P9-EMK-757

Integrated Coordinated Science for the 21st Century™

Dr. Michael Smith

Dr. John B. Southard

Dr. Arthur Eisenkraft

Gary Freebury

Dr. Robert Ritter

Ruta Demery

IT's ABOUT TIME®

HERFF JONES EDUCATION DIVISION

84 Business Park Drive, Armonk, NY 10504   Phone (914) 273-2233
Fax (914) 273-2227   Toll Free (888) 698-TIME (8463)   www.its-about-time.com

Creative/Art Director
John Nordland

Design/Production
Kadi Sarv
Kathleen Bowen
Burmar Technical
Corporation
Jon Voss

Physics Reviewer
Dr. John Roeder

Chemistry Reviewer
Dr. Carl Heltzel

Biology Reviewer
Dr. Arthur Eisenkraft
William H. Leonard
Myrna Hipol Estrata
Philip Estrada
Marissa Hipol
Laura Hajdukiewicz

Project Editor
Ruta Demery
*EarthComm, Active Physics,
Active Chemistry, Active Biology*

Project Managers
Ruta Demery
EarthComm, Active Physics
Barbara Zahm
*Active Physics
Active Chemistry, Active Biology*
John Nordland
*Integrated Coordinated
Science for the 21st Century*

Project Coordinators
Emily Crum
Matthew Smith
EarthComm

Technical Art
Stuart Armstrong
EarthComm
Burmar Technical Corporation,
Kadi Sarv
*Active Physics, Active Chemistry
Active Biology*

Illustrations
Tomas Bunk,
Dennis Falcon

Senior Photo Consultant
Bruce F. Molnia
EarthComm

Photo Research
Caitlin Callahan
EarthComm
Kathleen Bowen
EarthComm, Active Chemistry
Jon Voss
Kadi Sarv
Jennifer Von Holstein
Active Biology

Safety Reviewers
Dr. Ed Robeck
EarthComm, Active Biology
Gregory Puskar
Active Physics
Jack Breazale
Active Chemistry

Integrated Coordinated Science for the 21st Century™

All student activities in this textbook have been designed to be as safe as possible, and have been reviewed by professionals specifically for that purpose. As well, appropriate warnings concerning potential safety hazards are included where applicable to particular activities. However, responsibility for safety remains with the student, the classroom teacher, the school principals, and the school board.

EarthComm® is a registered trademark of the American Geological Institute. Registered names and trademarks, etc., used in this publication, even without specific indication thereof, are not to be considered unprotected by law.

Active Physics™ is a registered trademark of the American Association of Physics Teachers. Registered names and trademarks, etc., used in this publication, even without specific indication thereof, are not to be considered unprotected by law.

It's About Time® and *Active Chemistry*™ are registered trademarks of It's About Time, Inc. Registered names and trademarks, etc., used in this publication, even without specific indication thereof, are not to be considered unprotected by law.

EarthComm® text in this publication is copyrighted by the: American Geological Institute © Copyright 2003
National Science Foundation (grant no. ESI-9452789)

The *Active Physics*™ text in this publication is copyrighted by the: American Association of Physics Teachers © Copyright 2000

National Science Foundation (grant no. MDR-9150111)

The *Active Chemistry*™ text in this publication is copyrighted by: It's About Time, Inc. © Copyright 2003

The *Active Biology*™ text in this publication is copyrighted by: It's About Time, Inc. © Copyright 2004

All rights reserved. No part of this publication may be reproduced, stored in a retrieval system, or transmitted, in any form or by any means, electronic, mechanical, photocopying, recording, or otherwise, without the prior written permission of the copyright owner.

Care has been taken to trace the ownership of copyright material contained in this publication. The publisher will gladly receive any information that will rectify any reference or credit line in subsequent editions.

Printed and bound in the United States of America

ISBN #1-58591-279-4

2 3 4 5 D 08 07 06 05 04

This project was supported, in part, by the
National Science Foundation
Opinions expressed are those of the authors and not necessarily those of the National Science
Foundation or the donors of the American Geological Institute Foundation.

Integrated Coordinated Science for the 21st Century is an innovative core curricula assembled from four proven inquiry-based programs. It is supported by the National Science Foundation and developed by leading educators and scientists. The *EarthComm, Earth System Science in the Community* Unit 1 was developed by the American Geological Institute, under the guidance of Dr. Michael Smith, Director of Education and Outreach, and Dr. John Southard of MIT. Unit 2 *Active Physics*, was developed by the American Association of Physics Teachers, and the American Institute of Physics.

Both the *Active Physics* and *Active Chemistry* Unit 3, are projects directed by Dr. Arthur Eisenkraft, past president of NSTA. Unit 4, *Active Biology* was derived from materials that were originally developed by Biological Sciences Curriculum Study (BSCS). Each unit of this course has been designed and built on the National Science Education Standards... the same instructional model... and inquiry-based approach.

Principal Investigator, EarthComm

Michael Smith is Director of Education at the American Geological Institute in Alexandria, Virginia. Dr. Smith worked as an exploration geologist and hydrogeologist. He began his Earth Science teaching career with Shady Side Academy in Pittsburgh, PA in 1988 and most recently taught Earth Science at the Charter School of Wilmington, DE. He earned a doctorate from the University of Pittsburgh's Cognitive Studies in Education Program and joined the faculty of the University of Delaware School of Education in 1995. Dr. Smith received the Outstanding Earth Science Teacher Award for Pennsylvania from the National Association of Geoscience Teachers in 1991, served as Secretary of the National Earth Science Teachers Association, and is a reviewer for Science Education and The Journal of Research in Science Teaching. He worked on the Delaware Teacher Standards, Delaware Science Assessment, National Board of Teacher Certification, and AAAS Project 2061 Curriculum Evaluation programs.

Senior Writer, EarthComm

Dr. John B. Southard received his undergraduate degree from the Massachusetts Institute of Technology in 1960 and his doctorate in geology from Harvard University in 1966. After a National Science Foundation postdoctoral fellowship at the California Institute of Technology, he joined the faculty at the Massachusetts Institute of Technology, where he is currently Professor of Geology Emeritus. He was awarded the MIT School of Science teaching prize in 1989 and was one of the first cohorts of the MacVicar Fellows at MIT, in recognition of excellence in undergraduate teaching. He has taught numerous undergraduate courses in introductory geology, sedimentary geology, field geology, and environmental Earth Science both at MIT and in Harvard's adult education program. He was editor of the Journal of Sedimentary Petrology from 1992 to 1996, and he continues to do technical editing of scientific books and papers for SEPM, a professional society for sedimentary geology. Dr. Southard received the 2001 Neil Miner Award from the National Association of Geoscience Teachers.

Project Director, Active Physics and Active Chemistry

Arthur Eisenkraft teaches physics in the Bedford Public Schools in New York. Dr. Eisenkraft is the author of numerous science and educational publications. He holds U.S. Patent #4447141 for a Laser Vision Testing System (which tests visual acuity for spatial frequency).

Dr. Eisenkraft has been involved with a number of National Science Teachers Association (NSTA) projects and chaired many NSTA sponsored competitions including: the Toshiba/NSTA ExploraVisions Awards (1991 to the present); the Toyota TAPESTRY Grants (1990 to the present); the Duracell/NSTA Scholarship Competitions (1984 to 2000). He was a columnist and on the Advisory Board of *Quantum* (a science and math student magazine that was published by NSTA as a joint venture between the United States and Russia; 1989 to 2001). In 1993, he served as Executive Director for the XXIV International Physics Olympiad after being Academic Director for the United States Team for six years. He served on the content committee and helped write the National Science Education Standards of the NRC (National Research Council).

Dr. Eisenkraft has also been recognized with the following awards: Tandy Technology Scholar Award 2000, Presidential Award for Excellence in Science Teaching, 1986 from President Reagan; AAPT Distinguished Service Citation for "excellent contributions to the teaching of physics", 1989; Science Teacher of the Year, Disney American Teacher Awards in their American Teacher Awards program, 1991; Honorary Doctor of Science degree from Rensselaer Polytechnic Institute, 1993.

In 1999 Dr. Eisenkraft was elected to a 3-year cycle as the President-Elect, President and Retiring President of the NSTA, the largest science teacher organization in the world. Also in 1999, he was the sole recipient of an award for Excellence in Pre-College Physics teaching from AAPT.

He serves on numerous advisory boards including The Merck Institute of Science Education; BSCS; the National Academy of Sciences and EDC.

Dr. Eisenkraft has appeared on *The Today Show*, National Public Radio, Public Television, *The Disney Channel* and numerous radio shows. He serves as an advisor to the *ESPN Sports Figures Video Productions*.

He is a frequent presenter and keynote speaker at National Conventions. He has published over 80 articles and presented over 110 papers and workshops and has been featured in articles in *The New York Times, Education Week, Physics Today, American Journal of Physics* and *Physics Teacher*.

Content Specialist, Active Chemistry

Gary Freebury, a noted chemistry teacher, educator, and writer worked as the Project Manager and Editor for the 3 Prototype chapters of *Active Chemistry* which are currently being field tested and he will continue to serve as the Project Manager and Editor to the project. He will be responsible for the writing of any introductory materials, producing the table of contents, indices, glossary, and reference materials. He will have a critical role in maintaining the integrity of safety standards across all units. He will also coordinate any modifications, changes, and additions to the materials based upon pilot and field-testing results.

Mr. Freebury has been teaching chemistry for more than 35 years. He has been the Safety Advisor for Montana Schools, past director of the Chemistry Olympiad, past chairman of the Montana Section of the American Chemical Society (ACS), member of the Executive Committee of the Montana Section of the ACS, and a past member of the Montana Science Advisory Council. Mr. Freebury has been the regional director and author of Scope, Sequence and Coordination (SS&C) – Integrated Science Curriculum and Co-director of the National Science Foundation supported Chemistry Concepts four-year program. He earned a B.S. degree at Eastern Montana College in mathematics and physical science, and an M.S. degree in chemistry at the University of Northern Iowa.

UNIT 1: EARTHCOMM
PRIMARY AND CONTRIBUTING AUTHORS

Earth's Dynamic Geosphere

Daniel J. Bisaccio
Souhegan High School
Amherst, NH

Steve Carlson
Middle School, OR

Warren Fish
Paul Revere School
Los Angeles, CA

Miriam Fuhrman
Carlsbad, CA

Steve Mattox
Grand Valley State University

Keith McKain
Milford Senior High School
Milford, DE

Mary McMillan
Niwot High School
Niwot, CO

Bill Romey
Orleans, MA

Michael Smith
American Geological Institute

Tom Vandewater
Colton, NY

Understanding Your Environment

Geoffrey A. Briggs
Batavia Senior High School
Batavia, NY

Cathey Donald
Auburn High School
Auburn, AL

Richard Duschl
Kings College
London, UK

Fran Hess
Cooperstown High School
Cooperstown, NY

Laurie Martin-Vermilyea
American Geological Institute

Molly Miller
Vanderbilt University

Mary-Russell Roberson
Durham, NC

Charles Savrda
Auburn University

Michael Smith
American Geological Institute

Earth's Fluid Spheres

Chet Bolay
Cape Coral High School
Cape Coral, FL

Steven Dutch
University of Wisconsin

Virginia Jones
Bonneville High School
Idaho Falls, ID

Laurie Martin-Vermilyea
American Geological Institute

Joseph Moran
University of Wisconsin

Mary-Russell Roberson
Durham, NC

Bruce G. Smith
Appleton North High School
Appleton, WI

Michael Smith
American Geological Institute

Earth's Natural Resources

Chuck Bell
Deer Valley High School
Glendale, AZ

Jay Hackett
Colorado Springs, CO

John Kemeny
University of Arizona

John Kounas
Westwood High School
Sloan, IA

Laurie Martin-Vermilyea
American Geological Institute

Mary Poulton
University of Arizona

David Shah
Deer Valley High School
Glendale, AZ

Janine Shigihara
Shelley Junior High School
Shelley, ID

Michael Smith
American Geological Institute

Earth System Evolution

Julie Bartley
University of West Georgia

Lori Borroni-Engle
Taft High School
San Antonio, TX

Richard M. Busch
West Chester University
West Chester, PA

Kathleen Cochrane
Our Lady of Ransom School
Niles, IL

Cathey Donald
Auburn High School, AL

Robert A. Gastaldo
Colby College

William Leonard
Clemson University

Tim Lutz
West Chester University

Carolyn Collins Petersen
C. Collins Petersen Productions
Groton, MA

Michael Smith
American Geological Institute

Content Reviewers

Gary Beck
BP Exploration

Phil Bennett
University of Texas, Austin

Steve Bergman
Southern Methodist University

Samuel Berkheiser
Pennsylvania Geologic Survey

Arthur Bloom
Cornell University

Craig Bohren
Penn State University

Bruce Bolt
University of California, Berkeley

John Callahan
Appalachian State University

Sandip Chattopadhyay
R.S. Kerr Environmental Research Center

Beth Ellen Clark
Cornell University

Jimmy Diehl
Michigan Technological University

Sue Beske-Diehl
Michigan Technological University

Neil M. Dubrovsky
United States Geological Survey

Frank Ethridge
Colorado State University

Catherine Finley
University of Northern Colorado

Ronald Greeley
Arizona State University

Michelle Hall-Wallace
University of Arizona

Judy Hannah
Colorado State University

Blaine Hanson
Dept. of Land, Air, and Water Resources

James W. Head III
Brown University

Patricia Heiser
Ohio University

John R. Hill
Indiana Geological Survey

Travis Hudson
American Geological Institute

Jackie Huntoon
Michigan Tech. University

Teresa Jordan
Cornell University

Allan Juhas
Lakewood, Colorado

Robert Kay
Cornell University

Chris Keane
American Geological Institute

Bill Kirby
United States Geological Survey

Mark Kirschbaum
United States Geological Survey

Dave Kirtland
United States Geological Survey

Jessica Elzea Kogel
Thiele Kaolin Company

Melinda Laituri
Colorado State University

Martha Leake
Valdosta State University

Donald Lewis
Happy Valley, CA

Steven Losh
Cornell University

Jerry McManus
Woods Hole Oceanographic
Institution

Marcus Milling
American Geological Institute

Alexandra Moore
Cornell University

Jack Oliver
Cornell University

Don Pair
University of Dayton

Mauri Pelto
Nicolas College

Bruce Pivetz
ManTech Environmental Research
Services Corp.

Stephen Pompea
Pompea & Associates

Peter Ray
Florida State University

William Rose
Michigan Technological Univ.

Lou Solebello
Macon, Gerogia

Robert Stewart
Texas A&M University

Ellen Stofan
NASA

Barbara Sullivan
University of Rhode Island

Carol Tang
Arizona State University

Bob Tilling
United States Geological Survey

Stanley Totten
Hanover College

Scott Tyler
University of Nevada, Reno

Michael Velbel
Michigan State University

Ellen Wohl
Colorado State University

David Wunsch
State Geologist of New Hampshire

Pilot Test Evaluator

Larry Enochs
Oregon State University

Pilot Test Teachers

Rhonda Artho
Dumas High School
Dumas, TX

Mary Jane Bell
Lyons-Decatur Northeast
Lyons, NE

Rebecca Brewster
Plant City High School
Plant City, FL

Terry Clifton
Jackson High School
Jackson, MI

Virginia Cooter
North Greene High School
Greeneville, TN

Monica Davis
North Little Rock High School
North Little Rock, AR

Joseph Drahuschak
Troxell Jr. High School
Allentown, PA

Ron Fabick
Brunswick High School
Brunswick, OH

Virginia Jones
Bonneville High School
Idaho Falls, ID

Troy Lilly
Snyder High School
Snyder, TX

Sherman Lundy
Burlington High School
Burlington, IA

Norma Martof
Fairmont Heights High School
Capitol Heights, MD

Keith McKain
Milford Senior High School
Milford, DE

Mary McMillan
Niwot High School
Niwot, CO

Kristin Michalski
Mukwonago High School
Mukwonago, WI

Dianne Mollica
Bishop Denis J. O'Connell
High School
Arlington, VA

Arden Rauch
Schenectady High School
Schenectady, NY

Laura Reysz
Lawrence Central High School
Indianapolis, IN

Floyd Rogers
Palatine High School
Palatine, IL

Ed Ruszczyk
New Canaan High School
New Canaan, CT

Jane Skinner
Farragut High School
Knoxville, TN

Shelley Snyder
Mount Abraham High School
Bristol, VT

Joy Tanigawa
El Rancho High School
Pico Rivera, CA

Dennis Wilcox
Milwaukee School of Languages
Milwaukee, WI

Kim Willoughby
SE Raleigh High School
Raleigh, NC

Field Test Workshop Staff

Don W. Byerly
University of Tennessee

Derek Geise
University of Nebraska

Michael A. Gibson
University of Tennessee

David C. Gosselin
University of Nebraska

Robert Hartshorn
University of Tennessee

William Kean
University of Wisconsin

Ellen Metzger
San Jose State University

Tracy Posnanski
University of Wisconsin

J. Preston Prather
University of Tennessee

Ed Robeck
Salisbury University

Richard Sedlock
San Jose State University

Bridget Wyatt
San Jose State University

Field Test Evaluators

Bob Bernoff
Dresher, PA

Do Yong Park
University of Iowa

Field Test Teachers

Kerry Adams
Alamosa High School
Alamosa, CO

Jason Ahlberg
Lincoln High
Lincoln, NE

Gregory Bailey
Fulton High School
Knoxville, TN

Mary Jane Bell
Lyons-Decatur Northeast
Lyons, NE

Rod Benson
Helena High
Helena, MT

Sandra Bethel
Greenfield High School
Greenfield, TN

John Cary
Malibu High School
Malibu, CA

Elke Christoffersen
Poland Regional High School
Poland, ME

Tom Clark
Benicia High School
Benicia, CA

Julie Cook
Jefferson City High School
Jefferson City, MO

Virginia Cooter
North Greene High School
Greeneville, TN

Mary Cummane
Perspectives Charter
Chicago, IL

Sharon D'Agosta
Creighton Preparatory
Omaha, NE

Mark Daniels
Kettle Morraine High School
Milwaukee, WI

Beth Droughton
Bloomfield High School
Bloomfield, NJ

Steve Ferris
Lincoln High
Lincoln, NE

Bob Feurer
North Bend Central Public
North Bend, NE

Sue Frack
Lincoln Northeast High
Lincoln, NE

Rebecca Fredrickson
Greendale High School
Greendale, WI

Sally Ghilarducci
Hamilton High School
Milwaukee, WI

Kerin Goedert
Lincoln High School
Ypsilanti, MI

Martin Goldsmith
Menominee Falls High School
Menominee Falls, WI

Randall Hall
Arlington High School
St. Paul, MN

Theresa Harrison
Wichita West High
Wichita, KS

Gilbert Highlander
Red Bank High School
Chattanooga, TN

Jim Hunt
Chattanooga School of Arts
& Sciences
Chattanooga, TN

Patricia Jarzynski
Watertown High School
Watertown, WI

Pam Kasprowicz
Bartlett High School
Bartlett, IL

Caren Kershner
Moffat Consolidated
Moffat, CO

Mary Jane Kirkham
Fulton High School

Ted Koehn
Lincoln East High
Lincoln, NE

Philip Lacey
East Liverpool High School
East Liverpool, OH

Joan Lahm
Scotus Central Catholic
Columbus, NE

Erica Larson
Tipton Community

Michael Laura
Banning High School

Wilmington, CA

Fawn LeMay
Plattsmouth High
Plattsmouth, NE

Christine Lightner
Smethport Area High School
Smethport, PA

Nick Mason
Normandy High School
St. Louis, MO

James Matson
Wichita West High
Wichita, KS

Jeffrey Messer
Western High School
Parma, MI

Dave Miller
Parkview High
Springfield, MO

Rick Nettesheim
Waukesha South
Waukesha, WI

John Niemoth
Niobrara Public
Niobrara, NE

Margaret Olsen
Woodward Academy
College Park, GA

Ronald Ozuna
Roosevelt High School
Los Angeles, CA

Paul Parra
Omaha North High
Omaha, NE

D. Keith Patton
West High
Denver, CO

Phyllis Peck
Fairfield High School
Fairfield, CA

Randy Pelton
Jackson High School
Massillon, OH

Reggie Pettitt
Holderness High School
Holderness, NH

June Rasmussen
Brighton High School
South Brighton, TN

Russ Reese
Kalama High School
Kalama, WA

Janet Ricker
South Greene High School
Greeneville, TN

Wendy Saber
Washington Park High School
Racine, WI

Garry Sampson
Wauwatosa West High School
Tosa, WI

Daniel Sauls
Chuckey-Doak High School
Afton, TN

Todd Shattuck
L.A. Center for Enriched Studies
Los Angeles, CA

Heather Shedd
Tennyson High School
Hayward, CA

Lynn Sironen
North Kingstown High School
North Kingstown, RI

Jane Skinner
Farragut High School
Knoxville, TN

Sarah Smith
Garringer High School
Charlotte, NC

Aaron Spurr
Malcolm Price Laboratory
Cedar Falls, IA

Karen Tiffany
Watertown High School
Watertown, WI

Tom Tyler
Bishop O'Dowd High School
Oakland, CA

Valerie Walter
Freedom High School
Bethlehem, PA

Christopher J. Akin Williams
Milford Mill Academy
Baltimore, MD

Roseanne Williby
Skutt Catholic High School
Omaha, NE

Carmen Woodhall
Canton South High School
Canton, OH

Field Test Coordinator

William Houston
American Geological Institute

Advisory Board

Jane Crowder
Bellevue, WA

Arthur Eisenkraft
Bedford (NY) Public Schools

Tom Ervin
LeClaire, IA

Mary Kay Hemenway
University of Texas at Austin

Bill Leonard
Clemson University

Don Lewis
Lafayette, CA

Wendell Mohling
National Science Teachers
Association

Harold Pratt
Littleton, CO

Barb Tewksbury
Hamilton College

Laure Wallace
USGS

AGI Foundation

Jan van Sant
Executive Director

The American Geological Institute and EarthComm

Imagine more than 500,000 Earth scientists worldwide sharing a common voice, and you've just imagined the mission of the American Geological Institute. Our mission is to raise public awareness of the Earth sciences and the role that they play in mankind's use of natural resources, mitigation of natural hazards, and stewardship of the environment. For more than 50 years, AGI has served the scientists and teachers of its Member Societies and hundreds of associated colleges, universities, and corporations by producing Earth science educational materials, *Geotimes*–a geoscience news magazine, GeoRef–a reference database, and government affairs and public awareness programs.

So many important decisions made every day that affect our lives depend upon an understanding of how our Earth works. That's why AGI created *EarthComm*. In your *EarthComm* classroom, you'll discover the wonder and importance of Earth science by studying it where it counts—in your community. As you use the rock record to investigate climate change, do field work in nearby beaches, parks, or streams, explore the evolution and extinction of life, understand where your energy resources come from, or find out how to forecast severe weather, you'll gain a better understanding of how to use your knowledge of Earth science to make wise personal decisions.

We would like to thank the AGI Foundation Members that have been supportive in bringing Earth science to students. These AGI Foundation Members include: American Association of Petroleum Geologists Foundation, Anadarko Petroleum Corp., The Anschutz Foundation, Apache Canada Ltd., Baker Hughes Foundation, Barrett Resources Corp., Elizabeth and Stephen Bechtel, Jr. Foundation, BP Foundation, Burlington Resources Foundation, CGG Americas, Inc., ChevronTexaco Corp., Conoco Inc., Consolidated Natural Gas Foundation, Devon Energy Corp., Diamond Offshore Co., Dominion Exploration & Production, Inc., EEX Corp., Equitable Production Co., ExxonMobil Foundation, Five States Energy Co., Geological Society of America Foundation, Global Marine Drilling Co., Halliburton Foundation, Inc., Kerr McGee Foundation, Maxus Energy Corp., Noble Drilling Corp., Occidental Petroleum Charitable Foundation, Ocean Energy, Optimistic Petroleum Co., Parker Drilling Co., Phillips Petroleum Co., Santa Fe Snyder Corp., Schlumberger Foundation, Shell Oil Company Foundation, Southwestern Energy Co., Texas Crude Energy, Inc., Unocal Corp. USX Foundation (Marathon Oil Co.).

We at AGI wish you success in your exploration of the Earth System and your Community.

Michael J. Smith
Director of Education, AGI

Marcus E. Milling
Executive Director, AGI

UNIT 2: ACTIVE PHYSICS
PRIMARY AND CONTRIBUTING AUTHORS

Home

Jon L. Harkness
Active Physics Regional Coordinator
Wausau, WI

Douglas A. Johnson
Madison West High School
Madison, WI

John J. Rusch
University of Wisconsin, Superior
Superior, WI

Ruta Demery
Blue Ink Editing
Stayner, ON

Communication

Richard Berg
University of Maryland
College Park, MD

Ron DeFronzo
Eastbay Ed. Collaborative
Attleboro, MA

Harry Rheam
Eastern Senior High School
Atco, NJ

John Roeder
The Calhoun School
New York, NY

Patty Rourke
Potomac School
McLean, VA

Larry Weathers
The Bromfield School
Harvard, MA

Medicine

Russell Hobbie
University of Minnesota
St. Paul, MN

Terry Goerke
Hill-Murray High School
St. Paul, MN

John Koser
Wayzata High School
Plymouth, MN

Ed Lee
WonderScience, Associate Editor
Silver Spring, MD

Predictions

Ruth Howes
Ball State University
Muncie, IN

Chris Chiaverina
New Trier Township High School
Crystal Lake, IL

Charles Payne
Ball State University
Muncie, IN

Ceanne Tzimopoulos
Omega Publishing
Medford, MA

Sports

Howard Brody
University of Pennsylvania
Philadelphia, PA

Mary Quinlan
Radnor High School
Radnor, PA

Carl Duzen
Lower Merion High School
Havertown, PA

Jon L. Harkness
Active Physics Regional Coordinator
Wausau, WI

David Wright
Tidewater Comm. College
Virginia Beach, VA

Transportation

Ernest Kuehl
Lawrence High School
Cedarhurst, NY

Robert L. Lehrman
Bayside, NY

Salvatore Levy
Roslyn High School
Roslyn, NY

Tom Liao
SUNY Stony Brook
Stony Brook, NY

Bob Ritter
University of Alberta
Edmonton, AB, CA

Principal Investigators

Bernard V. Khoury
American Association of Physics
Teachers

Dwight Edward Neuenschwander
American Institute of Physics

Consultants

Peter Brancazio
Brooklyn College of CUNY
Brooklyn, NY

Robert Capen
Canyon del Oro High School
Tucson, AZ

Carole Escobar

Earl Graf
SUNY Stony Brook
Stony Brook, NY

Jack Hehn
American Association of
Physics Teachers
College Park, MD

Donald F. Kirwan
Louisiana State University
Baton Rouge, LA

Gayle Kirwan
Louisiana State University
Baton Rouge, LA

James La Porte
Virginia Tech
Blacksburg, VA

Charles Misner
University of Maryland
College Park, MD

Robert F. Neff
Suffern, NY

Ingrid Novodvorsky
Mountain View High School
Tucson, AZ

John Robson
University of Arizona
Tucson, AZ

Mark Sanders
Virginia Tech
Blacksburg, VA

Brian Schwartz
Brooklyn College of CUNY
New York, NY

Bruce Seiger
Wellesley High School
Newburyport, MA

Clifford Swartz
SUNY Stony Brook
Setauket, NY

Barbara Tinker
The Concord Consortium
Concord, MA

Robert E. Tinker
The Concord Consortium
Concord, MA

Joyce Weiskopf
Herndon, VA

Donna Willis
American Association of
Physics Teachers
College Park, MD

Safety Reviewer

Gregory Puskar
University of West Virginia
Morgantown, WV

Equity Reviewer

Leo Edwards
Fayetteville State University
Fayetteville, NC

Spreadsheet and MBL

Ken Appel
Yorktown High School
Peekskill, NY

Physics at Work

Barbara Zahm
Zahm Productions
New York, NY

Physics InfoMall
Brian Adrian
Bethany College
Lindsborg, KS

First Printing Reviewer
John L. Hubisz
North Carolina State University
Raleigh, NC

Unit Reviewers
George A. Amann
F.D. Roosevelt High School
Rhinebeck, NY

Patrick Callahan
Catasauqua High School
Center Valley, PA

Beverly Cannon
Science and Engineering
Magnet High School
Dallas, TX

Barbara Chauvin

Elizabeth Chesick
The Baldwin School
Haverford, PA

Chris Chiaverina
New Trier Township High School
Crystal Lake, IL

Andria Erzberger
Palo Alto Senior High School
Los Altos Hills, CA

Elizabeth Farrell Ramseyer
Niles West High School
Skokie, IL

Mary Gromko
President of Council of State Science
Supervisors
Denver, CO

Thomas Guetzloff

Jon L. Harkness
Active Physics Regional Coordinator
Wausau, WI

Dawn Harman
Moon Valley High School
Phoenix, AZ

James Hill
Piner High School
Sonoma, CA

Bob Kearney

Claudia Khourey-Bowers
McKinley Senior High School

Steve Kliewer
Bullard High School
Fresno, CA

Ernest Kuehl
Roslyn High School
Cedarhurst, NY

Jane Nelson
University High School
Orlando, FL

John Roeder
The Calhoun School
New York, NY

Patty Rourke
Potomac School
McLean, VA

Gerhard Salinger
Fairfax, VA

Irene Slater
La Pietra School for Girls

Pilot Test Teachers
John Agosta

Donald Campbell
Portage Central High School
Portage, MI

John Carlson
Norwalk Community
Technical College
Norwalk, CT

Veanna Crawford
Alamo Heights High School
New Braunfels, TX

Janie Edmonds
West Milford High School
Randolph, NJ

Eddie Edwards
Amarillo Area Center for Advanced
Learning
Amarillo, TX

Arthur Eisenkraft
Fox Lane High School
Bedford, NY

Tom Ford

Bill Franklin

Roger Goerke
St. Paul, MN

Tom Gordon
Greenwich High School
Greenwich, CT

Ariel Hepp

John Herrman
College of Steubenville
Steubenville, OH

Linda Hodges

Ernest Kuehl
Lawrence High School
Cedarhurst, NY

Fran Leary
Troy High School
Schenectady, NY

Harold Lefcourt

Cherie Lehman
West Lafayette High School
West Lafayette, IN

Kathy Malone
Shady Side Academy
Pittsburgh, PA

Bill Metzler
Westlake High School
Thornwood, NY

Elizabeth Farrell Ramseyer
Niles West High School
Skokie, IL

Daniel Repogle
Central Noble High School
Albion, IN

Evelyn Restivo
Maypearl High School
Maypearl, TX

Doug Rich
Fox Lane High School
Bedford, NY

John Roeder
The Calhoun School
New York, NY

Tom Senior
New Trier Township High School
Highland Park, IL

John Thayer
District of Columbia Public Schools
Silver Spring, MD

Carol-Ann Tripp
Providence Country Day
East Providence, RI

Yvette Van Hise
High Tech High School
Freehold, NJ

Jan Waarvick

Sandra Walton
Dubuque Senior High School
Dubuque, IA

Larry Wood
Fox Lane High School
Bedford, NY

Field Test Coordinator
Marilyn Decker
Northeastern University
Acton, MA

Field Test Workshop Staff
John Carlson
Marilyn Decker
Arthur Eisenkraft
Douglas Johnson
John Koser
Ernest Kuehl
Mary Quinlan
Elizabeth Farrell Ramseyer
John Roeder

Field Test Evaluators
Susan Baker-Cohen
Susan Cloutier
George Hein
Judith Kelley
all from Lesley College,
Cambridge, MA

Field Test Teachers and Schools

Rob Adams
Polytech High School
Woodside, DE

Benjamin Allen
Falls Church High School
Falls Church, VA

Robert Applebaum
New Trier High School
Winnetka, IL

Joe Arnett
Plano Sr. High School
Plano, TX

Bix Baker
GFW High School
Winthrop, MN

Debra Beightol
Fremont High School
Fremont, NE

Patrick Callahan
Catasaugua High School
Catasaugua, PA

George Coker
Bowling Green High School
Bowling Green, KY

Janice Costabile
South Brunswick High School
Monmouth Junction, NJ

Stanley Crum
Homestead High School
Fort Wayne, IN

Russel Davison
Brandon High School
Brandon, FL

Christine K. Deyo
Rochester Adams High School
Rochester Hills, MI

Jim Doller
Fox Lane High School
Bedford, NY

Jessica Downing
Esparto High School
Esparto, CA

Douglas Fackelman
Brighton High School
Brighton, CO

Rick Forrest
Rochester High School
Rochester Hills, MI

Mark Freeman
Blacksburg High School
Blacksburg, VA

Jonathan Gillis
Enloe High School
Raleigh, NC

Karen Gruner
Holton Arms School
Bethesda, MD

Larry Harrison
DuPont Manual High School
Louisville, KY

Alan Haught
Weaver High School
Hartford, CT

Steven Iona
Horizon High School
Thornton, CO

Phil Jowell
Oak Ridge High School
Conroe, TX

Deborah Knight
Windsor Forest High School
Savannah, GA

Thomas Kobilarcik
Marist High School
Chicago, IL

Sheila Kolb
Plano Senior High School
Plano, TX

Todd Lindsay
Park Hill High School
Kansas City, MO

Malinda Mann
South Putnam High School
Greencastle, IN

Steve Martin
Maricopa High School
Maricopa, AZ

Nancy McGrory
North Quincy High School
N. Quincy, MA

David Morton
Mountain Valley High School
Rumford, ME

Charles Muller
Highland Park High School
Highland Park, NJ

Fred Muller
Mercy High School
Burlingame, CA

Vivian O'Brien
Plymouth Regional High School
Plymouth, NH

Robin Parkinson
Northridge High School
Layton, UT

Donald Perry
Newport High School
Bellevue, WA

Francis Poodry
Lincoln High School
Philadelphia, PA

John Potts
Custer County District High School
Miles City, MT

Doug Rich
Fox Lane High School
Bedford, NY

John Roeder
The Calhoun School
New York, NY

Consuelo Rogers
Maryknoll Schools
Honolulu, HI

Lee Rossmaessler
Mott Middle College High School
Flint, MI

John Rowe
Hughes Alternative Center
Cincinnati, OH

Rebecca Bonner Sanders
South Brunswick High School
Monmouth Junction, NJ

David Schilpp
Narbonne High School
Harbor City, CA

Eric Shackelford
Notre Dame High School
Sherman Oaks, CA

Robert Sorensen
Springville-Griffith Institute and
Central School
Springville, NY

Teresa Stalions
Crittenden County High School
Marion, KY

Roberta Tanner
Loveland High School
Loveland, CO

Anthony Umelo
Anacostia Sr. High School
Washington, D.C.

Judy Vondruska
Mitchell High School
Mitchell, SD

Deborah Waldron
Yorktown High School
Arlington, VA

Ken Wester
The Mississippi School for
Mathematics and Science
Columbus, MS

Susan Willis
Conroe
High School
Conroe, TX

UNIT 3: ACTIVE CHEMISTRY
PRIMARY AND CONTRIBUTING AUTHORS

Active Chemistry Writers

Gary Freebury
Kalispell, MT

Mary Gromko
Colorado Springs, CO

Carl Heltzel
Transylvania University
Lexington, KY

John Roeder
The Calhoun School
New York, NY

Hannah Sevian
University of
Massachusetts – Boston
Campus, Boston, MA

Sandra Smith
Colorado Springs, CO

Michael Tinnesand
American Chemical
Society
Washington, D.C.

Active Chemistry Consultants

James Davis
Chemistry Professor
Emeritus Harvard
University

George Miller
University of California
at Irvine
Irvine, CA

Carlo Parravano
Merck Institute for
Science Education
Rahway, NJ

Maren Reeder
Merck Institute for
Science Education
Rahway, NJ

Active Chemistry Pilot Testers

Rob Adams
Wyoming, DE

Ina Ahern
Plymouth Regional
High School
Plymouth, NH

John Bibb
Georgetown, DE

Amy Biddle
Pinkerton Academy
Derry, NH

Robert Dayton
Rush-Henrietta
High School
Henrietta, NY

Barbara Duch
Education Resource Ctr.
Newark, DE

Gabriel Duque
North Miami
Senior High School
Miami, FL

Liz Garcia
Carson High School
Carson, CA

Laura Hajdukiewicz
The Bromfield School
Harvard, MA

Jonathon Haraty
SAGE School
Springfield, MA

Carl Heltzel
Transylvania University
Lexington, KY

Natalie Hiller
Philadelphia Public
Schools
Philadelphia, PA

Penny Hood
Stanwood High School
Stanwood, WA

Tamilyn Ingram
Menifee County
High School
Frenchburg, KY

Barbara Jeffries
Casey Co. High School
Liberty, KY

Diane Johnson
Lewis County
High School
Vanceburg, KY

Gerry LaFontaine
Toll Gate High School
Warwick, RI

Jo Larmore
Laurel, DE

Jeffrey Little
Pikeville High School
Pikeville, KY

Kathy Lucas
Casey Co. High School
Liberty, KY

Barbara Malkas
Taconic High School
Pittsfield, MA

Barbara Martin
Reading High School
Reading, MA

Robert Mayton
Allen Central
High School
Eastern, KY

Vicki Mockbee
Caesar Rodney
High School
Camden, DE

Brenda Mullins
Knott County
Central High School
Hindman, KY

Jim Nash
Stanwood High School
Stanwood, WA

Barry North
Rivendell Interstate
Regional High School
Orford, NH

Angela Pence
Wolfe County
High School
Campton, KY

Roy Penix
Prestonburg High School
Prestonburg, KY

Robin Ringland
Stanwood High School
Stanwood, WA

George Robertson
Stanwood High School
Stanwood, WA

Lance Rudiger
Potsdam High School
Potsdam, NY

John Scali
Newark, DE

Noreen Scarpitto
Reading High School
Reading, MA

Fred Schiess
Stanwood High School
Stanwood, WA

Hannah Sevian
Chelsea High School
Chelsea, MA

Angela Skaggs
Magoffin County
High School
Salyersville, KY

Mary Stoukides
Toll Gate High School
Warwick, RI

Jim Swanson
Saugus High School
Saugus, MA

Kathy Swingle
Rehoboth, DE

Jeffrey Scott Townsend
Powell Co. High School
Stanton, KY

Josh Underwood
Deming High School
Mount Olivet, KY

Elaine Weil
Berlin, MD

Jen Wilson
Wilmington, DE

UNIT 4: ACTIVE BIOLOGY
PRIMARY AND CONTRIBUTING AUTHORS

Active Biology Writers

Bob Ritter
Consultant, *Active Biology* and
Active Physics

Bob Ritter is presently the
principal of Holy Trinity High
School in Edmonton, Alberta. Dr.
Ritter began his teaching career in
1973. Since then he has had a
variety of teaching assignments.
He has worked as a classroom
teacher, Science Consultant, and
Department Head. He has also
taught Biological Science to
student teachers at the University
of Alberta. He is presently
involved with steering committees
for "At Risk High School
Students" and "High School
Science."

Dr. Ritter is author of many
publications. He has written
numerous biology textbooks and
laboratory manuals for middle and
high school students during the
past 25 years. He has also
developed a variety of professional
teaching materials. These include
*Teaching Controversial Issues,
Learning Strategies*, and *Teacher
and Student Perceptions about
Alternative Assessment.*

Dr. Ritter is frequently a presenter
and speaker at national and
regional conventions across Canada
and the United States. He has
initiated many creative projects,
including establishing a science-
mentor program in which students
would have an opportunity to work
with professional biologists. In
1993 Dr. Ritter received the Prime
Minister's Award for Science and

Technology Teaching. He has also
been honored as Teacher of the
Year and with an Award of Merit
for contribution to science
education.

Dr. Ritter was consultant and
contributing writer to the *Active
Biology* unit. He also developed
the assessment strategies and
rubrics for the *Active Physics*
teacher's guides.

Ruta Demery
Project Editor and
Contributing Writer, *EarthComm,
Active Physics*, *Active Chemistry*,
and *Active Biology*

Ruta Demery is an editorial
consultant. She has been engaged
in educational publishing for over
30 years. She has also worked as a
classroom science and mathematics
teacher in both middle school and
high school.

She has participated in the
development and publishing of
numerous innovative mathematics
and science books. She has also
been a contributing writer for a
variety of mathematics and science
textbooks and teacher's guides.
She brings to her work a strong
background in curriculum
development and a keen interest
in student assessment. When time
permits, she also leads workshops
to familiarize teachers with new
classroom materials.

Ruta Demery is presently involved
in editorial consulting on several
National Science Foundation
(NSF) projects. She was the
project editor for *EarthComm,
Active Physics*, *Active Chemistry*,
and *Active Biology*. She was
also a contributing writer for
Active Physics and *Active Biology*,
both students' and teachers'
editions.

Active Biology Consultants

Dr. Arthur Eisenkraft
Project Director of *Active Physics*
and *Active Chemistry*. Past
President of the National Science
Teachers Association (NSTA)

William H. Leonard, Ph.D.
Clemson University
Professor of Education
and Biology
Co-Author *Bio Comm*

Philip Estrada
Biology Teacher Hollywood
High School, LAUSD

Marissa Hipol
Biology Teacher Hollywood
High School, LAUSD

Laura Hajdukiewicz
Biology Teacher, Andover, MA

You can do any science. Here are the reasons why...

The following features make it that much easier to understand the science principles you will be studying. You will find that regardless of which science discipline you approach, whether it be Earth science, physics, chemistry, or biology, the way you go about learning each of them is the same. Every step along the way will prepare you for the following step. Using all these features together will help you actually learn about science and see how it works for you every day, everywhere. Look for these features in each chapter of *Integrated Coordinated Science for the 21st Century*.

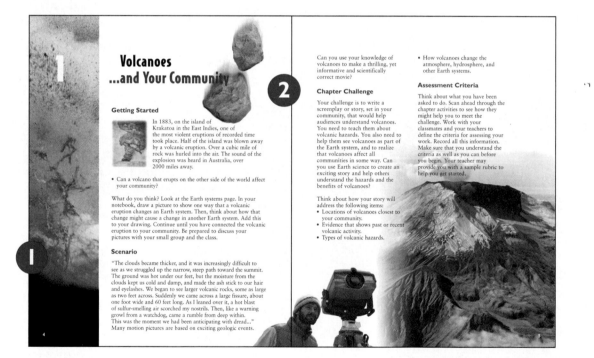

 **Scenario**

Each chapter begins with a realistic event or situation. You might actually have experienced the event, or you can imagine yourself participating in a similar situation at home, in school, or in your community. Chances are you probably never thought about the science involved in each case.

 Challenge

This feature presents you with a challenge that you can expect to complete by the end of the chapter. As you progress through the chapter you will accumulate all the knowledge you need to successfully complete the challenge.

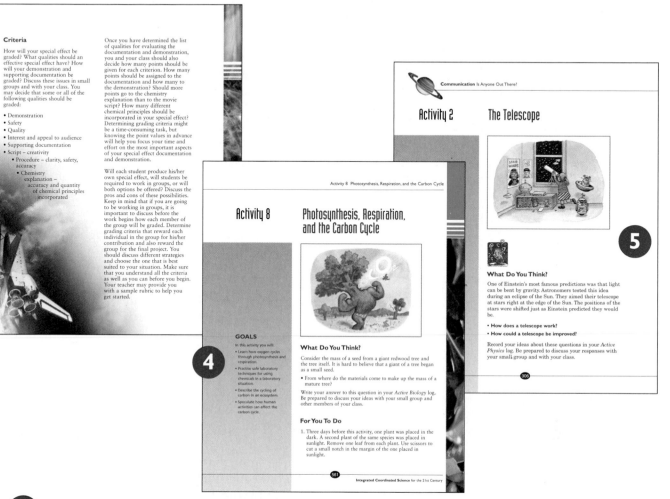

3 Criteria

Before you begin the chapter and the challenge, you and your classmates, along with your teacher, will explore exactly how you will be graded. You will review the criteria and expectations for solving the challenge, and make decisions about how your work should be evaluated.

4 Goals

At the beginning of each activity you are provided with a list of goals that you should be able to achieve by completing your science inquiry.

5 What Do You Already Know?

Before you start each activity you will be asked one or two questions to consider. You will have a chance to discuss your ideas with your group and your class. You are not expected to come up with the "right" answer, but to share your current understanding and reasoning.

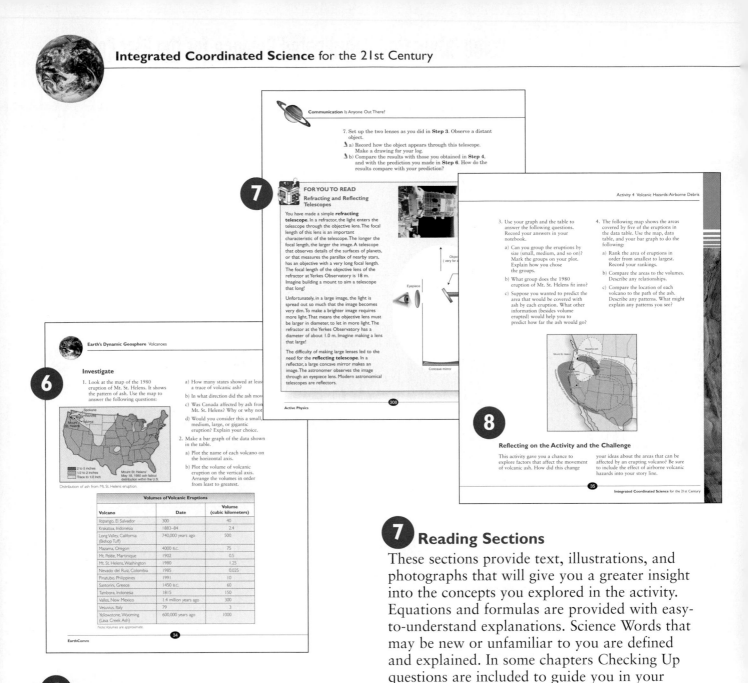

6 Investigate

In *Integrated Coordinated Science for the 21st Century* you learn by doing science. In your small groups, or as a class, you will take part in scientific inquiry by doing hands-on experiments, participating in fieldwork, or searching for answers using the Internet and reference materials.

7 Reading Sections

These sections provide text, illustrations, and photographs that will give you a greater insight into the concepts you explored in the activity. Equations and formulas are provided with easy-to-understand explanations. Science Words that may be new or unfamiliar to you are defined and explained. In some chapters Checking Up questions are included to guide you in your reading.

8 Reflecting on the Activity and the Challenge

Each activity helps to prepare you to be successful in the challenge. This feature gives you a brief summary of the activity. It will help you relate the activity that you just completed to the challenge. It's another piece of the chapter jigsaw puzzle.

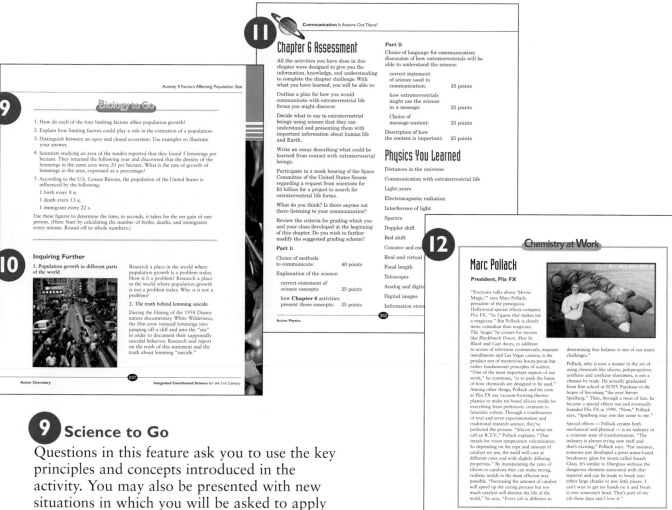

9 Science to Go

Questions in this feature ask you to use the key principles and concepts introduced in the activity. You may also be presented with new situations in which you will be asked to apply what you have learned. They are excellent as a study guide, helping you review and understand what is most important from the activity. You will also be provided with suggestions for ways in which you can organize your work and get ready for the challenge.

10 Inquiring Further

This feature stretches your thinking. It provides lots of suggestions for deepening your understanding of the concepts and skills developed in the activity. Also, if you're looking for more challenging or in-depth problems, questions, and exercises, you'll find them right here.

11 Chapter Assessment

How do you measure up? Here is your opportunity to share what you have actually learned. Using the activities as a guide, you can now complete the challenge you were presented at the beginning of the chapter.

12 Science at Work

Science is an integral part of many fascinating careers. This feature introduces some people working in different fields that involve the principles of science.

Table of Contents

Unit 1

EARTHCOMM
Earth's Dynamic Geosphere
Chapter 1: Volcanoes and Your Community

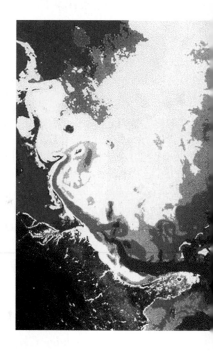

Chapter 3: Earthquakes and Your Community

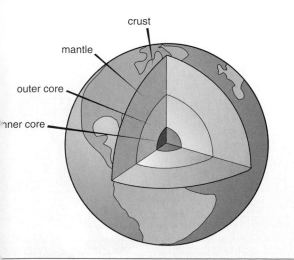

Unit 2

ACTIVE PHYSICS

Chapter 4: Let Us Entertain You

Chapter 5: Long-Distance Communication

Chapter 6: Is Anyone Out There?

Screen

Lens

Unit 3

ACTIVE CHEMISTRY

Chapter 7: The Periodic Table

Chapter 8: Cool Chemistry Show

Unit 4

ACTIVE BIOLOGY

Would you like to write a screenplay about volcanoes? Present a cool chemistry show to wow a group of elementary students? Look for and communicate with extraterrestrials? Or develop a booklet to help people to decide how to vote? This year science will be filled with fascinating challenges. This is *EarthComm*, *Active Physics*, *Active Chemistry*, and *Active Biology*. This is *Integrated Coordinated Science for the 21st Century*. It's a science course that introduces you to the fundamental laws and theories of four large disciplines of science and asks that you use your creativity, interest, and expertise to complete challenges in the same way that professionals do.

When scientists, artists, musicians, writers, and engineers are hired to solve a problem, their first responsibility is to understand the nature of the assignment. Often, they must do research to better acquaint themselves with the topic. The person assigning the job has a sense of what is needed, but does not know exactly what the final product will be. For instance, a movie producer may decide that a film about

volcanoes would be thrilling, yet informative. The producer would then hire a team of screenwriters to provide the script. This group of talented people will need a wide range of expertise. The team must image an exciting, yet realistic plot. They must also rely on someone who has knowledge about volcanoes, where they can occur, how they can be monitored, and the hazards that they can produce. In the first chapter of *EarthComm*, you will be required to write a screenplay about volcanoes. You will be helped along the way with activities that will give you the knowledge and expertise to be successful.

As you complete chapter challenges, you will begin to combine your science knowledge with your other interests and create something that will represent the best efforts of you and your team. You will be learning about the disciplines of physics, chemistry, Earth science, and biology. You will learn about volcanoes and earthquakes, and how they affect all the Earth systems. You will investigate how waves produce music. You will discover how the behavior of atoms and electrons can make some foods delicious and others poisonous. And you will understand that the extinction of one organism can affect an entire ecosystem.

Hundreds of teachers, professors, artists, editors, and science education professionals who have worked on these materials have taken into account the best information on how students can achieve and how students can be engaged in their own learning. We have taken the philosophy and recommendations of the National Science Education Standards and created a course that will engage you in asking the types of questions that scientists ask; will have you explore the world in the way that scientists explore the world; and will require you to show us that you really understand the meaning and implications of the scientific principles.

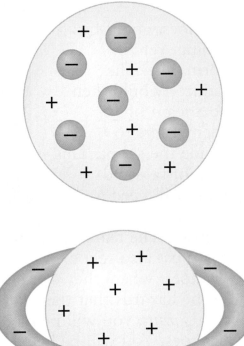

The development of the chapters in this book has been funded by the National Science Foundation. They have gone through a process that included feedback from students much like you in classrooms across the country. Based on that feedback, the materials have been improved so that you can learn science, enjoy what you are learning, and be successful in the course.

This year will be an introduction to four major sciences. Scientists in each discipline have ways of learning that are unique to their disciplines and yet the sciences are also similar. The energy released in an earthquake travels in waves, so does sound, as does the light that is given off when electrons move from one orbit to another. Measuring the waves involved in each of these examples requires different tools and different apparatus. You will be introduced to these sciences and will become acquainted with the similarities and differences among the disciplines.

You will begin to think like a scientist.

EARTH SYSTEMS

The **atmosphere** is the gaseous envelope that surrounds the Earth and consists of a mixture of gases composed primarily of nitrogen, oxygen, carbon dioxide, argon, and water vapor.

The **biosphere** is the life zone of the Earth and includes all living organisms, including humans, and all organic matter that has not yet decomposed.

The **cryosphere** is the portion of the climatic system consisting of the world's ice masses and snow deposits. This includes ice sheets, ice shelves, ice caps and other glaciers, sea ice, seasonal snow cover, lake and river ice, and seasonally frozen ground and permafrost.

The **geosphere** is the solid Earth that includes the continental and oceanic crust as well as the various layers of the Earth's interior.

The **hydrosphere** includes the water of the Earth, including surface lakes, streams, oceans, underground water, and water in the atmosphere.

Unit 1

EarthComm®
Earth System Science
in the Community

Earth's Dynamic Geosphere

Making Connections

You are about to begin a very active year continuing your exploration of science. This year, you will get chances to explore the world around you in a very meaningful way. *Integrated Coordinated Science for the 21st Century* includes *EarthComm*, *Active Physics*, *Active Chemistry*, and *Active Biology*.

To organize the understanding and investigation of the world, scientists have made up categories like Earth science, biology, chemistry, and physics. All of these fields are related. There are now fields like biochemistry, physical chemistry, and environmental science, which require an understanding of more than one branch of science.

What Do You Think?

• What is science?

• How are Earth science, physics, chemistry, and biology similar? How are they different?

Record your ideas about this in your log. Be prepared to discuss your response with your small group and the class.

For You To Try

• Bertrand Russell (1872-1970) an English philosopher and mathematician said that, "Science is what you know. Philosophy is what you don't know." Research to find quotes from other famous people about what they think that science is. Which one do you think comes closest to what you think that science is?

• Rarely does a week go by without a new scientific study or discovery being reported in the media. Review the news for the last few months to find what new studies or discoveries have been make recently. Research and report on one of these.

Chapter 1

Volcanoes
...and Your Community

Getting Started

In 1883, on the island of Krakatoa in the East Indies, one of the most violent eruptions of recorded time took place. Half of the island was blown away by a volcanic eruption. Over a cubic mile of rock was hurled into the air. The sound of the explosion was heard in Australia, over 2000 miles away.

• Can a volcano that erupts on the other side of the world affect your community?

What do you think? Look at the Earth systems page. In your notebook, draw a picture to show one way that a volcanic eruption changes an Earth system. Then, think about how that change might cause a change in another Earth system. Add this to your drawing. Continue until you have connected the volcanic eruption to your community. Be prepared to discuss your pictures with your small group and the class.

Scenario

"The clouds became thicker, and it was increasingly difficult to see as we struggled up the narrow, steep path toward the summit. The ground was hot under our feet, but the moisture from the clouds kept us cold and damp, and made the ash stick to our hair and eyelashes. We began to see larger volcanic rocks, some as large as two feet across. Suddenly we came across a large fissure, about one foot wide and 60 feet long. As I leaned over it, a hot blast of sulfur-smelling air scorched my nostrils. Then, like a warning growl from a watchdog, came a rumble from deep within. This was the moment we had been anticipating with dread..." Many motion pictures are based on exciting geologic events.

Can you use your knowledge of volcanoes to make a thrilling, yet informative and scientifically correct movie?

Chapter Challenge

Your challenge is to write a screenplay or story, set in your community, that would help audiences understand volcanoes. You need to teach them about volcanic hazards. You also need to help them see volcanoes as part of the Earth system, and to realize that volcanoes affect all communities in some way. Can you use Earth science to create an exciting story and help others understand the hazards and the benefits of volcanoes?

Think about how your story will address the following items:
• Locations of volcanoes closest to your community.
• Evidence that shows past or recent volcanic activity.
• Types of volcanic hazards.

• How volcanoes change the atmosphere, hydrosphere, and other Earth systems.

Assessment Criteria

Think about what you have been asked to do. Scan ahead through the chapter activities to see how they might help you to meet the challenge. Work with your classmates and your teachers to define the criteria for assessing your work. Record all this information. Make sure that you understand the criteria as well as you can before you begin. Your teacher may provide you with a sample rubric to help you get started.

Activity 1

Where are the Volcanoes?

GOALS

In this activity you will:

- Find the latitude and longitude of volcanoes nearest your community when given a map of historically active volcanoes.

- Search for and describe patterns in the global distribution of volcanoes.

- Make inferences about possible locations of future volcanic activity.

- Understand that most volcanism occurs beneath the ocean.

- Understand that map projections distort regions near the poles and eliminate some data.

Think about It

Volcanoes are one of nature's most feared, yet spectacular activities.

- Can volcanoes form anywhere on Earth? Why or why not?

What do you think? Record your ideas about this question in your *EarthComm* notebook. Be prepared to discuss your responses with your small group and the class.

Investigate

1. "Thought experiments" are experiments that scientists dream up and then run in their imagination, rather than in a real laboratory. They are a useful way to develop new ideas and insights into scientific problems. Here's a thought experiment for you to do, to help you understand the Mercator map projection. It wouldn't even be too difficult to do this in real life, if you could obtain the right materials.

Visualize a large, see-through plastic ball. Poke holes on opposite sides, and stick a wooden dowel or a chopstick through to make the North Pole and the South Pole. Install a bright light directly at the center of the ball, somehow. With a felt-tipped pen, draw a fake continent on the ball. Make the continent extend from near the Equator to near the North Pole. Now wrap a clear sheet of stiff plastic around the globe, to make a tight-fitting cylinder that's parallel to the Earth's axis. See the figure on the right for how to arrange this. Turn the light on, and observe how the border of your continent projects onto the plastic cylinder. Trace that image on the cylinder with the felt-tipped pen. Unwrap the cylinder from the globe, and lay it flat on the table. You now have a map with what's called a Mercator projection of your continent!

a) Describe how the image of your continent is changed in shape (distorted) when it is projected onto the cylinder.

b) If you drew a short east–west line with a certain length near the southern end of your continent, and another east–west line with the same length near the northern end of your continent, how would the lengths of the lines compare when they are projected onto the cylinder map?

c) If you drew a short north–south line with a certain length near the southern end of your continent, and another north–south line with the same length near the northern end of your continent, how would the lengths of the lines compare when they are projected onto the cylinder map?

d) How would the image of a continent that is centered on the North Pole project onto the cylinder map?

e) Which part of your map shows the least distortion?

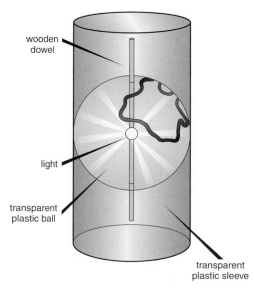

wooden dowel

light

transparent plastic ball

transparent plastic sleeve

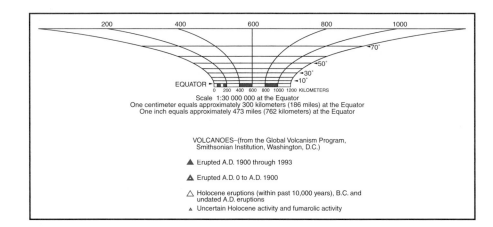

2. Obtain the USGS map called *This Dynamic Planet*. Look at the map key, also shown above, to learn the meaning of the various symbols and how to use the map scale.

   a) What do each of the four kinds of triangles represent?

   b) What do the solid red lines represent?

   c) Describe how the scale of the map changes with latitude.

   d) Does the map cover the entire Earth? Why or why not?

3. For each time interval of volcanic activity shown on the map, find the latitude and longitude of three volcanoes closest to your community.

   a) Make a data table to record your results. When complete, the data table should list 12 volcanoes.

   b) Compare your data with that of other groups in your class. Did your class agree on the locations of the nearest historically active volcanoes? How did you resolve any differences?

4. Obtain a copy of a world map. Use this map to summarize any patterns in the global distribution of volcanoes.

   a) When volcanoes follow a linear pattern, draw a thick line on the world map. Use the string of volcanoes within the Aleutian Islands and southern Alaska as an example.

   b) For the red lines that appear on the USGS map, draw thin lines on your copy of the map. See the examples in the Pacific Ocean near Oregon and Washington.

   c) Where volcanoes are less concentrated, outline (circle) the area that they cover. Try to be as accurate as possible. See the group of volcanoes in the Cascades as an example.

5. When your map is complete, answer the following questions in your notebook:

   a) Are most volcanoes found in random places or do they show a trend or pattern? Explain.

b) Does the USGS map show volcanoes that have not erupted during the last 10,000 years?

c) Does the USGS map show eruptions after 1993, or new volcanoes?

d) Does the USGS map show any volcanoes associated with the red lines in the ocean basins?

e) What information does the map give about the size or hazard of the volcanoes?

f) Suppose that tomorrow a volcano forms somewhere in the United States. Could it form in or near your state? Support your answer with evidence from this activity.

g) What are some limitations of the evidence you used?

Reflecting on the Activity and the Challenge

By looking at a world map of recent volcanic activity you found patterns in the data. This helped you to make inferences about the possible location of the next volcanic eruption in the United States. The data you looked at are incomplete. This may limit the conclusions you can draw. However, you now have some knowledge that will help you decide where in the United States you might "stage" a volcanic eruption.

Digging Deeper

THE GLOBAL DISTRIBUTION OF VOLCANOES

Volcanoes beneath the Sea

The USGS map *This Dynamic Planet* shows historical volcanic activity throughout the world. It tells a story about how our dynamic planet releases its internal storehouse of energy. No single source of data tells the whole story, but a map is a great place to begin.

On average, about 60 of Earth's 550 historically active volcanoes erupt each year. Geologists have long known that volcanoes are abundant along the edges of certain continents. The presence of volcanic rocks on the floors of all ocean basins indicates that volcanoes are far more abundant under water than on land.

→

Geo Words

mid-ocean ridge: a continuous mountain range extending through the North and South Atlantic Oceans, the Indian Ocean, and the South Pacific Ocean

rift valley: the deep central cleft in the crest of the mid-oceanic ridge

magma: naturally occurring molten rock material generated within the Earth

All of the Earth's ocean basins have a continuous mountain range, called a **mid-ocean ridge** extending through them. These ridges, over 80,000 km long in total, are broad rises in the ocean floor. They are usually in water depths of 1000 to 2000 m. *Figure 1* shows a vertical cross section through a mid-ocean ridge. At the crest of the ridge there is a steep-sided **rift valley**. **Magma** (molten rock) from deep in the Earth rises up into the rift valley to form submarine volcanoes. These volcanoes have even been observed by scientists in deep-diving submersibles. All of the floors of the oceans, beneath a thin layer of sediments, consist of volcanic rock, so we know that volcanoes form all along the mid-ocean ridges, at different times at different places. At a few places along the mid-ocean ridges, as in Iceland, volcanic activity is especially strong, and volcanoes build up high enough to form islands.

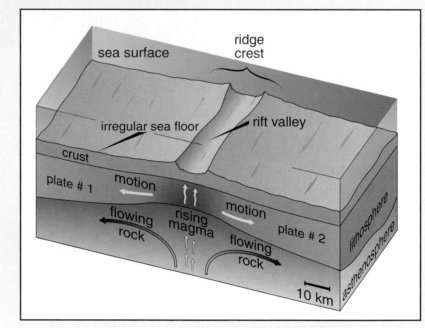

Figure 1 Cross section through a mid-ocean ridge.

Volcanoes on Land

Volcanoes that erupt on land are much more dangerous than volcanoes beneath the ocean. Eruptions along the western edge of the United States have formed the Cascades volcanic mountain range. They also form island chains, like the Aleutians in Alaska. Volcanoes like these are common in a narrow belt all around the Pacific Ocean. Geologists call this the "Ring of Fire." A famous example of an eruption along the Ring of Fire was the dramatic eruption of Mt. St. Helens in Washington in 1980.

Ring of Fire

Around the edges of the Pacific Ocean, the plates of the Pacific Ocean slide down beneath the continents. Look at *Figure 2* to see an example. The Nazca Plate, moving eastward from the East Pacific Ridge, slides down beneath the west coast of South America. The plate is heated as it sinks into the much hotter rocks of the deep Earth. The heat causes fluids, especially water, to leave the plate and rise into overlying hot rocks. The added water lowers the melting point of the solid rock. If enough water is added the rock melts and magma is formed. The magma rises upward, because it is less dense than the rocks. It feeds volcanoes on the overlying plate. Nearly four-fifths of volcanoes on land form where one plate slides beneath another plate.

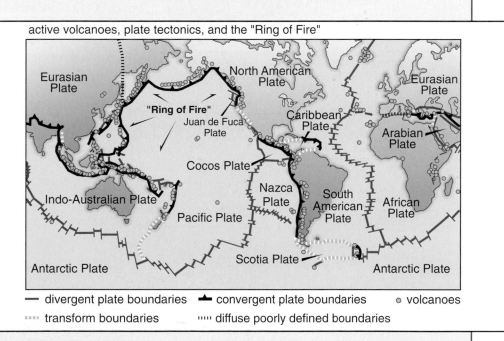

active volcanoes, plate tectonics, and the "Ring of Fire"

— divergent plate boundaries   ◣— convergent plate boundaries   ◦ volcanoes
····· transform boundaries   ''''' diffuse poorly defined boundaries

Figure 2 The plates of the Earth, and the "Ring of Fire" around the Pacific. The circles show active volcanoes.

Volcanoes Formed by Rifting on the Continents

Volcanoes in the East African rift valley form where two parts of the African continent are moving apart from each other. The process is very similar to what happens at mid-ocean ridges. The continental plate is stretched and broken. One of the breaks becomes the main one, and opens up to form the rift valley, as shown in *Figure 3*.

Geo Words

hot spot: a fixed source of abundant rising magma that forms a volcanic center that has persisted for tens of millions of years

map projections: the process of systematically transforming positions on the Earth's spherical surface to a flat map while maintaining spatial relationships

Mercator projection: a map projection in which the Equator is represented by a straight line true to scale, the meridians by parallel straight lines perpendicular to the Equator and equally spaced according to their distance apart at the Equator, and the parallels by straight lines perpendicular to the meridians and the same length as the Equator. There is a great distortion of distances, areas, and shapes at the polar regions

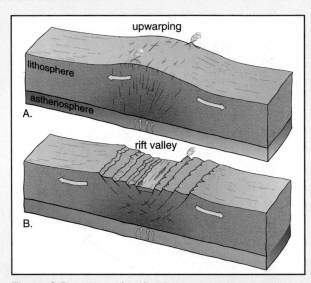

Figure 3 Formation of a rift valley on a continent.

In the United States, continental rifting long ago formed the rocks that make up the tall cliffs on the western bank of the Hudson River. These rocks formed when magma intruded the crust during this rifting. The rocks are seen for more than 80 km along the bank of the Hudson River and can be up to 300 m thick! Other evidence of magma formed during this rifting is found in many states along the East Coast.

Figure 4 Mount Kilimanjaro is a famous example of volcanism at a continental rift. Many other volcanoes in the East African rift valley have erupted in historic times.

Volcanoes at Hot Spots

Volcanoes discussed so far occur near the edges of plates. However, a small percentage of volcanoes occur in the interior of a plate. The Hawaiian Islands, shown in *Figure 5*, are an example. Studies of volcanic rock show that the islands get older to the northwest. Only the youngest island, the "big island" of Hawaii, has active volcanoes.

Here's how geologists explain the pattern of the Hawaiian Islands. Deep beneath Hawaii, there is a fixed source of abundant rising magma, called a **hot spot**. As the

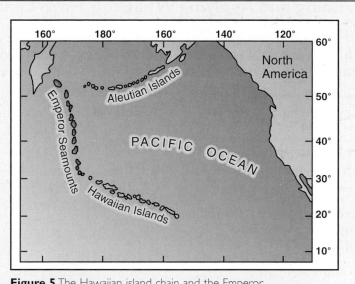

Figure 5 The Hawaiian island chain and the Emperor seamount chain.

Geo Words

seamount: a peaked or flat-topped underwater mountain rising from the ocean floor

Pacific Plate moves to the northwest, away from the East Pacific Ridge, it passes over the fixed hot spot. Magma from the hot spot punches its way through the moving plate to form a chain of islands. The sharp bend in the chain was formed when the direction of movement of the plate changed abruptly at a certain time in the past. Far to the northwest the chain consists of **seamounts**.

Map Projections

There is always a big problem in drawing a map of the world, because you have to try to show the curved surface of the Earth's globe on a flat sheet of paper. Many different ways of doing this, called **map projections**, have been developed, but they all have some kind of distortion. The USGS map uses a **Mercator projection**. As you move away from the Equator, the map becomes more and more distorted. For example, it makes all lines of latitude look like they are equal in length. This makes it difficult to measure distances on the map. Another problem is that the USGS map stops at 70° north and south latitude, because of the Mercator projection. This keeps you from seeing all of the data. For example, the USGS map cuts off the mid-ocean ridge north of Iceland. The scale of the map also presents a problem. The larger the area covered by the map, the less detail the map can show. In this case, the triangular symbols that represent volcanoes often overlap in areas with many volcanoes. This makes them difficult to count.

Check Your Understanding

1. What evidence do geologists have that volcanoes occur on the ocean floor?

2. What is the Ring of Fire, and where is it located?

3. Where do most volcanoes on land form?

4. How are rift valleys formed?

5. What are hot spots? Provide an example of a hot spot on Earth.

6. Why does the horizontal scale of a Mercator projection increase with latitude?

Understanding and Applying What You Have Learned

1. What difficulties did you have finding the latitude and longitude of volcanoes?

2. Where on Earth do most volcanoes occur? Explain your answer.

3. Are most volcanoes on land caused by the Earth's plates moving away from each other or moving toward each other? Explain your answer.

4. In your own words, describe the likely cause of historically active volcanoes in:

    a) The continental United States.
    b) The Aleutian Islands and southern Alaska.
    c) The Hawaiian Islands.

5. Based on your results from this investigation, list the five states that you think are most likely to experience the next volcanic eruption. Explain each choice.

6. Of the average of 60 volcanoes that erupt in any given year, how many are likely to erupt along the Ring of Fire?

7. Why did the Mercator projection not show volcanoes near the Earth's poles?

8. Do most volcanoes on land occur in the Northern Hemisphere or the Southern Hemisphere? Explain why you think this is so.

Preparing for the Chapter Challenge

Think about how you can help the audience understand why you chose the probable location of the volcanic eruption for your story. Explain the map that you made for this activity. Note the volcanic eruptions that are closest to your area. Explain where most volcanoes occur in the United States. You should also note where they have not happened recently.

Inquiring Further

1. **Eruptions near your community**

   Find out more about the historical eruptions at the volcanoes nearest your community. The Volcano World web site lists hundreds of historically active volcanoes. (Consult the AGI *EarthComm* web site for current addresses.) Your data table of latitudes and longitudes will help you to identify them.

2. **Volcanoes and the water on Earth (the hydrosphere)**

   Research to find answers to the following questions, and any other questions which you have formed:

- How do volcanoes at mid-ocean ridges affect the temperature of seawater?

- How do volcanoes change the chemistry of seawater?

- How does seawater affect the composition of the volcanic rock that is formed at the mid-ocean ridge?

- Would volcanoes affect a small body of seawater, such as the Red Sea, the same way as a large ocean like the Atlantic?

- Can a change in the volume of volcanic rock formed at mid-ocean ridges change sea level?

Activity 2

Volcanic Landforms

GOALS

In this activity you will:

- Make a topographic map from a model.

- Understand the meanings of contour line, contour interval, and relief.

- Interpret topographic maps.

- Recognize volcanic landforms on a topographic map, and predict where lava would flow on them.

- Understand basic relationships between magma composition and type of volcano formed.

Think about It

When most people think about volcanoes, they probably have in mind a steep-sided cone. Many volcanoes, however, have very gentle slopes.

- Why do different volcanoes have different shapes?

What do you think? Record your ideas about this question in your *EarthComm* notebook. Include a quick sketch for each question. Be prepared to discuss your responses with your small group and the class.

Investigate

1. Use a piece of paper and tape to make a model of a volcano. The model should be small enough to fit into a shoebox.

2. Draw horizontal curves on the model at regular heights above the table. To help you draw the lines, attach a strip of stiff cardboard at right angles to a centimeter ruler at the 1-cm mark, as shown in the diagram. Hold the ruler upright on the table, with the "zero" end down, and move it around the model so that the cardboard strip is near the surface of the model. Make a series of small dots on the model at this 1-cm height, and then connect the dots to form a horizontal curve. Repeat this with the cardboard strip attached at the 2-cm mark. Continue increasing the height above the table by 1 cm until you reach the top of the model.

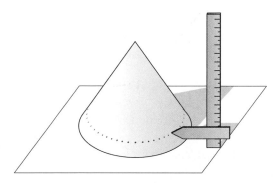

3. Place the model into a shoebox.

4. Clip an overhead transparency onto a clear clipboard. Lay the clipboard on the box.

5. Look straight down into the top of the shoebox at the lines you drew on the mountain. With a grease pencil or marker, trace the lines onto the transparency. Be sure to keep looking straight down, whenever you're tracing the lines! Also, it might help to keep one eye closed. These are contour lines, or lines of equal elevation above sea level.

6. Remove the transparency from the box. Write an elevation on each line of the transparency. Let each centimeter in height on the model represent 100 m in elevation on the map. The numbers should increase toward the center of the transparency.

7. Compare your map to the map of Mt. St. Helens shown below. Answer the following questions in your notebook and on your map:

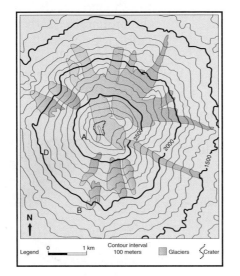

Legend 0 1 km   Contour interval 100 meters   ▨ Glaciers   ⌇ Crater

a) Describe two similarities between the maps.

b) Note the legend on the map of Mt. St. Helens. Add a legend to your map. Include a scale, north arrow, and contour interval.

c) What do the shaded regions on the map of Mt. St. Helens represent?

d) Why do the shaded regions cross the contour lines at right angles?

e) Which part of Mt. St. Helens is steeper, the slope between 1500 m and 2000 m, or the slope between 2000 m and 2500 m? Explain your answer.

f) What are the lowest and highest elevations on the map of Mt. St. Helens? What is the difference in elevation between these two points?

g) Note the locations A, B, C, and D on the map. If lava erupted at point A, would it flow to point B, C, or D? Explain why.

Reflecting on the Activity and the Challenge

You made a map from a model of a volcano. The map showed lines of equal elevation. The lines are contour lines, and the map is a topographic map. You can use topographic maps to predict volcanic hazards. Gravity pulls the lava erupted from volcanoes downhill. A topographic map shows the paths the lava might take. It might also help you to guess whether a certain region has volcanoes.

Digging Deeper

TOPOGRAPHY OF VOLCANIC REGIONS

Topographic Maps

Topographic maps have **contour lines**. These are curves that connect all points at the same elevation. The **contour interval** is the difference in elevation between adjacent contour lines. A **topographic map** shows how steep or gentle a slope is. It also shows the elevation and shape of the land. **Relief** is the difference in elevation between the highest and lowest points on the map.

The following are some important points to consider when interpreting topographic maps:

- Contour lines never cross (but two or more can run together, where there is a vertical cliff).
- The closer together the contour lines, the steeper the slope.
- Contour lines for closed depressions, such as a volcanic crater, are marked with "tick marks" (short lines at right angles to the contour line) pointing downslope, into the depression.
- On most topographic maps, every fifth contour line on a map is darker and its elevation is always marked.

Magma Composition

Volcanoes are often pictured as cone-shaped mountains. However, volcanoes come in many shapes and sizes. Ice, wind, and rain can change the shape of a volcano, both between eruptions and after the volcano becomes dormant. A large eruption or giant landslide can remove the top or side of a volcano. The chemical composition of magma can have an even greater effect on the shape the volcano takes as it forms.

Magma is a mixture of liquid, melted rock, and dissolved gases. The most abundant chemical elements in magma are silicon and oxygen. As the magma cools, minerals form. Silicon and oxygen are the building blocks of the most common minerals, called silicate minerals, that form from magmas. One silicon atom and four oxygen atoms become tightly bonded together to form an ion, called the silicate ion. These combine with ions of other elements, mainly aluminum, iron, calcium, sodium, potassium, and magnesium, to form silicate minerals.

When geologists make a chemical analysis of an **igneous rock**, a rock that formed when molten materials became solid, they express the results as percentages of several "oxides," such as SiO_2, Al_2O_3, or CaO. In one

Geo Words

contour lines: a line on a map that connects points of equal elevation of the land surface

contour interval: the vertical distance between the elevations represented by two successive contour lines on a topographic map

topographic map: a map showing the topographic features of the land surface

relief: the physical configuration of a part of the Earth's surface, with reference to variations of height and slope or to irregularities of the land surface

igneous rock: rock or mineral that solidified from molten or partly molten material, i.e., from magma

Geo Words

silica: material with the composition SiO_2

shield volcano: a broad, gently sloping volcanic cone of flat-dome shape, usually several tens or hundreds of square miles in extent

way, this is a fake, because real oxide minerals are a very small part of most igneous rocks. It's just a generally accepted practice. Because silicon and oxygen are the most abundant elements in magmas, the "oxide" SiO_2, called **silica**, is the most abundant "oxide." The percentage of silica in magma varies widely. This is important to know for two reasons. First, magmas rich in silica tend to have more dissolved gases. Second, silica content affects how easily magma flows. Magmas that are rich in silica do not flow nearly as easily as magmas that are poor in silica. Because of this, silica-rich magmas are more likely to remain below the Earth's surface, at shallow depths, rather than flowing freely out onto the surface. These two factors combine to make eruptions of silica-rich magmas likely to be dangerously explosive. Here's why: As the magma rests below the surface, the dissolved gases gradually bubble out, because the pressure on the magma is much less than it was down deep in the Earth, where the magma was formed. It's just like what happens when you pour a can of soda into a glass: the carbon dioxide dissolved in the soda gradually bubbles out of solution. Unlike your soda, however, the magma is so stiff that the bubbles can't readily escape. Instead they build up pressure in the magma, and that often leads to a catastrophic explosion. The table in *Figure 1* shows how magma properties relate to magma composition.

Properties of Magma as They Relate to Magma Composition			
Magma Property	**Magma Composition (percent silica content)**		
	Low Silica	**Medium Silica**	**High Silica**
Silica content (% SiO_2)	~ 50	~ 60	~ 70
Viscosity	lowest	medium	highest
Tendency to form lava	highest	medium	lowest
Tendency to erupt explosively	lowest	medium	highest
Melting temperature	highest	medium	lowest
Volume of an eruption	highest	medium	lowest

Figure 1

Adapted from *Earth Science*, 7th Edition, Tarbuck and Lutgens, 1994

Types of Volcanic Landforms

When low-silica magma erupts, lava tends to flow freely and far. If it erupts from a single opening (vent) or closely spaced vents, it forms a broad **shield volcano**, as shown in *Figure 2*.

Figure 2 Volcanoes such as these are called shield volcanoes because they somewhat resemble a warrior's shield. They are formed when low-silica magma erupts.

Figure 3 The eruption of low-silica magma along long, narrow openings in the Columbia Plateau flowed over a vast area. The result was a broad lava plateau that makes up the cliffs.

Silica-rich magmas are far less fluid. They often stop moving before they reach the surface. If they do reach the surface, they ooze slowly, like toothpaste squeezed out of a vertical tube. The thick, stiff lava forms volcanic domes with steep slopes, as shown in *Figure 4*. If the volcano's vent gets plugged, gases cannot escape and pressure builds up. The pressure can be released in a violent eruption that blasts pieces of lava and rock (pyroclastics) into the atmosphere.

➡

Geo Words

composite cone (stratovolcano): a volcano that is constructed of alternating layers of lava and pyroclastic deposits

caldera: a large basin-shaped volcanic depression, more or less circular, the diameter of which is many times greater than that of the included vent or vents

Figure 4 Silica-rich magma does not flow readily and often forms a volcanic dome such as the one shown in this photograph.

A **composite cone**, as shown in *Figure 5*, forms by many eruptions of material with medium or high silica content. They erupt violently when pressure builds up in the magma. After the explosion, gooey (viscous) lava oozes out of the top. The volcano becomes quiet. Over time, pressure may build up and repeat the cycle. Composite volcanoes are tall and have steep slopes because the lava does not flow easily.

Figure 5 Composite cones include the beautiful yet potentially deadly Cascades in the northwestern United States (Shasta, Rainier, Mt. St. Helens, etc.).

When a very large volume of magma is erupted, the overlying rocks may collapse, much like a piston pushing down in a cylinder. The collapse produces a hole or depression at the surface called a **caldera**, shown in *Figure 6*. A caldera is much larger than the original vent from which the magma erupted.

Figure 6 Calderas are deceptive volcanic structures. They are large depressions rather than conical peaks. Oregon's Crater Lake, formed nearly 7000 years ago, is an example of this type of volcano.

Check Your Understanding

1. Explain in your own words the meaning of a contour line, contour interval, relief, and topographic map.

2. Arrange corn syrup, water, and vegetable oil in order of low to high viscosity.

3. What is the silica content of magma that has a low viscosity?

4. Why do silica-poor magmas produce broad volcanoes with gentle slopes?

5. Why does high-silica magma tend to form volcanic domes with steep sides?

6. How is a caldera formed?

Understanding and Applying What You Have Learned

1. What is the contour interval on the topographic map of Mt. St. Helens?

2. Sketch a contour map of a volcano that shows:

   a) a gentle slope
   b) a steep slope
   c) a nearly vertical cliff
   d) a crater or depression at the top

3. Imagine that your paper model was a real volcano. Lava begins to erupt from the top. Shade your topographic map to show where a stream of lava would flow. Explain your drawing.

4. For the volcanoes shown in *Figures 2* and *5*, sketch a topographic map. Show what the volcano would look like from above. Apply the general rules for interpreting topographic maps. Include a simple legend.

5. Use the topographic map below, or obtain a topographic map of your state or region, to answer the questions.
   a) Record the contour interval, and the highest and lowest elevations. Calculate the relief.

b) Identify areas that look like the volcanic landforms you explored in this activity. Describe possible paths of lava flows.

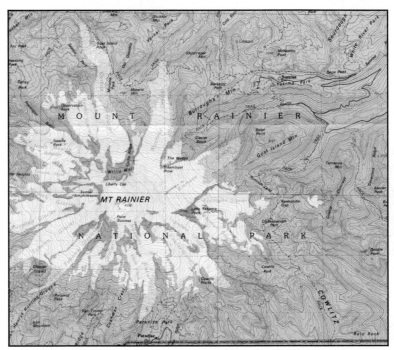

Preparing for the Chapter Challenge

In your story or play decide how you will convey to the audience the importance of using topographic maps to identify volcanic landforms. Indicate how the maps can also help geologists predict the paths of lava.

Inquiring Further

1. **Cascade volcano in your community**

   Build a scale model of a Cascade volcano and a scale model of your community. To do so, find a topographic map of a Cascade volcano. Trace selected contours on separate sheets of paper. Cut and glue each contour level onto pieces of card or foam board. Stack the board to make a three-dimensional model. Do the same using a topographic map of your community. Make sure that the scales of the maps match.

 Be cautious when cutting foam board.

Activity 3

Volcanic Hazards: Flows

GOALS

In this activity you will:

- Measure and understand how volume, temperature, slope, and channelization affect the flow of fluid.

- Apply an understanding of factors that control lava flows, pyroclastic flows, and lahars (mudflows).

- Apply understanding of topographic maps to predict lahar flow (mudflow) patterns from a given set of data.

- Describe volcanic hazards associated with various kinds of flows.

- Become aware of the benefits of Earth science information in planning evacuations and making decisions.

- Show understanding of the nature of science and a controlled experiment.

Think about It

Only one person in the entire city of St. Pierre, on Martinique in the Caribbean, survived the hot ash and rock fragments that swept over the city from the explosive eruption of Mt. Pelée in 1902. He was a prisoner in a dungeon deep underground.

- How do volcanoes affect the biosphere?

What do you think? Record your ideas about this question in your *EarthComm* notebook. Be prepared to discuss your responses with your small group and the class.

Cleveland High School
63171268

Investigate

Part A: Area of Lava Flow

1. Suppose a volcano produces twice the amount of lava than in a prior eruption. Write a hypothesis based upon the following question: What is the relationship between the volume of an eruption and the size of the area it covers?

   a) Record your hypothesis in your notebook.

2. Check your hypothesis to see if it could be disproved. A hypothesis must be a prediction that can be falsified. The statement "Some stars will never be discovered," cannot be disproved. Therefore, it is not a hypothesis.

3. In this investigation, you will use liquid soap to simulate flow during a volcanic eruption. Volcanic flows include lava, gases, and mixtures of solid particles and gases.

   a) In your notebook, set up a data table. The table should help you record the relationship between the volume of liquid soap and the surface area that the soap covers. You will do trials with 0.5, 1, 2, 4, 8, and 16 cm^3 (cubic centimeters) of liquid soap.

4. Place an overhead transparency of a square grid on a flat surface.

5. Pour 0.5 cm^3 of liquid soap onto the transparent graph paper.

6. When the soap stops flowing, measure the area of the flow.

   a) Record the area of the flow in your data table.

7. Wipe the surface clean. Repeat the trials using 1, 2, 4, 8, and 16 cm^3 of liquid soap.

   a) Record your data in your table. Look for patterns.

8. Develop a hypothesis and design a test for one of the following questions related to the flow of fluids. Remember that during scientific inquiry, you can return to the materials or your data and revise your procedures as needed.

   • What effect does temperature have on resistance to flow (viscosity)?

   • What happens to fluid when slope changes from steep to gentle?

   • What effects would you see if fluids moved through narrow channels?

   a) Write down your hypothesis.

   b) Record your procedure in your notebook.

   c) Describe the variables you investigated.

9. Present your procedure to your teacher for approval. Then run your test.

   a) Record your data.

   b) Summarize your conclusions.

   c) Was your hypothesis correct?

 Heat sources can cause burns. Hot objects and liquids look like cool ones. Feel for heat at a distance before touching.

 Clean up any spills immediately. Liquids being used can cause floors and equipment to be sticky or slippery.

Part B: Travel Time of Lahars

1. Examine the table of expected travel times of lahars (mudflows) triggered by a large eruption of Mt. St. Helens. The values in the table come from computer simulations and actual behavior of mudflows in the 1980 eruption.

Expected Travel Times for Lahars Triggered by a Large Eruption of Mt. St. Helens (USGS)		
Distance (via river channels) from Mt. St. Helens (km)	Estimated travel time (hours:minutes)	
	North Fork Toutle River	South Fork Toutle River, Pine Creek, Muddy River, Kalama River
10	0:37	0:11
20	1:08	0:30
30	1:37	0:54
40	2:16	1:21
50	2:53	1:49
60	3:27	2:20
70	3:48	2:53
80	4:43	3:31
90	6:36	4:18
100	8:50	5:12

2. Convert the travel times into minutes.

   a) Record the times in your notebook.

3. Make a graph of travel time (in minutes on the vertical axis) versus distance (in kilometers on the horizontal axis) for both data sets.

   a) Plot both data sets on the same graph.

   b) Connect the data points so that you can compare the data.

   c) Calculate an average velocity for mudflows along each fork of the Toutle River.

4. Answer the following questions in your notebook:

   a) Which area (North Fork or South Fork) is more likely to have a steeper gradient? Use the results of your investigation in **Activity 2** to support your answer.

   b) Explain the evidence in your graphs that suggests the gradients are not constant?

   c) Based on the information in the table, explain whether or not you think that a community located 50 km from Mt. St. Helens along either of these river valleys would have time to evacuate in the event of an unexpected massive eruption.

Reflecting on the Activity and the Challenge

In this activity, you found that temperature, volume, channels, and slope affect the flow of liquids. Analyzing data from a computer model, you predicted the flow of volcanic fluids down river valleys near Mt. St. Helens. You can now describe the volcanic hazards associated with various kinds of flows and factors which affect the flows. In your movie you may wish to locate a town in the path of a potentially dangerous flow.

Geo Words

lava: molten rock that issues from a volcano or fissure

lava flow: an outpouring of molten lava from a vent or fissure; also, the solidified body of rock so formed

viscosity: the property of a fluid to offer internal resistance to flow

pyroclastic flow: a high-density mixture of hot ash and rock fragments with hot gases formed by a volcanic explosion or aerial expulsion from a volcanic vent

Digging Deeper

FLOW-RELATED HAZARDS

Lava

Lava flows are streams of molten rock that come from vents and fissures in the Earth's crust. Lava flows destroy almost everything in their path. However, most lava flows move slowly enough for people to move out of the way. Slope and cooling affect the flow of lava. Lava flows faster on a steeper slope. As lava cools, it flows less and less easily. The term **viscosity** is used to describe a fluid's resistance to flow or internal friction. As lava cools, it becomes more viscous.

Lava that is low in silica is less viscous. (See *Figure 1* in the previous activity that shows the properties of magma as they relate to magma composition.) Flows of low-silica lava can travel tens

Figure 1 Lava tubes form when the surface of a flow cools and crusts over, but the interior of the flow is still fluid.

of kilometers from the source. Sometimes it sets up an internal "plumbing system." The surface may cool, crust over, and insulate the interior. This keeps the lava at a higher temperature as it moves away from the source. Evidence of this is found in the lava tubes, as shown in *Figure 1*, found in flows of low-silica lava. When lava breaks out of the leading edge of a flow, the lava can drain out. A hollow tube remains behind.

Basalt flows can move at speeds of up to 10 km/h (kilometers per hour) on steep slopes. On a shallow slope, basalt flows typically move less than one kilometer per hour. Basaltic lava flows confined within channels or lava tubes can travel at speeds of 45 km/h. Basaltic lava flows can cover a considerable area. The largest lava flow in recent history occurred in 1783 at Laki in Iceland. Lava erupted from the Laki fissure covered 500 km^2, an area roughly equal to 100,000 soccer fields.

Since the start of the eruption in 1983, lava flows erupted from the Kilauea volcano in Hawaii and entered communities repeatedly. The flows destroyed more than 180 homes, a visitor center in a national park, highways, and historical and archaeological sites. The village of Kalapana was buried in 1990 by 15–25 m of lava erupted during a period of seven months. See *Figure 2*.

It is sometimes possible to control the flow of lava. In 1973, lava flows at Heimaey, Iceland threatened to cut off a vital harbor. Citizens sprayed water onto the lava from ships in the harbor. This stopped the flow. Lava flows can also be diverted away from populated areas. Workers must carve a new channel or pathway through the landscape for the lava to follow.

Andesitic lava is cooler and has a higher silica content than basaltic lava. It moves only a few kilometers per hour. Andesitic lava rarely flows beyond the base of the volcano. Dacitic and rhyolitic lavas are even higher in silica and are even more viscous. Their lava usually forms steep mountains called lava domes, which extend only short distances from the vent.

Pyroclastic Flows

Topography plays a role in two other types of volcanic flows: pyroclastic flows and lahars. **Pyroclastic flows** are high-density mixtures of hot ash and rock fragments with hot gases. Pyroclastic flows occur in explosive eruptions. They move away from the vent at speeds up to 350 km/h. They often have two parts. A lower flow of coarse fragments moves along the ground. A turbulent cloud of ash rises above the lower flow. Both parts ride upon a cushion of air. This enables the material to move

Figure 2 The former village of Kalapana was buried by lava flows.

→

29

Geo Words

lahar: a wet mixture of water, mud, and volcanic rock fragments, with the consistency of wet concrete, that flows down the slopes of a volcano and its river valleys

rapidly. The more dense material follows the topography in a twisting path downslope. Pyroclastic flows are extremely dangerous. They destroy everything in their path. The pyroclastic flow produced by the Mt. St. Helens eruption, as shown in *Figure 3*, was impressive, but it was small compared to pyroclastic flows in prehistoric times.

Lahar

A **lahar** is a wet mixture of water, mud, and volcanic rock fragments, with the consistency of wet concrete, that flows down the slopes of a volcano and its river valleys. Lahars can carry rock debris ranging in size from clay, to gravel, to boulders more than 10 m in diameter.

Figure 3 Flow of pyroclastic materials from Mt. St. Helens destroyed everything in its path.

Check Your Understanding

1. Name two factors that influence the viscosity of a lava flow.

2. Describe two ways in which lava flows can be controlled.

3. What is a pyroclastic flow?

4. What is a lahar?

5. How are lahars formed?

6. Explain how topography influences volcanic flows.

Eruptions may trigger lahars. Heat from the eruption may melt snow and ice, or the eruption may displace water from a mountain lake or river. Lahars sometimes form when the erupted material dams the mountain's drainage, causing a lake to form. The lake may spill over the loose volcanic material and send water and debris down valley. Lahars are also formed when rain soaks the loose volcanic debris during or after an eruption, causing it to start to flow. As a lahar flows downstream, it poses a risk to everyone in the valley downstream. When a lahar finally comes to a stop, it can bury an entire village under many meters of mud.

Figure 4 On the left side of the photograph, the dark region extending down the side of Mt. St. Helens is an example of a lahar flow.

Understanding and Applying What You Have Learned

1. How does the volume of an eruption affect the area? Describe any mathematical pattern in your data.

2. When the Mauna Loa volcano erupted in 1984, lava flowed toward Hilo, Hawaii. It is an excellent example of how scientists used their understanding of the factors that control the flow of lava to predict where lava would flow and decide whether to evacuate residents. The map shows the path of a series of lava flows from Mauna Loa. Each flow is given a letter (A through G) in the order it happened.

    a) Look at flow D on the map. What is the elevation of the top of flow D, and what is the elevation of the Kulani Prison?
    b) How close did flow D get to the prison?
    c) Do you think that the prison was put on alert?

    d) Look at flow E on the map. The flow was channeled. Do you think it moved swiftly or slowly? Explain.
    e) Lava from flow E crossed an important road. It headed straight for the city of Hilo. The lava then broke through walls of the channel. What do you think happened to the width of the flow after it broke through the channel? How do you think this changed the speed of the flow?

3. Refer back to the reading that described the lava flow at Heimaey, Iceland.

    a) Why did spraying the lava flow with water slow it down?
    b) This was a very unusual circumstance. What factors made this effort successful?

4. Why might a lahar (mudflow of volcanic debris and water) affect a community more severely than a lava flow?

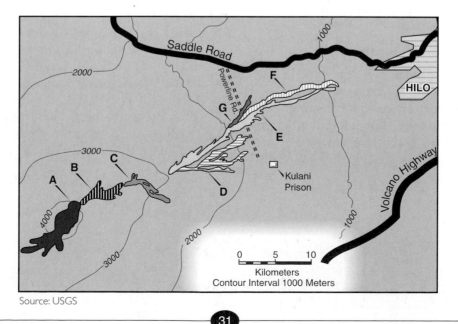

Source: USGS

Integrated Coordinated Science for the 21st Century

Preparing for the Chapter Challenge

Think about what you have learned about volcanic flows. Prepare a one-page information sheet to raise awareness of how flows affect communities. Focus on three or more of the following:

a) How local topography controls where lava would flow.

b) Major roads that must be protected to ensure evacuation.

c) Natural and developed areas most likely to be affected.

d) Areas least likely to be affected, and why.

e) Living things that would not escape advancing flows.

f) Ways that flows might be controlled (diverting the flow, using water, and so on).

Consider how you can creatively work this information into your story line.

Inquiring Further

1. **Research a famous lava flow**

   Search the web for information about the Columbia River basalt group in the northwest. Prepare a report to the class about the members of this famous basalt group in relation to largest, longest, thickest, cooling characteristics, effects on ancient topography, and cause.

2. **Lava and the biosphere**

   How have lava flows at Mauna Loa and Kilauea volcanoes affected Hawaiian communities? How does the lava that enters the Pacific Ocean in Hawaii affect coastal ecosystems? What kinds of organisms develop and thrive at the "black smokers" along mid-ocean ridges? Research the 1783 Laki fissure flow in Iceland. It was 40 km long and covered 500 km^2. How did it affect vegetation and livestock?

3. **Lava and the cryosphere**

   What happens when lava erupts from an ice-capped or snow-capped volcano? This is an issue in the Cascade volcanoes. Mt. Rainier, which overlooks Seattle, has 27 glaciers. Some insights might be gained from exploring the recent eruption at Grimsvotn in Iceland.

Activity 4   Volcanic Hazards: Airborne Debris

GOALS

In this activity you will:

- Understand why ash from volcanic eruptions can affect a much larger region than lava, pyroclastic flows, or lahars.

- Define tephra and describe some of the hazards it creates.

- Interpret maps and graph data from volcanic eruptions to understand the range in scale of volcanic eruptions.

- Understand that the explosive force of a volcano is not the only factor that determines its potential to cause loss of life and property.

- Interpret maps of wind speed and direction to predict the movement of volcanic ash.

Think about It

Volcanic ash put into the stratosphere from the great eruption of Krakatoa in Indonesia (see **Getting Started**) caused spectacular sunsets all around the world for many months.

- Could material from a volcanic eruption ever reach your community? Explain your ideas.

What do you think? Record your ideas about this question in your *EarthComm* notebook. Be prepared to discuss your responses with your small group and the class.

Investigate

1. Look at the map of the 1980 eruption of Mt. St. Helens. It shows the pattern of ash. Use the map to answer the following questions:

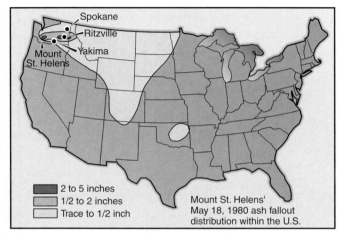

2 to 5 inches
1/2 to 2 inches
Trace to 1/2 inch

Mount St. Helens' May 18, 1980 ash fallout distribution within the U.S.

Distribution of ash from Mt. St. Helens eruption.

a) How many states showed at least a trace of volcanic ash?

b) In what direction did the ash move?

c) Was Canada affected by ash from Mt. St. Helens? Why or why not?

d) Would you consider this a small, medium, large, or gigantic eruption? Explain your choice.

2. Make a bar graph of the data shown in the table.

a) Plot the name of each volcano on the horizontal axis.

b) Plot the volume of volcanic eruption on the vertical axis. Arrange the volumes in order from least to greatest.

Volumes of Volcanic Eruptions		
Volcano	**Date**	**Volume (cubic kilometers)**
Ilopango, El Salvador	300	40
Krakatoa, Indonesia	1883–84	2.4
Long Valley, California (Bishop Tuff)	740,000 years ago	500
Mazama, Oregon	4000 B.C.	75
Mt. Pelée, Martinique	1902	0.5
Mt. St. Helens, Washington	1980	1.25
Nevado del Ruiz, Colombia	1985	0.025
Pinatubo, Philippines	1991	10
Santorini, Greece	1450 B.C.	60
Tambora, Indonesia	1815	150
Valles, New Mexico	1.4 million years ago	300
Vesuvius, Italy	79	3
Yellowstone, Wyoming (Lava Creek Ash)	600,000 years ago	1000

Note: Volumes are approximate.

3. Use your graph and the table to answer the following questions. Record your answers in your notebook.

   a) Can you group the eruptions by size (small, medium, and so on)? Mark the groups on your plot. Explain how you chose the groups.

   b) What group does the 1980 eruption of Mt. St. Helens fit into?

   c) Suppose you wanted to predict the area that would be covered with ash by each eruption. What other information (besides volume erupted) would help you to predict how far the ash would go?

4. The following map shows the areas covered by five of the eruptions in the data table. Use the map, data table, and your bar graph to do the following:

   a) Rank the area of eruptions in order from smallest to largest. Record your rankings.

   b) Compare the areas to the volumes. Describe any relationships.

   c) Compare the location of each volcano to the path of the ash. Describe any patterns. What might explain any patterns you see?

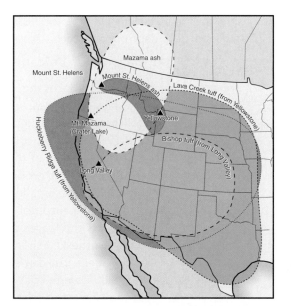

Reflecting on the Activity and the Challenge

This activity gave you a chance to explore factors that affect the movement of volcanic ash. How did this change your ideas about the areas that can be affected by an erupting volcano? Be sure to include the effect of airborne volcanic hazards into your story line.

Geo Words

tephra: a collective term for all the particles ejected from a volcano and transported through the air. It includes volcanic dust, ash, cinders, lapilli, scoria, pumice, bombs, and blocks

volcanic bomb: a blob of lava that was ejected while viscous and received a rounded shape (larger than 64 mm in diameter) while in flight

lapilli: pyroclastics in the general size range of 2 to 64 mm

ash: fine pyroclastic material (less than 2 mm in diameter)

Digging Deeper

AIRBORNE RELEASES

Particle Types

Tephra is a term for pieces of volcanic rock and lava that are ejected into the air. It ranges from less than 0.1 mm to more than one meter in diameter. Tephra is classified by size. Names for sizes of tephra include **volcanic bombs** (greater than 64 mm), **lapilli** (between 2 and 64 mm), and **ash** (less than 2 mm). Bombs and lapilli usually fall to the ground on or near the volcano. Ash can travel hundreds to thousands of kilometers. (See *Figure 1*.) The height of the ash and the wind speed control how far the ash travels.

Distribution

A volcanic eruption can send ash many kilometers into the atmosphere. Ash from the 1980 eruption of Mt. St. Helens reached a height of 19 km. Winds carried the ash to the east. Five days after the eruption, instruments in New England detected ash. An eruption at Yellowstone 2 million years ago produced 1000 times as much ash. An area of 1000 km^2 received one meter of ash. Ten centimeters of ash covered an area of 10,000 km^2. You could look at it this way: if the ash from Mt. St. Helens filled a shoe box, the ash from Yellowstone would fill a bedroom to a depth of a meter!

Hazards of Volcanic Ash

Volcanic ash presents many kinds of hazards. Ash that falls on homes, factories, and schools can collapse roofs. More than 300 people died after the 1991 eruption of Mt. Pinatubo in the Philippines. Most of these deaths were caused by roof collapse. At ground level, fine ash causes breathing problems in humans and animals. It can also damage automobile and truck engines. Ash that coats the leaves of plants interferes with photosynthesis. Ash injected higher into the atmosphere can damage aircraft. In the last 15 years, 80 commercial aircraft have been damaged as they flew through volcanic ash. The only death outside the immediate area of Mt. St. Helens occurred from the crash of a small plane that was flying through the ash. Ash that falls on the slopes of a volcano poses great risk. When soaked by rain, loose ash can form lahars. Years after the eruption, lahars remain a source of concern to communities at the base of Mt. Pinatubo.

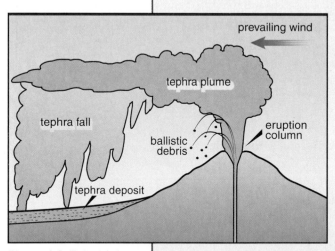

Figure I Ballistic debris refers to volcanic bombs and lapilli that fall on or near the volcano. Ash can travel much further.

Figure 2 Volcanic ash landing on buildings can result in death. Volcanic ash is also a hazard to airplanes on the ground as well as in the air.

Volcanic Explosivity Index

The table in *Figure 3* is a scale of eruption magnitude. The scale is known as **Volcanic Explosivity Index**, or VEI. The VEI is based on the volume of erupted material and the height it reaches. The size of an eruption depends upon several factors. Two important factors are the composition of the magma and the amount of gas dissolved in the magma. The viscosity of a magma depends on two things: the temperature of the magma, and its chemical composition. The higher the silica content of magma, the more viscous it is. The more viscous it is, the more likely it is for gas pressure to build. High-silica volcanoes, like Yellowstone, erupt extremely violently, but on a scale of tens or hundreds of thousands of years. Volcanoes with intermediate silica contents, like Mt. St. Helens, commonly produce violent eruptions with a frequency of hundreds or thousands of years. Silica-poor magmas, like those erupted at Kilauea, feed less explosive eruptions that occur more often.

Geo Words

Volcanic Explosivity Index: the percentage of pyroclastics among the total products of a volcanic eruption

Volcanic Explosivity Index (VEI)				
VEI	Plume Height	Volume	How often	Example
0	<100 m	1000's m^3	Daily	Kilauea
1	100–1000 m	10,000's m^3	Daily	Stromboli
2	1–5 km	1,000,000's m^3	Weekly	Galeras, 1992
3	3–15 km	10,000,000's m^3	Yearly	Ruiz, 1985
4	10–25 km	100,000,000's m^3	10's of years	Galunggung, 1982
5	>25 km	1 km^3	100's of years	St. Helens, 1980
6	>25 km	10's km^3	100's of years	Krakatoa, 1883
7	>25 km	100's km^3	1000's of years	Tambora, 1815

Figure 3

Check Your Understanding

1. Review any words from the **Digging Deeper** sections of the previous activities that are used in this section but may still be unfamiliar to you. Briefly explain the meaning of each of the following terms: lahar, pyroclastic flow, caldera.

2. In your own words explain the meaning of tephra and how volcanic bombs, lapilli, and ash relate to tephra.

3. Name two factors that can affect the distance that volcanic ash can travel.

4. How does the silica content of magma affect how explosive a volcano can be?

5. a) What does VEI represent?

   b) Is VEI on its own a good indicator of the dangers involved with a volcanic eruption? Explain your answer.

It might seem that the number of deaths caused by an eruption should always increase as the VEI increases. The table of VEI and deadliest eruptions in *Figure 4* shows that this is not the case. For example, mudflows after the 1985 eruption of Nevado del Ruiz (Colombia) killed more than 25,000 people. This was the worst volcanic disaster since Mount Pelée in 1902. However, both eruptions had a VEI below five. Of the seven most deadly eruptions since A.D. 1500, only Tambora and Krakatoa erupted with greater explosive force (VEI above 5).

Volcanic Explosivity Index (VEI) of the Deadliest Eruptions since 1500 A.D.			
Eruption	**Year**	**VEI**	**Casualties**
Nevado del Ruiz, Colombia	1985	3	25,000
Mount Pelée, Martinique	1902	4	30,000
Krakatoa, Indonesia	1883	6	36,000
Tambora, Indonesia	1815	7	92,000
Unzen, Japan	1792	3	15,000
Lakagigar (Laki), Iceland	1783	4	9000
Kelut, Indonesia	1586	4	10,000

Figure 4

Tambora erupted in 1815. It had a VEI of 7. Pyroclastic flows streamed down its slopes. Ash rose 44 km. About 150 km^3 of ash were erupted (about 150 times more than the 1980 eruption of Mt. St. Helens). A caldera formed when the surface collapsed into the emptying magma chamber. The Tambora caldera is 6 km wide and 1.1 km deep. Tephra fall, a tsunami (a giant sea wave caused by the explosion), and pyroclastic flows killed about 10,000 people. More than 82,000 people died from famine. It is thought that the ash shortened the growing season.

Understanding and Applying What You Have Learned

1. In your own words, compare the sizes of the areas affected by lava, pyroclastic flows, and ash falls.

2. Is volcanic ash a concern only in the western United States? Explain your answer.

3. Why do eruptions in Hawaii differ from the Mt. St. Helens eruption?

4. Look at your list of the three volcanoes that are closest to your community. Go to the AGI *EarthComm* web site to find out how to simulate the eruption of one of your three volcanoes on the Internet. Simulate the eruption of one of your three volcanoes.

   a) Print out and describe the paths of the ash from the simulation.
   b) What do the maps tell you about the prevailing wind directions for your community?
   c) Do the prevailing wind directions change seasonally in your area? If yes, how would this affect the pattern of ash fallout?

Preparing for the Chapter Challenge

In **Activity 1** you were asked to describe to your audience the place that you thought a volcanic eruption was most likely to occur. Did you leave the impression in your story that this was the only area to be affected by the eruption? Think about how your study of the movement and hazards of volcanic ash has changed your ideas. Be sure to include this information in your story.

Inquiring Further

1. **Make a model of tephra transport**

   Build a model of a volcano that has exploded (Mt. St. Helens). Run a tube up through the vent of the volcano. Mix a small amount of baby powder with some sand. Use a funnel to pour the sand mixture down the other end of the tube. Attach a bicycle pump to pump the sand out of the volcano. Use a fan or hair dryer to simulate winds.

   Devise a method to outline the distribution of material when there is no wind, weak wind, and strong wind. Compare how far the sand travels and how far the baby powder travels. Consider the factors of particle size, wind speeds, wind direction, and topography. As part of your **Chapter Challenge** you may wish to include a presentation and explanation of your model.

 Use eyewear whenever non-water liquids and/or particles such as sand are used. If this activity is done indoors use a large, clear area. Clean the area well when you are done. Sand on the floor can be slick.

Activity 5 — Volcanoes and the Atmosphere

GOALS

In this activity you will:

• Measure the amount of dissolved gas in a carbonated beverage.

• Understand that volcanoes emit gases such as water vapor, carbon dioxide, and sulfur dioxide.

• Describe how volcanoes are part of the hydrosphere and water cycle.

• Demonstrate awareness of how volcanoes can affect global temperatures.

• Recognize that volcanoes are part of interactive systems on Earth.

Think about It

Following the eruption of Tambora in Indonesia in 1815, snow fell in New England during each of the summer months that year!

• What else escapes from a volcano besides lava, rock, and ash?

What do you think? Record your ideas about this question in your *EarthComm* notebook. Be prepared to discuss your responses with your small group and the class.

Investigate

1. Use a can of your favorite carbonated soft drink to explore the quantity of gas that can be dissolved in a liquid under pressure.

   a) How many milliliters (mL) of liquid are in the can of soda?

   b) Predict how many milliliters of gas (carbon dioxide) a can of soda contains. Record and explain your prediction.

2. Obtain these materials: heat source, 1-liter Pyrex® beaker, water, rubber tubing (about 50 cm), smaller beaker or bottle, plastic container (shoebox size), modeling clay, safety goggles.

3. Devise a way to use the materials to measure the gas that escapes from the can of soda. Note: You will need to heat the soda after you have opened it. To do this safely, put the can in a water bath (container of water) and heat the water bath.

   a) Draw a picture of how you will set up your materials.

   b) Write down the procedures you will follow. Include the safety precautions you will take.

4. After your teacher has approved your design, set up your materials. Run your experiment.

   a) Record your results.

   b) How do your results compare to your prediction?

   c) Describe anything that might have affected your results.

 Plan your activity carefully in detail to avoid potential hazards.

Reflecting on the Activity and the Challenge

You worked with a material that resembled volcanic products. When you opened the can of soda, you lowered the pressure inside the can. This allowed carbon dioxide (the dissolved gas) to come out of solution. Dissolved gases emerge from the Earth's interior in much the same way.

Digging Deeper

VOLCANOES AND THE ATMOSPHERE

Volcanic Gases

Gases that escape in greatest abundance from volcanoes are water vapor, carbon dioxide, hydrogen chloride, and nitrogen. These and certain other gases have played an important role in the Earth system throughout the long span of geologic time, and they continue to do so at the present time.

The atmosphere of the Earth early in its history contained abundant carbon dioxide but no oxygen. After primitive algae made their appearance partway through Earth history, the carbon dioxide emitted by volcanoes was gradually converted to oxygen by photosynthesis.

Carbon dioxide is more dense than air and sometimes accumulates in a low spot near a volcanic eruption. High concentrations of carbon dioxide are hazardous, because they cause people and animals to suffocate.

Water vapor is an essential component of the Earth system. It is especially important for human communities, because it sustains life. When you think of the water cycle, do you think of volcanoes? Volcanoes release abundant water vapor. Most of the Earth's surface water seems to have been released from the Earth's interior by volcanoes throughout the Earth's history.

Some volcanoes emit sulfur dioxide gas in great abundance. Sulfur dioxide combines with water vapor and oxygen to form sulfuric acid. The sulfuric acid is washed out of the atmosphere by rain, over large areas downwind of the eruption. Rain that contains sulfuric acid, and certain other acids as well, is called acid rain. It is produced not only by volcanoes but also by power plants that burn coal containing sulfur. Acid rain damages plants both on land and in lakes.

Volcanoes and Climate Change

Volcanoes illustrate the complexity of Earth's systems, because the gases from volcanic eruptions can contribute both to global cooling and to global warming.

How do volcanoes affect climate? If the Earth system were simple, the task of answering that question might be easy. Suppose that volcanic activity is the independent variable. This is the variable that, when changed, causes a change in something else (the dependent variable). In a simple model, climate would be the dependent variable. You could plot volcanic activity over time and compare it to temperature (an aspect of climate that can be measured) over time. Temperature changes that follow volcanic events would allow you to make inferences about the effects of eruptions on climate. However, the Earth system is complex. Records of climate and volcanic activity are imperfect. Some volcanic products should warm the atmosphere (carbon dioxide, a greenhouse gas). Others should cool the climate (dust, which reduces sunlight). The task of understanding climate change is obviously very complicated. The evidence at hand, however, suggests that major volcanic eruptions can lower the average temperature of the Earth's surface by a few tenths of a degree Celsius for as long as a few years.

It is often thought that volcanic eruptions increase or cause rainfall near or downwind of the eruption. Volcanoes put dust into the air. Water droplets in clouds form around small dust particles. Eruptions can also heat the local atmosphere. This should increase convection, or circulation, of the atmosphere. Finally, some volcanic eruptions release great quantities of water vapor needed to form clouds and rain. However, a number of studies show that an increase in rainfall is rare after an eruption. The major eruption of Krakatoa in 1883 did not increase rainfall, and it occurred during the wet (monsoon) season. It seems that conditions in the atmosphere near a volcanic eruption have to be just right for rainfall to increase just because of the eruption.

Enormous quantities of sulfur dioxide gas from a volcanic eruption can be put all the way into the stratosphere (the upper layer of the atmosphere, above the weather). It then slowly reacts with water to form tiny droplets of sulfuric acid, less than a thousandth of a millimeter in diameter. Unlike in the troposphere (the lowest layer of the atmosphere), these sulfur dioxide droplets are not affected by the water cycle. They stay suspended in the stratosphere for as long as a few years. The sulfur dioxide droplets, as well as the large quantities of very fine volcanic ash particles that also reach the stratosphere during major volcanic eruptions, reflect sunlight and are thought to cause the global cooling that is often observed for a few years after a major volcanic eruption. For example, following the eruption of Tambora in Indonesia in 1815, many areas in the United States and Canada had unusually cold summer weather. In New England, 1815 was called the "year without a summer."

Check Your Understanding

1. What gases escape from volcanoes?

2. Why does the emission of carbon dioxide pose a threat near volcanic eruptions?

3. How are volcanoes connected to the water cycle?

4. a) How is acid rain formed?

   b) Are volcanoes the only source of acid rain?

5. Do volcanic eruptions increase or decrease the temperature of the Earth? Explain your answer.

Understanding and Applying What You Have Learned

1. Think about the air you are breathing. How much of it came from some distant volcano?

2. If a volcano erupted huge amounts of ash, would you expect global temperatures to go up or down? Why?

3. If warm air rises, why would hot gases from a volcano be a threat to people in the valley below? (Hint: think about volume's effect in your work with the lava flow lab.)

4. If a system consists of many parts that affect each other, how are volcanoes part of systems on Earth?

Preparing for the Chapter Challenge

Use the information in this activity to argue that volcanoes have affected virtually every community.

Consider ways in which you can include these arguments in your story line.

Inquiring Further

1. **Cascades eruptions**

   Examine the figure showing the eruptions of Cascade volcanoes during the last 4000 years.

   a) Which volcano has been most active? Which volcano has been least active? Explain.

   b) What three volcanoes do you think are most likely to erupt next?

   c) Visit the AGI *EarthComm* web site for a link to the USGS Cascades Volcano Observatory web site. Find out about their monitoring efforts.

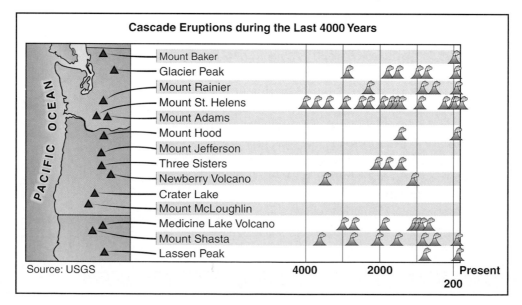

Cascade Eruptions during the Last 4000 Years

Source: USGS

Activity 6

Volcanic History of Your Community

GOALS

In this activity you will:

- Demonstrate awareness of the knowledge used to construct geologic maps.

- Examine and identify several common igneous rocks.

- Identify the distribution of active volcanoes on one map and rock types on a given geologic map.

- Recognize that volcanic rocks indicate a history of volcanic activity.

Think about It

Geologists can recognize volcanic eruptions dating back to early Earth history, over 3 billion years ago.

- If your community once had a volcanic eruption long ago, what evidence would be left behind?

What do you think? Record your ideas about this question in your *EarthComm* notebook. Be prepared to discuss your responses with your small group and the class.

Investigate

Part A: Rock Samples

1. Examine a set of rocks collected near a volcano.

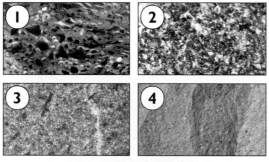

a) Record the sample number and briefly describe the physical characteristics of each rock.

b) Sort them into different groups by color (light, medium, dark).

c) Sort them again by texture (fine grains, large grains, mixture of sizes of grains, bubble holes).

2. Examine a set of rocks collected in your community.

a) Observe each rock, noting the size of the grains, color, and any other distinguishing features. Briefly describe each rock.

b) Note which ones you think might be volcanic.

c) Are all the rocks in the collection originally local? Explain.

  Soft rock material can come off rock samples as grit. Avoid contact with eyes.

Part B: Geologic Maps

1. Examine the geologic map of your state or region. Find your community on the map. An example of a geologic map is shown.

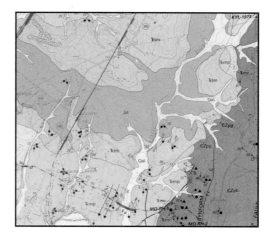

2. Look for patterns in the distribution of map colors (different rock types).

3. Compare the names of the rocks in the formations on the map with the names of rocks found in a reference book or field guide. Formation names followed by Basalt, Andesite, Dacite, Rhyolite, Ash, or Tuff indicate volcanic origin. Also, use any rock columns provided with the map and look for symbols that indicate volcanic rocks.

a) Record in your notebook the geologic age of any volcanic rocks you find on the map.

4. Using a measuring device and the map scale, determine how far your community is from the nearest volcanic rock unit.

a) Record this distance in your notebook.

Reflecting on the Activity and the Challenge

You have seen evidence that rocks formed by volcanic eruptions look different from those formed in other ways. They also vary greatly in their chemical composition. You can try to use what you have learned about the ages of the rocks in your area to decide on the probability of a volcano erupting in your community. Consider how you can share this knowledge with your audience.

Digging Deeper

IGNEOUS ROCKS

Introduction

Igneous rocks crystallize from cooling magma and lavas. Some igneous rocks form from magma that has cooled slowly beneath Earth's surface. The slow cooling allows crystals to form and grow, yielding coarse-grained igneous rocks such as granite. We know from laboratory work on melted rock that it takes extremely long times for large crystals to grow from a cooling magma. Such slow cooling can happen only deep within the Earth. These **intrusive igneous rocks**, also called **plutonic igneous rocks**, are made of crystals large enough to be seen with the naked eye. The sizes and shapes of bodies of intrusive igneous rocks vary greatly, from human scale to whole mountain ranges. Because intrusive igneous rocks form underground, they can only be seen where uplift and erosion have removed the overlying rocks.

Other igneous rocks, called **extrusive igneous rocks**, form from magma that is brought to the Earth's surface. Magma at or near the Earth's surface cools more rapidly, and crystals do not have time to grow to a large size. Sometimes, lava cools so fast that no crystals have a chance to form. Instead, the lava forms a kind of glass, called obsidian, as shown in *Figure 3*. Extrusive rocks are only one kind of volcanic rock. Remember from an earlier activity that pyroclastic volcanic rocks are also important.

Geo Words

intrusive igneous rock (plutonic igneous rock): igneous rock formed at considerable depth by the crystallization of magma

extrusive igneous rock: an igneous rock that has formed by eruption of lava onto the surface of the Earth

Figure 1 Granite is one kind of intrusive igneous rock formed by slow cooling of magma below Earth's surface.

Usually, the color of igneous rocks reflects the composition of the magma from which they form. Rocks from magmas high in silica (rhyolite and granite) tend to be lighter in color because their minerals are lighter in color, such as quartz, muscovite, and feldspar. These minerals are relatively poor in magnesium and iron, which are chemical elements that tend to make minerals dark.

Figure 2 Scoria is an extrusive igneous rock with a frothy texture.

Igneous rocks from magmas low in silica (basalt and gabbro) are darker in color, because they contain a large percentage of dark-colored minerals like pyroxenes, amphiboles, and dark micas. These minerals are relatively rich in magnesium and iron.

Figure 3 Obsidian is an extrusive igneous rock with a glassy texture.

Volcanic rocks of intermediate composition are mixtures of light and dark minerals that give the rock an intermediate color. A good example is andesite. It is named after the Andes Mountains, a mountain chain in South America that has many volcanoes.

In summary, igneous rocks crystallize from melted rock. They are divided into two types:

- Intrusive (plutonic) rocks are coarse-grained (>1 mm) and composed of crystals large enough to be seen with the naked eye. This implies slow cooling at depth.

- Extrusive (volcanic) rocks are fine-grained (<1 mm) and are composed mainly of crystals that are too small to be seen without a magnifying glass. This implies rapid cooling at or near the surface. Some may even be glassy, and many are filled with bubble holes, called vesicles.

Classification of Igneous Rocks				
Color	**Light**	**Intermediate**	**Dark**	**Dark**
Mineral composition	quartz (≥5%) plagioclase feldspar potassium feldspar iron-magnesium rich minerals (≤15%)	quartz (<5%) plagioclase feldspar potassium feldspar iron-magnesium rich minerals (15-40%)	no quartz plagioclase feldspar (~50%) no potassium feldspar iron-magnesium rich minerals (~40%)	nearly 100% iron magnesium rich minerals
Texture Crystals >10 mm	granite pegmatite	diorite pegmatite	gabbro pegmatite	
Crystals 1–10 mm	granite	diorite	gabbro	peridotite
Crystals <1 mm	rhyolite	andesite	basalt	
Glassy	obsidian		obsidian	
Frothy	pumice		scoria	

Figure 4

Rocks with Interesting Textures

Pumice, shown in *Figure 5*, feels like sandpaper. It is often light enough to float in water. Pumice forms when the gases inside the lava effervesce (bubble off) as pressure is released, just the way bubbles form when a can of soda, under pressure, is opened. The lava cools into a rock that is mostly tiny holes, with only very thin walls of rock between the holes. Much of the material blown out at first around Mt. St. Helens was pumice.

Figure 5 Pumice sample from Mt. St. Helens.

Obsidian is a glassy rock that was cooled so quickly from lava that crystals did not form. A broken surface of obsidian is usually smooth and shiny, just like a broken piece of glass (which it is!).

49

Tuff is a rock composed of pyroclastic material deposited from explosive eruptions. Some tuffs consist of ash that was put into the atmosphere by the eruption and then fell back to the surface downwind of the volcano. These tuffs may be lightweight, soft, and fragile, if they have not been buried deeply by later deposits. Other tuffs form from pyroclastic flows. These tuffs are often welded tightly together by the heat of the pyroclastic flow.

Scoria is a crusty-looking rock filled with holes made by gas bubbles trying to escape from the lava as it solidified. It is usually red or black, depending on the degree of oxidation of iron. Scoria is heavier to lift than pumice, because it doesn't have as great an abundance of holes. If you get to visit a cinder cone that is being mined, look at the cinders in the center and compare them to the cinders on the flank. The central cinders will be more oxidized and red and the outer samples darker and more like the basalt associated with the cone.

Types of Volcanic Rocks (based on silica content)

Basalt is dark and fine-grained. It is a low-silica rock. It is the most common rock on Earth and makes up the floors of all the oceans. Basalt covers about 70 percent of the surface of Earth. Basalt underlies the sediments on the floors of all the deep oceans of the Earth. Because the deep oceans occupy about 60 percent of the Earth's surface, basalt is the most common rock near the Earth's surface. On the continents, however, sediments and sedimentary rocks are much more common than basalt near the Earth's surface.

Andesite is a rock that is intermediate in silica content. It is also intermediate in color, typically gray, green, or brown. Andesite is typical of volcanic rocks from around the "Ring of Fire" in the Pacific Ocean. The ash from Mt. St. Helens was andesitic.

Dacite is a silica-rich rock that is between a rhyolite and an andesite in composition, somewhat like the difference between blue and violet in the color spectrum. It is lighter in color but not quite as silica rich as a rhyolite. It, too, is fine-grained but may have some visible crystals.

Rhyolite is usually light in color and has a fine-grained background. It forms from viscous lava that is high in silica. One of the identifying aspects of rhyolite is that it has visible quartz crystals that are not often seen in other volcanic rocks. These quartz crystals form because of (and are evidence of) rhyolite's high silica content. Perhaps the most famous rhyolite is the rock found in Yellowstone National Park. It came from one of the most massive volcanic eruptions known in Earth history.

Check Your Understanding

1. How can you distinguish intrusive igneous rock from extrusive igneous rock?

2. What is the difference between the way intrusive and extrusive igneous rock is formed?

3. Which chemical elements tend to make minerals dark?

Understanding and Applying What You Have Learned

1. Examine the sketch of the volcano. Some rocks shown on the sketch are extrusive, some are intrusive, and others are not igneous. Label a copy of the sketch to point out the following:

   a) Two locations of intrusive igneous rocks.
   b) Two locations of extrusive igneous rocks.

2. Consider what you know about volcanic hazards.

   a) Why is it important to study rocks?
   b) What information can be learned by looking at the geologic evidence in your community?

Cross section of a composite volcano. Rocks that form from the material shown in this diagram include extrusive igneous (erupted out of the volcano), intrusive igneous (cooled and crystallized inside the volcano or elsewhere beneath the surface), and non-igneous (metamorphic or sedimentary rock).

Preparing for the Chapter Challenge

You have now completed a variety of studies about volcanoes and volcanic rocks. Think about what you have learned about the relationships between rock types and volcanoes. Use the information you have learned about the distribution of rocks in your region to write a paragraph about the potential for a volcano to affect your community. Design a creative way to include geologic evidence about past eruptions in your movie script.

Inquiring Further

1. **Volcanoes as natural resources**

   Volcanoes provide energy to some communities. The Geothermal Education Office explains how heat associated with volcanic activity can be converted into electrical energy.

   Volcanoes also provide materials that are used for a variety of applications. Visit the Volcano World web site and compile a list of metals and other materials mined from volcanoes.

   Consult the AGI *EarthComm* web site for current addresses.

2. **Simulating gases in igneous rock**

   How does all the gas in pumice form? Acquire some bread dough (from the store or make from a recipe). Note the characteristics of the dough. Cut an end off to examine the interior. Set the dough out for a while and watch what happens. If you bake it, look at the interior again. It is not exactly the same as a volcano because the bubble holes in lava come from gases evolving out of solution, but it will give you the idea of how the gases are formed.

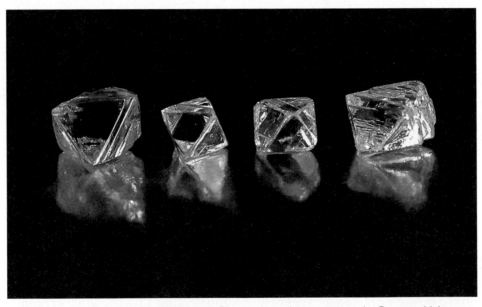

Volcanoes yield many materials that we use. Diamonds are just one example. Can you think of any others?

Activity 7

Monitoring Active Volcanoes

GOALS

In this activity you will:

- Understand some of the changes that occur prior to volcanic eruptions.
- Describe volcanic monitoring systems.
- Design and build an instrument to monitor changes which occur prior to volcanic eruptions.

Think about It

Many volcanologists (geoscientists who study volcanoes) have been killed while observing active volcanoes, when the activity of the volcano increases unexpectedly.

- How would you be able to tell that a volcano was about to erupt?

What do you think? Record your ideas about this question in your *EarthComm* notebook. Be prepared to discuss your responses with your small group and the class.

Investigate

1. Read the report issued from the Montserrat Volcano Observatory. The report was released one day before an eruption.

2. Identify all the evidence that signaled an impending eruption.

   a) In your notebook, write down each kind of event that signals volcanic activity.

Montserrat Volcano Observatory Daily Report 3/25/99 to 3/26/99

A slight change in the nature and level of seismicity was observed during the period under review. There were nineteen (19) earthquakes, nineteen (19) rockfalls and three (3) regional events. An increase in small earthquakes that are thought to be associated with rock fracturing due to dome growth was noted. About one hundred and thirty-four (134) of these small events were recorded on the Gages and Chances Peak Seismographs. The southern and eastern EDM [electronic distance measurement] triangles were measured today. The very small changes in the elevation of the land measured were consistent with the recent trends. Visual observations were made early this morning from the helicopter in excellent viewing conditions and subsequently from Chances Peak. The dome continues to steam and vent gas from various locations. The focus of activity has shifted from the two previously active areas (near Farrell's and to the north of Castle Peak) to two new areas located on the eastern and western sectors of the dome. Rockfalls may continue to occur in the area north of Castle Peak. The rockfalls in this area have been the source of the recent ash clouds.

---

3. As a group, select one of the changes that occurs prior to an eruption. Discuss how you might design an instrument (or a model of an instrument) that would monitor the change. The instrument should be one that you could transport to an observation site. You should also be able to construct it from readily available materials. To learn more about volcano monitoring techniques, read the **Digging Deeper** section: "Volcano Monitoring."

   a) Sketch your design in your notebook.

   b) Label the parts of the instrument and list the materials from which it will be built.

4. Write a brief manual for the instrument. Be sure to specify the following:

   a) What the instrument does.

   b) Where on or near the volcano to place it.

   c) How to position it on the site.

   d) How to operate it.

   e) How to record observations.

5. Exchange your manual with another group and construct the instrument they have designed. If possible, take it to a test site and follow the procedures to take and record observations.

Reflecting on the Activity and the Challenge

Understanding how volcanoes are monitored can help you appreciate how scientists strive to keep people informed and safe from volcanic hazards. You looked at the aspects of the design of instruments that made them easy to understand, construct, and operate as well as the relative costs and savings associated with developing and maintaining monitoring systems. You can now share with your audience the general advantages and disadvantages of different monitoring systems. Perhaps you could have a scene in your movie showing a debate in which a town council must decide whether or not to purchase monitoring equipment.

Geo Words

seismology: the study of earthquakes and of the structure of the Earth

Digging Deeper

VOLCANO MONITORING

The technology that geologists use is likely to be more sophisticated and expensive than the instruments you designed and constructed. However, they follow the same principles and observe the same changes. In emergencies, particularly in remote regions or in underdeveloped countries, simple monitoring techniques may provide the response time needed to save lives and property. Since the United States Geological Survey (USGS) cannot afford to monitor all volcanoes, on-site and local monitoring information can provide clues to the need for more sophisticated equipment.

Only 25% of the world's active volcanoes are monitored. Most potentially active volcanoes are not monitored due to a lack of funding. In response to this problem, the USGS developed a mobile volcano monitoring system. This system allows scientists to quickly install monitoring equipment and assess the potential hazard when a volcano becomes restless. The USGS sent this system to Mt. Pinatubo, Philippines in 1991 to help the Philippine Institute of Volcanology and Seismology monitor their volcano. (**Seismology** is the study of earthquakes and the structure of the Earth.) The lessons learned from monitoring volcanoes around the world help USGS scientists further prepare for eruptions in the United States. This system is not capable of stopping nor can it be designed to stop any natural occurrence. Its purpose is to provide forecasts to local populations and agencies for the health and welfare of their communities. Everyone must realize that the forces involved in a volcanic eruption cannot be stopped and must be allowed to take their course.

Figure 1 Many potentially active volcanoes around the world are not monitored due to a lack of funding.

Mt. Pinatubo erupted cataclysmically in June 1991. Fortunately for the residents of the island, monitoring prevented property losses of at least $250 million and saved an estimated 5000 lives. While 300 lives were lost and some $50 million were spent preparing for and monitoring the eruption, the estimated savings in human life far outweighed the costs associated with the monitoring program.

Volcano monitoring involves the recording and analyses of measurable phenomena such as ground movements, earthquakes, variations in gas compositions, and deviations in local electrical and magnetic fields that reflect pressure and stresses induced by the subterranean magma movements. To date, monitoring of earthquakes and ground deformation before, during, and following eruptions has provided the most reliable criteria in predicting volcanic activity, although other geochemical and geophysical techniques hold great promise.

Most of the commonly used monitoring methods were largely pioneered and developed by the Hawaiian Volcano Observatory (HVO). The HVO began monitoring in 1912. It has been operated continuously by the U.S. Geological Survey since 1948. Years of continuous observations of Kilauea and Mauna Loa, two of the world's most active volcanoes, have led to new instruments and measurement techniques. This work has increasingly been used in the study of other active volcanoes the world over. Moreover, early major advances in seismic research at HVO contributed significantly to subsequent systematic investigations of earthquake and related crustal processes, now conducted as part of the U.S. Geological Survey's Earthquake Hazards Reduction Program.

The volcanic plumbing and reservoir system beneath Kilauea can be pictured schematically as a balloon buried under thin layers of sand and plaster. When magma is fed into the reservoir (analogous to air filling a balloon), the internal pressure increases, and the sand-plaster surface layers are pushed upward and outward in order to accommodate the swelling or inflation. The net effects of such inflation include the steepening of slope of the volcano's surface; increases in horizontal and vertical distances between points on the

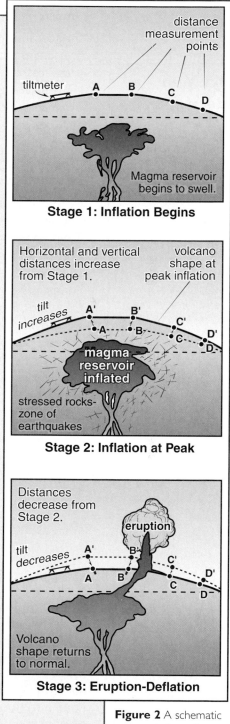

Stage 1: Inflation Begins

Stage 2: Inflation at Peak

Stage 3: Eruption-Deflation

Figure 2 A schematic representation of changes in a volcano prior to and following an eruption.

Check Your Understanding

1. Can monitoring equipment be used to prevent a volcano from erupting? In your answer explain what monitoring equipment can do.

2. What does monitoring a volcano involve?

3. What external evidence indicates that a reservoir in a volcano is being "fed" with magma?

4. Is a tiltmeter a sensitive measuring device? Explain your answer.

surface; and, in places, the fracturing of rock layers stretched beyond the breaking point. Such rupturing of materials adjusting to magma-movement pressures results in earthquakes. A shrinking or rapidly draining reservoir to feed surface eruptions (analogous to deflating or popping the balloon) would produce the opposite effects: flattening of slopes, reduction in distances between surface points, and decrease in earthquake frequency.

Changes in slope in a real volcano can be measured precisely by various electronic mechanical "tiltmeters" or field tilt surveying techniques. Tiltmeters can detect the change in slope of a kilometer-long board raised by the thickness of a dime placed under one end. Similarly, an instrument that uses a laser beam can measure minute changes in horizontal distances. Tiny changes in vertical distances can be measured by making a series of precise leveling surveys. Such changes can be easily detected to a precision of only a few parts per million. The notion of one part per million can be compared to putting one drop of Kool-Aid® in 16 gallons of water. The frequency, location, and magnitude of earthquakes generated by magma movement can easily and accurately be determined by data obtained from a properly designed seismic network. The Hawaiian Volcano Observatory has recently expanded its seismic networks to 45 stations to continuously record the earthquake activity of Kilauea and Mauna Loa.

The monitoring of earthquakes and changes in volcano shape is not sufficient for predicting eruptions, however. The proper analysis of data requires a basic understanding of the prehistoric eruptive record and behavior of a volcano. Such glimpses into a volcano's prehistoric past are critically important because historic records extend over too short a time to permit the making of reliable predictions of future behavior.

Understanding and Applying What You Have Learned

1. Use the following questions to analyze your experiences designing, devising written plans, understanding the plans of other groups, and using monitoring instruments. In your notebook, record your responses.

   a) What aspect of your design would have worked well?

   b) What aspect of another group's design would have worked well?

   c) How useful do you think such devices would be in an emergency where expensive monitoring instruments were not readily available?

   d) How does elevation and slope of a volcano change prior to an eruption?

e) How could you measure changes in the elevation of a volcanic dome?

f) What changes in volcanic gases indicate an ensuing eruption?

g) How does seismic activity change prior to an eruption?

h) Did the class design at least one piece of equipment to measure change in slope? Elevation? Gases? Seismicity?

i) If you answered no to one of the questions in (**h**), think of two potential reasons why the instrument was not developed.

2. Describe three methods of monitoring an active volcano.

a) Which monitoring system is least reliable, and why?

b) Which monitoring systems are most dangerous to those who monitor an active volcano, and why?

c) Which monitoring systems would be most useful in your community, and why?

d) What aspects of volcano monitoring are most challenging for geologists? For communities? Explain your answers.

3. Why is weather monitored more closely than volcanic activity in the United States?

Preparing for the Chapter Challenge

Summarize the monitoring systems you would recommend for your community. Include a justification of their cost in relationship to the hazard information they might provide. Also, indicate the type of monitoring equipment you would recommend be used in the community in which you "stage" a volcanic eruption. Use this summary in your response to the **Chapter Challenge**.

Describe how the movie relates to what you have studied about volcanic hazards and volcano monitoring systems in this chapter.

Inquiring Further

1. **Volcanic hazards of Mt. Rainier**

   View the movie *Perilous Beauty: The Hidden Dangers of Mount Rainier*, U.S. Department of the Interior, USGS. This movie is the result of in-depth research into the volcanic hazards of Mt. Rainier.

Integrated Coordinated Science for the 21st Century

Earth Science at Work

ATMOSPHERE: *Air Traffic Controller*
Air traffic controllers are responsible for the safe passage of aircraft in their airspace.

BIOSPHERE: *Produce Manager*
Customers expect to find an ample supply of fresh produce throughout the year.

CRYOSPHERE: *Geohydrologist*
Some geologists are involved in the study of global water, its properties, circulation, and distribution. Mountain rivers and streams would be one area that they would investigate.

GEOSPHERE: *Commodities Supplier*
Some industries rely on an ample supply of sulfur in their manufacturing processes.

HYDROSPHERE: *Fisheries Worker*
In the fishing industry, income depends on the quality and the quantity of the catch.

How is each person's work related to the Earth system, and to volcanoes?

Chapter 2

Plate Tectonics
...and Your Community

Getting Started

Plate tectonics is a scientific theory. A scientific theory is a well-tested concept that is supported by experimental or observational evidence. It explains a wide range of observations. The theory of plate tectonics explains the formation, movement, and changes of the outer, rigid layer of the Earth, called the lithosphere.

- How do you think the Earth's lithosphere formed?
- How do you know that the Earth's lithosphere moves?
- List some ways that the Earth's lithosphere changes.

What do you think? Write down your ideas about these questions in your notebook. Be prepared to discuss your ideas with your small group and the class.

Scenario

A middle-school science teacher in your community has been asked to teach a unit on plate tectonics to her class and has asked for your help. To her students, the fact that they are riding on Earth on a floating plate makes about as much sense as riding on a magic carpet. The students feel that because plate tectonics is "just a theory" that scientists have "made up," there is no need for them to learn about it, or try to understand it. Also, they believe it is totally irrelevant to their lives.

The teacher hopes that her students might be more likely to listen to local high school students. She would like you to convince her class of the significance of plate tectonics in their lives. She wants you to explain to her class the key science concepts behind the theory. She thinks that it would help her students if they could see how research, evidence, modeling, and technology support plate tectonics.

Can the EarthComm students meet this challenge and help a middle-school class to understand why the theory of plate tectonics is important to learn about and understand?

Chapter Challenge

Think about how you can use the theory of plate tectonics to help middle-school students understand scientific theories. You might want to prepare a PowerPoint™ presentation, a web page, or a three-panel poster display. Your project will need to address:

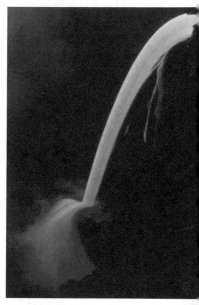

- Evidence for movement and changes in the geosphere over time.
- The flow of matter and energy in the Earth.
- The nature of the Earth's interior.
- How plate tectonics accounts for the features and processes that geoscientists observe in the Earth.
- How the theory of plate tectonics developed.

Assessment Criteria

Think about what you have been asked to do. Scan ahead through the chapter activities to see how they might help you meet your challenge. Work with your classmates and your teachers to define the criteria for judging your work. Record all this information. Make sure that you understand the criteria as well as you can before you begin. Your teacher may provide you with a sample rubric to help you get started.

Activity 1

Taking a Ride on a Lithospheric Plate

GOALS

In this activity you will:

• Determine the direction and rate of movement of positions within the plate on which your community is located, using data from the Global Positioning System and a computer model.

• Predict the position of your community in the near future, and "retrodict" its position in the recent past, by extrapolating from data already collected.

• Recognize that the rate and direction of plate motion is not necessarily constant.

• Describe several lines of evidence for plate motion.

Think about It

The motion of anything (you, your automobile, a lithospheric plate, or the Milky Way Galaxy!) has to be described in relation to something else.

• How can you locate your position on the Earth's surface?
• How would you be able to determine whether your position on the Earth has moved?

What do you think? Record your ideas about these questions in your *EarthComm* notebook. Include sketches as necessary. Be prepared to discuss your responses with your small group and the class.

Investigate

Part A: Data from the Global Positioning System

1. Data from Global Positioning System (GPS) satellites will help you find out if the position of your community has changed over time. The map shows measurements of movements at GPS recording stations in North America. Each station has a four-character symbol. Arrows show the rate and direction of motion of the Earth's surface at that station. Longer arrows indicate faster motion than shorter arrows. The motions shown are relative to the GPS frame of reference, which you can think of as "attached" to the Earth's axis of rotation.

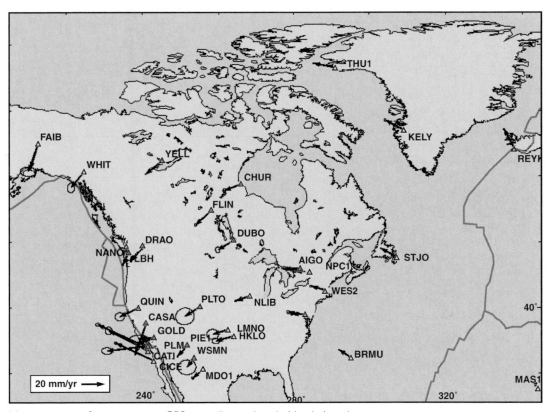

Measurements of movements at GPS recording stations in North America.

a) Find the WES2 station (in the northeastern United States). How do you know that the WES2 station has moved over time?

b) In what compass direction is the WES2 station moving? Be specific.

c) The arrow in the lower left corner of the map is a scale. It shows the length of a "20 mm/yr" arrow. Is the WES2 station moving more than or less than 20 mm/yr? Explain.

d) Are all stations on the map moving at the same speed? Explain.

e) Are all stations on the map moving in the same direction? Explain.

f) What is the general or average direction of movement of North America?

2. A series of measurements of the location and elevation of a GPS station over time is called a GPS time series. The graph shows the GPS time series for the WES2 station. The solid sloping lines on the three graphs are the "best-fit" lines through the data points.

Use the map and the time series to answer the following questions:

a) How many years of data does the time series show?

b) Were measurements recorded continuously or only at certain times? Explain your answer.

3. The top graph shows movement of the station to the north or south. Northward movement is indicated by positive values, and southward movement is shown by negative values. Find the calculation above the top graph. How many millimeters per year did WES2 move? Convert

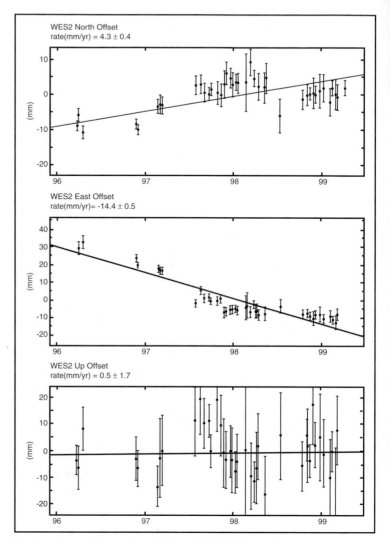

The location and elevation of GPS station WES2 over time. The vertical lines above and below each point are called "error bars". They show the uncertainty in the measurement. They tell you that the real value might lie anywhere within the error bar.

this value to centimeters per year. In which direction did it move?

a) Record the rate (in cm/yr) and the direction of motion in your notebook.

4. The middle graph shows movement to the east or west. Eastward movement is indicated by positive values, and westward movement is shown by negative values. Find the calculation above the middle graph. How many millimeters per year did WES2 move? Convert this value to centimeters per year. In which direction did it move?

   a) Record the rate (in cm/yr) and direction of motion in your notebook.

5. The bottom graph shows the movement up or down.

   a) Has the WES2 station always stayed at the same elevation? Explain.

6. Do the speed and direction of motion of WES2 shown in the graphs match the direction and length of the arrow shown on the map?

7. Look at the "best-fit" line in the top and middle graphs.

   a) Did the WES2 station move at a constant speed since 1996? Explain your answer.

   b) What additional data would you need to decide whether the differences between the measured data points and the best-fit straight line are due to the overall motion of the plate or are caused by processes in the local area around the WES2 station?

8. Obtain a GPS time series for a station nearest your community.

   a) Record the directions and rates of motion in cm/yr for the station nearest your community.

Part B. Data from a Computer Model

1. Computer models that use geologic data also provide information about the changes in position of your community over time. To use this model, you will need to know the latitude and longitude of your school in decimal format.

   Find your school (or another familiar place) on your local topographic map. Latitude and longitude are used to identify a position on the Earth's surface. Latitude is a measure of location in degrees, minutes, and seconds north or south of the equator. Therefore, it is found on the left or right side of the map. Longitude is a measure of location in degrees, minutes, and seconds east or west of the Prime Meridian, which passes through Greenwich, England. Therefore, it is found on the top or bottom of the map.

   a) Record the latitude and longitude of the position you chose in degrees, minutes, and seconds. (These "minutes" and "seconds" are *not* the same as the familiar minutes and seconds of time! They describe positions on a circular arc.)

   b) Convert the latitude and longitude values to a decimal format. An example for you to follow is provided on the following page.

Example:

42° (degrees) 40' (minutes) 30" (seconds) north latitude
Each minute has 60".
30" divided by 60" equals 0.5'.
This gives a latitude of 42° 40.5' north.
Each degree has 60'.
40.5' divided by 60' equals 0.675°.
The latitude in decimal format is 42.675° north.

2. Obtain a world outline map showing lithospheric plates, similar to the one shown.

   a) Place a dot on the map to represent the location of your community and label it with an abbreviation.

b) In your notebook, record the name of the plate your community lies within. Record the name of a plate next to your community.

3. Visit the Relative Plate Motion (RPM) Calculator web site. (See the *EarthComm* web site for more information.) The RPM calculator determines how fast your plate is moving relative to another plate that is assumed to be "fixed" (non-moving). At the web site, enter the following information:
   • The latitude and longitude of your community (decimal format).
   • The name of the plate on which your community is located.
   • The name of the "fixed" reference plate adjacent to your plate. Use the African Plate as the reference plate.

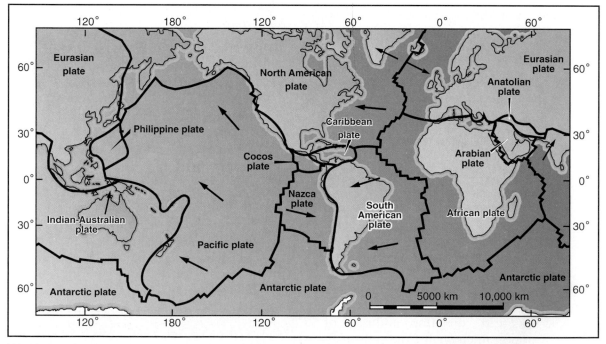

World map of major lithospheric plates. Arrows show the relative motions of the plates relative to the African Plate, which happens to be moving slowest relative to the Earth's axis of rotation.

Once you have entered the data, run the model. Print the results. (A sample printout for the location of station WES2 is provided for you.) Record the following information in your notebook:

a) The rate of movement of the plate on which your community is located (in centimeters per year).

b) Its direction of motion. (Note that direction is given in degrees, starting from 0°, clockwise from north. For example, 90° is directly east, 180° is directly south and 270° is directly west.)

c) In your own words, describe the motion of your plate over time.

d) How do the results from the computer model compare to those obtained from GPS data?

NUVEL-1A Calculation Results
Calculation results are as follows:

Relatively fixed plate = Africa
Relatively moving plate = North America
Latitude of Euler pole = 78.8 degree
Longitude of Euler pole = 38.3 degree
Angular velocity = 0.24 degree/million years
Latitude inputted = 42.364799 degree
Longitude inputted = −71.293503 degree
Velocity = 2.11 cm
Direction = 283.39 degree

e) What data does GPS provide that the plate motion calculator does not?

Reflecting on the Activity and the Challenge

So far, you have learned that when you use GPS data collected over time, you can find the speed and direction of movement of your plate. You can also use data from a computer model to show that your community is moving as part of the movement of a large plate. You are riding on a piece of the Earth's lithosphere! Your maps show how your community, along with the plate on which it rides, has moved over time. You can also predict its future position. You have now gathered some evidence to help you explain to the middle school students that their community is in fact moving.

<table>
<tr><td valign="top">

Geo Words

crust: the thin outermost layer of the Earth. Continental crust is relatively thick and mostly very old. Oceanic crust is relatively thin, and is always geologically very young

mantle: the zone of the Earth below the crust and above the core. It is divided into the upper mantle and lower mantle with a transition zone between

lithosphere: the outermost layer of the Earth, consisting of the Earth's crust and part of the upper mantle. The lithosphere behaves as a rigid layer, in contrast to the underlying asthenosphere

asthenosphere: the part of the mantle beneath the lithosphere. The asthenosphere undergoes slow flow, rather than behaving as a rigid block, like the overlying lithosphere

</td></tr>
</table>

Digging Deeper

MEASURING THE MOTION OF LITHOSPHERIC PLATES

The Interior Structure of the Earth

Refer to *Figure 1* as you read this section. The thin, outermost layer of the Earth is called the **crust**. There are two kinds of crust: continental and oceanic. The continental crust forms the Earth's continents. It is generally 30–50 km thick, and most of it is very old. Some continental crust has been dated as old as four billion years! The geological structure of the continental crust is generally very complicated, as you will learn in a later chapter. In contrast, the oceanic crust is only 5–10 km thick, and it is young in terms of geologic time. All of the oceanic crust on the Earth is younger than about 200 million years.

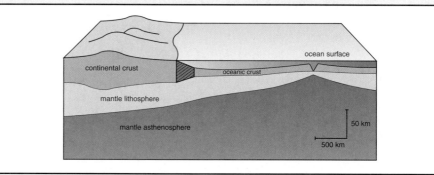

Figure 1 A schematic cross section through the outer part of the Earth. Note that the vertical and horizontal scales are very different. The diagram has a lot of "vertical exaggeration". If the diagram had been drawn without distortion, all of the layers would look much thinner. The boundary between continental crust and oceanic crust, shown by the shaded box, will be described later in the chapter.

Beneath the Earth's crust is the **mantle**. The rocks of the mantle are very different in composition from the crust, and the boundary between the crust and the mantle is sharp and well defined. The uppermost part of the mantle, which is cooler than below, moves as a rigid block, carrying the crust with it. The upper rigid part of the mantle, together with the crust, is called the **lithosphere**. The Earth's plates are composed of the lithosphere. At greater depths, the mantle is hot enough that it can flow very slowly, just like a very stiff liquid. That part of the mantle is called the **asthenosphere**.

In terms of composition and origin, the crust and the mantle are very different, but in terms of how they move, they behave in the same way. On the other hand, the lithosphere part of the mantle is the same in composition as the asthenosphere part of the mantle, but in terms of how they move, they behave very differently.

Measuring Plate Motions with GPS

The **Global Positioning System (GPS)** consists of 24 satellites that orbit the Earth at a height of 20,200 km. Receivers at stations on Earth (such as WES2 in Westport, Massachusetts) use the signals from satellites to calculate the location of the station. Geoscientists have set up a network of targets all over the world in order to monitor the movement of lithospheric plates. Steel spikes pounded into the ground (preferably embedded in solid rock) make up the targets, as shown in *Figure 2.* A high-precision GPS receiver is then mounted on a tripod and positioned directly above the target. The targets are revisited over a period of months or years. The receiver measures the distance to four or more GPS satellites and then uses stored data on satellite locations to compute the location of the target. Changes in horizontal and vertical positions can be detected within several millimeters.

Geo Words

Global Positioning System (GPS): a satellite-based system for accurate location of points on the Earth

Figure 2 A GPS receiver mounted in rock is used to measure changes in the elevation of this volcano.

GPS data collected at stations all over the world confirm that the surface of the Earth is moving. However, GPS time series show data for only the last several years. GPS is a new technology, and a global network of GPS stations has existed for less than a decade. How do we know that the surface of the Earth has been moving for a longer period of time? The answer to this question comes from the study of rocks.

Sea-Floor Spreading

The computer model at the Plate Motion Calculator web site uses several sources of geologic data. One source comes from the study of the magnetism of rocks that make up the sea floor. All magnets and ➡

materials that have magnetism have a north and south direction, or magnetic polarity. In the middle of the 20th century, geoscientists noted that they could group rocks by their magnetic polarity. Rocks with normal magnetic polarity match that of the Earth's magnetic field (the north end of the rock's "compass needle" points toward magnetic north.) The other group has magnetic minerals with reversed polarity(the north end of the rock's compass needle points south).

It was known that as lava cools to form **basalt** (an iron-rich volcanic rock that makes up the ocean floor), its iron minerals (such as magnetite) become magnetized and "lock in" the polarity of the Earth's magnetic field. Beginning in the 1950's, scientists began noting patterns in the magnetism of rocks on the ocean floor, as shown in *Figure 3*. The alternating belts of higher and lower than average magnetic field strength were of normal and reverse polarity, respectively.

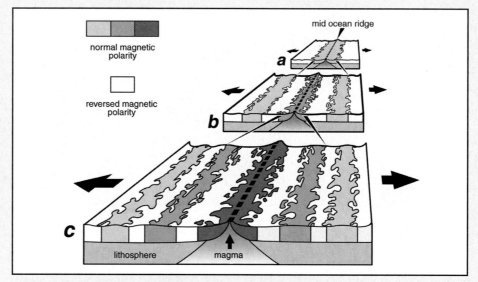

Figure 3 The formation of magnetic striping. New oceanic crust forms continuously at the crest of the mid-ocean ridge. It cools and becomes increasingly older as it moves away from the ridge crest with sea-floor spreading: a. the spreading ridge about 5 million years ago; b. about 2 to 3 million years ago; and c. present day.

In 1963, two scientists, F.J. Vine and D. H. Matthews, proposed the revolutionary theory of sea-floor spreading to explain this pattern. According to their theory, the matching patterns on either side of the **mid-ocean ridge** could be explained by new ocean crust forming at the ridge and spreading away from it. As ocean crust forms, it obtains the polarity of the Earth's magnetic field at that time. Over time, the strength of the Earth's magnetic field changes. When new ocean crust forms at the center of the spreading , it obtains a new kind of magnetic polarity. Over time, a series of magnetic "stripes" are formed.

Since the theory of sea-floor spreading was proposed, core samples of volcanic rock taken from the ocean floor have shown that the age of the rock increases from the crest of the ridge, just as the theory predicts. What's more, by measuring both the age and magnetic polarity of rocks on land, geologists have developed a time scale that shows when the magnetic field has reversed its polarity. Because the magnetic striping on the ocean floor records the reversals of the Earth's magnetic field, geoscientists can calculate the average rate of plate movement during a given time span. These rates range widely. The Arctic Ridge has the slowest rate (less than 2.5 cm/yr), and the East Pacific Ridge has the fastest rate (more than 15 cm/yr). The computer model in the plate motion calculator uses spreading rates from ocean ridges throughout the world to compute plate motion.

Geologic data is also used to find the direction of movement of the plate. Surveys of the depth of the ocean floor, mainly since the 1950s, revealed a great mountain range on the ocean floor that encircles the Earth, as shown in *Figure 4*. This mid-ocean ridge zig-zags between the continents, winding its way around the globe like the seams on a baseball. The mid-ocean ridge is

Geo Words

basalt: a kind of volcanic igneous rock, usually dark colored, with a high content of iron

mid-ocean ridge: a chain of undersea ridges extending throughout all of the Earth's ocean basins, and formed by sea-floor spreading

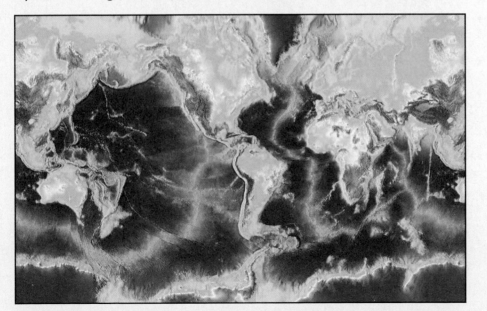

Figure 4 Map of the world ocean floor. The crest of the mid-ocean ridge system is shown as a broad light blue line throughout the ocean floor. The flanks of the mid-ocean ridges slope gradually down to the deeper part of the oceans, nearer the continents.

1. What is the difference between the lithosphere and the asthenosphere?

2. What does the abbreviation GPS stand for?

3. From where does a GPS receiver get its signal?

4. Why are GPS data not enough to confirm that the Earth's surface has been moving for many years?

5. What has caused the "zebra pattern" in the rock of the ocean floor?

6. What is the significance of the patterns of offsets along mid-ocean ridges?

not straight; it is offset in many places (*Figure 5*). The offsets are perpendicular to the axis of the ridge. When combined with knowledge that the ocean floor is spreading apart at mid-ocean ridges, geologists realized that the offsets are parallel to the direction the plates are moving. By mapping the orientations of these offsets, and entering this data into the computer model, the plate motion calculator is able to generate the directions of plate motions. Comparisons between GPS measurements and results from geologic computer models show very good agreement, within 4%.

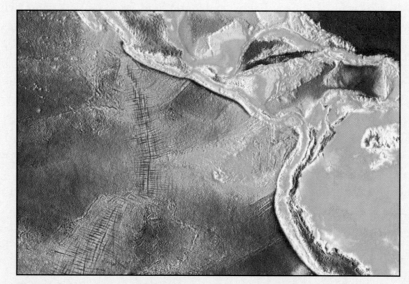

Figure 5 This map shows the network of fractures along the mid-ocean ridge in the eastern Pacific Ocean floor. Because the ocean floor spreads away from both sides of the ridge, the fractures indicate the direction of plate motion.

Understanding and Applying What You Have Learned

1. Describe the direction and the rate of movement for the plate on which you live.

2. Examine the scale of the USGS topographic map of your community. Given the rate of plate motion in your community, estimate the minimum number of years that it would take for a change in the location of your school to be detected on a topographic map.

3. How does GPS provide evidence that the surface of the Earth moves over time?

4. Describe at least one advantage of using GPS technology to gather evidence of plate motion.

5. How do studies of the magnetism of rocks on the sea floor provide evidence that the surface of the Earth moves over time?

6. What evidence examined in this activity suggests that the direction and rate of motion of plates is not constant?

7. Look at the world map in the **Investigate** section showing the relative motion of plates. This map shows how plates move relative to each other.

   a) Look at the names of the plates. On what basis does it appear that the plates were named?

   b) Write down the name of your plate and all the plates that border it. Describe the motion of your plate relative to all the plates that border it.

   c) How might the differences in motion of these plates affect the Earth's lithosphere?

Preparing for the Chapter Challenge

In your notebook, write a paragraph to convince the middle-school students that your community is moving as part of the movement of a much larger segment of the Earth's lithosphere. Describe the evidence used to make this determination.

Inquiring Further

1. **Technology used to detect plate motions**

   Explore how GPS allows plate movement to be measured. Excellent web sites that describe how GPS works can be found on the *EarthComm* web site.

2. **Investigating scales of motion**

   Plate motion is extremely slow. Make a list of other things you know about (or have heard about) that move or take place slowly. Possible examples include growth of fingernails, grass, tree height, tree-trunk diameter, and so on. Find out how fast they move. Compare the rate of these motions to the rate of movements of plates.

3. **Study animations of plate motions**

   Visit the *EarthComm* web site for the address of animated images of the motions of lithospheric plates. Describe how the motions shown in the animations match your analysis from this activity.

Activity 2

Plate Boundaries and Plate Interactions

GOALS

In this activity you will:

- Classify and label the types of movement at plate boundaries, using a world map that shows relative plate motion.
- Identify the distribution of plates by means of the world map of relative plate motions.
- Describe the present plate-tectonic setting of your community, and infer possible past plate-tectonic activity based on your knowledge.

Think about It

New plates are created at certain places on Earth, and existing plates are consumed at certain other places. The total surface area of the Earth stays the same, so the creation of new plates has to be exactly equal to the consumption of existing plates.

- Where do you suppose you would have the most "interesting" ride on a plate? Would it be at the center, on a leading edge, on a trailing edge, or somewhere else on the plate?

What do you think? Record your ideas about these questions in your *EarthComm* notebook. Include sketches as necessary. Be prepared to discuss your response with your small group and the class.

Investigate

Part A: Observing Plate Motions and Plate Interactions

1. Obtain the equipment shown in the following diagram.

2. Use the equipment to model a steady sea-floor spreading and subduction, as follows: One student holds the two rolled-up dowels in one place, loosely, so that they can turn but not shift their position. Another student holds the stapled piece of 2×4 lumber "continent" and pulls it away from the rolled-up dowels. A third student holds the dowel and piece of 2×4 lumber "subduction zone" at the other end loosely in place. A fourth student pulls the paper strip from under the piece of 2×4 lumber "subduction zone." Be sure to unroll

the paper strips at the same rate, so that the numbers of the stripes stay matched up as they appear.

a) What does the area at the rolled paper strips on the dowels represent?

b) What does the section of paper between the dowels and the continental lithosphere (the piece of 2×4 lumber) represent?

c) What happens to the length of this section of paper as the dowels are unrolled?

d) As the dowels are unrolled, what happens to the width of the section of paper between the dowels and the subduction zone (the other piece of 2×4 lumber)?

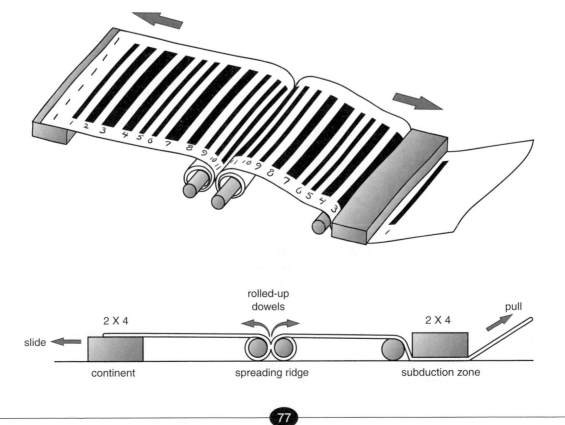

Integrated Coordinated Science for the 21st Century

3. Use the equipment to model a collision of a spreading ridge and a subduction zone, as follows: Begin with the materials arranged in the same way at the end of **Step 1**. While two students pull the paper strips to unwind the two rolled-up dowels, the student holding those dowels slides them slowly toward the subduction zone. The student operating the subduction zone needs to make sure that the stripes appearing at the spreading ridge continue to have their numbers matched up.

a) What happens to the length of the strip of paper between the dowels and the "continent" side in this situation?

b) What happens to the length of the strip of paper between the dowels and the "subduction" zone?

c) At what "place" does the spreading ridge eventually arrive?

4. Think about the following questions, and write a brief answer to each in your notebook.

a) In the first part of the modeling (**Step 2**), how long will the ocean on the "subduction" side last?

b) In the second part of the modeling (**Step 3**), what do you think would happen in real life when the spreading ridge arrives at the subduction zone?

c) In the second part of the modeling (**Step 3**), how would the ocean on the "continent" side change after the spreading ridge arrives at the subduction zone?

d) In both cases, what do you think would happen in real life if the

continent became blocked in its movement away from the spreading ridge by something happening on the other side of the continent?

Part B: How Transform Faults Are Formed

1. When the theory of plate tectonics was young, back in the 1970s, there was an experiment to see how divergent plate boundaries are formed. Scientists might describe this experiment as "beautiful" or "elegant." It was small enough to be done on a table top. You can run it as a "thought experiment." A diagram of the setup is shown below. Use a shallow square pan. Fill it with melted wax, and heat the bottom of the pan to keep the wax melted. Cool the surface of the wax with a fan, so that it crusts over to form "lithosphere." Install roller cylinders along opposite edges of the top of the pan. These two rollers can be rotated outward in opposite directions to pull the solid surface of the wax apart.

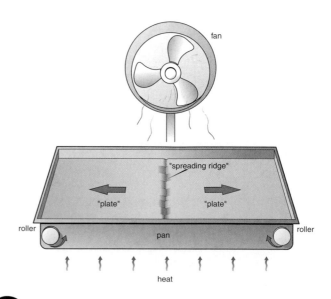

a) Predict what will happen to the crust of wax when the rollers are rotated. Assume that everything is adjusted right (composition of the wax; heating at the bottom; cooling at the top; speed of the rollers).

b) If a break were to occur in the surface wax, what do you think would happen to the liquid wax below?

2. In the actual experiment, the "lithosphere" broke along a crack across the middle of the pan. As the two "plates" on either side of the crack were formed, new "lithosphere" formed as the liquid wax welled up into the crack and solidified. The amazing thing about the experiment was that the original crack was formed with exactly the same pattern of ridge-crest segments and transform faults that can be seen in the real mid-ocean ridges!

a) Were your predictions correct? How do you explain any differences between what happened and your predictions?

b) What does the experiment suggest about the age of the transform faults compared to the mid-ocean ridges?

Part C: Plate Boundaries on World Maps

1. Look at the world map in the **Investigate** section of the previous activity, which shows the relative motion of the plates. Observe what it shows about how plates move relative to each other. Answer the following:

a) Name two plates that are moving toward each other (colliding/converging).

b) Name two plates that are moving apart (diverging).

c) Name two plates that are sliding past each other.

2. Use a blank world map to make a map that shows the three major types of plate boundaries.

a) On the map, color the boundary line that separates two converging plates. Do not outline both of the plates completely; highlight only the boundary between the two plates.

b) Using two other colors, highlight the divergent plate boundaries, (where plates are moving away from one another) and the plate boundaries, where plates slide past one another (called transform boundaries). Make a key that shows this color code.

Part D: The Plate-Tectonic Setting of Your Community

1. Describe the plate-tectonic setting of your community. Refer to your world map and the map *This Dynamic Planet* (United States Geological Survey) in your work.

a) How far is your community from the nearest plate boundary?

b) What type of plate boundary is it?

c) How might your community change its position relative to plate boundaries in the future?

Reflecting on the Activity and the Challenge

You have seen that plates can interact in three different ways: they can converge, diverge, or move parallel to each other. You have gained some experience in recognizing the three kinds of plate boundaries on world maps. You are better prepared for a later activity, on the different kinds of landforms that develop at the different kinds of plate boundaries, and how earthquakes and volcanoes are caused at or near plate boundaries. You are now in a better position to help middle-school students understand one of the key concepts of plate tectonics: the material of the ocean floors is always much younger than the oceans themselves!

Geo Words

divergent plate boundary: a plate boundary where two plates move away from one another

Digging Deeper

THE DYNAMICS OF PLATE BOUNDARIES

Types of Plate Boundaries

Plate boundaries are geologically interesting areas because they are where the action is! Geologists use three descriptive terms to classify the boundaries between plates: 1) divergent boundaries are where two plates move away from each other; 2) convergent boundaries are where two plates move toward each other; and 3) transform boundaries are where two plates slide parallel to each other.

Divergent Plate Boundaries

You have already learned some things about **divergent plate boundaries** in **Activity 1**, because mid-ocean ridges are divergent plate boundaries. The mid-ocean ridges are places where mantle asthenosphere rises slowly upward. As it rises, some of the rock melts to form magma. Why does melting happen there? To understand that, you need to know that the melting temperature of rock decreases as the pressure on the rock decreases. As the mantle rock rises, its temperature stays about the same, because cooling takes a long time. However, the pressure from the overlying rock is less, so some of the rock melts. The magma then rises up, because it is less dense than the rock. It forms volcanoes in the central valley of the mid-ocean ridge. Geoscientists in deep-diving submersibles can watch these undersea volcanoes! Because of the great water pressure in the deep ocean, and also the cooling effect of the water, these volcanoes behave differently from volcanoes on land. The lava oozes out of cracks in the rocks, like toothpaste out of a tube. Some of the magma stays below the sea floor and crystallizes into rock there. All of these new igneous rocks, at the sea floor and below, make new oceanic crust, which then moves away from the ridge crest. This would be a good time to go back to **Activity 1** and review the material on sea-floor spreading.

In the investigation you modeled how the "continent" moved farther and farther from the "spreading ridge." Look back again at the world map of lithospheric plates in **Activity 1**. In both the North Atlantic Ocean and the South Atlantic Ocean, there is no plate boundary along the coastlines on either side of the ocean. That tells you that the Atlantic Ocean is getting wider as time goes on. Why? Because new lithosphere is being created all the time at the mid-ocean ridge but is not being consumed at the edges of the continents. Does that make you wonder what would happen if you could make time run backward and watch the ocean shrink? At some time in the past, there was no Atlantic Ocean!

A new ocean begins when hot mantle material begins to move upward beneath a continent. Geoscientists are still not certain about why that happens. The lithosphere of the continent bulges upward and is stretched sideways. Eventually it breaks along a long crack, called a rift. See *Figure 1* for what a newly formed **rift valley** looks like. Magma rises up to feed volcanoes in the rift. As the rift widens, the ocean invades the rift. A new ocean basin has now been formed, and it gets wider as time goes on.

Geo Words

rift valley: a large, long valley on a continent, formed where the continent is pulled apart by forces produced when mantle material rises up beneath the continent

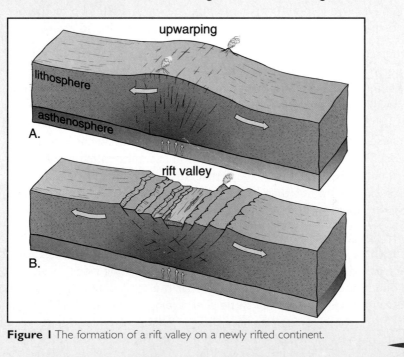

Figure 1 The formation of a rift valley on a newly rifted continent.

Geo Words

convergent plate boundary: a plate boundary where two plates move toward one another

subduction: the movement of one plate downward into the mantle beneath the edge of the other plate at a convergent plate boundary. The downgoing plate always is oceanic lithosphere. The plate that stays at the surface can have either oceanic lithosphere or continental lithosphere

Convergent Plate Boundaries

At a **convergent plate boundary**, two plates are moving toward each other. Your common sense tells you that one of them has to go under the other. (Would it surprise you to hear that common sense is important to a scientist, even though sometimes common sense can fool you?) There are three kinds of places where this happens. These are described below. In a later activity you will learn much more about the landforms that are produced at convergent plates boundaries, and how earthquakes and volcanoes are associated with convergent plate boundaries.

In some places, two oceanic lithospheric plates are converging. There are good examples along the western edge of the Pacific Ocean. Look back at the world map of lithospheric plates in **Activity 1**. The Pacific Plate and the Indo-Australian Plate are moving toward one another in the South Pacific, and the Pacific Plate and the Philippine Plate are moving toward one another in the Western Pacific. Look at the lower part of *Figure 2*. One plate stays at the surface, and the other plate dives down beneath it at some angle. This process is called **subduction**, and so these plate boundaries are called subduction zones. Where the downgoing plate first bends downward, a deep trench is formed on the ocean floor. These trenches are where the very deepest ocean depths are found. As the plate goes down into the mantle asthenosphere, magma is produced at a certain depth. The magma rises up to the ocean floor to form a chain of volcanic islands, called a volcanic island arc.

Other subduction zones are located at the edges of continents. Look at the upper part of *Figure 2*. The west coast of South America, where the Nazca Plate and the South American Plate are converging, is a good example. In places like this, the downgoing plate is always oceanic lithosphere and the plate that remains at the surface is always continental lithosphere. That's because the continental lithosphere is less dense than the oceanic lithosphere. Ocean–continent subduction is similar in many ways to ocean–ocean subduction, except that the volcanic arc is built at the edge of the continent, rather than in the ocean. The Andes mountain range in western South America is an example of a continental volcanic arc.

The third kind of convergent boundary is where two continental lithospheric plates have collided with each other. Think back to the investigation. You were asked what would happen when the "spreading ridge" arrives at the "subduction zone." If you suspected that the spreading ridge would go down the subduction zone, never to be seen again, you were right! If you had continued the investigation after the spreading ridge had disappeared, what would have happened? As the plate that was on the other side of the

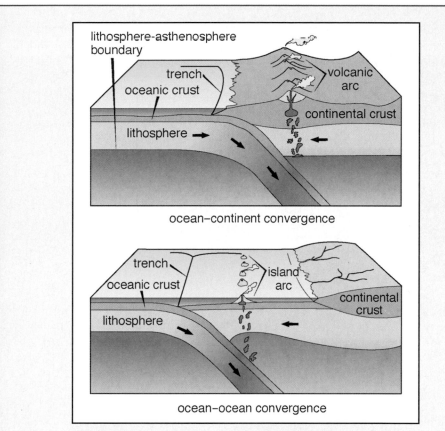

Figure 2 Cross sections through subduction zones. The upper cross section shows subduction of an oceanic lithospheric plate beneath a continental lithospheric plate (ocean–continent subduction). The lower cross section shows subduction of an oceanic lithospheric plate beneath another oceanic lithospheric plate (ocean–ocean subduction).

Geo Words

suture zone: the zone on the Earth's surface where two continents have collided and have been welded together to form a single continent

spreading ridge was consumed down the subduction zone, the continent on the other side of the ocean would have moved closer and closer to the subduction zone. This is how two continents can come together at a subduction zone. Remember that continental lithosphere is much less dense than the mantle, so continental lithosphere cannot be subducted. The subduction stops! The continent that was coming along toward the subduction zone keeps working its way under the other continent, for hundreds of kilometers, until finally the friction between the two continents is so great that plate movement stops. The zone where two continents have met and become welded into a single continent is called a **suture zone**. There is only one good example on today's Earth: the Indian Plate has collided with the Eurasian Plate and is still working its way under it.

Geo Words

transform plate boundary: a plate boundary where two plates slide parallel to one another

transform fault: a vertical surface of slippage between two lithospheric plates along an offset between two segments of a spreading ridge

See *Figure 3*. There is a good reason why the Tibetan Plateau is the largest area of very high elevations in the world: the continental lithosphere is much thicker there because one continent has moved under another.

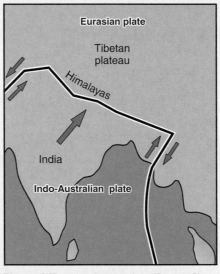

Figure 3 The Himalayas and the Tibetan Plateau were formed by the collision of the Indian Plate with the Eurasian Plate. The Indian Plate is being shoved horizontally underneath the Eurasian Plate, so the continental crust in the Himalayas and the Tibetan Plateau is much thicker than normal.

Transform Plate Boundaries

At **transform boundaries**, plates slide past one another. The surface along which the plates slide is called a **transform fault**. As you saw in **Activity I** in the material about mid-ocean ridges, transform faults connect the offsets along mid-ocean spreading ridges. Most are short, but a few are very long. The most famous transform fault forms the boundary between the North American Plate and the Pacific Plate, in California. It is several hundred kilometers long. You can see from the map in *Figure 4* that the San Andreas Fault connects short segments of spreading ridges at its northern and southern ends.

The movement along the transform fault is limited to the distance between the two segments of ridge crest. *Figure 5* is a sketch map of a mid-ocean ridge, showing segments of the ridge crest offset by transform faults. Between Points I and 2, Plates A and B are sliding past each other.

The transform fault extends only between Points 1 and 2. To the left of Point 1, Plate A is in contact with itself along the east-west line, and to the right of Point 2, Plate B is in contact with itself along the east-west line. Since the plates are rigid, there is no slipping movement along the east-west lines, which are like "dead" transform faults!

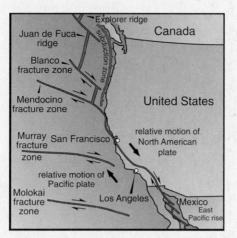

Figure 4 Plates showing a transform boundary.

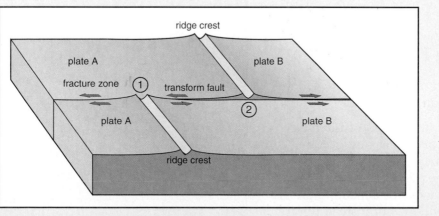

Figure 5 Sketch map of a mid-ocean ridge, showing segments of the ridge crest offset by transform faults.

Check Your Understanding

1. Name the three types of boundaries between lithospheric plates.

2. How and where are rift valleys formed?

3. How can ocean basins change in size?

4. Convergent plate boundaries can be in three different settings. What are they?

5. Describe subduction.

6. Why is it that transform faults can be used to figure out the directions of plate movements? Why can't subduction zones also be used for that?

7. What happens when two continents collide along a convergent plate boundary?

Understanding and Applying What You Have Learned

1. Design an investigation, with the materials like the ones you used in this activity, to model the creation of a new ocean basin.

2. Identify on a world map of lithospheric plates one example of each of the following settings:

   a) an established divergent boundary;

   b) a young divergent zone (continental rift zone);

   c) an ocean–ocean convergent boundary;

   d) an ocean–continent convergent boundary;

   e) a continent–continent collision zone:

   f) the interior of a plate;

   g) a transform plate boundary.

Preparing for the Chapter Challenge

Reflect on your answers to the above. Write a short summary (one or two paragraphs) describing what you have learned so far about how plate movements and their interactions at plate boundaries can change the arrangement of continents and ocean basins on the Earth. Be prepared to include this summary in your **Chapter Challenge**.

Inquiring Further

1. **Evolution of the Biosphere at Mid-Ocean Ridges**

   Recently, new forms of life have been discovered at mid-ocean ridges. They thrive in the presence of superheated, mineral-rich water. This life does not depend upon the Sun for energy, but instead upon the energy and matter from Earth's interior. How has life evolved in such environments? For further information check the *EarthComm* web site.

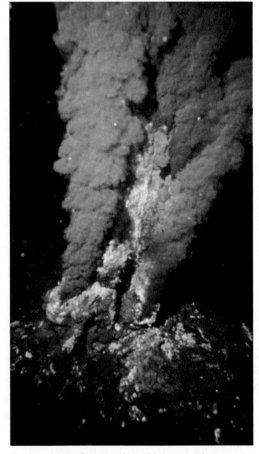
Black smokers form at the mid-ocean ridges.

Activity 3

What Drives the Plates?

GOALS

In this activity you will:

- Calculate the density of liquids and compare their densities with their position in a column of liquid.

- Observe the effects of temperature on the density of a material.

- Examine natural heat flow from within The Earth.

- Understand the results of uneven heating within The Earth.

- Understand the causes of the movement of lithospheric plates.

Think about It

Geoscientists are still uncertain about the most important forces that drive the plates.

- What causes the movement of the lithospheric plates?

What do you think? Record your ideas about this question in your *EarthComm* notebook. Be prepared to discuss your responses with your small group and the class.

Investigate

Part A: Effects of Density on the Position of Material

1. Obtain 30 mL each of water, pancake syrup, and vegetable oil. Suppose you were to carefully pour a small volume of each liquid into one graduated cylinder or clear tube.

   a) Predict what you think will happen. Sketch and explain your prediction.

2. One at a time, carefully pour 10 mL of each liquid into a cylinder or clear tube.

   a) Record your observations.

   b) Do your observations support your predictions?

   c) Does the order in which you pour the liquids make a difference in what you observe?

3. Develop a method to determine the density of each of the three liquids using a graduated cylinder, 10 mL of each liquid, and a balance scale. Density is mass per unit volume. Thus, the density of each liquid equals the mass of liquid (in grams) divided by the volume (10 mL).

   a) Write down your procedure for finding the density of each liquid.

   b) Make a data table to record your measurements and calculations for each liquid.

   c) After your teacher has approved your procedure, determine the density of each liquid.

   ⚠ Follow your teacher's safety advice about using a heat source. Hot corn syrup can cause burns. Clean up spills immediately.

4. Compare your calculations with your observations in **Step 2**.

   a) Describe how the densities you calculated explain what you observed.

   b) If layers of materials of different densities within the Earth behave like layers of liquids of different densities, what would you predict about the position of the rock layers of different densities in the Earth?

Part B: Effects of Temperature on Density of a Material

1. Pour about a 5 cm thick layer of corn syrup into a Pyrex® beaker or wide aluminum pan. Place the pan on a heat source.

2. Place three pieces of balsa wood on the syrup.

   a) Predict what you think will happen to the wood as the corn syrup is heated. Record your ideas in your notebook.

3. Observe the wood. Record any changes every 5 min for 20 to 30 min.

   a) Use diagrams to record the changes you observe.

   b) Do your observations support your predictions? What do you think caused the results you observed?

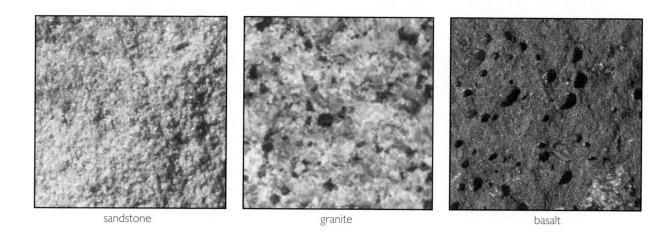

sandstone   granite   basalt

Part C: Density of Earth Materials

1. Collect samples of rock from your community and also obtain samples of granite, basalt, and sandstone.

2. If you can, predict qualitatively the density of the samples. Which sample appears to be least dense? Which appears to be most dense?

    a) Record your predictions in your notebook.

3. Develop a method to find the density of each rock sample using the sample, water, a graduated cylinder, and a balance scale. Density is mass per unit volume. Thus, the density of each rock equals the mass of rock (in grams) divided by the volume of rock (in cubic centimeters). Note that 1 mL = 1 cm³.

    a) Write down your procedure for finding the density of each rock sample.

    b) Make a data table to record your measurements and calculations for each rock.

    c) After your teacher has approved your procedure, determine the density of each rock sample.

4. Compare your calculations with your predictions.

    a) How does the density of the rock from your community compare with the densities of granite, sandstone, and basalt?

Part D: Forces Causing Subduction of Lithospheric Plates

1. Partly fill a large, rectangular tub with warm water. Wait until any tiny air bubbles have disappeared. The water has to be perfectly clear.

2. Very slowly and carefully, put a few ounces of liquid dish detergent in the water and mix it slowly and carefully with a mixing spoon. If any soap bubbles or foam remain on the water surface, scrape them off with a damp sponge.

3. Cut a piece of the vinyl plastic to be about six inches wide and about twelve inches long. Trim a flat, clear-plastic ruler with the scissors to be the same width as the plastic sheet. (The ruler should sink in water.) Tape the ruler to one end of the plastic sheet.

4. Dip the ruler end of the plastic sheet into the water to a depth of about 1 cm. Immediately place the plastic sheet on the water surface. Do this by holding the ends up, and letting the sagging middle part of the sheet touch the water surface first, to avoid trapping air bubbles under the sheet. Observe what happens. Repeat this step as many times as you need to make careful observations.

   a) Record your observations. Include a description of the motion of the plastic sheet in the water.

   b) What is the force that makes the plastic behave as it did?

   c) How does this demonstration show what happens in a subduction zone?

Reflecting on the Activity and the Challenge

You have seen evidence that liquids of varying densities will form layers in a container with the densest liquid on the bottom. You have also shown by modeling that a solid floating on a liquid seems to move away from a source of heat. You have seen evidence that different rocks are likely to have varying densities. Finally, you have made a direct observation of one of the main forces that cause subduction. These investigations will help you understand the Earth's interior and the flow of matter and energy in the Earth. You should now be able to explain why lithospheric plates can float and what might cause them to move.

 Keep work area clean and dry.

 Have paper towels ready for the wet plastic that is taken out of the tub.

Digging Deeper

THE EARTH'S INTERIOR STRUCTURE

Evidence for Earth's Layered Structure

Density (mass per unit volume) refers to how concentrated the mass (atoms and molecules) in an object or material is. Less dense material tends to rise upward and float on more dense material. Here are some everyday examples: a less dense solid floats in a more dense liquid; a more dense solid sinks to the bottom of a less dense liquid; a less dense liquid floats on a more dense liquid. Rocks in the Earth's crust (oceanic crust consists mainly of basalt; continental crust consists mainly of less dense rocks like granite) are less dense than the rocks of the underlying mantle. The crust "floats" on the more dense interior material.

Several kinds of evidence reveal that density varies within the Earth. Laboratory experiments in high-pressure apparatus show that rocks deep in the Earth are more dense than the same rocks when they are at the surface. The weight of the overlying rock puts pressure on rock below, making it more dense. The most dense material should be at the center of the Earth, where the pressure is greatest.

A second line of evidence comes from calculations of the average density of the Earth. You cannot put the Earth on a balance scale to find its mass, but the mass can be found indirectly using Newton's Law of Gravitation. According to that law, the gravitational force (F) between any two objects in the universe can be expressed this way:

$$F = \frac{gm_1m_2}{d^2}$$

where m_1 and m_2 stand for the masses of two objects,

d stands for the distance between them, and

g stands for the gravitational constant (known from experiments).

Because the Earth exerts a certain force on a body (like you) with a certain mass m_1 on the Earth's surface, some 6400 km from its center, the known values can be substituted into the equation and the mass of the Earth (m_2) can be calculated. Dividing the mass of the Earth by its volume gives an average density of the Earth (in metric units) of 5.5 g/cm³. The density of the rocks commonly found at the surface (granite, basalt, and sandstone) is much lower. The average density of surface rocks is 2.8 g/cm³. The density of ➡

Geo Words

density: the mass per unit volume of a material or substance

91

Geo Words

core: the solid, innermost part of the Earth consisting mainly of iron

the Earth's interior must be much greater than 2.8 g/cm³ for the entire Earth to average 5.5 g/cm³. This is partly due to the effect of compression, but also partly because the material in the Earth's core is mostly iron, which is much more dense than rocks, even when it is not under great pressure.

The speed of earthquake (seismic) waves within the Earth generated by earthquakes also provides convincing evidence about the properties of rock in the Earth. Scientists have learned that these waves travel faster the deeper they are in the Earth. It's known from laboratory experiments that earthquake (seismic) waves that travel at 4.8 km/s at the surface travel at 6.4 km/s at a depth of 1600 km. The reason why the speed of seismic waves increases downward in the mantle is complicated. In the laboratory, scientists use special equipment to measure the speeds of seismic waves in different rocks. They can determine how the speed of seismic waves changes with changes in temperature, pressure, and rock type.

Studies also show that change in density is not uniform with depth. Instead, there are distinct jumps or changes in density. By studying the changes in the speed of earthquake (seismic) waves as they pass through the Earth, scientists have concluded that the Earth's interior structure is layered. The thickness and the composition of the layers are shown in the table in *Figure 1*.

Layer	Thickness (km)	Composition	Temperature (°C)	Density (g/cm³)
Continental crust	30–60	Granitic silicate rock (>60% silica)	20–600	~2.7
Oceanic crust	5–8	Basaltic silicate rock (<50% silica)	20–1300	~3.0
Mantle	2800	Solid silicate	100–3000	~5
Outer core	2150	Liquid iron-nickel	3000–6500	~12
Inner core	1230	Solid iron-nickel	7000	~12

Figure 1 The composition of the layers of the Earth.

Using the evidence they have observed, geoscientists divide Earth into four main layers: the inner **core**, the outer core, the mantle, and the crust, as shown in *Figure 2*. The core is composed mostly of iron. It is so hot that the outer core is molten. The inner core is also hot, but under such great pressure that it remains solid. Most of the Earth's mass is in the mantle. The mantle is composed of iron, magnesium, and aluminum silicate minerals. At over 1000°C, the mantle is solid rock, but it can deform slowly in a plastic manner. The crust is much thinner than any of the other layers, and is composed of the least dense rocks.

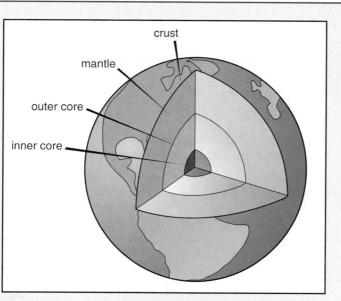

Figure 2 Schematic diagram showing the layered structure of the Earth's interior.

Geo Words

thermal convection: a pattern of movement in a fluid caused by heating from below and cooling from above. Thermal convection transfers heat energy from the bottom of the convection cell to the top

The Flow of Matter and Energy within the Earth

The temperature of the Earth increases with depth. This can be observed directly in mines and in oil wells. Sources of the Earth's internal heat include the decay of radioactive elements, the original heat of Earth's formation, and heating by the impact of meteorites early in Earth's history. The Earth can be thought of as a massive heat engine. The transfer of heat from Earth's interior to its surface drives the movements of the Earth's crust and mantle.

Temperature affects the density of materials. Hot-air balloons show this effect well. When the air inside a balloon is heated it expands (increases in volume). The mass of the balloon stays the same, but the volume increases. When the ratio of mass to volume drops, the density drops. Therefore, heating makes the balloon less dense than the surrounding air. The hot-air balloon begins to rise. Similarly, as rocks in the interior of the Earth are heated enough, their density decreases. The less dense rock rises slowly over time, unless the rocks are too rigid to allow flow.

In the activity, you heated corn syrup and observed the movement of balsa wood. Why did the balsa wood move? The answer lies in the process of **thermal convection**. Heating lowers the density of the corn syrup at the bottom of the container. This causes it to rise. As the corn syrup approaches the upper surface, it flows to the side, making room for more corn syrup rising from below. As it moves to the side, it cools. As it cools, it becomes more dense, and it sinks back to the bottom of the container. At the bottom of the container it is heated and rises again. This kind of density-driven circulation is called thermal convection, as shown in *Figure 3*. Thermal convection transfers heat energy from one place to another by the movement of material.

In 1929, the geologist Arthur Holmes elaborated on the idea that the mantle undergoes thermal convection. He suggested that this thermal convection is like a conveyor belt. He reasoned that rising mantle material can break a continent apart and then force the two parts of the broken continent in opposite directions. The continents would then be carried by the convection currents.

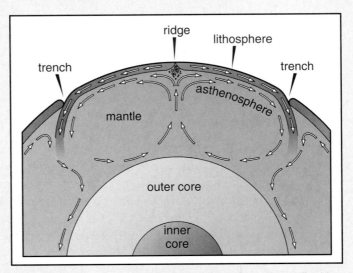

Figure 3 One possible pattern of thermal convection in the Earth's mantle. Convection cells like this might provide at least some of the driving force for the movement of lithospheric plates.

According to this hypothesis of mantle convection, material is heated at the core–mantle boundary. It rises upward, spreads out horizontally, cools, and sinks back into the interior. These extremely slow-moving convection cells might provide the driving force that moves the lithospheric plates (see *Figure 3*). Material rises to the surface at places where lithospheric plates spread apart from one another. Material sinks back into the Earth where plates converge. Although the idea was not widely appreciated during Holmes' time, mantle convection cells became instrumental in the development of the theory of plate tectonics.

Mantle convection can't be observed directly, the way you could have observed convection in the corn syrup if you had put some tiny marker grains in the syrup. Geoscientists are sure that the mantle is convecting, but they are still unsure of the patterns of convection. The patterns probably don't look much like what is shown in *Figure 3*! Geoscientists now think that the lithospheric plates themselves play a major part in driving the convection, rather than just being passive riders on top of the convection cells. Do you remember from **Activity 1** that the mid-ocean ridges are broad, and they slope gradually down to the deep ocean nearer the continents? That means that the plates on either side of the ridge crest slope downward away from the ridge crest, and they tend to slide downhill under the pull of gravity! In this way, they help the convection cell to keep moving, instead of the other way around. Also, you probably know that most materials expand when they are heated and shrink when they are cooled. As the plates in the ocean cool, they become more dense than the deeper mantle because they have almost the same composition but they are not as hot. They sink into the mantle of their own accord, just as in **Part D** of the investigation. In that way they help to keep the convection cell moving.

Check Your Understanding

1. How can the density of the Earth be calculated?

2. How does the density of the Earth provide evidence that the interior of the Earth is denser than the surface?

3. Name three main layers of the Earth.

4. Why is the inner core of the Earth solid, even though it is hot?

5. How are convection currents set up?

6. What part of the Earth's interior layers are in motion due to density differences?

Understanding and Applying What You Have Learned

1. Look at the map of lithospheric plates near South America and the relative "horizontal" motion between these plates.

   a) At point A, the two plates are moving away from each other. What is happening between them?

   b) At point B, two plates are moving toward each other. What happens as they continue to push toward each other if they have:

      (i) Different densities

      (ii) The same density

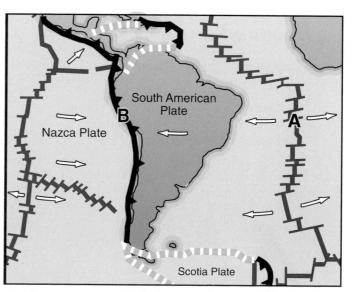

Map of the Nazca and South American plates.

2. Draw two pictures side by side. Make one the experiment with corn syrup and balsa wood. Make the other the Earth's interior structure. Show where heating and cooling occur, and use arrows to indicate the movement of material (the flow of matter and energy in both systems). Label the parts in each diagram and show how they correspond to each other.

3. What evidence is there at the Earth's surface for unequal heating somewhere within the Earth?

4. List some natural processes that occur when heat from the Earth's interior is transferred to the surface.

5. Use your understanding of density to calculate the missing values in the table below:

Object	Mass (g)	Volume (cm³)	Density (g/cm³)
Iron	41.8		7.6
Quartz	39.75	15.0	
Gold		8.0	19.3

Preparing for the Chapter Challenge

Reflect on your answers to the above. Write an essay that describes the Earth's interior structure and the flow of matter and energy within the Earth. Refer to the evidence you examined and the models you explored. Sketch and label a drawing or two to illustrate the main ideas. Be prepared to include this summary in your **Chapter Report.**

Inquiring Further

1. **Investigating Driving Forces for Plate Motions**

   What questions do you have about the driving forces behind plate tectonics? Develop a plan that would help you find an answer to one of your questions. Record your plan in your notebook. What further information might help you answer your questions?

Activity 4

Effects of Plate Tectonics

GOALS

In this activity you will:

- Use maps to examine the distribution of earthquakes and volcanoes to the location of plate boundaries.

- Explain the location, nature, and cause of volcanic arcs in terms of plate tectonics.

- Explain the location, nature, and cause of hot spots.

- Explain how plate-tectonic processes have caused continents to grow through geologic time.

- Explain how plate-tectonic processes produce landforms.

- Explain how plate tectonics can affect the interior of a continent.

Think about It

Rocks high in the Himalayas, almost 8000 m (29,028 ft) above sea level, contain fossils of marine animals.

- Why are most high mountain ranges located at or near plate boundaries?

What do you think? Record your ideas about this question in your *EarthComm* notebook. Include sketches as necessary. Be prepared to discuss your response with your small group and the class.

Investigate

1. Compare the distribution of volcanoes and earthquakes shown on the following map with the map of crustal plates you created in **Activity 2**.

   a) Describe any differences between the distribution of volcanoes along plate boundaries and within plate interiors.

   b) Describe any differences between the distribution of earthquakes along plate boundaries and within plate interiors.

2. To model the rise of magma through the Earth, fill a tall, transparent jar almost up to the brim with honey. Put a very small volume of vegetable oil (about 5 mL, one teaspoon) on top of the honey. Screw on the lid. Try not to leave any air in the container. Turn the container upside down quickly and set it on a tabletop. Make your observations and answer the following questions:

   a) What does the honey represent?

   b) What does the vegetable oil represent?

   c) Describe and explain the behavior of the vegetable oil.

   d) What do you think are the similarities and differences between the behavior of this model and the rise of magma in the Earth?

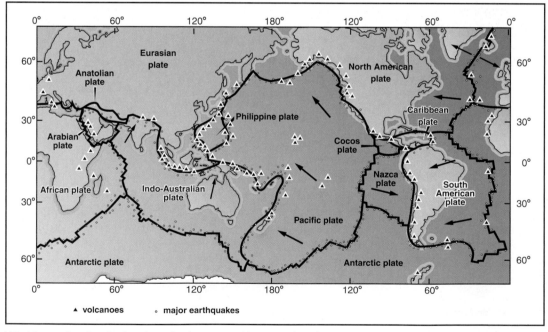

World map showing the location of volcanoes and large earthquakes.

⚠ Be sure the lid is on tight before the jar is turned over. Clean up spills immediately.

3. The diagram shows a cross section with two subduction zones, a spreading ridge, and a continental rift. Note the two zones where an oceanic plate is being subducted (plunged) under another plate. Volcanoes are common in a zone that is located a certain distance away from the trench where the subducted plate first bends downward.

In your group, develop as many hypotheses as you can think of for why the volcanoes occur, and why they are located where they are. Here are four important facts you might need to use or think about in developing your hypotheses:

(i) The downgoing plate is cooler than the mantle.

(ii) The composition of the downgoing plate is slightly different from the composition of the mantle. (Why?)

(iii) The oceanic crust on the downgoing plate contains water, which was added to the igneous rocks when they formed.

(iv) Friction generates heat.

a) Record your group's hypothesis.

b) In a class discussion, compare the hypotheses you developed in your group with those of other groups. Were their hypotheses different from yours and still seemed reasonable?

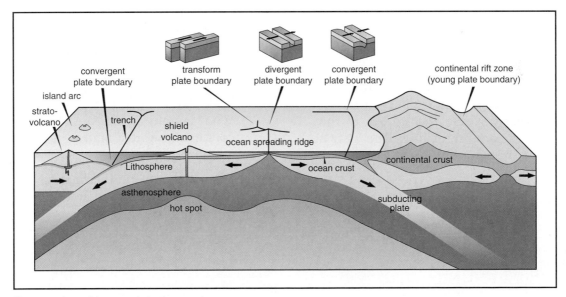

Cross-section with two subduction zones.

4. Look again at the diagram of the cross section with two subduction zones. Use the cross section to answer the following questions:

   a) Under what two types of plates is the oceanic lithosphere being subducted?

   b) What differences between oceanic volcanic arcs and continental volcanic island arcs can you see or infer from the cross section?

   c) On a copy of the map of volcanoes and earthquakes, circle two continental volcanic arcs and three oceanic volcanic arcs.

   d) In which part of the world are most volcanic arcs located? What does that suggest about the plate-tectonic setting of that part of the world?

5. To understand why volcanic arcs are called arcs, look at the Andes Mountains on a topographic map. The Andes are topped with volcanoes that are part of a volcanic arc. They appear to run along a straight line. Run a string or thread along their length on a globe.

   a) What is the shape of the line on the globe? Why are lines of volcanoes called arcs?

   b) Using the cross section of the subduction zones, explain why few volcanoes occur very far inland within a continent.

   c) If volcanic rock is found far inland within a continent, what is one possible reason why it is there?

6. One reason why volcanic rock might be located in the interior of a plate is illustrated on the cross section of the subduction zones where a hot spot is shown in the middle of one of the oceanic plates.

   a) Where does it appear that the hot spot originated?

   b) Is it related to subduction?

   c) Where does the hot spot begin to produce a pool of magma?

7. The map on the next page shows hot spots around the world:

   a) Where are most hot spots?

   b) Are they clustered or randomly located?

   c) What famous area of the continental United States sits over a hot spot?

   d) What sits atop another famous hot spot in the United States?

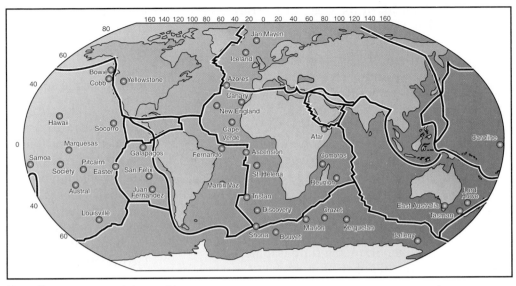

Map of hot spots around the world.

8. To model the growth in size at a subduction zone, set up pieces of lumber and a plastic sheet as shown in the diagram. With a table knife, spread a thin (about 2 mm) layer of cream cheese on the part of the plastic sheet that rests on the upper surface of the 2 × 6. Try to keep the layer as even in thickness as you can. Spread a layer of the cheese spread, of about the same thickness, over the layer of cream cheese.

Have one student hold the piece of 2 × 4 in place, pressing down on it gently. Another student very slowly pulls the loose end of the sheet of plastic out from under the 2 × 4. Observe what happens to the layer of cream cheese and cheese spread as "subduction" proceeds.

a) In your notebook, write a description of the process you observe. Be sure to note how the body of material at the subduction zone changes its shape, as well as its volume through time.

⚠️ Keep work area clean. Have damp paper towels ready to wipe up spills and clean hands as required.

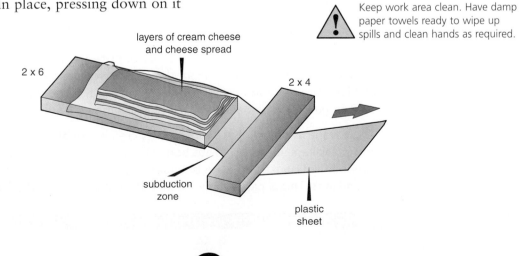

layers of cream cheese and cheese spread

2 x 6

2 x 4

subduction zone

plastic sheet

9. After all of the sheet of plastic has been consumed down the subduction zone, make a cut through the accumulated cream cheese and cheese spread, to see the internal structure of the new material at the subduction zone. The cut should be vertical, and parallel to the direction of subduction. Clear away all the material from one side of the cut and examine the face of the cut.

a) In your notebook, draw a sketch of what the cut looks like. Show the topographic profile of the top of the material, and also any internal structures you observe.

b) Is there a limit to the height of the "mountain range" that is formed at the subduction zone?

c) Did any of the cream cheese and cheese spread go down the subduction zone (under the 2 × 4)? In a real subduction zone, what would happen to such material? (This is not a perfect model of what happens to oceanic sediment at a subduction zone, but it gives you the flavor of it. Geoscientists love to make puns.)

Reflecting on the Activity and the Challenge

In this activity you have observed features on the Earth's surface that are created as a result of crustal plate movements and activity within the geosphere. You have also seen that plate-tectonic processes can cause plates to grow in size. Finally, you have seen that plate movements can cause earthquakes that can be associated with specific plate boundaries. You will need to consider these surface features and disturbances created by plate motions in order to complete your **Chapter Challenge**.

Geo Words

plate tectonics: the field of study of plate motion

Digging Deeper

"BUILDING" FEATURES ON EARTH'S SURFACE

Plate Tectonics

You can now see why the field of study of plate motion is called **plate tectonics**. Tectonics comes from the Greek word *tekton*, which means builder. Plate tectonics refers to the building of the features on Earth's surface due to deformation caused by plate movements.

You have learned that plate movements create mountain ranges, trenches, and rift valleys at or near plate boundaries. Also, there is a clear relationship between volcanoes and plate boundaries, and between earthquakes and plate boundaries. This is particularly evident around the rim of the Pacific Ocean, where the subduction of oceanic plates around much of the rim results in volcanic arcs and earthquakes.

Oceanic Trenches

The deepest valleys on Earth are in the ocean, where they can't be seen except from special deep-diving submersibles. Where an oceanic plate is subducted under another plate, it bends downward as it enters the subduction zone. The valley that is formed above the zone of bending is called a trench. Oceanic trenches are very deep. Many are deeper than 10,000 m, which is twice the average depth of the deep ocean. The word "valley" is a bit misleading, because trenches are wide, and their side slopes are not very steep. You can easily spot the locations of trenches in most world atlases, because they are shown with the darkest blue shading on maps of the world's oceans. Trenches are common in many places in the western Pacific, where there is ocean–ocean subduction. There is a long trench along the west coast of South America, where the Nazca Plate is being subducted under the continent.

Volcanoes at Plate Boundaries

You know already that volcanoes are common along mid-ocean ridges, where basalt magma rises up from the asthenosphere to form new oceanic crust. Volcanoes are also common along subduction zones, where they form volcanic arcs. At a depth of 200 to 300 kilometers, magma is produced above the subducted plate, and rises toward the surface because it is less dense than the surrounding rock. At first it was thought that the magma was produced as rock near the top of the downgoing plate and was heated by friction, but geoscientists are now convinced that the melting is for a different reason. When the oceanic crust is first produced, at the mid-ocean ridges, a lot of water is combined with certain minerals in the igneous rocks. As the pressure and temperature increase down the subduction zone, this water is driven off, and it rises upward from the plate. It's known that the melting temperature of the mantle rock above the plate is lowered when water is added to it. This causes some of the mantle rock to melt. This is a good way to explain why melting doesn't start until the plate has reached a certain depth down the subduction zone, and then stops at a slightly deeper depth. The "Ring of Fire" around the Pacific Ocean is caused by this melting at subduction zones all around the Pacific.

Hot Spots

Not all volcanoes are associated with mid-ocean ridges and subduction zones. Hot spots, which originate at the boundary between the mantle

➡️

103

and the outer core, are narrow plumes of unusually hot mantle material. These plumes rise up through the mantle and melt the rock at the base of the lithosphere, creating pools of magma. This magma then rises to the surface, resulting in hot spot volcanoes.

Some hot spots are located under continents. The hot spot producing the hot springs at Yellowstone National Park is an example. One theory suggests that the bulge created by a hot spot may initiate the rifting of a continent. It is thought that a hot spot lies below, and is responsible for, the Rift Valley of Africa. There is also evidence suggesting that the New Madrid fault, which runs down the Mississippi River Valley, may represent an aborted rift zone originally created by a series of hot spots. The largest series of earthquakes in the United States, outside of Alaska, occurred on the New Madrid fault in the early 19th century, ringing bells as far away as Philadelphia and causing the Mississippi River to run backwards for a short time! In this way, plate tectonics can even affect areas that are within the heart of a continent.

Mountains at Plate Boundaries

Most of the great mountain ranges of the world are located near convergent plate boundaries. When someone says "mountain ranges" to you, which of them do you think of? The Alps in Europe, the Himalayas in southern Asia, the Andes in South America, and the coastal mountain ranges in western North America are some examples. Mountain ranges like those are built in mainly two ways. You already know that the magma that is generated above the subducted plate rises up to form a chain of volcanoes. Much of the magma remains below the surface and cools to form large underground masses of igneous rock called batholiths. The combination of volcanoes at the surface and batholiths deep in the Earth adds a lot of new rock to the area above the subduction zone, and makes the elevation of the land much higher. Also, many subduction zones experience compression, when the two plates are pushed together by plate movements elsewhere. In places like that, great masses of rock are pushed together and stacked on top of one another in complicated structures, to form high mountains. This happens also where two continents collide with each other, as in the Himalayas.

Growth of Continents at Subduction Zones.

During the long travels of an oceanic plate from a mid-ocean ridge to a subduction zone, a hundred meters or more of oceanic sediment is deposited on the top of the plate. In **Part 6** of the investigation, you saw how a lot of this sediment is scraped off and added to the edge of the other plate. This material, which is deformed into very complicated structures, is turned into rock by heat and pressure. It becomes a solid part of the other plate. When material is added to the edge of a continent in this way, the continent grows larger at its edge. Continents also grow as the igneous rock of volcanoes and batholiths are added to the continent above the subduction zone, as described above. The growth of a continent along its edge in these ways is called **continental accretion**. This has been going on through geologic time, making the continents larger and larger.

Earthquakes and Plate Tectonics

As plates move past each other at plate boundaries, they don't always slide smoothly. In many places the rocks hold together for a long time and then slip suddenly. You will learn more in **Chapter 3** about how earthquakes are caused in this way. Earthquakes along mid-ocean ridges are common because of movement along the transform faults that connect segments of the ridge crest. Only where transform faults are on land or close to land, as in California, are these earthquakes likely to be hazardous. As you saw in **Activity 2**, the famous San Andreas fault in California is a transform fault. Earthquakes at subduction zones and continent–continent collision zones are a bigger problem for human society, because these areas are so common on the Earth, especially around the rim of the Pacific and along a belt that stretches from the Mediterranean to southeast Asia. Earthquakes in subduction zones happen at depths that range from very shallow, near the trench, to as deep as hundreds of kilometers, along the subducted plate. Earthquakes in continent–continent collision zones happen over wide areas as one continent is pushed under the other.

Geo Words

continental accretion: the growth of a continent along its edges

Check Your Understanding

1. Why is plate tectonics a suitable name for the study of plate motion. Explain.

2. What geographic features would you expect to see at plate boundaries.

3. How do geoscientists suggest that "hot spots" are related to plate tectonics.

4. In your own words explain the process of continental accretion.

Understanding and Applying What You Have Learned

1. Review your work with earthquakes and volcanoes one more time.

   a) Summarize where most earthquakes are located compared to plate boundaries.

   b) Summarize where most volcanoes are located compared to plate boundaries.

2. Although most earthquakes and volcanoes are associated with plate boundaries, they are not always located directly along the boundaries. Considering boundaries between oceanic and continental plates:

   a) Why are volcanoes usually found on the continental side of a plate boundary?

   b) Why are earthquakes usually found on the continental side of a plate boundary?

3. Many volcanoes and earthquakes are found far from modern plate boundaries. Write a paragraph giving one idea you think might explain how at least some of them have formed. Be sure to point out examples by describing their location.

4. Make a list of the various plate-tectonic settings where mountain ranges are likely to be produced. For each item on the list, draw a cross section that shows the mountain range and how it relates to the plate-tectonic setting. For each item, give an example from somewhere in the world.

Preparing for the Chapter Challenge

In this activity you have learned that plate tectonics has an influence on every part of the world. Surface features and movements caused by plate tectonics are not only at plate boundaries, but also at locations far from modern plate boundaries. Write a paragraph, based on what you now know of movements or features in your region that indicate plate-tectonic activity (whether it is nearby or far away). Carefully list your evidence so you can present it to the middle-school class.

Inquiring Further

1. **Plate tectonics and the local climate**

   Distant mountain ranges and plateaus created by plate tectonics can affect air flow in many ways, affecting local climate and thus vegetation, soil, wildlife, and drainage patterns. Research and report on how your local region has been affected directly or indirectly by plate tectonics. You may even wish to include some of this research in your **Chapter Challenge**.

Activity 5

The Changing Geography of Your Community

GOALS

In this activity you will:

- Use several present-day distributions of minerals, rock formations, and fossils to help figure out the distribution of continents.

- Construct a map showing the position of continents 250 million years ago by reversing the present direction of plate motion.

- Recognize a convergence of presently widely scattered minerals, rock formations, and fossils when all the continents were part of Pangea.

- Compare present average community motions with that of the past 250 million years, by calculating the average yearly rate of motion over the last 250 million years.

- Describe the context in which the hypothesis of continental drift was proposed and why it was subjected to criticism.

- Show that your community has moved through different ecological regions over time.

Think about It

The plates forming the Earth crust can be compared to pieces of newspaper torn from the same page.

- How would you be able to decide if the pieces all came from the same page?
- How could you convince someone else that the pieces came from the same page?

What do you think? Record your ideas about these questions in your *EarthComm* notebook. Include sketches as necessary. Be prepared to discuss your responses with your small group and the class.

Investigate

1. Begin your work individually. Obtain four copies of the diagram, showing the outline of the continents at sea level, as well as the boundary between the continental crust and the oceanic crust. The diagram also shows the location of rock formations, mountain ranges, and fossil plants and animals. Cut out the continents on the first sheet along the edges of the continental shelves, which in most places are close to the boundaries betwen the oceanic lithosphere and the continental lithosphere.

   a) Why cut the pieces at the boundaries between the continental and oceanic crust?

   b) In which ecological region is your community today: tropics, subtropics, mid-latitudes, subpolar, or polar?

   c) Coal deposits originated in the swamps of tropical forests. Are the coal deposits shown on the map in the tropics today?

   d) Where do you find mountains similar in structure to the Appalachian Mountains?

   e) Where do you find rock formations similar to those in South America?

   f) Glossopteris is an extinct seed fern that had leaves like ferns of today. It produced seeds too large to travel by air or float on water. Where are fossils of these ferns located today?

   g) Mesosaurus is an extinct freshwater reptile that thrived during the Triassic Period (245 to 208 million years ago). Where are fossils of this reptile found today?

2. Rearrange the cut pieces on a blank piece of paper as the continents now appear and tape them in place.

   a) Label the outlines "Present."

   b) Draw a border around the map.

   c) Sketch in and label the Equator and latitude lines at 30° and 60° north and south.

   d) Title the map "Present."

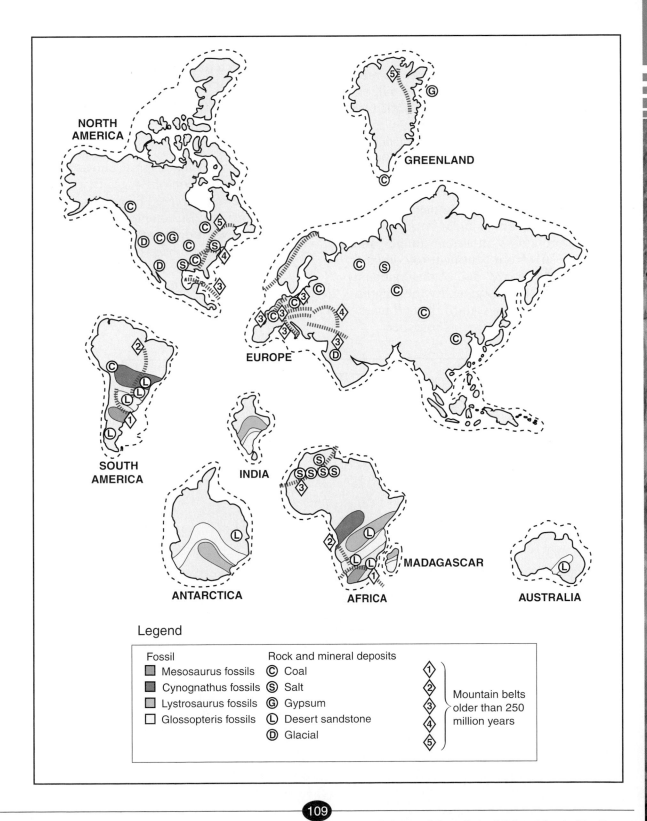

Legend

Fossil
- Mesosaurus fossils
- Cynognathus fossils
- Lystrosaurus fossils
- Glossopteris fossils

Rock and mineral deposits
- C Coal
- S Salt
- G Gypsum
- L Desert sandstone
- D Glacial

1
2
3   Mountain belts
4   older than 250
5   million years

Integrated Coordinated Science for the 21st Century

3. Cut out the continents from the second sheet. Try to arrange them on another piece of paper, as they would have appeared 250 million years ago, before the Atlantic Ocean and the Indian Ocean began to open. You can do this by using two methods: (a) moving each continent in the direction opposite of that shown by the arrows on the map of plate motions on page 68; (b) matching similar rock formations, mountain ranges, and fossils from continent to continent. Try to move each of the continents at the speeds given by the lengths of the arrows, until they all meet. Tape the continents together.

a) Draw a border around the map.

b) Sketch in and label the Equator and latitude lines at 30° and 60° north and south.

c) Title this map, "250 million years ago."

d) The following diagram shows the reconstruction of Pangea that is generally accepted by geoscientists. Your reconstruction is likely to be somewhat different, because the evidence you had is less detailed. Compare your map with the following map, and adjust the positions of the continents on your map as required.

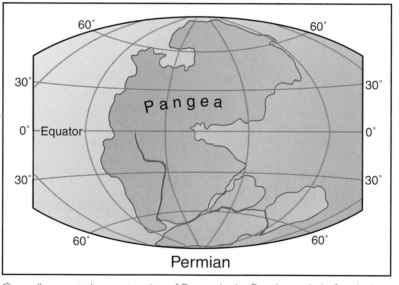

Generally accepted reconstruction of Pangea, in the Permian period of geologic time, 225 million years ago.

4. Use your adjusted map, "250 million years ago" to answer the following questions:

   a) Which two continents fit together best?

   b) Why do you think the continents do not fit together exactly?

   c) From the map of Pangea, what can you say about the latitude and longitude of your community 250 million years ago?

   d) In what ecological region was your community 250 million years ago?

   e) Many coal deposits were created before 280 million years ago in the tropics. Where were they 250 million years ago? Does this make sense? Explain your answer.

   f) Do the Appalachian Mountains line up with other mountain ranges that they resemble?

   g) Do rock formations in South America line up with other formations that they resemble?

   h) How does *Glossopteris* appear to have migrated to its present fossil distribution, since its seeds could not be carried by the wind or float on water?

   (i) How does *Mesosaurus* appear to have migrated to its present fossil locations, since it could not swim in the salty ocean?

5. Cut out the continents from the third sheet, in the same way as before. Arrange them on a new piece of paper, as they might appear 250 million years in the future. You can do so by starting with the present distribution of the continents and then moving each in the direction and at the speed shown by the arrows on the map of plate motions. Remember that some plates will be subducted under others.

   a) What will fill the spaces between the continents in the future?

   b) What will happen to the Mediterranean Sea? What will be created in southern Europe?

   c) Where will the southern coast of California be in 250 million years?

   d) In what latitude and in which ecological region might your community lie in 250 million years?

   e) How might the change in ecological region affect your community?

   f) Why might your prediction regarding the future location of your community and continent be in error?

Reflecting on the Activity and the Challenge

You have seen that by moving the continents "in reverse," in directions opposite to their present movement, you can make the continents fit together fairly well as a single continent. You have also seen that features like rock formations, mountain ranges, and fossil plants and animals that are similar but are now separated by wide oceans are brought together when the continents are assembled into the single large continent of Pangea. You have gotten some idea about how far a particular place on a continent might have moved in the 250 million years since Pangea broke apart.

Digging Deeper

DEVELOPMENT OF THE PLATE TECTONICS THEORY

In this activity, you examined some of the evidence that supports the idea that the continents of the Earth have moved during geologic time. Two features of the Earth were the subject of intense study in the late 1800s— the discovery of similar fossils on continents that are now separated widely by oceans, and the origin of mountain ranges. Both played a part in the early stages of the development of theory of plate tectonics.

In the late 1800s, an Austrian geologist named Eduard Suess (1831–1914) tried to solve a basic geological question: how do mountain ranges form? He based his model of mountain formation on some of the same principles that you explored in this chapter. Suess stated that as the Earth cooled from a molten state, the more dense materials contracted and sank toward the center, and the least dense materials "floated" and cooled to form the crust. He then speculated that mountain ranges formed from the contraction and cooling of the Earth. He likened this to the way that an apple wrinkles and folds as it dries out and shrinks.

Suess went on to explain the origins of oceans, continents, and the similarities of fossils on different continents now separated by oceans. In his model, during the cooling process, parts of the Earth sank deeper than others, forming the ocean basins. Suess claimed that certain parts of the sea floor and continents could rise and sink as they adjusted to changes in the cooling earth. This led him to propose land bridges between continents. Suess coined the term Gondwanaland for a former continent made up of central and southern Africa, Madagascar, and peninsular India. These areas all contained similar fossils that were hundreds of millions of years old. According to Suess, the land bridges allowed various animals and plants to migrate and spread without crossing an ocean.

Although other geologists proposed different models to explain mountains, oceans, and fossils, all generally agreed that the Earth's crust moved up and down, but not very far sideways. Land bridges were often cited as allowing various kinds of organisms to move between continents now separated by oceans. According to Suess and others, the land bridges sank into the ocean long ago and no longer exist.

Not all geologists accepted the theory of a contracting Earth. In 1912, the German geoscientist Alfred Wegener (1880–1930) proposed the hypothesis of continental drift. He saw a variety of problems with the contraction theory. One difficulty was the severe compression of the Alps. The Alps are a young mountain range. Rock layers in the Alps are severely folded and stacked up on top of one another, indicating a great horizontal shortening of original distances, as shown in *Figure 1*. Wegener thought that contraction could not produce such great shortening of the Earth's crust. He also thought that contraction should produce uniform "wrinkles" in the Earth, not narrow zones of folding. The discovery of radioactive heat in Wegener's time also provided evidence against cooling. Heat from radioactive decay in the Earth would work against the cooling and contraction process.

Figure 1 Wegener used the severe compression of the Alps as evidence to support his hypothesis of continental drift.

Geo Words

Pangea: Earth's most recent supercontinent which was rifted apart about 200 million years ago

According to Wegener, about 200 millions years ago, a huge supercontinent called **Pangea** (Greek for *all land*) broke into separate continents that moved apart. Wegener claimed that compression at the leading edge of the moving continent led to the formation of mountains. Wegener's hypothesis allowed him to explain the different ages of the different mountain belts. He claimed that the timing of the breakup was variable, with some parts of Pangea separating earlier than others. His evidence included the puzzle-like fit of the continents and the similarity of rocks, geologic structures, and fossils on opposite sides of the Atlantic Ocean. Wegener's hypothesis eliminated the need for (now sunken) land bridges that once connected widely separated continents.

But how did continents move? Wegener thought that the material beneath the Earth's lithosphere acts like a slow-moving fluid. If this is true for vertical movements, it should also be true for horizontal movements. To visualize Wegener's argument, think about a piece of candy taffy or "silly putty." At the right temperature, taffy that will shatter when struck with a hammer will deform by flowing rather than by breaking when a force is applied slowly and constantly. Although other geologists saw folded mountains as evidence of contraction, Wegener saw folded mountains as evidence of horizontal compression caused by movement of the continents. The presence of folded mountains convinced Wegener that forces within the Earth are powerful enough to move continents. A quote from Wegener summarizes his ideas about the way that all the geological evidence "fit together":

"It is just as if we were to refit the torn pieces of a newspaper by matching their edges and then check whether the lines of print run smoothly across. If they do, there is nothing left to conclude but that the pieces were in fact joined this way. If only one line was available to the test, we would still have found a high probablility for the accuracy of fit, but if we have *n* number of lines, this probability is raised to the *nth* power."

The reaction to Wegener's hypothesis was mixed. Some scientists accepted his arguments. Others argued that it would be impossible for continents to "plow through" the ocean floor (see *Figure 2*). Most geoscientists rejected Wegener's hypothesis. At an international meeting in 1926 devoted to the discussion of continental drift, only a handful of scientists were sympathetic to Wegener's ideas. One scientist raised 18 different arguments against Wegener's evidence! Although his evidence for drift was strong, the mechanism he proposed for the drift of the continents was inadequate.

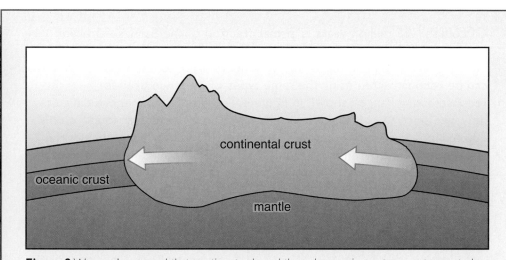

Figure 2 Wegener's proposal that continents plowed through oceanic crust was not accepted by many other geologists.

Convincing evidence began to emerge after World War II, as the sea floor was explored and mapped extensively. By the late 1960s, the theory of plate tectonics had been developed based on many types of evidence. Today, this evidence is considered so abundant and convincing that almost all geoscientists accept the theory. Much of the evidence that Wegener used to support his hypothesis supports plate tectonics. However, new evidence has emerged that provides a more plausible mechanism for the movement of the Earth's lithosphere.

Using evidence such as magnetic striping on the ocean floor (described in **Activity 1**), ages of ocean-floor basalts, outlines of continental plates, and the locations of similar fossils and rock types on widely spaced continents, geologists have reconstructed the record of the breakup of the supercontinent Pangea. Pangea started to break up about 200 million years ago, as continental rifts (divergent zones) began to open and oceanic crust began to form. As Pangea continued to be rifted apart, oceanic crust formed between the northern continents (called Laurasia) and the southern continents (called Gondwana). New ocean floor also was formed between Antarctica and Australia and between Africa and South America. India started to separate from Antarctica and travel northward.

The maps shown in *Figure 3* summarize what has been reconstructed as the breakup of Pangea, from 225 million years ago to the present. As you can see, continents that are now connected were not always that way, and continents that are now widely separated once were part of the same land mass.

Geo Words

supercontinent: a large continent consisting of all of the Earth's continental lithosphere. Supercontinents are assembled by plate-tectonic processes of subduction and continent–continent collision

Of course, 225 million years is a small fraction of the Earth's 4.5 billion year history. There may be rocks in your community much older than 225 million years. The positions of the continents prior to 225 million years ago can be reconstructed using the same types of evidence used for reconstructing Pangea, shown in *Figure 4*. The task is much more difficult, however, since the oldest oceanic crust geologists have ever found is only 200 million years old. Thus, the evidence for the earlier geography of the Earth must be gathered from the continents. Old mountain belts such as the Appalachians of North America and the Urals (which separate Europe from Asia) help locate ancient collision zones between continents of the past. Rock types and fossils provide evidence for the locations of ancient seas, glaciers, mountains and ecological regions. Continents like Pangea, which consist of all of the Earth's continental lithosphere in one single piece, are called **supercontinents**. Geoscientists are fairly sure that there was at least one earlier supercontinent before Pangea, and maybe others as well. The cycle of assembly, breakup, and reassembly of supercontinents is called the Wilson Cycle.

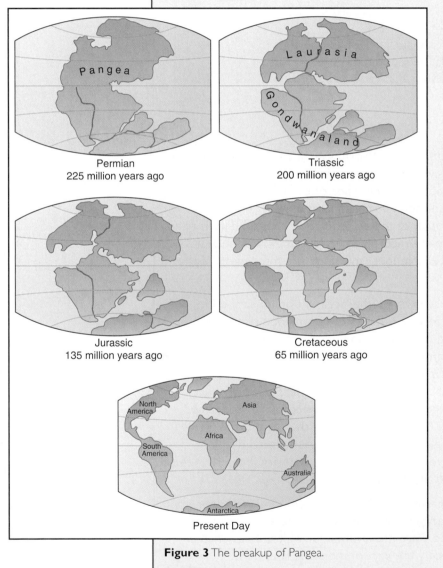

Figure 3 The breakup of Pangea.

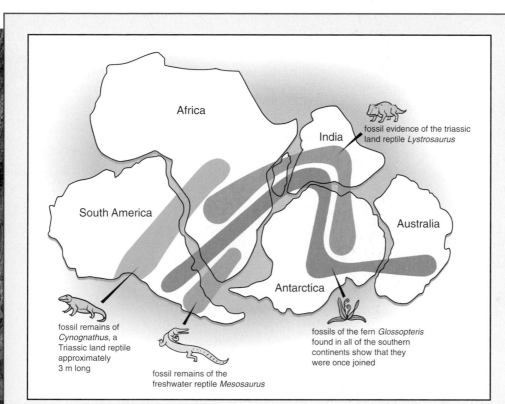

Geo Words

paleomagnetism: the record of the past orientation and polarity of the Earth's magnetic field recorded in rocks containing the mineral magnetite

Figure 4 Evidence used to reconstruct Pangea.

Paleomagnetism

You learned in **Activity 1** that the mineral magnetite "locks" the Earth's magnetic field into its atomic structure as it cools. Geoscientsts collect rock samples containing magnetite and measure the past magnetism the rocks record (called **paleomagnetism**). They do this by putting the sample in a special room that is arranged so that the present Earth's magnetic field is canceled out. The Earth's magnetic field has the same pattern that would be observed if there were a giant bar magnet inside the Earth, lying along the Earth's axis of rotation. There isn't really a big magnet in the Earth; the magnetic field is thought to exist because of movements of liquid iron in the Earth's core. *Figure 5* shows how the lines of the Earth's magnetic field are arranged. The angle that the magnetic field lines make with the Earth's surface changes from the Equator to the poles. Near the Equator the lines are nearly horizontal, and near the poles they are nearly vertical. This means that the paleomagnetism of a rock sample can tell you the latitude of the sample when it formed, called the paleolatitude. Measurement of paleolatitudes is one of the things geoscientists use to reconstruct past supercontinents like Pangea. The big problem is that there is no way of measuring paleolongitude, because the magnetic field lines are always oriented about north–south! That's why no longitude lines are shown on the map of Pangea in the investigation.

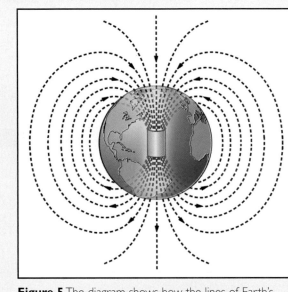

Figure 5 The diagram shows how the lines of Earth's magnetic field are arranged.

Check Your Understanding

1. How did Suess explain the formation of mountain ranges?

2. What evidence was found to contradict Suess's proposal that the Earth is cooling and shrinking?

3. What evidence did Wegener use to support his theory of the breakup of Pangea?

4. How did Wegener propose that the continents move horizontally?

5. How was fossil evidence used to reconstruct Pangea?

Understanding and Applying What You Have Learned

1. Geoscientists often try to figure out paleogeography (the geography of land and sea in the geologic past) using the clues given on your continent puzzle pieces. What additional evidence would you need to be more confident about your "225 Million Years Ago" map?

2. Paleoclimatology is also used to show how continents were connected in the past. What type of climate data might have been helpful to you in making your "225 Million Years Ago" map?

3. Why was the theory of continental drift questioned when it was first proposed by Alfred Wegener?

4. What discoveries helped scientists begin to accept the idea that parts of the Earth's lithosphere move? Why were the more modern clues not available in Wegener's time?

5. New scientific theories often take many years to be accepted by the scientific community. Explain why this is so, using the theory of plate tectonics as an example.

6. The theory of plate tectonics is now accepted by almost all geoscientists. The theory overcomes the objections many scientists had to the idea of continents moving around the globe. How does plate tectonics explain the seeming movement of continents through rigid oceanic crust?

7. Describe what has happened to the lithosphere under the Atlantic Ocean during the last 200 million years. What has happened to the lithosphere under the Pacific Ocean? How does this information support the theory of plate tectonics?

Preparing for the Chapter Challenge

In your notebook, write a brief essay describing how the arrangement of continents and oceans in the geologic past can be figured out, and what are the limitations to doing this.

Try to devise a way of animating the movements of all of the continents from the time of the breakup of Pangea to the present time, so that the middle-school students can watch the movements with their own eyes. Write up your ideas in your notebook. Compare your ideas with those of others in the class.

Inquiring Further

1. **History of science**

   The history of the development of the theory of plate tectonics is a fascinating one. A very important piece of evidence that supported plate tectonic theory was the discovery of paleomagnetism in ocean bottom basalts. How was this paleomagnetic evidence of sea-floor spreading discovered?

   Write down in your notebook at least one additional question you have about the geologic history of your community. How would you go about gathering information to answer these questions? Write your ideas in your notebook.

2. **Plate tectonics and the Earth system**

   Write an essay explaining how Earth systems would change if plate tectonics were to "stop." You might begin with something directly connected to plate tectonics, such as volcanism or mountain building. For example, *"If plate tectonics were to cease, then global volcanism..."*

Earth Science at Work

ATMOSPHERE: *Meteorologist*
In predicting weather patterns, meteorologists must take into account the geological features of the surrounding land.

BIOSPHERE: *Paleontologist*
Geoscientists study the fossils of plants and animals and their relationship to existing plants and animals in order to "reconstruct" the geologic past.

CRYOSPHERE: *Tour Guides*
Some of the most spectacular scenery can be found on and off the shores of Alaska. Tourists are interested in the geography of the areas they visit.

GEOSPHERE: *Civil Engineer*
Transportation networks, whether within a city, or within the country, are a vital lifeline in today's society. The public relies on safe roads and bridges.

HYDROSPHERE: *Harbor Master*
Harbor masters and marina operators are responsible for the vessels that are tied up at their docks. Millions of dollars worth of boats could be housed in a single marina.

How is each person's work related to the Earth system, and to plate tectonics?

Chapter 3

Earthquakes
...and Your Community

Getting Started

An average of about 350,000 earthquakes are detected on Earth each year.

- What causes an earthquake?
- How can an earthquake affect your community?

What do you think? In your notebook, draw a picture that shows a side view of the Earth's crust. Show what causes an earthquake, and how an earthquake can affect a community. Write a caption to explain your drawing. Be prepared to discuss your picture and ideas with your small group and the class.

Scenario

The following description of the 1906 San Francisco earthquake was written by author Jack London:

"Within an hour after the earthquake shock, the smoke of San Francisco's burning was a lurid tower visible a hundred miles away.

"...There was no opposing the flames. There was no organization, no communication. The earthquake had smashed all the cunning adjustments of a twentieth century city. The streets were humped into ridges and depressions, and piled with the debris of fallen walls. Dynamite was lavishly used, and man crumbled many of San Francisco's proudest structures himself into ruins, but there was no withstanding the onrush of the flames. The troops were falling back and driving the refugees with them. From every side came the roaring of flames, the crashing of walls, and the detonations of dynamite."

Can you use your knowledge of earthquakes to develop a plan to ensure that your community would be prepared to deal with an earthquake?

Chapter Challenge

In many states of the U.S., damaging earthquakes can happen at any time. If you live along the Pacific Coast, in a mountain belt, or in the central Midwest, they may even be a very great hazard. Your community has asked your school to assess the earthquake hazard in your area and to find ways to reduce any damage. You have been asked to present these plans to the public as a public service message (video or audio) and in a brochure.

Think about how your message and brochure will address the following items:
- Educate the public about why earthquakes occur.
- Explain how earthquakes transmit energy.
- Explain the effects associated with earthquakes.
- Suggest ways to reduce the damage caused by earthquakes.

Assessment Criteria

Think about what you have been asked to do. Scan ahead through the chapter activities to see how they might help you prepare your brochure. Work with your classmates and your teacher to define the criteria for judging your work. Record all this information. Make sure that you understand the criteria as well as you can before you begin. Your teacher may provide you with a sample rubric to help you get started.

Activity 1   An Earthquake in Your Community

GOALS

In this activity you will:

• Generate and describe two types of waves.

• Determine the relative speeds of compressional and shear waves.

• Simulate some of the motions associated with earthquakes.

• Infer the origin of earthquakes and the mechanism of transfer of seismic wave energy.

Think about It

In some earthquakes, the ground shakes back and forth so much that small objects are overturned, hanging objects and doors swing, and pictures are knocked out of plumb.

• If you have experienced an earthquake, describe your most vivid memory. If you have not experienced an earthquake, what would you expect to see, feel, and hear?

What do you think? Record your ideas about this question in your *EarthComm* notebook. Be prepared to discuss your response with your small group and the class.

Investigate

Part A: Rupture and Rebound

1. Obtain two "L"-shaped wooden blocks that have a slot cut in their short lengths, as shown in the diagram. Place the blocks so that the slots line up. Put a thin piece (less than 1 mm) of Styrofoam® into the two slots so that it connects the two blocks.

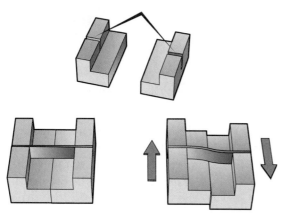

2. Put on your safety glasses. Holding the two blocks together, move the blocks parallel to each other, but in opposite directions. Do this very slowly. Gradually increase the offset between the blocks without breaking the Styrofoam.

   a) Record and sketch your observations in your notebook.

3. Continue to increase the offset until the Styrofoam snaps. Watch carefully what happens to the Styrofoam as it ruptures.

   a) Record and sketch your observations in your notebook.

   b) Did you feel a vibration in the wood? When?

Part B: A Thought Experiment on Rupture and Friction

1. The experiment with the Styrofoam strip shows some important things about the cause of earthquakes, but it's not a very realistic model of rocks. "Thought experiments" are experiments that scientists dream up and then run in their imagination, rather than in a real laboratory. They are a useful way to develop new ideas and insights into scientific problems. Here's a thought experiment that gets you closer to the real thing.
   Suppose you could make a "fake rock" that is just like a real rock, except that its strength is so much less that you can easily break it with your hands.
   Hold the two sides of the rock as you did to break the Styrofoam. As you gradually increase the sliding (shearing) force on the rock, it bends, just like the Styrofoam, but because it is much stiffer, like a real rock, you probably wouldn't be able to see the bending. Eventually the rock breaks along a line, and the two sides spring back to their original shape. "Seismic" waves are generated.

Styrofoam should not splinter. Do not substitute other material.

125

a) If you started to apply a shearing force again, with the two halves still pressed together, what do you think you would observe? Why would you need to exert some force to make the two halves slide past one another, even though they are already cut by a fracture?

b) Imagine pouring some liquid containing a bit of glue down

into the fracture and waiting for the glue to set. The rock regains some of its strength. What happens when you again apply a greater and greater "sliding" force to the "healed" block of rock? Do you expect the force needed for rupture to be greater than originally, less, or the same? Why?

Part C: Vibration

1. Place a Slinky® on the floor. Have one person in your group hold one end of the Slinky and a second person hold the other end. Back away from each other so that the Slinky stretches out about 5 m long.

2. Have one person hold the end of the Slinky in a fist and then hit the back of the fist with the other hand. The palm should be facing the Slinky. Observe the motion of the Slinky. Repeat the pulse until each member of your group can describe the motion of the Slinky. Observe the direction the Slinky moves compared to the direction in which the pulse is moving.

   a) Record your observations.

3. With the Slinky stretched out about 5 m, have a person at one end quickly jerk the end of the Slinky back and forth (left to

right). Observe the motions of the Slinky. Repeat the pulse until each member of your group can describe the resultant motion of the Slinky. Observe the direction the Slinky moves compared to the direction in which the pulse is moving.

   a) Record your observations.

4. To compare the two types of vibrations (wave motion) that you observed in the Slinky, stretch out two Slinkys along the floor, about 5 m. Starting at the same end at the same time, have one student strike their fist while the other student jerks the Slinky back and forth. Observe what happens. Try the movements several times until you are confident in your observations.

   a) Which of the two wave types arrives at the other end first (which one is faster)?

A stretched Slinky can move unpredictably when released. Spread out so that you can work without hitting anyone. Release the stretched Slinky gradually.

Reflecting on the Activity and the Challenge

In the experiments, you observed rupture, energy release, and energy transmission. These are the main processes in the occurrence of earthquakes.

In the experiment with the Styrofoam, you gradually applied a force to a solid material (the Styrofoam strip). The force caused the strip to bend. Bending like that is called elastic deformation. If you had removed the force before the strip broke, the strip would have returned to its original shape. Rocks in the Earth's crust behave in the same way. The material broke when the force exceeded the strength of the material. This instantly released the energy you had stored in the material by applying a force to bend it. In your model, you felt the sudden release of energy during rupture as a vibration in the wood. As the Styrofoam strip broke, its ends "jumped" a short distance in opposite directions, to straighten themselves out again.

In the thought experiment with the weak, fake rock, the force you applied caused the rock to rupture and slide along a fault plane. Friction along the fault plane made it necessary for you to apply a non-zero force to get the two halves to slide past one another even after they were cut by the fault. After the fault was partly healed, some force was still needed for the rock to slip along the fault plane again.

Energy can be transmitted from one place to another without permanent movement of the material. In the experiment with the Slinky, the energy of motion you put into the solid (the Slinky) by shaking it at one end was transmitted away from the source, without the Slinky changing its position after the waves had passed. Earthquake waves similar to the ones that you modeled carry the energy of the earthquake for long distances as they travel through the Earth.

Digging Deeper

WHAT IS AN EARTHQUAKE?

Earthquakes

An **earthquake** is a sudden motion or shaking of the Earth as rocks break along an extensive surface within the Earth. The rock masses on either side of the fault plane slip past one another for distances of as much as ten meters during the brief earthquake. The rocks break because of slowly built-up bending. The sudden release of energy as rock ruptures causes intense vibrations called **seismic waves** or earthquake waves.

Geo Words

earthquake: a sudden motion or shaking in the Earth caused by the abrupt release of slowly accumulated strain

seismic (earthquake) waves: a general term for all elastic waves in the Earth, produced by earthquakes or generated artificially by explosions

Geo Words

fault: a fracture or fracture zone in rock, along which the rock masses have moved relative to one another parallel to the fracture

shear strength: the shear force needed to break a solid material

elastic rebound: the return of a bent elastic solid to its original shape after the deforming force is removed

friction: the force that resists the motion of one surface against another surface

focus: the point of an earthquake within the Earth where rupture first occurs to cause an earthquake

epicenter: the point on the Earth's surface directly above the focus of an earthquake

fault scarp: the cliff formed by a fault that reaches the Earth's surface

Geoscientists explain the occurrence of earthquakes in the following way. A **fault** is a surface between two large blocks or regions of rock, along which there has been rupture and movement in the past. Faults are very common in the rocks of the Earth's crust. Large-scale forces within the Earth's crust push the fault blocks in opposite directions. Most of these forces are caused by the movements of the Earth's plates.

As the forces gradually build up over time, the blocks are bent on either side of the fault, the same as with the Styrofoam strip. The region of bending can extend for very long distances away from the fault. All rocks have a shear strength. The **shear strength** of a rock is the force that is needed to break the rock when it is acted upon by forces in two opposite directions. Eventually the forces overcome the shear strength of the rock, and the rock breaks along the fault plane. The blocks then suddenly slip for some distance against each other to undo the bending, and stored energy is released. The straightening movement is called **elastic rebound**.

Usually, the rocks in a fault zone have already been ruptured by earlier earthquakes. Why don't they just slip continuously as force is applied? The answer is that in some places, they do slip continuously. In most places, however, the fault becomes "locked" and doesn't move again for a long time. There are two reasons for this. One reason is that there is a lot of **friction** along the fault plane, because the rock surfaces are rough and are pressed together by the great pressure deep in the Earth. You can see for yourself how effective this rock friction is, by gluing sandpaper to two wooden blocks and then trying to slide the sand-papered surfaces past one another while you squeeze the blocks together. The other reason is that new minerals tend to be deposited along the fault by slowly flowing water solutions. This new mineral material acts as a "cement" to restore some of the shear strength of the rock.

Earthquakes usually occur at some depth below the surface. The place in the Earth along the fault where rupture occurs is called the earthquake **focus**, as shown in *Figure 1*. The **epicenter** is the geographic point on the Earth's surface directly above the focus. Once a fracture starts, it spreads rapidly in all directions along the fault plane. It often reaches the Earth's surface. Where it does, the motion on the fault can cause a sharp step in the land surface, called a **fault scarp**. Fault scarps can be as much as a few meters high. Horizontal motions along a fault can cause roads or fences to be offset, by as much as 10 to 15 m.

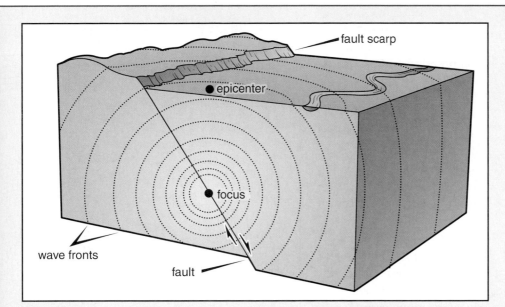

Figure 1 The relationship between the focus and the epicenter of an earthquake.

Earthquake or Seismic Waves

When an earthquake occurs by rupture along a fault, the elastic energy of bending is released and seismic waves spread out in all directions from the focus. Earthquakes produce several kinds of seismic waves. The different kinds of waves travel through rocks at different speeds, and each kind of wave causes a different kind of motion in the rock as it passes by. The various kinds of waves arrive at some distant point on the Earth at different times, depending on their relative speed and their path though the Earth. (See *Figure 2*.)

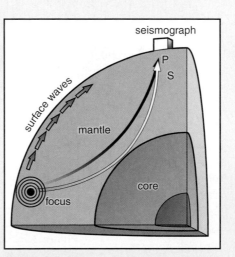

Figure 2 Earthquakes produce several types of seismic waves.

Geo Words

primary wave (P wave): a seismic wave that involves particle motion (compression and expansion) in the direction in which the wave is traveling

secondary wave (S wave): a seismic wave produced by a shearing motion that involves vibration perpendicular to the direction in which the wave is traveling. It does not travel through liquids, like the outer core of the Earth

surface wave: a seismic wave that travels along the surface of the Earth

Check Your Understanding

1. What is an earthquake?

2. Explain how seismic waves are generated by an earthquake.

3. What is the relationship between the focus and the epicenter of an earthquake?

4. Use a diagram to describe the differences between P waves, S waves, and surface waves.

5. Rank P waves, S waves, and surface waves in order from fastest to slowest.

Compressional waves (*Figure 3a*) cause rapid compression and expansion of rock as they pass through the Earth. As the waves pass, the rock material is moved back and forth in the direction of wave motion. Compressional waves are the first to reach a location away from the focus, so they are called **primary waves**, or just P waves. P waves are similar to sound waves. They can move through solids, liquids, and gases. They move through solid rock at a speed of about five kilometers per second, or about fifteen times the speed of sound in air.

Shear waves arrive at a location after compressional waves, so they are called **secondary waves**, or just S waves. Shear waves (*Figure 3b*) move rock material at right angles to the direction of their motion. S waves can travel only through solids, not through fluids. They move through rock at a speed of about three kilometers per second.

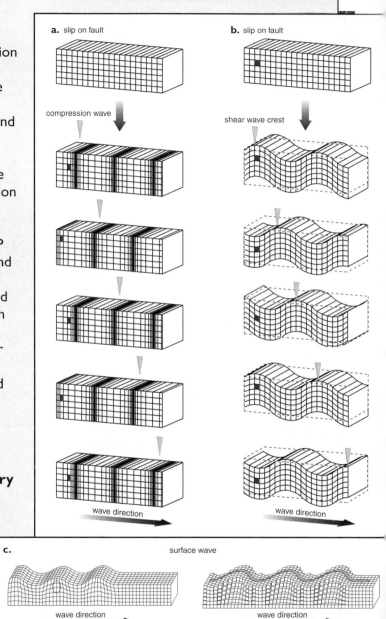

Figure 3 This diagram shows how **a.** primary (compressional), **b.** secondary (shear), and **c.** surface waves move through the Earth.

Surface waves, which travel along the Earth's surface, are the last to arrive at a location. They travel slower than S waves. There are two kinds of surface waves. One kind creates an up-and-down rolling motion of the ground, very much like a wave on a water surface (*Figure 3c.i*). The other kind of surface wave shakes the ground sideways (*Figure 3c.ii*). Surface waves usually cause the most movement at the Earth's surface, and therefore the most damage.

Understanding and Applying What You Have Learned

1. What kinds of motion would you expect to feel in an earthquake?

2. What effects might earthquake motions have on buildings, roads, and household furnishings?

3. Of the types of earthquake waves discussed in this section, which do you think are the most dangerous? Why?

4. Many people have some common beliefs about earthquakes. One of these is that earthquakes occur more frequently in areas of warm climates.

   a) How would you design an investigation that might test this idea?

   b) Do you have information available to you that either supports or contradicts this idea?

   c) Write a short paragraph either supporting or refuting this belief.

5. What other ideas about earthquakes did you have before doing these activities that were either supported or contradicted by what you have learned through your investigation? Describe your original ideas and how they were either confirmed or refuted.

6. Some faults are frequently active and produce numerous small earthquakes. Other faults are rarely active but produce large earthquakes. Based on the activities you completed, propose factors that might influence the number and size of earthquakes produced by a fault.

7. In the rupture activity, you provided the energy needed to break the styrofoam. Use this idea to describe why earthquakes reveal that Earth is a dynamic planet.

Preparing for the Chapter Challenge

Write a background summary for the brochure you will prepare for your **Chapter Challenge**. Include a concise, simple, but accurate explanation for the cause of earthquakes, how they transmit energy, and how different types of seismic waves move. Be sure to address any common beliefs that you may know to be false. This section should be no longer than one page. Include diagrams as appropriate.

Inquiring Further

1. **Forming questions to investigate**

   Write down other questions you have about the causes of earthquakes and their effects. How would you go about gathering information to answer these questions? Write your ideas in your notebook.

2. **Using seismic waves to study the Earth's interior**

   How do we know about the structure and composition of the interior of the Earth? Study of the distribution and effects of earthquakes, and especially of the transmission of seismic waves, has enabled geoscientists to develop many answers. To learn more about the details of the Earth's structure revealed by the study of seismic waves, visit the *EarthComm* web site.

3. **Using seismic waves to explore for oil and gas**

   Understanding the behavior of seismic waves allows geoscientists to use them as tools to study deep layers of the Earth. Find out how exploration geologists use seismic waves to draw inferences about the layers of sedimentary rock in which they find oil and gas deposits. Consult the *EarthComm* web site.

4. **Earth science careers**

   Do you think you would like to study earthquakes for a career? To see what a seismologist does at work, visit the *EarthComm* web site.

Marine seismic vessel.

Activity 2

Detecting Earthquake Waves

GOALS

In this activity you will:

- Construct a simple seismometer.
- Record motion in two dimensions and also within a fixed time frame.
- Understand how seismometers record earthquake waves.
- Recognize P waves, S waves, and surface waves on seismograms.
- Read a graph to determine the distance to the earthquake focus.
- Locate the epicenter from time–distance graphs.

Think about It

Some of the energy released by an earthquake takes the form of seismic waves. Surface waves are responsible for most earthquake destruction.

- What specific observations would you want to make to study an earthquake?
- How could you detect and record the arrival of earthquake waves: P waves, S waves, and surface waves?

What do you think? Record your ideas about these questions in your *EarthComm* notebook. Be prepared to discuss your responses with your small group and the class.

Investigate

1. Attach one end of a spiral spring or thick rubber band to a small, heavy weight (a non-lead fishing-line sinker would work well). Attach the other end of the spring or rubber band to the bottom of a rectangular, open-sided storage box, such as a small milk crate. Turn the box upside down so that the weight is suspended and hanging freely.

2. Move the frame of the box rapidly back and forth (horizontally). Now move the box vertically up and down. Move it back in forth in one direction, then back and forth in the other direction.

   a) In your notebook, write a careful description of what you observe.

   b) Are the motions you generate similar to the motions produced by the Slinky in **Activity 1**, or different?

 Be sure the spring and weight are securely fastened to the crate.

c) How would you describe the motions of the weight in comparison to the motions you impart to the box?

3. Obtain a piece of heavy paper or light cardboard and a very soft pencil or thin felt-tipped marker. Hold the marker firmly in place above the paper so that its tip is just touching the paper. This can be done by having the member of your group with the steadiest hand hold the marker in place above the paper. Have another group member move the paper under the marker in order to write the word "Earthquake" in cursive. Move only the paper, not the pen.

   a) Record what you observe and how this writing is achieved.

4. Drag the paper across the table smoothly toward you (with the tip of the marker touching the paper). Then pull the paper toward you again, but this time jiggle it back and forth perpendicular to the direction in which you're pulling.

   a) What does the line look like when the paper was pulled smoothly toward you?

   b) What does the resulting line look like when the paper was jiggled?

5. Repeat **Step 4,** but this time use a timer or the second hand on a watch to record the time it takes to pull the paper through. Use a roll of adding machine paper this time so you have a strip of paper a meter or so long. Have a third person make a little mark on the edge of the paper strip every second as you move the strip along.

6. Examine a record of a real earthquake as shown in the figure below.

   a) Is the size (height) of the recorded wave the same for the entire duration shown on the seismogram?

   b) Is the shape of the recorded wave the same for the entire duration shown on the seismogram?

7. Make or obtain a copy of the diagram showing a real earthquake.

   a) Label the arrival of the P wave and the S wave.

   b) How much time separates the arrival of the two waves?

   c) Use the diagram and the difference in arrival times to determine the distance from the focus to the seismometer.

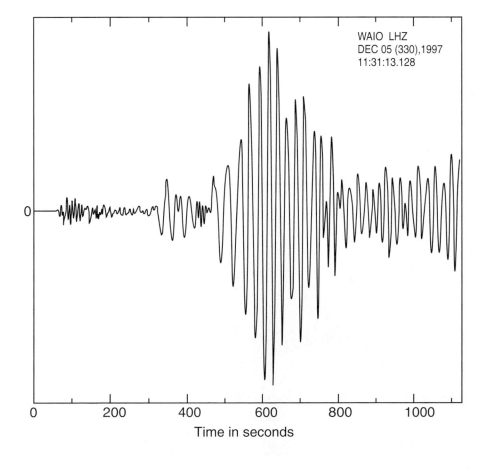

WAIO LHZ
DEC 05 (330),1997
11:31:13.128

Time in seconds

Reflecting on the Activity and the Challenge

You constructed a simple instrument that recorded passing vibrations. Your instrument used a stationary mass (like the fishing-line sinker) to provide a fixed reference against which vertical and horizontal movement could be compared. By marking time on your record, you could determine the "arrival" of the waves you generated. What you created is a very simple seismometer. A seismometer is a device for measuring shaking. You also made a seismogram, or record of shaking. Geologists use similar (but more complex) instruments to record passing earthquake waves. Time is also marked on their records. This allows the arrival times of P waves, S waves, and surface waves to be determined.

Geo Words

seismometer: an instrument that measures seismic waves. It receives seismic impulses and converts them into a signal like an electrical voltage

Digging Deeper

RECORDING EARTHQUAKE WAVES

Seismometers

A **seismometer** works on the principle of inertia, the tendency for a mass at rest to remain at rest. Seismometers similar to the device you built were first used in the 1800s. They had a cylinder coated with soot and a stylus that scratched a mark as it registered vibrations. In today's instruments (*Figure 1*), the relative motion between the mass and its frame creates an electric signal. The signal is then amplified and transmitted to a recording destination. The destination may be a) ink pens writing on paper, b) a narrow beam of light that leaves a record of the vibrations on photographic paper, c) a device that records a magnetic signal on tape, or d) a computer screen. It takes three seismometers to record all the motions of the ground during an earthquake. Two horizontal cylinders at right angles to each other record sideways motions (north–south, east–west). The third cylinder is vertical. It records up and down motions.

Figure 1 In the 1960s, a worldwide network of seismometers was developed to verify nuclear test-ban treaties. When a nuclear device is tested, seismometers around the world record the seismic waves that result from the blast.

Instruments used to detect earthquakes also record any motion of the ground to which they are attached. These motions can be natural (earthquakes, landslides) or caused by humans (large trucks, passing airplanes and helicopters, blasting during construction, nuclear bombs).

Interpreting Seismograms

A **seismogram** is a written or mechanically produced record of earthquake waves. *Figure 2* shows a seismogram recorded at Dallas, Texas. Note the separation of P waves and S waves on the seismogram. This seismogram was recorded about 1600 km from the earthquake's focus. If it had been recorded near the focus, the two waves would appear much closer together. All the waves are produced during the rupture. As distance from the focus increases, the separation and arrival times between the wave types increase because they travel at different speeds.

Geo Words

seismogram: the record made by a seismometer

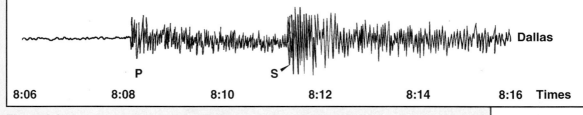

Figure 2 Seismogram recorded in Dallas, Texas.

P waves travel the fastest through the Earth, so they arrive first at a distant station. S waves arrive shortly after. Waves that arrive after the direct P waves complicate the seismogram. Various reflected and refracted P and S waves bounce off (are reflected at) layers of Earth's interior and eventually reach the station.

Using Travel-Time Curves

P and S waves travel at different speeds , so they arrive at different times at a seismological station. The difference in their arrival times increases with the distance from the focus. Travel-time curves (see *Figure 3* on the next page) show this relationship.

Integrated Coordinated Science for the 21st Century

Check Your
Understanding

Check Your Understanding

1. What is the function of a seismometer?

2. a) How many seismometers do you need at a given place to fully record the motions arising from earthquake waves?

   b) How should these seismometers be oriented, and why?

3. What is a seismogram?

4. What information is provided by a travel-time curve?

The graph shows the data from a magnitude 8 earthquake in the Kuril Islands on 3 December 1995. Here you can see the relationship between distance and the difference in arrival times for P waves and S waves.

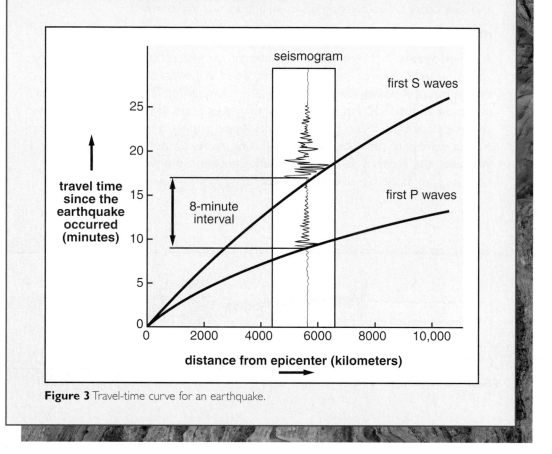

Figure 3 Travel-time curve for an earthquake.

Understanding and Applying What You Have Learned

1. a) Where would be the best place to put a seismometer in your school? Why would you choose this location?

   b) Where would be the worst place(s) in your school to put a seismometer? Why should this (these) location(s) be avoided?

   c) Where in your community might be a good place to put a seismometer? Why?

   d) At what locations in your community is it unwise to place a seismometer? Why?

2. a) How are the devices you worked with in this activity good models of a modern seismometer?

   b) In what respects are they poor models?

   c) What could you do to improve your models?

3. What advantages would be gained by having more seismometers at a particular location?

4. Not all vibrations of the Earth are made by natural earthquakes.

   a) Write in your notebook as many things as you can think of that could cause strong vibrations of the Earth's surface.

   b) How might you be able to distinguish seismograms of "natural" earthquakes from "human-made" earthquakes?

Preparing for the Chapter Challenge

Write a summary of this activity for your brochure. Include a concise, simple, but accurate description of how to detect earthquake waves and locate epicenters. Also record where to place a seismometer at your school (or somewhere else in your community). Explain why you chose this location.

Inquiring Further

1. **History of science**

   The study of earthquakes has a fascinating history. Humans have always felt the effects of earthquakes. Early civilizations interpreted the shaking of the Earth in different ways. How have the methods used to study earthquakes changed over time? Use electronic or print resources to prepare a report.

2. **Recent seismic activity**

   Visit the *EarthComm* web site for a description of how to conduct an on-line investigation into seismic waves that travel complicated paths within the Earth.

3. **Virtual earthquakes**

   Find out about the Virtual Earthquake web site at the *EarthComm* web site. Practice

In AD 132, a Chinese scholar named Chang Heng made one of the earliest known devices used to record the occurrence of an earthquake.

using seismographs to find an earthquake epicenter. Simulate an earthquake in the region of your choice. Print out a record of your results. Include the seismograms and the map showing the epicenter location, but do not do the magnitude activity at this time.

Activity 3 How Big Was It?

GOALS

In this activity you will:

• Rank the effects of earthquakes.

• Map the intensity of earthquakes.

• Interpret a map of earthquake intensity to infer the general location of the epicenter.

• Identify geologic materials that pose special problems during earthquakes.

• Explain how the magnitude of an earthquake is determined.

Think about It

Earthquakes can be so small that people can't feel them. They can be so great that the seismic energy of a magnitude 8 earthquake would supply one day's worth of electrical energy for the entire U.S.

• What factors would you look at to "measure" the size of an earthquake?
• What factors are most important for different uses? What measurements would interest each of the following: a seismologist? a city planner? a homeowner? you?

What do you think? Record your ideas about these questions in your *EarthComm* notebook. Be prepared to discuss your responses with your small group and the class.

Investigate

Part A: Measurement of Earthquake Effects

1. The reports listed below describe the effects of an earthquake felt in many cities in the eastern U.S.

   a) In your group, rank the effects in order of intensity. Assign numerical values to your ranking. Be prepared to explain your ranking system.

Newspaper data:

Detroit, MI: "Did you feel the earthquake? Last night a slight earth tremor was felt in this area."

Pittsburgh, PA: "Items Broken By Earthquake. Small Earthquake Awakens Many."

Syracuse, NY: "Mayor's 10th-floor office chandelier sways in the earthquake."

Baltimore, MD: "Citizens dash outside as earthquake brings down plaster in many homes."

Philadelphia, PA: "Doors and windows rattle as earthquake strikes."

Cleveland, OH: "Earthquake felt on top of new 23-story department store."

Roanoke, VA: "Pedestrians report parked cars rocked back and forth by earthquake."

Charleston, SC: "Almost no one here notices earthquake."

New York City: "Skyscraper offices sway in earthquake."

Washington, DC: "Chimneys tumble, new prefabricated buildings collapse in violent earthquake felt here."

Richmond, VA: "Furniture moved about by earthquake, but no major damage reported."

Winston-Salem, NC: "Patients in hospital report that building shakes in earthquake."

Atlanta, GA: "Earthquakes reported north of here apparently miss Atlanta."

Indianapolis, IN: "Few people here feel recently reported earthquake."

2. Use the data and your ranking to map the intensity of earthquake effects on the map of the Eastern United States.

   a) Draw several curves on the map connecting points or regions of equal intensity.

   b) Label each curve with the intensity value it represents.

   c) Attach your intensity scale.

3. Use the map to answer the following questions:

   a) Describe any pattern you observe.

   b) What can you infer about the probable location of the epicenter of the earthquake? Provide a reason.

4. Share your results with the class.

   a) How do the rankings of earthquake effects compare?

   b) How close were the estimates of the epicenter of the earthquake?

   c) What problems did you have finding the epicenter?

   d) What other information do you think would have helped you to locate the earthquake more accurately?

   e) How would you describe your measurement scale? Is it qualitative or quantitative?

   f) What property or properties of the earthquake were you measuring? Explain.

Part B: Measurement of Earthquake Wave Amplitude

1. Visit the *EarthComm* web site to find the location of the Virtual Earthquake web site. Simulate a new earthquake.

   a) Follow the directions to calculate the magnitude of the earthquake.

   b) How does the amplitude (height) of a seismic wave change when the size of an earthquake changes?

   c) How would you expect the amplitude as recorded on a seismogram to change as you get farther from the epicenter?

Reflecting on the Activity and the Challenge

To reduce earthquake risks, the potential effects of earthquakes should be studied. You made an intensity scale by ranking the effects of earthquakes on people and structures. You used the distribution of intensities to find the general area where an earthquake started. On the Virtual Earthquake web site, you learned that the amplitude of seismic waves on a seismogram is used to measure magnitude. For most earthquakes, both intensity and magnitude decrease as you move farther away from the epicenter. Intensity requires human observers. Magnitude requires a seismometer.

Digging Deeper

DESCRIBING EARTHQUAKES

Earthquake Intensity

The effects of an earthquake on the Earth's surface, including people and buildings, are an indication of its intensity. Intensity scales are based on certain key responses to the shaking of an earthquake. Examples include people awakening, damage to brick and stone structures, and movement of furniture. The intensity scale currently used in the United States is called the Modified Mercalli Intensity scale. There is no mathematical or quantitative basis for the scale. It is simply a ranking based on observed effects, as with the activity you just completed.

Earthquake intensity is a measure of the actual effects at a certain location. This makes an intensity value more meaningful than magnitude values to a non-scientist. The maximum observed intensity often occurs near the epicenter, but there are important exceptions to this rule. During the 1985 Mexico City earthquake and the 1989 Loma Prieta earthquake, the areas with maximum intensity were not nearest to the epicenter. In the Mexico City earthquake, the epicenter was hundreds of kilometers away, yet areas within the city experienced much higher intensities.

Modified Mercalli Scale of Earthquake Intensity	
Value	**Description of Effects**
I	• not felt, except rarely by a few
II	• felt by few, especially on upper floors of buildings • delicately suspended objects may swing
III	• felt indoors by some • vibration similar to a passing truck • not always recognized as an earthquake
IV	• felt indoors by many, outdoors by few • awakens some sleeping people • dishes, windows, and doors rattle, walls creak • standing cars rock • hanging objects swing
V	• felt indoors by mostly everyone, outdoors by many • awakens most sleeping people • some dishes break, windows and plaster walls crack • small unstable objects overturned • hanging objects and doors swing considerably, pictures knocked out of plumb • some liquid spilled from full containers

continued on next page

Integrated Coordinated Science for the 21st Century

Modified Mercalli Scale of Earthquake Intensity *(continued)*	
Value	**Description of Effects**
VI	• felt by everyone • general excitement and some fear • slight damage to poorly built structures • considerable amount of glassware and windows broken • some furniture overturned, and some heavy furniture moved • pictures and books fall from walls and shelves • some fallen plaster and damaged chimneys • small bells ring
VII	• everyone frightened, some have difficulty standing • negligible damage to well-designed, well-built structures, slight to moderate in well-built ordinary structures, considerable in poorly built or designed structures • weak chimneys broken • large church bells ring • trees and bushes shaken, water in lakes and ponds disturbed, some stream banks collapse
VIII	• general fear, approaching panic • slight damage to structures designed to withstand earthquakes, considerable damage to ordinary structures, great damage in poorly built or designed structures • heavy furniture overturned • chimneys and monuments topple • sand and mud ejected from the ground • changes in flow of wells and springs
IX	• general panic • considerable damage to structures designed to withstand earthquakes, well-designed buildings shifted off of foundations, great damage and partial collapse of substantial buildings • ground noticeably cracked • some underground pipes cracked
X	• severe damage to well-built wooden structures, most masonry structures and foundations destroyed, well-built brick walls cracked • bridges severely damaged or destroyed • ground severely cracked • considerable landslides from steep slopes and river banks • sand and mud on beaches shifted • water splashes over banks of canals, rivers, and lakes • underground pipes broken • open cracks and wavy patterns in concrete and asphalt • railroad tracks slightly bent

continued on next page

Modified Mercalli Scale of Earthquake Intensity *(continued)*	
Value	**Description of Effects**
XI	• few structures remain standing • bridges destroyed • broad fissures in the ground • Earth slumps and landslides in soft, wet ground • sand and mud-charged water ejected from the ground • underground pipelines completely out of service • railroad tracks greatly bent
XII	• total damage to all works of construction • numerous rock and landslides, river banks slump • waves seen on the ground • objects thrown up in the air

The Effect of Local Geologic Conditions on Intensity

Often, although not always, seismic waves increase in amplitude when they pass from solid bedrock to softer material near the Earth's surface, like sand, mud, or landfill material. The physical processes that cause this change are complicated, but you can get some idea of them by thinking about how a soft gelatin-like material responds to a source of shaking, compared to a much more rigid material like metal or rock. An earthquake that shook Mexico City in 1985 showed how local geologic conditions influence the intensity (and damage) of an earthquake. It caused about $4 billion in damage and killed at least 8000 people. The earthquake epicenter was about 300 km from Mexico City. Soft sand and clay deposits from an old lake bed under part of the city amplified (increased) the ground motions by a factor of 75 times. The amplification of shaking caused selective damage to tall buildings. Nearby structures on bedrock were relatively undamaged.

Another geologic process that affects earthquake intensity is liquefaction. Liquefaction is the temporary change of water-saturated soil and sand from a solid to a liquid state. Areas like the Marina district in San Francisco experienced very high intensities during the Loma Prieta earthquake. Studies revealed liquefaction of the wet landfill on which the district was built. The earthquake was centered 80 km south of the city. Nearby parts of the city built on hard bedrock did not experience intensities as high as in the Marina district.

Check Your Understanding

1. Why is the intensity value of an earthquake more meaningful than magnitude to a non-scientist?

2. Use the Modified Mercalli Scale to determine the intensity of the earthquake for each of the following observations:

   a) "I was awakened from a deep sleep and observed the door to the bedroom swinging back and forth."

   b) "I thought it very unusual to see a small wooden decoy vibrate on the table beside my chair."

   c) "I noticed waves on the pond, and could hear the church bells ring."

3. Is the greatest intensity of an earthquake always found at the epicenter? Explain your answer.

4. What geological conditions influence the intensity of an earthquake?

5. What does an earthquake magnitude scale measure?

Earthquake Magnitude

Earthquake magnitude is a measure of the amplitude of the seismic waves recorded on a seismogram. Charles F. Richter, a seismologist at the California Institute of Technology, developed the first magnitude scale in the 1930s. His basic idea was to observe the maximum amplitude recorded on a seismogram at a known distance from an earthquake. Earthquakes could be ranked quantitatively by size or strength. The amplitude measured is the "swing" of the stylus. The wider the swing, the "stronger" the vibrations, and therefore the stronger the earthquake. You modeled this in **Activity 2**.

The original Richter scale was developed only for shallow earthquakes detected in southern California by a certain type of seismometer. Since then it has been modified for more general use. Modern measurements of magnitude are still based on the amplitude of the recorded waves. However, more sophisticated methods are used today. Depending on which magnitude a seismologist is using to calculate the magnitude of an earthquake, the various magnitudes can vary by one unit or more.

An important aspect of magnitude scales is that they are logarithmic, based on powers of 10. This means that seismic wave amplitudes increase by 10 times for each unit of the scale. For example, the measured amplitude in a magnitude 6 earthquake is 10 times the measured amplitude in a magnitude 5 earthquake.

Understanding and Applying What You Have Learned

1. The Magnitude/Intensity Comparison table below compares the magnitude and intensity scales. The intensities listed are those typically observed at locations near the epicenter of earthquakes of different magnitudes. If intensity and magnitude measure different characteristics of earthquakes, how can such a chart be compiled? Why isn't it like comparing apples to oranges?

2. What is the highest intensity/magnitude that you would consider exciting to experience, but not dangerous? Explain your reasoning.

3. The following table shows the number of earthquakes per year of a given magnitude.

   Use the table to answer the following questions:

   a) Roughly how many earthquakes occur in a given year?
   b) Do humans feel most earthquakes?
   c) How many earthquakes did you hear about in the last year?
   d) What were their approximate magnitudes?
   e) Does this generate a bias in your perception of the number of earthquakes that happen per year and their size? Explain your answer.

Magnitude/Intensity Comparison	
Magnitude	**Intensity**
1.0–3.0	I
3.0–3.9	II–III
4.0–4.9	IV–V
5.0–5.9	VI–VII
6.0–6.9	VIII–IX
7.0 and higher	X or higher

Number of Earthquakes per Year of Given Magnitudes		
Description	**Magnitude**	**Number per Year**
Great earthquake	Over 8.0	1 or 2
Major earthquake	7.0 to 7.9	18
Destructive earthquake	6.0 to 6.9	120
Damaging earthquake	5.0 to 5.9	800
Minor earthquake	4.0 to 4.9	6000
Smallest usually felt by humans	3.0 to 3.9	49,000
Detected but not felt	2.0 to 2.9	300,000

Gutenberg, B, and Richter, C.F., 1954, *Seismicity of the Earth and Associated Phenomena*, Princeton University Press, Princeton, NJ.

Preparing for the Chapter Challenge

As a group, put together a text box for your brochure explaining how earthquakes are measured. You may use diagrams or charts. The box should contain a simple but accurate explanation of the two methods. It should also explain the advantages and limitations of each method. Remember that this will only be a sidebar for your brochure. It will help people to understand the meanings of terms you use in the rest of the brochure.

Inquiring Further

1. **Reporting earthquakes**

   Does your community experience frequent earthquakes? Maybe you would like to help seismologists when an earthquake happens in your community. The Earthquake Felt Report Form allows you to contribute your intensity observations directly to seismologists so that they can construct isoseismal maps. Visit the *EarthComm* web site page now to find the address that will let you know the kinds of observations you need to detect and record.

2. **Determine the intensity of an earthquake from a description**

   Do you know someone who has experienced an earthquake? If so, ask the individual to describe the experience to you. Compare the person's descriptions to the Mercalli Intensity Scale. Are the descriptions of earthquake effects in the Mercalli intensity scale consistent with the person's experience? Use the scale to rate the intensity of an earthquake they experienced. If they recall the approximate magnitude of the earthquake they experienced, how well does the magnitude/intensity chart match their experience?

3. **Investigate earthquake measurement**

   Write down other questions you have about the ways earthquakes are measured. How would you go about gathering information to answer these questions? Write your ideas in your notebook. Visit the *EarthComm* web site for suggestions of useful web sites to explore.

Activity 4

Earthquake History of Your Community

GOALS

In this activity you will:

- Recognize patterns in the global distribution of earthquakes.

- Interpret maps and research written information to determine the earthquake history of the community and region.

- Examine correlations between faults and earthquakes on a regional and community scale.

- Assess the likelihood of future earthquakes in the community.

- Interpret graphical data to examine long-term trends in the number of earthquakes in the United States.

Think about It

Earthquakes occur all over the world, every day, but not many are strong enough for people to feel them.

- Is there a general pattern to where earthquakes occur on Earth?
- Has an earthquake occurred in your community? Could it occur in your community?

What do you think? Record your ideas about these questions in your *EarthComm* notebook. Be prepared to discuss your responses with your small group and the class.

Investigate

1. In your group, take a close look at the USGS map *This Dynamic Planet*. You may wish to use the map below instead. Discuss the following questions within your group and record your ideas.

   a) How would you describe the pattern of earthquakes around the Earth?

   b) Are earthquakes concentrated in any particular areas on the Earth's surface? If so, what other phenomena and features correspond to these areas?

   c) Are patterns different for ocean and continental areas?

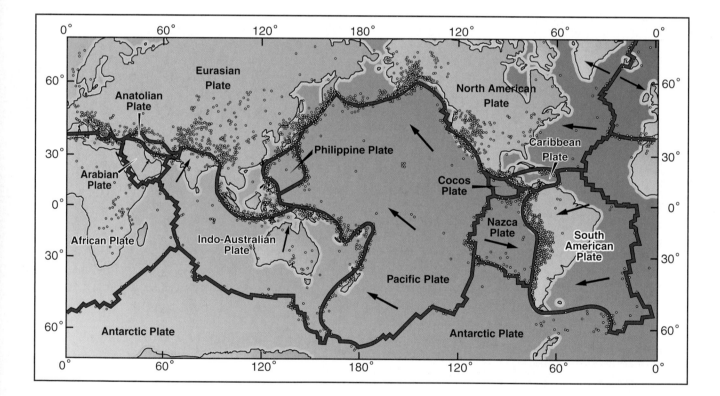

2. The next figure shows two maps of California. One map shows the San Andreas Fault system and other large faults. The other map shows recent earthquakes for a period of a week.

   a) Describe the distribution and arrangement of earthquakes in California.

   b) Do earthquakes correlate with identified large faults?

   c) Do earthquakes occur in areas without identified large faults?

   d) In your small group, discuss what a fault is and what causes one to occur. Record your ideas.

3. Obtain a map of the world and a geologic map of your state (with latitude and longitude marked). If possible, obtain a geologic map of your region (with latitude and longitude marked). Use electronic and print resources to answer the following questions. Visit the *EarthComm* web site for suggested Internet sites to visit and explore.

   a) Plot notable earthquakes of the world on the world map.

   b) Plot important earthquakes of the United States and Canada on the world map (or a map of North America).

   c) Write down the criteria you used to determine if an earthquake was notable or important.

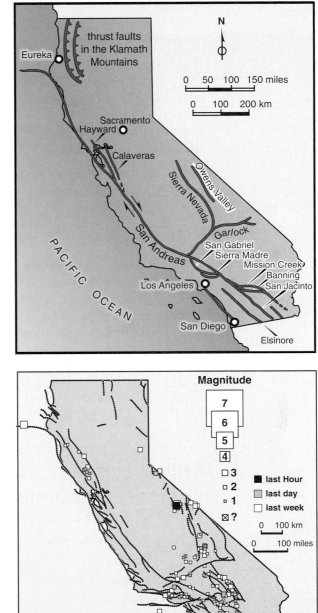

d) Plot earthquakes that have occurred within 200–500 km of your community on your state and/or regional map.

e) Find out about, list, and mark on your maps the locations, sizes, dates, and any other information you can get about past earthquakes in your state, region, or community.

f) Share with other groups so that each has information about worldwide, continental, regional, and state earthquake distributions.

4. Look at the geologic map of your community or state. Locate faults on the map.

a) Describe the relationship between the location of faults and the locations of earthquakes in your community or state.

Reflecting on the Activity and the Challenge

You found that most earthquakes occur along linear belts in oceans. You also found scattered or broad bands of earthquakes on most continents. You looked at maps of fault zones and earthquakes in California. This showed that most earthquakes happen near faults. Your work with local maps helped you to look for local patterns and relationships. Compiling information on past earthquakes helped you to think about the potential risk of earthquakes in your state, region, and community. This will help you explain to the public the risk of an earthquake in your area, as well as the magnitude of this risk.

Geo Words

transform fault: a vertical surface of slippage between two lithospheric plates along an offset between two segments of a spreading ridge

Digging Deeper

THE GLOBAL DISTRIBUTION OF EARTHQUAKES

Earthquake Patterns and Plate Tectonics

Earth's plates move relative to one another at their boundaries. In some places, two plates slide past one another along **transform faults**. Earthquakes are common along transform faults, like the

San Andreas Fault in California. In other places, plates move away from each other or toward each other. These motions also cause forces in the rocks near the plate boundaries. When the forces build up to be greater than the strength of the rocks, the rocks break, causing an earthquake. Thus, you should expect to see many earthquakes near plate boundaries. The concentration of earthquakes along plate boundaries is very high.

The depths of earthquake foci also match the types of boundaries. Shallow-focus earthquakes occur at mid-ocean ridges and transform faults. At **subduction zones**, where one plate dives beneath another to great depths in the Earth's mantle, earthquakes range from shallow-focus ones to very deep-focus ones.

Areas of Risk in the United States

Risk is the impact of natural **hazards** on people. The size of the natural hazard, how often they occur, how close they are to people, and population density affect risk. Certain locations in the United States have had large earthquakes in recorded history. This puts them at higher risk from earthquakes again than at other places.

The map in *Figure 1* shows earthquake risks for the United States. The map is based mainly on earthquake history. The areas at highest risk are near plate boundaries. Southern Alaska is near a subduction zone. California has a very long transform fault (the San Andreas Fault), which extends from north of San Francisco all the way to the Gulf of California, in Mexico. Large earthquakes have also happened far from plate

Geo Words

subduction zone: a long, narrow belt in which one plate descends beneath another

risk: the potential impact of a natural hazard on people or property

hazard: a natural event, like an earthquake, that has the potential to do damage or harm

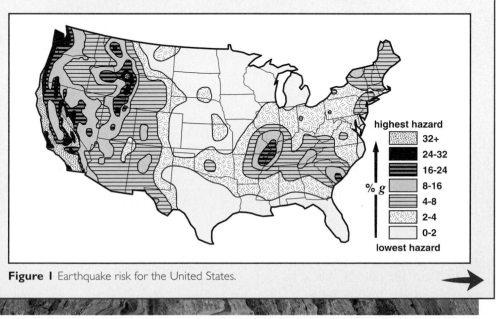

highest hazard

32+
24-32
16-24
% *g* 8-16
4-8
2-4
0-2

lowest hazard

Figure 1 Earthquake risk for the United States.

Check Your Understanding

1. Why do scientists use the distribution of earthquakes as evidence to support the theory of plate tectonics?

2. In general, where is the highest risk of earthquakes?

boundaries. This suggests a zone of weakness and/or high stress in the crust. These earthquakes are not as easy to understand as the ones that happen at plate boundaries. Keep in mind that the forces produced by plate motions are transmitted all the way across the plates. Here's an example of that from everyday life: when you squeeze a brick from its ends or try to pull it apart, the forces you apply act throughout the brick, not just at its ends. Some areas within plates have unusually weak rocks, for a number of geologic reasons. In these areas, the forces that build up within the plates cause the rocks to break, causing an earthquake. Here are some examples: New Madrid, Missouri; Charleston, South Carolina; and parts of southern Quebec.

The legend of the map is in units of percentage of one *g*, the acceleration due to gravity, which is how fast an object gains speed when it is dropped. You have felt "*g* forces" yourself, when an airplane makes a sharp turn or when an elevator or an automobile stops suddenly. You would feel them if you were caught in an earthquake, too! Shaking during an earthquake causes an object that's attached to the ground, like a building, to move back and forth. How fast its velocity changes as it moves back and forth can be described in units of *g*.

Understanding and Applying What You Have Learned

1. The table on the following page shows major earthquakes in the United States. Use the data to address the following questions:

    a) When was the last major earthquake in the eastern United States?

    b) How might the time interval between major earthquakes influence your thoughts about the danger from earthquakes?

    c) What is the likelihood of major earthquakes in western states compared to the eastern states?

    d) Has the frequency of earthquakes in the western states been increasing over time? Explain.

    e) Note the low number of deaths from the New Madrid earthquake in Missouri. Would you expect the same number of deaths if an earthquake of that size took place today? Explain your answer.

    f) How can you explain that there was only one major earthquake in the 1700s but there were 15 major earthquakes during the 1900s?

Major Earthquakes in the United States			
Year	Nearest City/ Epicenter	Richter Magnitude	Number of Deaths– Comments
1755	Boston/Cape Ann, MA	6	Buildings damaged
1811 1812	Memphis, TN/New Madrid, MO	7.8	8 in 3 separate earthquakes
1812	San Juan Capistrano mission San Gabriel, CA	7	40 – roof of church caved in
1857	Los Angeles/Ft. Tejon, CA	8.0	1 – San Andreas Fault
1868	San Jose, CA	7.0	30 – Hayward Fault
1872	Bishop, CA/Lone Pine, CA	8.0	27 – Sierra Nevada Fault
1886	Charleston, SC	6.8	100 – Liquefaction of soil
1925	Santa Barbara, CA	6.3	13 – Unnamed offshore fault
1933	Long Beach, CA	6.3	120 – inspired codes of construction of schools
1934	Salt Lake City/Kosmo, UT	6.6	0 – Wasatch Fault System
1949	Seattle/Puget Sound, WA	7.1	8 – Area of occasional earthquakes
1952	Bakersfield/Kern County, CA	7.7	12 – White Wolf Fault
1954	Reno/Dixie Valley, NV	7.1	0 – Epicenter in rural area
1959	Bozeman/Hebgen Lake, MT	7.3	28 – In landslide caused by earthquake
1964	Anchorage/ Prince William Sound, AK	9.2	131 by tsunami and landslides; tsunami kills 11 in CA
1971	Los Angeles/San Fernando Valley, CA	6.4	65 – buildings and highway bridges collapse
1975	Kalapana, Hawaii	7.2	2 – tsunami damage
1983	Coalinga, CA	6.5	1 – older buildings destroyed
1987	Whittier, CA	5.9	8 – $358 million damage
1989	San Francisco – Oakland/Loma Prieta, CA	7.1	62 – Most in overpass collapse; over $6 billion damage
1991	Arcadia/Sierra Madre, CA	6	2 – $18 million damage
1992	Yucca Valley and Big Bear Lake, CA	7.4 and 6.5	2 – over 170 injured; Extensive ground cracking in remote area

2. Refer to the *This Dynamic Planet* map to answer these questions:

   a) Are all linear belts of earthquakes found with volcanoes?

   b) Do patterns depend on whether or not the earthquakes happen on continents or under oceans?

   c) Do you think this map is complete? Explain.

   d) How does seismic risk correlate with the edges of the continents?

3. The distribution of major earthquakes in the eastern states appears to be random. Unlike the western states, there are no linear belts. How might this make preparing the public for future earthquakes more difficult?

Preparing for the Chapter Challenge

Write a background summary for the brochure for your **Chapter Challenge**. Discuss the earthquake history of your state and community. Note any major earthquakes. Also, note the frequency of earthquakes that have been felt, and the maximum magnitude the public should prepare for. Make your summary concise, easy to understand, and accurate. It should fit on one page. Include maps and diagrams as needed.

Inquiring Further

1. **Earthquakes of magnitude 7 or greater**

   Use electronic or print resources to answer the following questions. Visit the *EarthComm* web site for suggested electronic resources.

   a) What is the maximum number of earthquakes with magnitude 7 or greater that occurred in one year from 1900 to 1989?

   b) On average, how many earthquakes of this size happen in a given year?

   c) Describe any patterns that you see in the data.

   d) Can you suggest any natural forces that might cause the observed variation in the number of earthquakes over time? Explain.

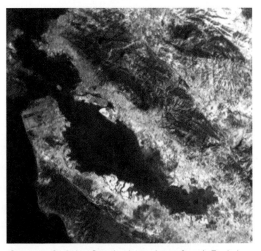

Can you find the San Andreas (transform) Fault in this Landsat image of the San Francisco Bay Area?

Activity 5

Lessening Earthquake Damage

GOALS

In this activity you will:

- Assign earthquake intensity based on observed effects.

- Describe the effects of passing earthquake waves.

- Recognize the secondary effects of earthquakes.

- Relate variations in intensity to the nature of the underlying geologic material.

- Identify places in your community with high and low risk from earthquakes.

- Outline steps to increase personal safety during an earthquake.

Think about It

In Japan, earthquake dangers are very great. All Japanese schools have regular earthquake drills, just as you have fire drills in your school.

- What damage do passing earthquake waves cause?
- How can you protect yourself in an earthquake?

What do you think? Record your ideas about these questions in your *EarthComm* notebook. Be prepared to discuss your responses with your small group and the class.

Investigate

1. At 4:48 a.m. on November 29, 1975, a magnitude 7.2 earthquake rocked the Island of Hawaii and neighboring islands. Construct a map of the earthquake intensities (as you did in **Activity 3**), using the observations listed below, the intensity scale, and a map of the islands.

Island of Hawaii

Hilo: Extensive damage to downtown area. Minor cracks in road, water pipes, concrete walls, plaster, and floors. Minor cracks and floor-to-wall separations a few millimeters wide in steel-reinforced concrete structures at the hospital, several schools, and libraries. In some of these buildings 5 to 10 mm vertical drops in some floor sections. Breaks in swimming pools. Shelved items in markets fell or tumbled over. Glass windows shattered. Breakage of chinaware. Collapse of stonewalls. Houses shifted from foundations. Cracking and crumbling of brick fireplace chimneys.

Hawaii Volcanoes National Park and Volcano: Extensive ground cracking caused heavy road damage. Water tanks damaged. Water lines broke. Some fireplace chimneys collapsed. At the Hawaiian Volcano Observatory, violent ground motion lasted half a minute, with many loose objects moved or turned over. Numerous rock falls in the crater.

Kurtistown: Damage to seven residential homes: cracked concrete steps, house and garage moved off foundation, chinaware broken from falling from cupboards.

Hawaii Paradise Park: One house shifted off foundation; cabinets toppled off walls.

Kalapana: A wood frame house shifted 1 m off the foundation.

Mountain View: Foundation of water tank cracked, Plexiglas cracked, television set shifted off stand and fell to floor, rock wall damaged.

Pahoa: Three homes moved from foundation. Other damage included a broken water line and a collapsed water tank.

Naalehu: The foundation of one ranch house cracked, and the roof was damaged.

Pahala: Doors distorted and house moved from concrete foundation. Furniture and stereo fell.

Laupahoehoe: Landslides along steep road cut along coastal road between Laupahoehoe and Honomu. Loose objects fell off shelves in homes.

Keaau and Pepeekeo: Moderate ground shaking and unstable objects moved.

Kailua-Kona: Loose objects fell off shelves. Strong shaking. Rock falls in Kealakekua.

Honokaa: Landslides on coast road. Loose objects fell off shelves.

Kohala: Some loose objects moved. Shaking felt by many people.

Island of Maui

Wailuku: Hanging objects moved slightly. Not recognized as an earthquake at first (thought to be a passing truck).

Island of Oahu

Honolulu: Felt indoors by a few sensitive people.

Island of Kauai

Lihue: Felt indoors by a few sensitive people.

a) Mark the places of equal intensity on your map. Seismologists call maps showing areas of equal intensity isoseismal maps.

b) List three effects directly related to the earthquake.

c) List three secondary effects, events triggered by the earthquake, noted in the above descriptions.

d) On which island was the earthquake located? In which quadrant of the island was the earthquake located?

e) Do(es) the area(s) of highest intensity correspond to the earthquake epicenter? If not, speculate why.

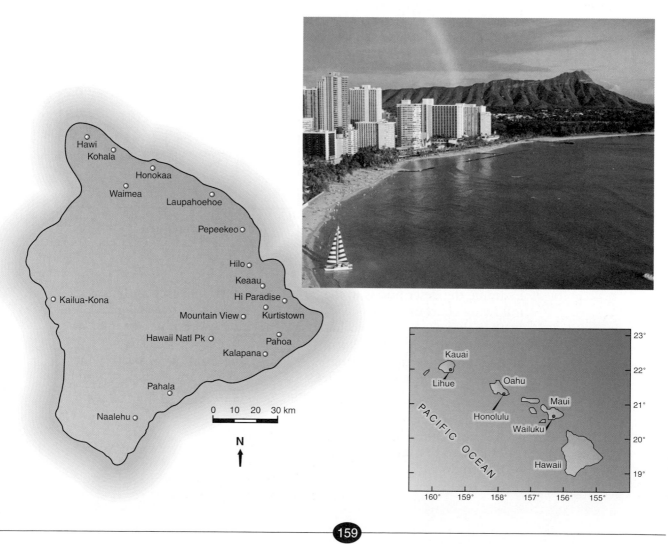

2. The figure below shows the location of three seismometers in San Francisco and the seismograms recorded at each station for a magnitude 4.6 aftershock of the Loma Prieta earthquake.

   a) What is the underlying geology at each seismometer?

   b) Which station(s) experienced low-amplitude waves during the aftershock?

   c) Which station(s) experienced high-amplitude waves during the aftershock?

   d) Describe any correlation between underlying geology and amplitude of seismic waves?

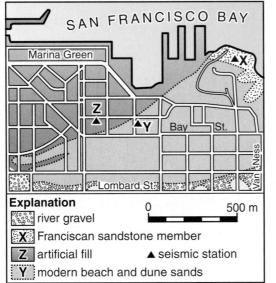

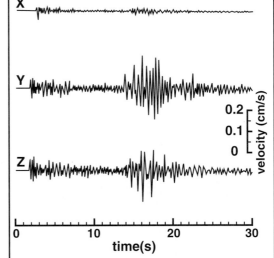

3. Examine the descriptions in the following chart of major earthquakes around the world, including a description of both geologic changes and resulting destruction (damage, loss of life).

   a) List phenomena associated directly with earthquakes that were not noted in the San Francisco or Hawaii descriptions.

   b) List phenomena that were triggered by earthquakes that were not noted in the San Francisco or Hawaii descriptions. Record your observations in your notebook.

Recent Seismic Events of Special Interest (IRIS)			
Event	**Magnitude**	**Geologic Changes**	**Destruction**
1. Northern Iran (5/97 & 6/97)	7.3	Landslides, rare sequence of large earthquakes	1567 killed, 2300 injured, 50,000 homeless, extensive damage
2. Windward Islands (4/97)	6.7	One of the largest known earthquakes in or near Trinidad or Tobago	None reported
3. S. Xinjiang, China (7/96)	5.2	Nuclear weapons test	None reported
4. Sakhalin Island (5/95)	7.5	None noted	1989 killed, 750 injured
5. Kobe, Japan (1/95)	6.8	Surface faulting for 9 km with horizontal displacement of 1.2 to 1.5 m, soil liquefaction	5502 killed, 36, 896 injured, 310,000 homeless, severe damage
6. Kuril Islands (10/94)	8.3	Tsunami with heights up to 346 cm	10 killed or missing, extensive damage throughout islands
7. Northern Bolivia (1/94)	8.2	At 637 km depth, the largest deep earthquake, first earthquake from this part of S. America to have been felt in N. America, including Canada	Several people killed
8. Northridge, CA (1/94)	6.8	A maximum uplift of 15 cm occurred, many rock slides, ground cracks, soil liquefaction	60 killed, 7000 injured, 20,000 homeless, severe damage
9. Southern India (9/93)	6.3	Large intraplate earthquake devastation	9748 killed, 30,000 injured, extreme devastation
10. Republic of South Africa (5/93)	3.8	Mine collapse	Several people killed
11. Flores Region (12/92)	7.5	Tsunami run-up of 300 m with wave heights of 25 m on Flores, landslides, ground cracks	2200 killed or missing
12. Switzerland (11/92)	3.7	Accidental explosion of a munitions cavern	6 killed
13. Northern Colombia (10/92)	7.3	Explosion of a mud volcano, landslides, soil liquefaction, small island emerged from the Caribbean Sea off San Juan de Uraba	10 killed, 65 injured, 1500 homeless
14. Landers, CA (6/92)	7.6	Surface faulting along a 70-km segment with up to 5.5 m of horizontal displacement and 1.8 m of vertical displacement	1 killed, 400 injured, substantial damage

continued on next page

Recent Seismic Events of Special Interest (IRIS) *(continued)*			
Event	**Magnitude**	**Geologic Changes**	**Destruction**
15. Northern India (10/91)	7.0	2 events 1.6 s apart, landslides, 30 m deep crack	2000 killed 1800 injured, 18,000 buildings were destroyed
16. Luzon, Philippines (7/90)	7.8	Landslides, soil liquefaction, surface faulting	1621 killed, 3000 injured, severe damage
17. Western Iran, (6/90)	7.7	Landslides	40,000–50,000 killed, 60,000 injured 400,000 homeless, extensive damage
18. Loma Prieta, CA (10/89)	7.1	Maximum intensity in part of Oakland and San Francisco, landslides, soil liquefaction, small tsunami at Monterey	60 killed, 3757 injured, $5.6 billion damage
19. Macquarie (1/95)	8.2	Small tsunami along coasts of Tasmania and in Australia. Largest oceanic earthquake ever recorded	None reported
20. Turkey-USSR Border (12/88)	6.8	Surface faulting 10 km in length with a maximum throw of 1.5 m	25,000 killed, 19,000 injured, 500,000 homeless, $6.2 billion damage

4. Look into the municipal building code in your community (contact your town or city government office).

   a) Does part of the code address earthquake risks?

   b) What parts of the code are applicable to reducing earthquake risk, both primary (due to Earth shaking) and secondary (aftereffects)?

   c) Has the code been upgraded in recent years?

5. Examine a detailed map of your community. A USGS 7.5-minute topographic quadrangle would work well.

   a) Assign risk factors to the highway system, access to hospitals, the power grid, police and fire services, and other community services that would come into play in the case of an earthquake catastrophe.

   b) In case of an earthquake, what kinds of damage might occur that could cause even more damage to the community and its occupants than the shaking of the Earth itself?

   c) Report your findings and your ideas about building codes and community safety to the class.

Reflecting on the Activity and the Challenge

You learned that ground motion (shaking) happens with every felt earthquake. Ground motion is the leading cause of damage to materials and buildings. Your **isoseismal map** showed that the epicenter and the area of maximum intensity do not always coincide. The effects of an earthquake depend in large part on the rocks and soil in a region. The motion from earthquakes can trigger landslides and tsunamis, and break gas lines and water lines. You also looked at local structures that might be at risk from earthquakes. You now have the information to provide recommendations on ways to reduce damage from an earthquake.

Digging Deeper

REDUCING EARTHQUAKE HAZARDS

Direct Hazards

The main effect of earthquakes is shaking of the ground as seismic waves pass through an area. The main result of ground shaking is the collapse of buildings. Motion along a fault can break power lines, pipelines, roads, bridges, and other structures that cross the fault.

Indirect Hazards

Fire is a secondary hazard in cities. Fire can cause much more damage than ground movement during an earthquake. In the 1906 San Francisco earthquake, 70% of the damage was due to fire. Fires occur when ground motion breaks fuel lines, tanks, and power lines. Often, water lines are also disrupted or broken. This reduces the water available to fight the fires. One of the ways to reduce the risk of heavy fire damage is to place many valves in the water and fuel pipelines. If one part of the pipeline is damaged, those pipes can be isolated from the system.

Landslides are another serious secondary effect of earthquakes. Earthquakes can trigger the failure of unstable slopes. The best way to minimize this hazard is not to build in areas with unstable slopes. Because buildings already exist in such areas, it is difficult to reduce the risk.

When an undersea or nearshore earthquake occurs, a **tsunami**, also called a seismic sea wave, can be generated. Tsunamis are like the ripples that form when you throw a rock in a pond, except very much larger. Tsunamis form when a large area of the ocean floor rises or falls suddenly in an earthquake. This causes waves to move away from the area. In the open ocean, the waves have very long wave lengths (greater than 500 km), but heights of only a →

Geo Words

isoseismal map: a map showing the lines connecting points on the Earth's surface at which earthquake intensity is the same

tsunami: a great sea wave produced by a submarine earthquake (or volcanic eruption or landslide)

Integrated Coordinated Science for the 21st Century

Check Your Understanding

1. What are the direct hazards of an earthquake?

2. Why are fires able to cause extensive damage after an earthquake?

3. What is a tsunami?

4. Why is it difficult to prepare against the destruction caused by a tsunami?

meter or so. The waves are so long and so low that ships at sea can't tell they are passing by! If you have been to the seashore, you probably have noticed that ordinary ocean waves get much higher and then break as they move into shallower water. The same thing happens with tsunami waves, only more so. As they come onshore, the waves build to heights as great as 30 m.

One of the difficulties in preparing for tsunamis is their great speed. They move very fast (1000 km/hour) over very long distances in the ocean. On average, there are two destructive tsunamis in the Pacific basin each year. An early warning system now monitors sea level around the Pacific. A tsunami can take several hours to travel across the Pacific. If a tsunami is detected, its estimated time of arrival is sent to areas in danger so that people can be evacuated. This early warning system has had many successes, but also some failures, since it was begun in 1948. It works well for areas far from the earthquake, but it is not very effective for areas close by, because the waves move so fast.

Personal Safety in an Earthquake

The Federal Emergency Management Agency provides safety rules for earthquakes. Earthquakes strike suddenly, violently, and without warning. Identifying potential hazards ahead of time and advance planning can reduce the dangers of serious injury or loss of life from an earthquake.

Understanding and Applying What You Have Learned

1. In a major earthquake, where in your school and in your community would you be safest? What places pose the greatest risk from the effects of an earthquake? Explain why you selected these locations.

2. If you live in an earthquake-prone area, your school may also have regular earthquake drills.

   If your school has a regular drill, examine the drill and evaluate its appropriateness.

If your school has no earthquake drill plan, describe how you would develop such a plan for your school. Think about the following questions:

- Where will students go when the shaking stops?

- How will this be accomplished?

Write down your ideas as a sequence of steps.

Preparing for the Chapter Challenge

Develop an overall community response and evacuation plan for earthquakes. Take into account the kinds of damage that may block roads, injure people, and collapse buildings. Note any steep slopes that might generate landslides during an earthquake.

Be sure to address the following issues:

- If a community mitigation (making less severe) plan already exists, how well does it address the important issues? Are there places where the current plan can be improved?

- Are there parts of your community where the physical conditions of the ground itself creates special risks of earthquake damage?

- Are there other areas where people and structures are more likely to be safer?

Inquiring Further

1. **Forming questions to investigate**

   Write down other questions that you have about ways to reduce the severity of earthquakes in your communities and around the world. How would you go about gathering information to answer these questions? Write your ideas in your notebook.

2. **The Pacific Tsunami Warning Center**

   The Pacific Tsunami Warning Center has provided successful advance warnings of potentially dangerous tsunami that may affect areas distant from the original earthquake. Find out about this tsunami warning system.

   a) Record in your notebook your ideas and any information you find on tsunamis and tsunami prediction.

   b) Why is it possible to predict a tsunami, but not an earthquake, in time to save lives?

   c) If your community is near the ocean, find out how well your community is prepared to deal with a tsunami warning.

Activity 6 Designing "Earthquake-Proof" Structures

GOALS

In this activity you will:

- Determine factors that influence the stability of buildings.

- Build models to assess the behavior of buildings during ground motion.

- Design reinforcements to structures and re-test their structures.

- Compare real structural failures to failure of their models.

- Suggest structural improvements for local buildings.

- Identify types of motion that lead to structural failure.

- Identify geologic conditions that enhance ground motion.

- Measure the natural frequency of different objects.

- Learn that natural frequency is a control on the stability of structures.

Think about It

During earthquakes, some buildings stand up well to the shaking while others collapse immediately.

- What influences the extent of damage to a building during an earthquake?
- Where is the safest place to be in a building during an earthquake?

What do you think? Record your ideas about these questions in your *EarthComm* notebook. Be prepared to discuss your responses with your small group and the class.

Investigate

Part A: Modeling the Response of Buildings to Shaking

1. Obtain the materials you need for this investigation. These include wooden dowels (about 4 cm diameter would be good to start with, but perhaps others that have a larger or smaller diameter as well), large sheets of heavy-gauge mat board or corrugated cardboard, and map pins. You may want to find other materials of your own to test some of the models you develop further. Read the steps carefully so that you are familiar with the suggested methods.

2. On a table that can easily be shaken sideways, build a model using the dowels as pillars and sheets of mat board. Construct a model of a 4-story parking garage, a tall square building, or an overhead freeway. Do not fasten these together first. Assemble them just by stacking.

3. Design your investigation so that you will be testing one variable at a time, if possible.

   a) Record which variable you will investigate.

4. Once your structure is complete, shake the table very gently for 5 s and observe whatever happens to the structure. Then shake it for 10 s, 20 s, and 30 s.

   a) Record what you observe each time.

⚠️ Work in an unobstructed area. As the structures topple, pieces will fall unpredictably. Do not use material that can break or cause injury as they fall. Keep feet and hands clear of falling objects.

5. Repeat your test and vary the "magnitude" of shaking (keeping the time and direction the same). Also, repeat the test and vary the direction of shaking, by moving to a different position around the table (keeping the "magnitude" and time the same). Observe what happens.

   a) Record your results.

   b) Was your building more or less resistant than you thought?

   c) How was the stability of your building affected by the violence of shaking? By the duration of the shaking?

   d) Does it matter from which direction the vibration comes?

6. Try other shapes of buildings, similar to buildings in your community, and use other kinds of materials if you wish to create more "realistic" models.

   a) Record your procedure and results carefully so that your experiment could be repeated and verified by others.

   b) Is there a difference between tall and short structures?

   c) Is there a difference between narrow and wide structures?

7. You should make your structures collapse eventually, because what you want to know is just how resistant the structures are to shaking. To determine the limits of your structures, you must continue the experiments until the structures fail.

167

Rebuild the structures you tested, but this time construct them so that they will not collapse, even with prolonged shaking. Identify materials like push pins, string, additional cardboard, tape, and paper binders that may help to reinforce your structure. Once your group has discussed several options, test them. Try to subject the rebuilt structures to as many of the types of wave motion you learned about in **Activity 2** as you can.

a) How did you add strength to your buildings?

b) Which methods of reinforcement worked the best?

8. The photographs show actual damage that happened to a bridge and buildings in real earthquakes.

a) How does the damage you observe in the photos resemble the kind of collapse and damage that you observed in your models?

b) For each case, can you suggest the type of force (compression, extension, or shear) that caused the structure to fail?

c) For each case, can you tell if the underlying geologic materials played a role in increasing the intensity of waves or causing damage?

Part B: Modeling the Response of Buildings of Various Heights to Shaking

1. Obtain the following materials: two square pieces of wood board, each about 10 cm on a side; a 30-cm (10") thin metal strip; a small C-clamp; and a lump of modeling clay, about half the size of a fist (about 100 gm).

2. Attach the two pieces of wood together with nails or wood screws to make an "L"-shaped wooden base. Set it on a table with one side horizontal and the other side upright. Clamp the metal strip blade vertically to the top of the upright piece of wood, as shown in the diagram.

3. Mold the modeling clay into a ball, and push it onto the top of the metal strip. Measure the distance from where the blade is clamped, up to the center of the ball.

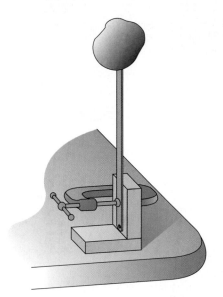

⚠ Stand back of the swinging metal strip. Avoid pulling back the metal strip to extreme bends. It is possible for all or part of the clay ball to come off. Position yourself to avoid being hit.

a) Set up a table to record the measurements for this activity.

b) Record the initial position of the clay ball.

4. Hold or clamp the wooden base to a table. Pull the ball to one side and let it go. You are modeling how a tall building sways back and forth when it is disturbed by the ground motion of an earthquake, or even by a strong gust of wind. Measure the period of the oscillation by timing how long it takes for several oscillations and then dividing the time by the number of oscillations.

a) Record your measurements.

b) Repeat your measurements for shorter buildings, by pushing the ball down the metal strip to three or four different heights. Record any observations and measurements.

c) Plot a graph with oscillation period on the vertical axis and the height of the ball on the horizontal axis.

d) How does the oscillation period depend on the height of the ball?

5. Put the ball back at the top of the metal strip. Slide the wood base on the table in a regular back-and-forth motion. Measure the period of the sliding by timing how long it takes for several cycles.

a) Estimate and record how far the ball moves away from the upright "neutral" position during one oscillation cycle. It's easier to do this if you prepare a centimeter grid on a piece of poster board and then staple the grid onto the wooden base so that you can view the swaying of the ball in front of the grid.

b) Repeat the last step for several different sliding periods, from very slow (less than one cycle per second) to as fast as you can easily measure. Record your measurements.

c) Plot a graph with sliding period on the horizontal axis and estimated ball displacement on the vertical axis. Draw a smooth curve through your data points.

d) What is the shape of the curve?

e) What is the relationship between the sliding period that produces the greatest displacement and the natural period of the oscillation, which you measured earlier?

6. Use the results of your investigation to answer the following questions:

a) Will earthquakes affect all buildings equally?

b) Are large earthquakes required to damage tall buildings?

c) If you had to design a tall building to withstand an earthquake, how might you use the results of this investigation to help you?

7. Within your groups, examine the data you have gathered during the two parts of the activity investigations and draw some conclusions about structures and their ability to withstand earthquake shaking.

a) Record your conclusions. Have representatives from each group report to the class.

b) Record the similarities and differences among the group results, and suggest possible explanations for these differences.

Reflecting on the Activity and the Challenge

In this activity, you used various materials to make models of buildings. With these models, you examined the influence of design, support, and size on the stability of a building. You also saw that magnitude, duration, and direction of shaking are important influences. By rebuilding some structures, you recognized that improvements could be made to add stability.

By examining damage from past earthquakes you gained insights about the interaction between building design and earthquake forces. You used a model to explore the relationship between height and stability and calculate the natural oscillation period of an object. You can use this information as part of your public service message.

Digging Deeper

BUILDINGS AND GROUND MOTION

Introduction

Severe earthquakes can cause major damage to buildings in any community. The problems are made worse by the loss of electric power, gas, and communication lines. Damage to roads often disrupts transportation. One of the problems is that it is difficult to build realistic small models that will behave like full-scale structures during an earthquake. Not all earthquakes produce the same ground motion. Areas with different underlying Earth materials react differently to the same shaking. However, certain design elements will help buildings and other structures to withstand ground motion.

Duration of Shaking

The duration of an earthquake can affect the extent of damage. For example, buildings made of reinforced concrete may withstand a 20-s main shock, yet collapse in a smaller-magnitude earthquake that lasts longer.

Direction of Motion

Many earthquakes in the San Fernando Valley of California caused horizontal displacement and ground motion. Structures that had collapsed in the past were rebuilt to withstand this kind of motion. The motion of the 1994 Northridge earthquake, however, had a strong vertical component. Many of the rebuilt structures and freeways collapsed again.

Underlying Earth Materials

Underlying Earth materials have a strong influence on the motions of structures during an earthquake. In the San Francisco earthquake of 1906, buildings on filled land (loose, wet soil) suffered much more damage than buildings built on bedrock. The same pattern was repeated in the 1989 Loma Prieta earthquake. Damage was high in the Marina district (**Activity 5**). This same part of San Francisco was hit hard in 1906. Buildings in Mexico City were affected greatly by the earthquake of 1985, although the epicenter was far away. Mexico City is built on a basin filled with weak layers of volcanic ash and gravel, sand, and clay. Acapulco, which was much closer to the epicenter, suffered less damage, because it stands firmly on bedrock. It's not easy to specify exactly why this happens. Materials like soils and sediments, which are much less rigid than bedrock, respond to the passage of seismic waves with much greater wave amplitudes. You can think of it this way: rocks and gelatin are both elastic solids, and both will vibrate when you hit them, but you know that the gelatin will shake more than the rock!

Resonance

Sometimes, particular structures are affected by ground motion when others are not. All structures have a natural period of oscillation or swaying, as you determined in the investigation. When the shaking of the ground during an earthquake happens to be close to the natural oscillation period of a building, the swaying of the building is at its maximum and contributes to building collapse. When the oscillation that is imposed on the building is nearly the same as the natural oscillation period of the building, the swaying is greatly intensified. This is called **resonance**. You all know about resonance from when you were little kids on a swing. The swing has a natural period of oscillation, so when you "pump" to go higher, you pumped at about the same period as the natural period. Pumping at a different period got you nowhere!

The 1985 earthquake in Mexico City caused severe damage or destruction to about 500 buildings. Ground vibrations were amplified by the vibrational properties of tall buildings. This caused 10 to 14-story buildings to sway even more (at a period of 1 to 2 s) and resulted in damage to many structures. Nearby shorter and taller buildings were not damaged.

Materials

Building materials also make a difference. Stone, brick, wood, concrete, and adobe all have different responses to the forces they experience during an earthquake. Building design must take into account not only the structural elements but also the material from which the structure is made.

Geo Words

resonance: a condition in which a vibration affecting an object has about the same period as the natural vibration period of the object

Check Your Understanding

1. In addition to damage to buildings, what other problems are associated with earthquakes?

2. Name five factors that affect the amount of damage caused by an earthquake.

3. Why were structures rebuilt to withstand earthquakes still heavily damaged during the 1994 Northridge earthquake?

4. Why was the Marina district of San Francisco so severely damaged during the 1989 Loma Prieta earthquake?

5. Why is earthquake risk greater on filled land with soft ground than on solid bedrock?

6. In the 1985 earthquake of Mexico City why were some buildings heavily damaged or destroyed, while surrounding shorter and taller buildings were not?

Understanding and Applying What You Have Learned

1. What are some of the major problems involved in getting your community to prepare for earthquake damage?

2. What modifications could be made to buildings of your community?

3. What types of scientists and professionals should be consulted in earthquake planning?

4. Suggest the kinds of areas where you think that buildings should not be constructed.

5. Which communities should prohibit the construction of tall buildings? Explain your reasoning.

Preparing for the Chapter Challenge

As a group, develop a set of recommendations to make to your town council and school board about how to minimize damage in your community from a major earthquake. Address the design of new structures and possible changes to older structures in your community. Write these recommendations as a list to include in your brochure. Be sure to address the following issues:

- suggestions for new building developers,

- suggestions for homeowners, and

- suggestions for local government and businesses.

Inquiring Further

1. **Earthquake engineering**

   The National Information Service for Earthquake Engineering provides an excellent overview of numerous structures as well as photographs of earthquake-resistant design. Visit the *EarthComm* web site for more information on how to locate this data.

   Compare their structures to the ones you built early in the activity. The service also has a description of shake tables, the large platforms used to test structural designs during simulated earthquake vibrations.

Earth Science at Work

ATMOSPHERE: *Firefighter*
The public depends on the availability of adequate firefighting equipment and the quick response time of the emergency personnel.

BIOSPHERE: *Insurance Agent*
Insurance agents need to consider the risks involved in insuring a building, and the lives and property of its owners.

CRYOSPHERE: *Ski Instructor*
Professional ski instructors arrange for helicopter skiing trips into remote mountain areas not accessible by roads. They are responsible for the safety of their clients.

GEOSPHERE: *Architect*
When designing a building, an architect must carefully calculate the forces that will act on the structure.

HYDROSPHERE: *Dam Maintenance Worker*
Dams are one of the engineering marvels of this world. Their maintenance is vital to their operation.

How is each person's work related to the Earth system, and to earthquakes?

Unit 2

Active Physics™

Communication

Making Connections

You have just completed the first unit of learning in *Integrated Coordinated Science for the 21st Century*. The unit was related to Earth science. You are now going to start a unit of *Active Physics*, called Communication.

When studying Earth science, you discovered that energy released during an earthquake is transmitted through the Earth as waves. You explored different types of waves. The first activity in the physics unit also deals with making waves. However, your first *Active Physics* challenge is to provide a sound and light show. That definitely seems different than developing a plan to ensure that your community would be prepared to deal with an earthquake. What is the connection?

What Do You Think?

• What is a wave?

• What does a wave do?

• What are the different types of waves? How are they different? How are they the same?

Record your ideas about this in your log. Be prepared to discuss your response with your small group and the class.

For You To Try

• With your classmates, make a "people wave," like the ones you see at sports' stadiums. Think about which way the wave moves, and which way you move.

• Identify similarities and differences between ocean waves and sound waves.

• Go to the side of a large building and try to create an echo.

Chapter 4

LET US ENTERTAIN YOU

Let Us Entertain You

Scenario

Most entertainment today comes from the communication of sound and light signals. You look forward to television shows, movies, and rock concerts. The sound signals that entertain you come from voices or musical instruments. Light signals make the images you see on TV or in the movies. Specially designed light patterns add to the effect of a rock concert.

Challenge

You have been made part of a committee to design a two- to four-minute sound and light show to entertain other students your age. But unlike the professionals, you have neither the funds nor the technology available to rock stars or MTV™ productions. All the sounds you use must come from musical instruments or sound makers that you build yourself, or from human voices. Some of these sounds may be prerecorded and then played back during your show. If your teacher has a laser and is willing to allow you to use it, you may do so. All other light must come from conventional household lamps.

Criteria

Work with your classmates to agree on the relative importance of the following assessment criteria. Each item in the list has a point value given after it, but your class must decide what kind of grading system to use.

1. The variety and number of physics concepts used to produce the light and sound effects: (30 points)

   four or more concepts: 30 points

   three concepts: 25 points

   two concepts: 20 points

   one concept: 10 points

2. Your understanding of the physics concepts: (40 points)

   Following your production, you will be asked to:

   a) Name the physics concepts that you used. (10 points)
   b) Explain each concept. (10 points)
   c) Give an example of something that each concept explains or an example of how each concept is used. (10 points)
   d) Explain why each concept is important. (10 points)

   As a class, you will have to decide if your answers will be in an oral report or a written report.

3. Entertainment value: (30 points)

   Your class will need to decide on a way to assign points for creativity. Note that an entertaining and interesting show need not be loud or bright.

You will have a chance later in the chapter to again discuss these criteria. At that time, you may have more information on the concepts and how you might produce your show. You may want to then propose changes in the criteria and the point values.

Activity 1   Making Waves

GOALS

In this activity you will:

• Observe the motion of a pulse.

• Measure the speed of a wave.

• Observe standing waves.

• Investigate the relationship among wave speed, wavelength, and frequency.

• Make a model of wave motion.

What Do You Think?

One of the largest tsunamis (tidal waves) grew from about 0.7 m high in the open ocean to 35 m high when it reached shore.

• **How does water move to make a wave?**

• **How does a wave travel?**

Record your ideas about these questions in your *Active Physics* log. Be prepared to discuss your responses with your small group and with your class.

For You To Do

1. In an area free of obstacles, stretch out a Slinky® so the turns are a few centimeters apart. Mark the positions of the end of the Slinky by sticking pieces of tape on the floor. Measure the distance between the pieces of tape.

   a) Record the distance between the pieces of tape in your log.

2. With the Slinky stretched out to the tape, grab the spring near one end, as shown in the drawing, and pull sideways 20 cm and back. To move it correctly, move your wrist like snapping a whip. Observe what happens. You have made a **transverse pulse**.

   a) In what direction does the spring move as the **pulse** goes by?

   b) A dictionary definition of transverse is: "Situated or lying across." Why is transverse a good name for the wave you observed?

Physics Words

transverse pulse or wave: a pulse or wave in which the motion of the medium is perpendicular to the motion of the wave

amplitude: the height of a wave crest; it is related to a wave's energy

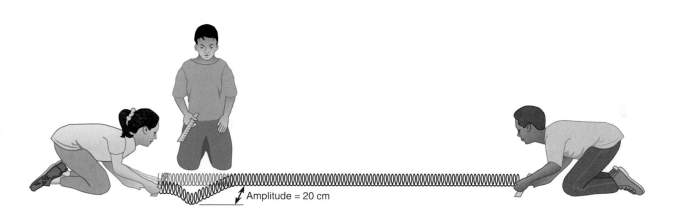

Amplitude = 20 cm

c) Measure and record the **amplitude** of the wave. The distance you disturbed the spring is called the *amplitude*. The amplitude tells how much the spring is displaced.

Physics Words

periodic wave:
a repetitive series of pulses; a wave train in which the particles of the medium undergo periodic motion (after a set amount of time the medium returns to its starting point and begins to repeat its motion)

standing wave: the superposition of two waves traveling in opposite directions characterized by lack of vibration at certain points, between which areas of maximum vibration occur periodically; produced whenever a wave is confined within boundaries, as in the vibrating of a musical instrument

crest: the highest point on a wave

wavelength: the distance (measured in the direction of propagation) between two identical points in consecutive cycles of a wave

frequency: the number of waves produced per unit time; the frequency is the reciprocal of the amount of time it takes for a single wavelength to pass a point

3. After you have experimented with making pulses, measure the speed of the pulse. You will need to measure the time it takes the pulse to go the length of the spring. Take several measurements and then average the values.

✎ a) Record your data in the second and third rows of a table like the one below.

Amplitude	Time for pulse to travel from one end to the other	Average time	Speed = $\dfrac{\text{length of spring}}{\text{average time}}$

4. Measure the speed of the pulses for two other amplitudes, one larger and one smaller than the value used in **Step 3**.

✎ a) Record the results in the table in your log.

✎ b) How does the speed of the pulse depend on the amplitude?

5. Now make waves! Swing one end back-and-forth over and over again along the floor. The result is called a **periodic wave**.

✎ a) Describe the appearance of the periodic wave you created.

6. To make these waves look very simple, change the way you swing the end until you see large waves that do not move along the spring. You will also see points where the spring does not move at all. These waves are called **standing waves**.

7. The distance from one **crest** (peak) of a wave to the next is called the **wavelength**. Notice that you can find the wavelength by looking at the points where the spring does not move. The wavelength is twice the distance between these points. Measure the wavelength of your standing wave.

✎ a) Record the wavelength of your standing wave in your log.

Crest

Amplitude

|← 1 wavelength →|

Trough

Standing wave

8. You can also measure the wave frequency. The frequency is the number of times the wave moves up and down each second. Measure the **frequency** of your standing wave. Hint: Watch the hands of the person shaking the Slinky. Time a certain number of back-and-forth motions. The frequency is the number of back-and-forth motions of the hand in one second.

a) Record the wave frequency in your log. The unit of frequency is the hertz (Hz).

9. Make several different standing waves by changing the wave frequency. Try to make each standing wave shown in the drawing. Measure the wavelength. Measure the frequency.

a) Record both in a table like the one below.

Wavelength (m/cycle)	Frequency (cycles/s or Hz)	Speed (m/s) wavelength × frequency

b) For each wave, calculate the product of the wavelength and the frequency. Compare these values with the average speed of the pulse that you found in **Steps 3** and **4** above.

10. All the waves you have made so far are transverse waves. A different kind of wave is the **compressional** (or **longitudinal**) **wave**. Have the members of your group stretch out the Slinky between the pieces of tape and hold the ends firmly. To make a compressional wave, squeeze together part of the Slinky and let it go. Measure the speed of the compressional wave and compare it with the speed of the **transverse wave**.

a) Record your results in a table partly like the one after **Step 3**.

b) In what direction does the Slinky move as the wave goes by?

Physics Words

compression pulse or wave: a longitudinal pulse or wave caused by means of the compression of a fluid, as a sound wave in air

longitudinal pulse or wave: a pulse or wave in which the motion of the medium is parallel to the direction of motion of the wave motion

transverse pulse or wave: a pulse or wave in which the motion of the medium is perpendicular to the motion of the wave

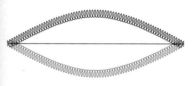

Wavelength = twice slinky length

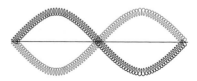

Wavelength = slinky length

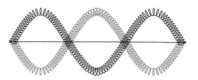

Wavelength = 2/3 slinky length

Wavelength

c) A dictionary definition of compressional is: "*a.* The act or process of compressing. *b.* The state of being compressed." A dictionary definition of longitudinal is: "Placed or running lengthwise." Explain why compressional or longitudinal wave is a suitable name for this type of wave.

11. To help you understand waves better, construct a wave viewer by cutting a slit in a file card and labeling it as shown.

2.0 cm
1.5 cm
1.0 cm
0.5 cm
0.0 cm
−0.5 cm
−1.0 cm
−1.5 cm
−2.0 cm

12. Make a drawing of a transverse wave on a strip of adding machine tape. Place this strip under the wave viewer so you can see one part of the wave through the slit.

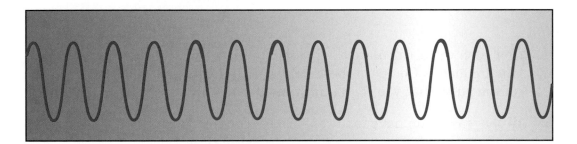

13. With the slit over the tape, pull the tape so that the wave moves. You will see a part of the wave (through the slit) going up and down.

14. Draw waves with different wavelengths on other pieces of adding machine tape. Put these under the slit and pull the adding machine tape at the same speed.

a) Describe what you see.

Wave Vocabulary

In this activity, you were able to send energy from one end of the Slinky to the other. You used chemical energy in your muscles to create mechanical energy in your arms that you then imparted to the Slinky. The Slinky had energy. A card at the other end of the Slinky would have moved once the wave arrived there. The ability to move the card is an indication that energy is present. The total energy is transferred but it is always conserved.

Of course, you could have used that same mechanical energy in your arm to throw a ball across the room. That would have also transferred the energy from one side of the room to the other. It would also have moved the card.

There is a difference between the Slinky transferring the energy as a wave and the ball transferring the energy. The Slinky wave transferred the energy, but the Slinky basically stayed in the same place. If the part of the Slinky close to one end were painted red, the red part of the Slinky would not move across the room. The Slinky wave moves, but the parts of the Slinky remain in the same place as the wave passes by. A wave can be defined as a transfer of energy with no net transfer of mass.

Leonardo da Vinci stated that "the wave flees the place of creation, while the water does not." The water moves up and down but the wave moves out from its center.

In discussing waves, a common vocabulary helps to communicate effectively. You observed waves in the lab activity. We will summarize some of the observations here and you can become more familiar with the terminology.

Physics Words

trough: the lowest point on a wave

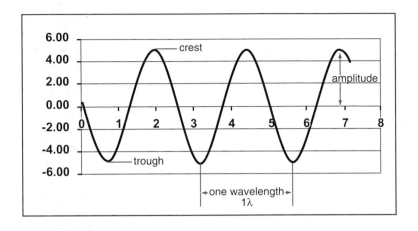

A periodic wave is a repetitive series of pulses. In the periodic wave shown in the diagram, the highest point is called the crest. The lowest point is called the **trough**. The maximum disturbance, the amplitude, is 5.00 cm. Notice that this is the height of the crest or the height of the trough. It is *not* the distance from the crest to the trough.

The wavelength of a periodic wave is the distance between two consecutive points in phase. The distance between two crests is one wavelength or 1 λ (the Greek letter lambda is used to signify wavelength). The wavelength of the wave in the diagram is 2.5 cm.

The amplitude of a periodic wave is the maximum disturbance. A large amplitude corresponds to a large energy. In sound, the large amplitude is a loud sound. In light, the large amplitude is a bright light. In Slinkies, the large amplitude is a large disturbance.

The wavelength of the wave in the diagram is 2.5 cm. It is the distance between two crests or the distance between two troughs.

The frequency is the number of vibrations occurring per unit time. A frequency of 10 waves per second may also be referred to as 10 vibrations per second, 10 cycles per second, 10 per second, 10 s^{-1}, 10 Hz (hertz). The human ear can hear very low sounds (20 Hz) or very high sounds (20,000 Hz). You can't tell the frequency by examining the wave in the diagram. The "snapshot" of the wave is at an instant of time. To find the frequency, you have to know how many crests pass by a point in a given time.

The period, T, of a wave is the time it takes to complete one cycle. It is the time required for one crest to pass a given point. The period and the frequency are related to one another. If three waves pass a point every second, the frequency is three waves per second. The period would be the time for one wave to pass the point, which equals 1/3 s. If 10 waves pass a point every second, the frequency is 10 waves per second. The period would be the time for 1 wave to pass the point, which equals 1/10 second.

Mathematically, this relationship can be represented as:

$$T = \frac{1}{f} \quad \text{or} \quad f = \frac{1}{T}$$

Points in a periodic wave can be "in phase" if they have the same displacement and are moving in the same direction. All crests of the wave are "in phase."

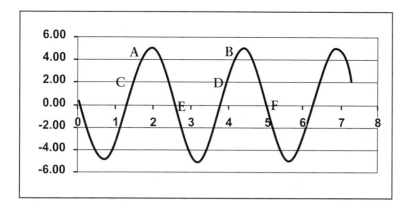

In the wave shown, the following pairs of points are in phase:

- A and B

- C and D

- E and F

Physics Words

node: a spot on a standing wave where the medium is motionless

A **node** is a spot on a standing wave where the medium is motionless. There are places along the medium that do not move as the standing wave moves up and down. The locations of these nodes do not change as the standing wave vibrates.

PHYSICS TALK

Calculating the Speed of Waves

You can find the speed of a wave by measuring the distance the crest moves during a certain change in time.

$$\text{speed} = \frac{\text{change in distance}}{\text{change in time}}$$

In mathematical language:

$$v = \frac{\Delta d}{\Delta t}$$

where $v =$ speed

$d =$ distance

$t =$ time

Suppose the distance the crest moves is 2 m in 0.2 s. The speed can be calculated as follows:

$$v = \frac{\Delta d}{\Delta t}$$

$$= \frac{2 \text{ m}}{0.2 \text{ s}}$$

$$= 10 \text{ m/s}$$

The distance from one crest of a wave to the next is the wavelength. The number of crests that go by in one second is the frequency. Imagine you saw five crests go by in one second. You measure the wavelength to be 2 m. The frequency is 5 crests/second, so the speed is (5 × 2)=10 m/s. Thus, the speed can also be found by multiplying the wavelength and the frequency.

speed = frequency × wavelength

In mathematical language:

$$v = f\lambda$$

where $v =$ speed

$f =$ frequency

$\lambda =$ wavelength

Standing waves happen anywhere that the length of the Slinky and the wavelength have a particular mathematical relationship. The length of the Slinky must equal $\frac{1}{2}$ wavelength, 1 wavelength, $1\frac{1}{2}$ wavelengths, 2 wavelengths, etc. Mathematically, this can be stated as:

$$L = \frac{n\lambda}{2}$$

where L is the length of the Slinky,

λ is the wavelength

n is a number (1,2,3...)

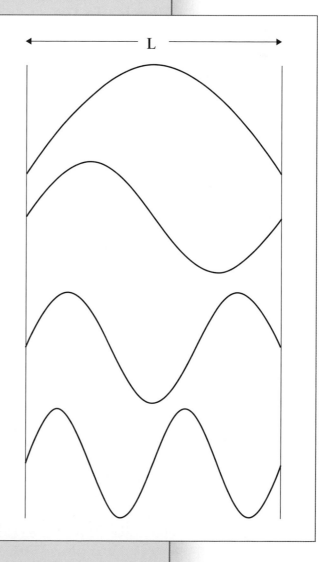

Reflecting on the Activity and the Challenge

Slinky waves are easy to observe. You have created transverse and compressional Slinky waves, and measured their speed, wavelength, and frequency. For the challenge, you may want to create musical instruments. You will receive more guidance in doing this in the next activities. Your instruments will probably not be made of Slinkies. You may, however, use strings that behave just like Slinkies. When you have to explain how your instrument works, you can relate its production of sound in terms of the Slinky waves that you observed in this activity.

Physics To Go

1. a) Four characteristics of waves are amplitude, wavelength, frequency, and speed. For each characteristic, tell how you measured it when you worked with the Slinky.
   b) For each characteristic, give the units you used in your measurement.
   c) Which wave characteristics are related to each other? Tell how they are related.

2. a) Suppose you shake a long Slinky slowly back and forth. Then you shake it rapidly. Describe how the waves change when you shake the Slinky more rapidly.
   b) What wave properties change?
   c) What wave properties do not change?

3. Suppose you took a photograph of a wave on a Slinky. How can you measure wavelength by looking at the photograph?

4. Suppose you mount a video camera on a tripod and aim the camera at one point on a Slinky. You also place a clock next to the Slinky, so the video camera records the time. When you look at the video of a wave going by on the Slinky, how could you measure the frequency?

5. a) What are the units of wavelength?
   b) What are the units of frequency?
   c) What are the units of speed?
   d) Tell how you find the wave speed from the frequency and the wavelength.
   e) Using your answer to **Part (d)**, show how the units of speed are related to the units of wavelength and frequency.

6. a) What is a standing wave?
   b) Draw a standing wave.
   c) Add labels to your drawing to show how the Slinky moves.
   d) Tell how to find the wavelength by observing a standing wave.

7. a) Explain the difference between transverse waves and compressional waves.

   b) Slinky waves can be either transverse or compressional. Describe how the Slinky moves in each case.

8. a) When you made standing waves, how did you shake the spring (change the frequency) to make the wavelength shorter?

   b) When you made standing waves, how did you shake the spring (change the frequency) to make the wavelength longer?

9. Use the wave viewer and adding machine tape to investigate what happens if the speed of the wave increases. Pull the tape at different speeds and report your results.

Activity 2   Sounds in Strings

GOALS

In this activity you will:

- Observe the effect of string length and tension upon pitch produced.

- Control the variables of tension and length.

- Summarize experimental results.

- Calculate wavelength of a standing wave.

- Organize data in a table.

What Do You Think?

When the ancient Greeks made stringed musical instruments, they discovered that cutting the length of the string by half or two-thirds produced other pleasing sounds.

- **How do guitarists or violinists today make different sounds?**

Record your ideas about this question in your *Active Physics* log. Be prepared to discuss your responses with your small group and with your class.

For You To Do

1. Carefully mount a pulley over one end of a table. Securely clamp one end of a string to the other end of the table.

2. Tie the other end of the string around a mass hanger. Lay the string over the pulley. Place a pencil under the string near the clamp, so the string can vibrate without hitting the table, as shown in the drawing.

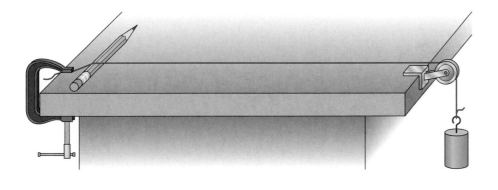

⚠️ **Make sure the area under the hanging mass is clear (no feet, legs). Also monitor the string for fraying.**

3. Hang one 500-g mass on the mass hanger. Pluck the string, listen to the sound, and observe the string vibrate.

✎ a) Record your observations in your log in a table similar to the following:

4. Use a key or some other small metal object. Press this object down on the string right in the middle, to hold the string firmly against the table. Pluck each half of the string.

✎ a) Record the result in your table.

5. To change the string length, press down with the key at the different places shown in the diagrams on the next page. Pluck each part of the string.

✎ a) Record the results in your table.

195

Length of vibrating string	Load on mass hanger	Pitch (high, medium, low)

6. When you pluck the string, it does not move at the ends. Look at the drawing under **Step 9** of the **For You To Do** section of **Activity 1**. Measure the length of your string, and find the wavelength of the vibration for each string length.

Physics Words

pitch: the quality of a sound dependent primarily on the frequency of the sound waves produced by its source

📝 a) Record the wavelength in your table.

📝 b) Look over the data in your table. Make a general statement about what happens to the **pitch** you hear as you change the length of the string.

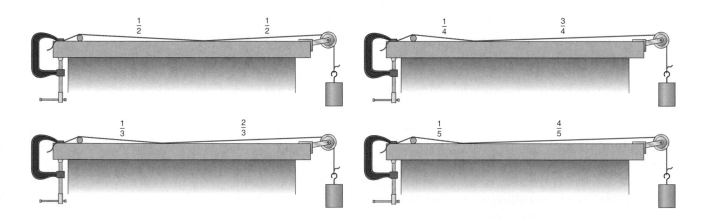

7. Remove the key, so the string is its original length. Pluck the string. To investigate the effect of tightening the string, add a second 500-g mass to the mass hanger. Pluck the string again, observe the vibration, and listen to the pitch of the sound.

✎ a) Make up a table to record your data in your log.

✎ b) Add a description of the pitch of the sound to your table. Continue adding weights and observing the sound until the total mass is 2000 g.

✎ c) Look over your data. As the mass increases, the string becomes tighter, and its tension increases. Make a general statement about what happens to the pitch you hear as you change the tension on the string.

FOR YOU TO READ

Changing the Pitch

Sound comes from vibration. You observed the vibration of the string as it produced sound. You investigated two of the variables that affect the sound of a vibrating string.

When you pushed the vibrating string down against the table, the length of the string that was vibrating became shorter. Shortening the string increased the pitch (resulted in a higher pitch). In the same way, a guitarist or violinist pushes the string against the instrument to shorten the length that vibrates and increases the pitch.

Also, when you hung weights on the end of the string, that increased the pitch too. These weights tightened the string, so they created more tension in it. As the string tension increased, the pitch of the sound also increased. In tuning a guitar or violin, the performer changes the string tension by turning a peg attached to one end of a string. As the peg pulls the string tighter, the pitch goes up.

Combining these two results into one expression, you can say that increasing the tension or decreasing the length of the string will increase the pitch.

The string producing the pitch is actually setting up a standing wave between its endpoints. The length of the string determines the wavelength of this standing wave. Twice the distance between the endpoints is the wavelength of the sound. The pitch that you hear is related to the frequency of the wave. The higher the pitch, the higher the frequency. The speed of the wave is equal to its frequency multiplied by its wavelength.

$$v = f\lambda$$

where v = speed

f = frequency

λ = wavelength

If the speed of a wave is constant, a decrease in the wavelength will result in an increase in the frequency or a higher pitch. A shortened string produces a higher pitch.

Reflecting on the Activity and the Challenge

Part of the challenge is to create a sound show. In this activity you investigated the relationship of pitch to length of the string and tension of the string: the shorter the string, the higher the pitch; the greater the tension, the higher the pitch. You also learned that the string is setting up a standing wave between its two ends, just like the standing wave that you created in the Slinky in **Activity 1**. That's the physics of stringed instruments! If you wanted to create a stringed or multi stringed instrument for your show, you now know how to adjust the length and tension to produce the notes you want. If you were to make such a stringed instrument, you can explain how you change the pitch by referring to the results of this activity.

Physics To Go

1. a) Explain how you can change the tension of a vibrating string.

   b) Tell how changing the tension changes the pitch.

2. a) Explain how you can change the length of a vibrating string.

   b) Tell how changing the length changes the sound produced by the string.

3. How would you change both the tension and the length and keep the pitch the same?

4. Suppose you changed both the length and the tension of the string at the same time. What would happen to the sound?

5. a) For the guitar and the piano, tell how the performer plays different notes.

   b) For the guitar and the piano, tell how the performer (or tuner) changes the pitch of the strings to tune the instrument.

6. a) Look at a guitar. Find the tuners (at the end of the neck). Why does a guitar need tuners?

   b) What is the purpose of the frets on a guitar?

   c) Does a violin or a cello have frets?

   d) Why do a violinist and cellist require more accuracy in playing than a guitarist?

7. a) Using what you have learned in this activity, design a simple two-stringed instrument.

   b) Include references to wavelength, frequency, pitch, and standing waves in your description.

   c) Use the vocabulary of wavelength, frequency, and standing waves from **Activity One** to describe how the instrument works.

Stretching Exercises

1. Set up the vibrating string as you did in the **For You To Do** above. This time you will measure the frequency of the sound. Set up a frequency meter on your computer. Pick up the sound with a microphone. Investigate how changing the length of the string changes the frequency of the sound. Create a graph to describe the relationship.

2. Set up the vibrating string, computer, and microphone as you did in **Stretching Exercise 1**. This time, investigate how changing the string tension changes the frequency of the sound. Create a graph to describe the relationship.

Inquiry Investigation

Design an investigation to find how the diameter (thickness) of the string, or the type of material the string is made from affects the pitch you hear. Submit your design to your teacher for approval before proceeding to carry out your experiments.

Activity 3

Sounds from Vibrating Air

GOALS

In this activity you will:

- Identify resonance in different kinds of tubes.
- Observe how resonance pitch changes with length of tube.
- Observe the effect of closing one end of the tube.
- Summarize experimental results.
- Relate pitch observations to drawings of standing waves.
- Organize observations to find a pattern.

What Do You Think?

The longest organ pipes are about 11 m long. A flute, about 0.5 m long, makes musical sound in the same way.

- **How do a flute and organ pipes produce sound?**

Record your ideas about this question in your *Active Physics* log. Be prepared to discuss your responses with your small group and with your class.

For You To Do

1. Carefully cut a drinking straw in half. Cut one of the halves into two quarters. Cut one of the quarters into two eighths. Pass one part of the straw out to one member of your group.

2. Gently blow into the top of the piece of straw.

a) Describe what you hear.

b) Listen as the members of your group blow into their straw pieces one at a time. Describe what you hear.

c) Write a general statement about how changing the length of the straw changes the pitch you hear.

3. Now cover the bottom of your straw piece and blow into it again. Uncover the bottom and blow again.

a) Compare the sound the straw makes when the bottom is covered and then uncovered.

b) Listen as the members of your group blow into their straw pieces, with the bottom covered and then uncovered. Write a general statement about how changing the length of the straw changes the pitch you hear when one end is covered.

⚠ **Make sure the outsides of the tubes are dry.**

4. Obtain a set of four test tubes. Leave one empty. Fill the next halfway with water. Fill the next three-quarters of the way. Fill the last one seven-eighths of the way.

5. Give each test tube to one member of your group. Blow across your test tube.

a) Describe what you hear.

b) Listen as the members of your group blow, one at a time, across their test tubes. Record what you hear.

c) What pattern do you find in your observations?

d) Compare the results of blowing across the straws with blowing across the test tubes. How are the results consistent?

PHYSICS TALK

Vibrating Columns of Air

The sound you heard when you blew into the straw and test tube was produced by a standing wave. If both ends of the straw are open, the air at both ends moves back and forth. The drawing shows the movement of the air as a standing wave.

Tube is open at both ends.
1/2 wavelength fits in straw.

When you covered the other end of the straw, you prevented the air from moving at the covered end. The drawing shows the movement of the air as a standing wave.

Tube is closed at one end.
1/4 wavelength fits in straw.

The velocity of a wave is equal to the frequency multiplied by the wavelength. Therefore,

$$\text{frequency} = \frac{\text{wave speed}}{\text{wavelength}}$$

Using mathematical symbols:

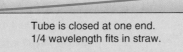

$$f = \frac{v}{\lambda}$$

As the wavelength increases, the frequency decreases. The wavelength in the open straw is half the wavelength in the straw closed at one end. This equation predicts that the frequency of the standing wave in the open straw is twice the frequency of the standing wave in the straw closed at one end.

FOR YOU TO READ

Compressing Air to Make Sound

Sound is a compression wave. The molecules of air bunch up or spread apart as the sound wave passes by.

At the end where the tube is closed, the air cannot go back-and-forth, because its motion is blocked by the end of the tube. That's why the wave's amplitude goes to zero at the closed end. At the open end, the amplitude is as large as it can possibly be. This back-and-forth motion of air at the open end makes a sound wave that moves from the tube to your ear.

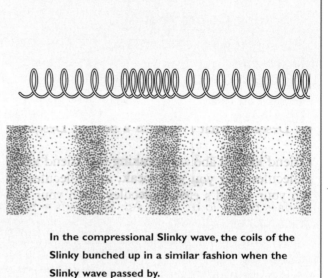

In the compressional Slinky wave, the coils of the Slinky bunched up in a similar fashion when the Slinky wave passed by.

Wave Diffraction

As the sound wave leaves the test tube in this activity, it spreads out. In the same way, when you speak to a friend, the sound waves leave your mouth and spread out. You can speak to a group of friends because the sound leaves your mouth and moves out to the front and to the sides.

This ability of the sound wave to spread out as it emerges from an opening is called diffraction. The smaller the opening, the more spreading of the sound. The spreading of the wave as it emerges from two holes can be shown with a diagram.

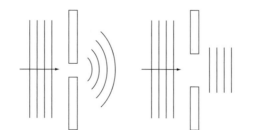

The wave on the left is going through a small opening (in comparison to its wavelength) and diffracts a great deal. The wave on the right is going through a large opening (in comparison to its wavelength) and shows little diffraction.

Cheerleaders use a megaphone to limit the diffraction. With a megaphone, the mouth opening becomes larger. The sound wave spreads out less and the cheering crowd in front of the cheerleader hears a louder sound.

A new musical instrument that you can make uses a straw instead of a test tube.

Take a straw and cut the ends to form a "v" as shown below.

Flatten the "v" end of the straw and blow this "trumpet." You can shorten the trumpet, decrease the wavelength of the standing wave and increase the frequency of the sound. Try making a sound. As you emit the sound, use scissors to cut ends off the straw. Listen to the different tones.

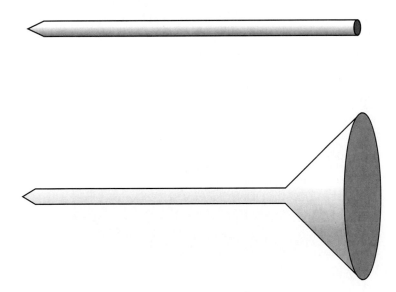

You can probably make a trombone by inserting one straw within another.

The sound diffracts from the small opening. You can add a horn to the end of the straw and limit the diffraction. The effect will be that the sound appears louder because it doesn't spread out. You can make a horn out of a piece of paper, as shown.

You may want to adapt this idea of a trumpet and a megaphone and make diffraction a part of your light and sound show.

Reflecting on the Activity and the Challenge

In this activity you have observed the sounds produced by different kinds of pipes. If the pipe is cut to a shorter length, the pitch of the sound increases. Also, when the pipe is open at both ends, the pitch is much higher than if the pipe were open at only one end. You have seen how simple drawings of standing waves in these tubes help you find the wavelength of the sound. If the tube is closed at one end, the air has zero displacement at that end. If the tube is open at one end, the air has maximum displacement there.

For your sound show, you may decide to create some "wind" instruments using test tubes or straws, or other materials approved by your teacher. When it comes time to explain how these work, you can refer to this activity to get the physics right.

Physics To Go

1. a) You can produce a sound by plucking a string or by blowing in a pipe. How are these two ways of producing sound similar?

   b) How are these two ways different?

2. a) For each piece of straw your group used, make a full-sized drawing to show the standing wave inside. Show both the straw closed at one end and open at both ends.

   b) Next to each drawing of the standing waves, make a drawing, at the same scale, of one full wavelength. You may need to tape together several pieces of paper for this drawing.

   c) Frequency times the wavelength is the wave speed. The speed is the same for all frequencies. From your answer to **Part (b)**, what can you predict about the frequencies of the standing waves in the straw pieces?

   d) How well do your predictions from **Part (c)** agree with your observations in this activity?

3. a) What is the length, in meters, of the longest organ pipe?

   b) Assume this pipe is closed at one end. Draw the standing wave pattern.

   c) For this pipe, how long is the wavelength of this standing wave?

   d) Why does a long wavelength indicate that the frequency will be low? Give a reason for your answer.

4. a) Suppose you are listening to the sound of an organ pipe that is closed at one end. The pipe is 3 m long. What is the wavelength of the sound in the pipe?

   b) The speed of sound in air is about 340 m/s. What is the frequency of the sound wave?

   c) Now suppose you are listening to the sound of an organ pipe that is open at both ends. As before, the pipe is 3 m long. What is the wavelength of the sound in the pipe?

   d) What is the frequency of the sound wave?

5. Suppose you listen to the sound of an organ pipe that is closed at one end. This pipe is only 1 m long. How does its frequency compare with the frequency you found in **Question 4, Part (b)**?

6. Waves can spread into a region behind an obstruction.

   a) What is this wave phenomenon called?

   b) Draw a diagram to illustrate this phenomenon.

Stretching Exercises

1. If you have a good musical ear, add water to eight test tubes to make a scale. Play a simple piece for the class.

2. Obtain a two-to-three meter long piece of a seven- to ten-centimeter diameter plastic pipe, like that used to filter water in small swimming pools. In an area free of obstructions, twirl the pipe overhead. What can you say about how the sound is formed? Place some small bits of paper on a stool. Twirl the pipe and keep one end right over the stool. What happens to the paper? What does that tell you about the air flowing through the pipe? Try to play a simple tune by changing the speed of the pipe as you twirl it.

3. Carefully cut new straw pieces, as you did in **For You To Do**, **Step 1**. This time you will measure the frequency of the sound. Set up a frequency meter on your computer. Place the microphone near an open end of the straw. As before, each person blows into only one piece of straw. Make the sound and record the frequency. Now cover the end of the straw and predict what frequency you will measure. Make the measurement and compare it with your prediction. Repeat the measurements for all four lengths of straw. Record your results, and tell what patterns you find.

Activity 4   Making Sound Electronically

GOALS

In this activity you will:

- Identify locations from rectangular coordinates.

- Wire an electronic circuit to produce sound.

- Observe how resistors and capacitors can determine the frequency of an oscillator.

- Observe that sound is produced by vibration.

What Do You Think?

You have seen products, like greeting cards or toys, that produce sound.

- **How is sound produced by these "instruments?"**

- **How expensive and complex could it be to produce sounds this way?**

Record your ideas about these questions in your *Active Physics* log. Be prepared to discuss your responses with your small group and with your class.

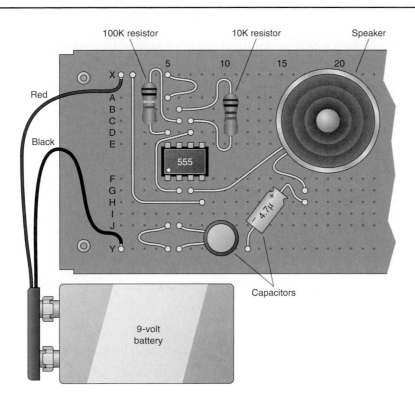

100K resistor   10K resistor   Speaker

Red

Black

555

4.7μ

Capacitors

9-volt
battery

For You To Do

1. Obtain the equipment shown in the diagram from your teacher. Use the diagram to identify each piece.

2. Find the socket board and turn it as shown in the drawing. Look at the diagram. See how each row (across) and each column (up and down) are labeled. Notice that the 555 timer is already shown installed on the board.

   a) In your log, make a drawing of the 555 timer as it is shown above. On your drawing, label the coordinates of each of the corner pins.

3. Find the four connection wires. Be sure that about 1 cm of insulation has been removed from each end. Connect them as follows:

   • Connect one wire from X5 TO A5.

   • Connect one wire from J5 to Y5.

   • Connect one wire from D7 to G6.

   • Connect one wire from X2 to H8.

   When you have finished, compare your wiring with the drawing.

Physics Words

resistor: an electric device used to impede (resist) the flow of electrons in conductors

capacitor: a component of an electrical circuit used to temporarily store charge

4. The **resistors** are small cylinders with colored bands. You can connect them in either direction. Find the resistor with brown, black, and yellow bands. Connect this resistor to D5 and C6.

5. Find the resistor with brown, black, and orange bands. Connect this resistor to B6 and C7.

6. Find the **capacitor** that says 4.7 μ and has a "+" sign at one end and a "−" sign at the other. A capacitor is a small cylinder with two wires coming out of the edge of the disk. Connect the "+" wire to H17. Connect the "−" wire to Y12.

7. Find the other capacitors. These capacitors are disks. Connect one of these capacitors to J6 and Y6.

8. Connect the speaker to G7 and G17.

9. Connect the red wire of the battery clip to X1 and the black wire to Y1.

10. Look at the battery and battery clip. Compare what you see with the drawing. Snap the clip onto the battery, as shown. Observe what happens.

    🖊 a) Record in your log what happens.

11. Return to the circuit board and do the following:

    🖊 a) Go back to the capacitor that you connected to J6 and Y6. Replace this with one of the other capacitors. What happens?

    🖊 b) Replace it with the third capacitor. What happens?
    🖊 c) Switch the two resistors. What happens?
    🖊 d) How do you think the sound wave changed when you changed capacitors or resistors? What did you hear?

12. Make the pitch of the sound as low as you can.

    🖊 a) Which capacitor are you using? Where are the resistors?
    🖊 b) Gently touch the speaker cardboard while the tone is sounding. What do you feel?

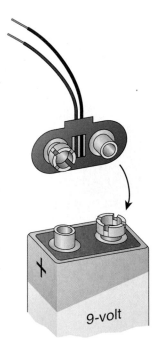

9-volt

FOR YOU TO READ
Good Vibrations

Sound is produced by vibration. The vibration of the speaker produces the sound waves you heard in this activity.

The vibrating speaker moves back and forth. When it moves forward, it compresses the air in front of it and pushes the air molecules closer together, as shown in the drawing. When the speaker moves back, it lets the air molecules move further apart.

The air molecules near the speaker are first moved closer together and then farther apart. Sound is a compressional wave. The air molecules move back and forth along the direction the wave is traveling. The wave moves from the speaker to you. When this wave reaches your ears, you hear the sound the speaker makes.

Reflecting on the Activity and the Challenge

In this activity you have learned how to build a simple **circuit** that produces sounds. You have discovered that by changing the parts, you can control the pitch of the sound. You felt the vibrations in the material of the speaker that produces the sound. With what you have learned about sound, you know that a different pitch means a different frequency. So you have made a device that could be part of a musical instrument, since you can make sounds and control the pitch of the sound. Perhaps you can use this electronics technology in your sound and light show. You might build a circuit with several capacitors connected to push buttons, so the audience could play different notes by pushing these buttons.

Physics To Go

1. a) How did you change your circuit to change the pitch of the sound?

   b) Describe the changes that increased the pitch.
   c) Describe the changes that decreased the pitch.

2. a) In a rock concert, what do you feel in your chest when the bass is playing its lowest notes?

   b) How does that compare to what you felt when you touched the speaker in the above activity?

Physics Words

circuit: a route laid out with wires that connect circuit components along which electrical current flows

circuit diagram: a drawing that uses a special set of symbols to represent the electrical components and wiring in an electric circuit

3. The illustration shows a **circuit diagram** of the circuit you built. This drawing shows the wires

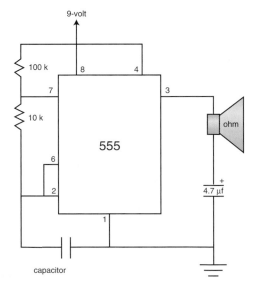

and connections in a special way. Show that the diagram describes the circuit you built.

4. Invent and describe a way in which to replace the capacitors very quickly so that notes can be played in succession.

5. Create a design for an electronic piano where each key produces a different note. Make a list of the materials you will need for this piano. What would be the price you would expect that someone may spend for such an instrument?

Stretching Exercises

1. Work with other groups of students to make a musical instrument out of the circuits that you make in this activity. Find a way to tune each group's circuit so that each one plays a musical note. Perform a tune for the class.

2. Use an oscilloscope to observe the signal that your circuit sends to the speaker. Report your findings to the class.

3. Set up a continuity tester by wiring up a light bulb and a battery. Use your tester to find out which sockets in your socket board are connected together. Make a drawing of the board to show the connections.

Activity 5

Reflected Light

What Do You Think?

Astronauts placed a mirror on the moon in 1969 so that a light beam sent from Earth could be reflected back to Earth. By timing the return of the beam, scientists found the distance between the Earth and the moon. They measured this distance to within 30 cm.

- **How are you able to see yourself in a mirror?**

- **If you want to see more of yourself, what can you do?**

Record your ideas about these questions in your *Active Physics* log. Be prepared to discuss your responses with your small group and with your class.

GOALS

In this activity you will:

- Identify the normal of a mirror.

- Measure angles of incidence and reflection.

- Observe the relationship between the angle of incidence and the angle of reflection.

- Observe changes in the reflections of letters.

- Identify patterns in multiple reflections.

Active Physics

For You To Do

1. Place a piece of paper on your desk. Carefully aim the laser pointer, or the light from a ray box, so the light beam moves horizontally, as shown.

2. Place a glass rod in the light beam so that the beam spreads up-and-down. Shine the beam on the piece of paper to be sure the beam passed through the glass rod.

3. Carefully stand the plane mirror on your desk in the middle of the piece of paper. Draw a line on the paper along the front edge of the mirror. Now remove the mirror and draw a dotted line perpendicular to the first line, as shown. This dotted line is called the **normal.**

⚠ **Do not use mirrors with chipped edges. Make sure the ends of the glass rod are polished.**

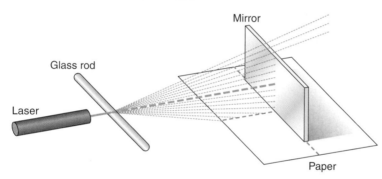

Mirror
Glass rod
Laser
Paper

⚠ **Never look directly at a laser beam or shine a laser beam into someone's eyes. Always work above the plane of the beam and beware of reflections from shiny surfaces.**

4. Aim the light source so the beam approaches the mirror along the normal. Be sure the glass rod is in place to spread out the beam.

🖎 a) What happens to the light after it hits the mirror?

5. Make the light hit the mirror at a different angle.

🖎 a) What happens now?

🖎 b) On the paper, mark three or more dots under the beam to show the direction of the beam as it travels to the mirror. The line you traced shows the *incident ray*. Also make dots to show the light going away from the mirror. This line shows the *reflected ray*. Label this pair of **rays** to show they go together.

6. Turn the light source so it starts from the same point but strikes the mirror at different angles. For each angle, mark dots on the paper to show the direction of the incident and reflected rays. Also, label each pair of rays.

Physics Words

normal: at right angles; perpendicular

ray: the path followed by a very thin beam of light

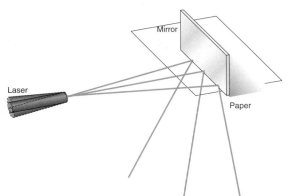

7. Most lab mirrors have the reflecting surface on the back. In addition, the light bends as it enters and leaves the glass part of the mirror. In your drawing, the rays may not meet at the mirror surface. Extend the rays until they do meet.

✎ a) Measure these angles for one pair of your rays.

8. Turn off the light source and remove the paper. Look at one pair of rays. The diagram shows a top view of the mirror, the normal, and an incident and reflected ray. Notice the **angle of incidence** and the **angle of reflection** in the drawing. Using a protractor, measure these angles for one pair of rays.

✎ a) Record your data in a table.

✎ b) Measure and record the angles of incidence and reflection for all of your pairs of rays.

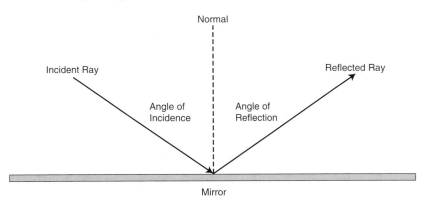

Physics Words

angle of incidence: the angle a ray of light makes with a perpendicular to the surface at the point of incidence

angle of reflection: the angle a reflected ray make with a perpendicular to the surface at the point of reflection

image: the likeness of a physical object formed by a lens, mirror or other optical instrument

reflection: the return of light or sound waves from a surface; the action of bouncing or folding back

✎ c) What is the relationship between the angles of incidence and reflection?

✎ d) Look at the reflected rays in your drawing. Extend each ray back behind the mirror. What do you notice when you have extended all the rays? The position where the rays meet is the location of the **image** of the light source. All of the light rays leave one point in front of the mirror. The reflected rays all seem to emerge from one point behind the mirror. Wherever you observed the **reflection**, you would see the source at this point behind the mirror.

✎ e) Tape a copy of your diagram in your log.

9. Hold the light source, or any object, near the mirror and look at the reflection. Now hold the object far away and again look at the reflection.

a) How is the position of the reflection related to the position of the object?

10. Set up a mirror on another piece of paper, and draw the normal on the paper. Write your name in block capital letters along the normal (a line perpendicular to the mirror). Observe the reflection of your name in the mirror.

a) How can you explain the reflection you see?

b) Which letters in the reflection are closest to the mirror? Which are farthest away?

c) In your log, make a sketch of your name and its reflection.

11. Carefully stand up two mirrors so they meet at a right angle. Be sure they touch each other, as shown in the drawing.

12. Place an object in front of the mirrors.

a) How many images do you see?

b) Slowly change the angle between the mirrors. Make a general statement about how the number of images you see changes as the angle between the mirrors changes.

FOR YOU TO READ

Images in a Plane Mirror

An object like the tip of a nose reflects light in all directions. That is why everybody in a room can see the tip of a nose. Light reflects off a mirror in such a way that the angle of incidence is equal to the angle of reflection. You can look at the light leaving the tip of a nose and hitting a mirror to see how an image is produced and where it is located. Each ray of light leaves the nose at a different angle. Once it hits the mirror, the angle of incidence must equal the angle of reflection. There are now a set of rays diverging from the mirror. If you assume that the light always traveled in straight lines, you can extend these rays behind the mirror and find where they "seem" to emerge from. That is the location of the image.

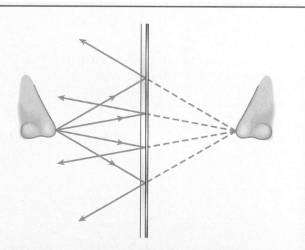

The mirror does such a good job in reflecting that it looks as if there is a tip of a nose (and all other parts of the face) behind the mirror. If you measure the distance of the image behind the mirror, you will find that it is equal to the distance of the nose (object) in front of the mirror. This can also be proven using geometry.

Diffraction of Light

As you begin to study the reflection of light rays, it is worthwhile to recognize that light is a wave and has properties similar to sound waves.

In studying sound waves, you learned that sound waves are compressional or longitudinal. The disturbance is parallel to the direction of motion of the wave. In sound waves, the compression of the air is left and right as the wave travels to the right. We saw a similar compressional wave using the compressed Slinky.

Light waves are transverse waves. They are similar to the transverse waves of the Slinky. In a transverse wave, the disturbance is perpendicular to the direction of the wave. In the Slinky, the disturbance was up and down as the wave traveled to the right. In light, the fields (the disturbance) are perpendicular to the direction of motion of the waves.

You also read that sound waves diffract—they spread out as they emerge from small openings. You can find out if light waves spread out as they emerge from a small opening. Try this. Take a piece of aluminum foil. Pierce the foil with a pin to create a succession of holes, one smaller than the next. Shine the laser beam through each hole and observe its appearance on a distant wall. You will be able to observe the diffraction of light.

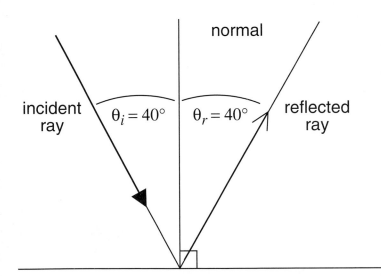

Reflecting on the Activity and the Challenge

In this activity you aimed light rays at mirrors and observed the reflections. From the experiment you discovered that the angle of incidence is equal to the angle of reflection. Therefore, you can now predict the path of a reflected light beam. You also experimented with reflections from two mirrors. When you observed the reflection in two mirrors, you found many images which made interesting patterns.

This activity has given you experience with many interesting effects that you can use in your sound and light show. For instance, you may want to show the audience a reflection in one mirror or two mirrors placed at angles. You can probably create a kaleidoscope. You will also be able to explain the physics concept you use in terms of reflected light.

Physics To Go

1. How is the way light reflects from a mirror similar to the way a tennis ball bounces off a wall?

2. a) What is the normal to a plane mirror?
   b) When a light beam reflects from a plane mirror, how do you measure the angle of incidence?
   c) How do you measure the angle of reflection?
   d) What is the relationship between the angle of incidence and the angle of reflection?

3. Make a top-view drawing to show the relationships among the normal, the angle of incidence, and the angle of reflection.

4. a) Suppose you are experimenting with a mirror mounted vertically on a table, like the one you used in this activity. Make a top-view drawing, with a heavy line to represent the mirror and a dotted line to represent the normal.
   b) Show light beams that make angles of incidence of 0°, 30°, 45°, and 60° to the normal.
   c) For each of the above beams, draw the reflected ray. Add a label if necessary to show where the rays are.

5. a) Stand in front of a mirror.

b) Move your hand toward the mirror. Which way does the reflection move?

c) Move your hand away from the mirror. Which way does the reflection move?

d) Use what you learned about the position of the mirror image to explain your answers to **Parts (b)** and **(c)**.

6. Suppose you wrote the whole alphabet along the normal to a mirror in the way you wrote your name in **Step 10**.

a) Which letters would look just like their reflections?

b) Write three words that would look just like their reflections.

c) Write three letters that would look different from their reflections.

d) Draw the reflection of each letter you gave in **Part (c)**.

7. Why is the word "Ambulance" written in an unusual way on the front of an ambulance?

Stretching Exercises

1. Carefully tape together three small mirrors to make a corner reflector. Shine a flashlight down into the corner. Where does the reflected beam go?

2. Build a kaleidoscope by *carefully* inserting two mirrors inside a paper towel holder. Also, you can use three identical mirrors. Do not force the mirrors into the tube. Tape the edges of the mirrors together, with the mirrored surfaces inside. Describe what you see through your kaleidoscope.

3. Carefully tape together one edge of two mirrors so they can move like a hinge, with the mirrored surfaces facing each other. Place a small object between the mirrors. Investigate how the number of images you see depends on the angle between the mirrors. You will need a protractor to measure this angle. Plot a graph of the results. What mathematical relationship can you find between the angle and the number of images?

Activity 6   Curved Mirrors

GOALS

In this activity you will:

- Identify the focus and focal length of a curved mirror.

- Observe virtual images in a convex mirror.

- Observe real and virtual images in a concave mirror.

- Measure and graph image distance vs. object distance for a convex mirror.

- Summarize observations in a sentence.

What Do You Think?

The curved mirror of the Palomar telescope is five meters across. Mirrors with varying curvatures are used in amusement parks as fun-house mirrors. Store mirrors and car side-view mirrors are also curved.

- **How is what you see in curved mirrors different from ordinary flat mirrors?**

Record your ideas about this question in your *Active Physics* log. Be prepared to discuss your responses with your small group and with your class.

For You To Do

1. Carefully aim a laser pointer, or the light from a ray box, so the light beam moves horizontally, as you did in **Activity 5**. Place a glass rod in the light beam so that the beam spreads up-and-down. See the upper diagram under **Step 3** of the **For You To Do** section in **Activity 5**.

2. Place the convex mirror in the light beam, as shown in the drawing.

3. Shine a beam directly at the center of the mirror. This is the *incident* beam. Show its path by placing three or more dots on the paper, as you did in **Activity 5**. Connect the dots to make a straight line. Find the reflected ray and mark its path in a similar way. Label the two lines so you will know they go together.

4. You will move the light source sideways to make a series of parallel beams. To make sure the incident beams are parallel, line up each one with the dots you made to show the incoming beam in **Step 3**. Mark the path of the incoming ray with three dots.

5. Each parallel beam makes a reflected beam. Show the path of each of these reflected rays. Label each incident and reflected beam so you will know that they go together.

✎ a) Write a sentence to tell what happens to the parallel beams after they are reflected.

✎ b) Make a drawing in your *Active Physics* log to record the path of the light.

6. Remove the mirror. With a ruler, extend each reflected ray backwards to the part of the paper that was behind the mirror.

✎ a) You probably noticed that all the lines converge in a single point. The place where the extended rays meet is called the **focus** of the mirror. The distance from this point to the mirror is called the **focal length**. Measure and record this focal length.

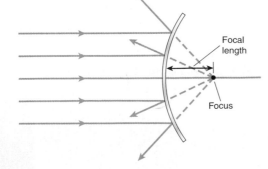

Glass rod

Laser

Paper

⚠ **Never look directly at a laser beam or shine a laser beam into someone's eyes. Always work above the plane of the beam and beware of reflections from shiny surfaces.**

Physics Words

focus: the place at which light rays converge or from which they appear to diverge after refraction or reflection; also call focal point

focal length: the distance from the center of a lens or mirror to its focal point

Focal length

Focus

7. Turn the convex mirror around to form a concave mirror. To help you remember this name, think of the concave mirror as "caving in." Repeat **Steps 3** through **5** for this mirror.

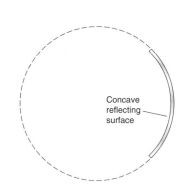

Concave reflecting surface

a) Write a sentence to tell what happens to the parallel beams after they are reflected from the concave mirror.

b) Make a drawing in your *Active Physics* log to record the path of the light. The place where the beams cross is called the focus. The distance from the focus to the mirror is the focal length.

c) Measure and record the focal length.

d) How do concave and convex mirrors reflect light differently? Record your answer in your log.

8. Use a concave mirror that your teacher has supplied. Use a 40-W light bulb or a candle as a light source, which will be called the "object." Carefully mount your mirror so it is at the same height as the light source. Place a light bulb about a meter away from the mirror. Put the bulb slightly off the center line, as shown, so that an index card will not block the light from hitting the mirror.

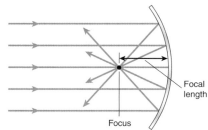

Focal length

Focus

9. Try to find the image of the object on an index card. Move the card back and forth until the image is sharp. The image you found is called a *real* image because you are able to project it on a card.

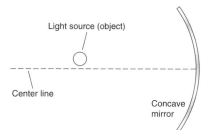

Light source (object)

Center line

Concave mirror

a) Record the distance of the bulb from the mirror and the image on the file card from the mirror. Put your results in the first line of a table like the one below.

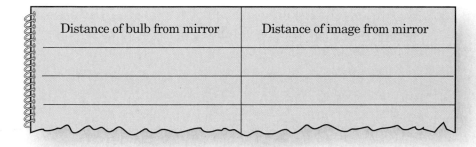

Distance of bulb from mirror	Distance of image from mirror

10. Carefully move the mirror closer to the object. Find the sharp image, as before, by moving the index card back and forth.

a) Record the image and object distances in your table.

b) Repeat the measurement for at least six object locations.

c) Draw a graph of the image distance (*y*-axis) versus the object distance (*x*-axis).

d) Write a sentence that describes the relationship between the image distance and the object distance.

11. A mathematical relation that describes concave mirrors is

$$\frac{1}{f} = \frac{1}{D_o} + \frac{1}{D_i}$$

where

f is the focal length of that particular mirror,

D_o is the object distance

D_i is the image distance

You have measured D_o and D_i. Calculate $\frac{1}{D_o}$ and $\frac{1}{D_i}$. Find their sum for each pair of data.

a) Record your calculations in your log.

b) Are your sums approximately equal? If so, you have mathematically found the value of $\frac{1}{f}$ for the mirror you used.

12. A convex mirror cannot form a real image that can be projected onto a screen. It can form an image behind the mirror, like the plane mirror of **Activity 5**.

a) Record in your log descriptions of the image in a convex mirror when the mirror is held close and when the mirror is held far from the object.

PHYSICS TALK

Making Real Images

To find how a concave mirror makes a real image, you can view a few rays of light. Each ray of light obeys the relation you found for plane mirrors (angle of incidence = angle of reflection). In this case, you choose two easily drawn rays.

Look at the drawing. It shows rays coming into a concave mirror from a point on a light bulb. One ray comes in parallel to the dotted line, which is the axis of the mirror. This ray reflects through the focus. The other ray hits the center of the mirror. This ray reflects and makes the same angle with the mirror axis going out as it did coming in. Where these rays meet is the image of the top of the light bulb.

The next drawing shows the same mirror, but with the object much further from the mirror. Notice how the image in this second drawing is much smaller and much closer to the focus.

As you have seen, the position of the object and image are described by the equation below.

$$\frac{1}{f} = \frac{1}{D_o} + \frac{1}{D_i}$$

Look at the graph of this equation. Notice that as the object distance decreases, the image distance becomes very large. As the object distance increases, the image distance moves toward the focal length (f). Also, notice that neither the object distance nor the image distance can be less than the focal length.

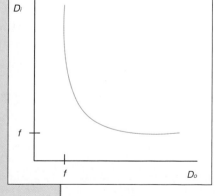

227

Reflecting on the Activity and the Challenge

You have observed how rays of light are reflected by a curved mirror. You have seen that a concave mirror can make an upside-down, real image (an image on a screen). You have also seen that the image and object distances are described by a simple mathematical relationship. You have also seen that there is no real image in a convex mirror, and the image is always smaller than the object.

You may want to use a curved mirror in your sound and light show. You may want to project an image on a screen or produce a reflection that the audience can see in the mirror. What you have learned will help you explain how these images are made.

Since the image changes with distance, you may try to find a way to have a moving object so that the image will automatically move and change size. A ball suspended by a string in front of a mirror may produce an interesting effect. You may also wish to combine convex and concave mirrors so that some parts of the object are larger and others are smaller. Mylar could be shaped to make some kind of fun-house mirror.

Remember that your light show will be partially judged by creativity and part will be judged by the application of physics principles. This activity has provided you with some useful principles that can help with both criteria.

Physics To Go

1. a) Make a drawing of parallel laser beams aimed at a convex mirror.
   b) Draw lines to show how the beams reflect from the mirror.

2. a) Make a drawing of parallel laser beams aimed at a concave mirror.
   b) Draw lines to show how the beams reflect from the mirror.

3. a) Look at the back of the spoon. What do you see?
   b) Look at the inside of the spoon. What do you see?

228

4. a) If you were designing a shaving mirror, would you make it concave or convex? Explain your answer.
   b) Why do some make-up mirrors have two sides? What do the different sides do? How does each side produce its own special view?
   c) How does a curved side mirror on a car produce a useful view? How can this view sometimes be dangerous?
   d) Why does a dentist use a curved mirror?

5. a) A student found the real image of a light bulb in a concave mirror. The student moved the light bulb to different positions. At each position, the student measured the position of the image and the light bulb. The results are shown in the table on the right. Draw a graph of this data.
   b) Make a general statement to summarize how the image distance changes as the object distance changes.
   c) If the object were twice as far away as the greatest object distance in the data, estimate where the image would be.
   d) If the object were only half as far from the mirror as the smallest object distance in the data, estimate what would happen to the image.

D_i (cm)	D_o (cm)
549	15
56	25
20	50
18	91
14	142

6. A ball is hung on a string in front of a flat mirror. The ball swings toward the mirror and back. How would the image of the ball in the mirror change as the ball swings back and forth?

7. a) A ball is hung on a string in front of a concave mirror. The ball swings toward the mirror and back. How would the image of the ball in the mirror change as the ball swings back and forth?
   b) How could you use this swinging ball in your light show?

8. Outdoors at night, you use a large concave mirror to make an image on a card of distant auto headlamps. You make the image on a card. What happens to the image as the car gradually comes closer?

Activity 7   Refraction of Light

GOALS

In this activity you will:

• Observe refraction.

• Measure angles of incidence and refraction.

• Measure the critical angle.

• Observe total internal reflection.

What Do You Think?

The Hope Diamond is valued at about 100 million dollars. A piece of cut glass of about the same size is worth only a few dollars.

• **How can a jeweler tell the difference between diamond and cut glass?**

Record your ideas about this question in your *Active Physics* log. Be prepared to discuss your responses with your small group and with your class.

For You To Do

1. Place an acrylic block on a piece of white paper.

2. Carefully aim a laser pointer, or the light from a ray box, so the light beam moves horizontally, as you did in **Activity 5**. Place a glass rod in the light beam so that the beam spreads up-and-down. See the upper diagram under **Step 3** of the **For You To Do** section in **Activity 5**.

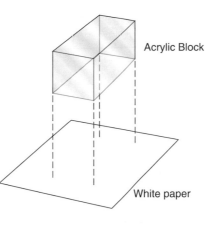

Acrylic Block

White paper

⚠ **Never look directly at a laser beam or shine a laser beam into someone's eyes. Always work above the plane of the beam and beware of reflections from shiny surfaces.**

3. Shine the laser pointer or light from the ray box through the acrylic block. Be sure the beam leaves the acrylic block on the side opposite the side the beam enters. Mark the path of each beam. You may wish to use a series of dots as you did in **Activity 5**. Label each path on both sides of the acrylic block so you will know that they go together.

4. The angle of incidence is the angle between the incident laser beam and the normal, as shown in the diagram. Choose two other angles of incidence and again mark the path of the light, as you did in **Step 3**. As before, label each pair of paths.

5. Trace the outline of the acrylic block on the paper, and remove the acrylic block. Connect the paths you traced to show the light beam entering the acrylic block, traveling through the acrylic block and emerging from the acrylic block. Draw a perpendicular line at the point where a ray enters or leaves the acrylic block. Label this line the normal.

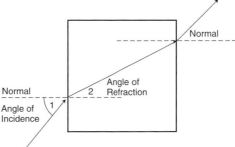

Normal

Angle of Refraction

Normal

Angle of Incidence

Physics Words

critical angle: the smallest angle of incidence at which a light ray passing from one medium to another can be totally reflected

index of refraction: a property of a medium that is related to the speed of light through it; it is calculated by dividing the speed of light in vacuum by the speed of light in the medium

angle of refraction: the angle a refracted ray makes with the perpendicular to the surface separating the two media traversed by the ray

Snell's Law: describes the relationship between the index of refraction and the ratio of the sine of the angle of incidence and the sine of the angle of refraction

6. Measure the angles of incidence (the angle in the air) and refraction (the angle in the acrylic block).

a) Record your measurements in tables like the one shown.

Angle of incidence	Angle of refraction	Sine of angle of incidence	Sine of angle of refraction	$\dfrac{\sin \angle i}{\sin \angle R}$

b) Use a calculator to complete the chart by finding the sines of the angles (sin button on calculator).

c) Is the value of $\dfrac{\sin \angle i}{\sin \angle R}$ a constant? This value is called the index of refraction for the acrylic block.

7. Set up the acrylic block on a clean sheet of white paper. This time, as shown in the drawing, aim the beam so it leaves the acrylic block on the side, rather than at the back.

8. Make the first angle of incidence (angle 1) as small as possible, so the second angle of incidence (angle 2) will be as large as possible. Adjust angle 1 so that the beam leaves the acrylic block parallel to the side of the acrylic block, as shown. Measure the value of angle 2.

a) Record the value of angle 2. It is called the **critical angle**.

b) What happens to the beam if you make angle 2 greater than the critical angle?

c) What you observed in **Part (b)** is called "total internal reflection." What is reflected totally, and where?

9. It is possible to bend a long, rectangular acrylic block so the light enters the narrow end of the acrylic block, reflects off one side of the acrylic block, then reflects off the other and back again to finally emerge from the other narrow end. Try to bend an acrylic block rectangle so that the light is reflected as described.

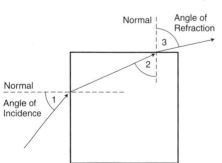

FOR YOU TO READ

Snell's Law

Light refracts (bends) when it goes from air into another substance. This is true whether the other substance is gelatin, glass, water or diamond. The amount of bending is dependent on the material that the light enters. Each material has a specific index of refraction, *n*. This **index of refraction** is a property of the material and is one way in which a diamond (very high index of refraction—lots of bending) can be distinguished from glass (lower index of refraction—less bending). The index of refraction is a ratio of the sine of the angle of incidence and the sine of the **angle of refraction.**

Index of refraction: $n = \dfrac{\sin \angle i}{\sin \angle R}$

This equation is referred to as **Snell's Law.**

As light enters a substance from air, the light bends toward the normal. When light leaves a substance and enters air, it bends away from the normal. If the light is entering air from a substance, the angle in that substance may be such that the angle of refraction is 90°. In this special case, the angle in the substance is called the critical angle. If the angle in the substance is greater than this critical angle, then the light does not enter the air but reflects back into the substance as if the surface were a perfect mirror. This is the basis for light fibers where laser light reflects off the inner walls of glass and travels down the fiber, regardless of the bend in the fiber.

Reflecting on the Activity and the Challenge

The bending of light as it goes from air into a substance or from a substance into air is called **refraction** It is mathematically expressed by Snell's Law. When light enters the substance at an angle, it bends toward the normal. When light leaves the substance at an angle, it bends away from the normal. As you create your light show for the **Chapter Challenge**, you may find creative uses of refraction. You may decide to have light bending in such a way that it spells out a letter or word or creates a picture. You may wish to have the light travel from air into glass to change its direction. You may have it bend by different amounts by replacing one material with another. Regardless of how you use refraction effects, you can now explain the physics principles behind them.

Physics To Go

1. A light ray goes from air into acrylic block. In general, which is larger, the angle of incidence or the angle of refraction?

2. a) Make a sketch of a ray of light as it enters a piece of acrylic block and is refracted.

   b) Now turn the ray around so it goes backwards. What was the angle of refraction is now the angle of incidence. Does the turned-around ray follow the path of the original ray?

3. A light ray enters acrylic block from air. Make a diagram to show the angle of incidence, the angle of refraction, and the normal at the edge of the acrylic block.

4. Light rays enter the acrylic block from air. Make drawings to show rays with angles of incidence of 30° and 60°. For each incident ray, sketch the refracted ray that passes through the acrylic block.

5. a) Light is passing from air into an acrylic block. What is the maximum possible angle of incidence that will permit light to pass into the acrylic block?

   b) Make a sketch to show your answer for **Part (a)**. Include the refracted ray (inside the acrylic block) in your sketch.

6. a) A ray of light is already inside an acrylic block and is heading out. What is the name of the maximum possible angle of incidence that will permit the light to pass out of the acrylic block?

   b) If you make the angle of incidence in **Part (a)** greater than this special angle, what happens to the light?

   c) Make a sketch to show your answer for **Part (b)**. Be sure to show what happened to the light.

7. a) Make a drawing of a light ray that enters the front side of a rectangular piece of acrylic block and leaves through the back side.

   b) What is the relationship between the direction of the ray that enters the acrylic block and the direction of the ray that leaves the acrylic block?

   c) Use geometry, and your answer to **Question 2 (b)**, to prove your answer to **Part 7 (b)**.

234

8. You have seen the colored bands that a prism or cut glass or water produce from sunlight. Light that you see as different colors has different wavelengths. Since refraction makes these bands, what can you say about the way light of different wavelengths refracts?

Stretching Exercises

1. Cover the acrylic block with a red filter. Shine a red laser beam into the acrylic block, as you did in **For You To Do**, **Steps 1** through **3**. What happens? How can you explain what happens?

2. Find some $\frac{1}{2}$" diameter clear tubing, about 2 m long. Plug one end. Pour clear gelatin in the other end, through a funnel, before the gelatin has had time to set. Arrange the tubing into an interesting shape and let the gelatin set. You may wish to mount your tube on a support or a sturdy piece of cardboard, which can be covered with interesting reflective material. Fasten one end of the tube so laser light can easily shine straight into it. When the gelatin has set, turn on the laser. What do you see?
   This phenomena is called total internal reflection.

3. Place a penny in the bottom of a dish or glass. Position your eye so you can just see the penny over the rim of the glass. Predict what will happen when you fill the glass with water. Then try it and see what happens. How can you explain the results?

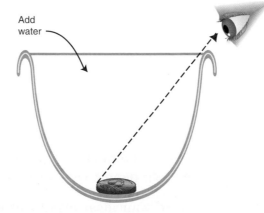

Add water

4. Place an empty, clear drinking glass over a piece of a newspaper. When you look through the side of the glass near the bottom, you can see the printing on the newspaper. What do you think will happen if you fill the glass with water? Try it and see. How can you explain the result? Does it help to hold your fingers over the back of the glass?

Activity 8   Effect of Lenses on Light

GOALS

In this activity you will:

• Observe real images.

• Project a slide.

• Relate image size and position.

What Do You Think?

Engineers have created special lenses that can photograph movie scenes lit only by candlelight.

• **How is a lens able to project movies, take photographs, or help people with vision problems?**

Record your ideas about this question in your *Active Physics* log. Be prepared to discuss your responses with your small group and with your class.

For You To Do

1. Look at the **lens** your teacher has given you.

✎ a) Make a side-view drawing of this lens in your log. This is a *convex* lens.

2. Point the lens at a window or at something distant outside. Use a file card as a screen. Look for the image on the file card. Move it back and forth until you see a sharp image of the distant object.

✎ a) Describe what you see. Is the image large or small? Is it right-side-up or upside-down? Is it reversed left-to-right? This image is called "real" because you can project it on the screen.

Focus

Focal length

3. Measure the distance between the image and the lens. If the object is very far away, this distance is the focal length of the lens. The position of this image is the focus of the lens. It is the same location that parallel rays of light would converge.

✎ a) Approximate the object distance.

✎ b) Measure the image distance.

✎ c) Record your object and image distance. Note that the image distance is also the focal length of the lens.

Physics Words

lens: a curved, ground and polished piece of glass or other transparent material used for the refraction of light

4. Set up a 40-W light bulb or a candle to be a light source. Mount the lens at the same height as the light source. If you are using a light bulb, point it right at the lens, as shown.

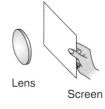

Lens

Screen

Light

⚠ **Do not use lenses with chipped edges. Mount lenses securely in a holder. Use only light sources with enclosed or covered electrical contacts. Keep flammables/combustibles away from the candle holder.**

5. Place the light bulb about a meter away from the lens. Try to find the image of the light bulb on a screen. The screen can be a file card or a sheet of paper.

a) Record your results in a table including the distance and appearance of the image.

6. Adjust the position of the object to create a larger image.

a) Describe how the position of the object, the image, and the size of the image have changed. Record the results. in a table.

7. Create an object by carefully cutting a hole in the shape of an arrow in an index card. Have someone in your group hold the card close to the light bulb.

a) Can you see the object on the screen? Describe what you see.

b) Have the person holding the object move it around between the light bulb and the convex lens. What happens?

8. Project the object onto the wall. Can you make what you project larger or smaller?

a) In your log indicate what you did to change the size of the image.

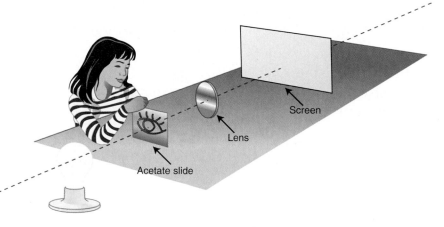

Screen

Lens

Acetate slide

9. Create a slide by drawing with a marking pen on clear acetate. Try placing a 100-W light bulb and the slide in different positions.

a) Describe how you can project a real, enlarged image of your slide onto a screen or wall.

b) How can you use the lens to change the size of the image?

c) Explore the effect of different lenses. In your log record how you think this effect might be part of your light and sound show.

Caution: Lamps get very hot. Be careful not to touch the bulb or housing surrounding the bulb.

Lens Ray Diagrams

You are probably more familiar with images produced by lenses than you are with images from curved mirrors. The lens is responsible for images of slides, overhead projectors, cameras, microscopes, and binoculars.

Light bends as it enters glass and bends again when it leaves the glass. The **converging lens** is constructed so that all parallel rays of light will bend in such a way that they meet at a location past the lens. This place is the *focal point*.

Physics Words

converging lens: a parallel beam of light passing through the lens is brought to a real point or focus (convex lens)

principal axis: the line drawn through the point of sight perpendicular to the perspective plane

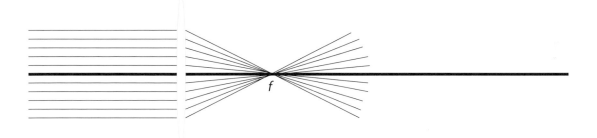

If an object is illuminated, it reflects light in all directions. If these rays of light pass through a lens, an image is formed.

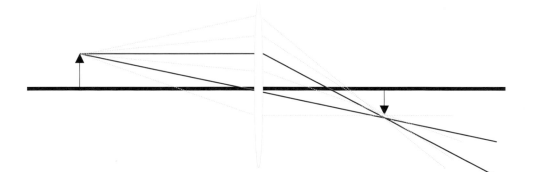

Although all of the light rays from the object help to form the image, you can locate an image by looking at two easy rays to draw—the ray that is parallel to the **principal axis** and travels through the focal point and the ray that travels through the center of the lens undeflected. (These rays are in red in the diagram.)

You can use this technique to see how images that are larger (movie projector), smaller (camera), and the same size (copy machine) as the object can be created.

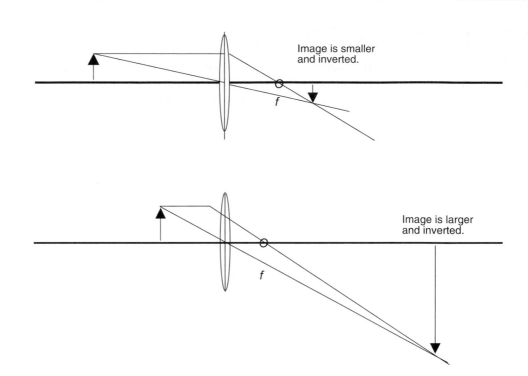

Image is smaller
and inverted.

f

Image is larger
and inverted.

f

If the object is close to the lens (an object distance smaller than
the focal distance), then an image is not formed. However, if
you were to view the rays emerging, they would appear to have
come from a place on the same side of the lens as the object. To
view this image, you put your eye on the side of the lens
opposite the object and peer through it—it's a magnifying glass!

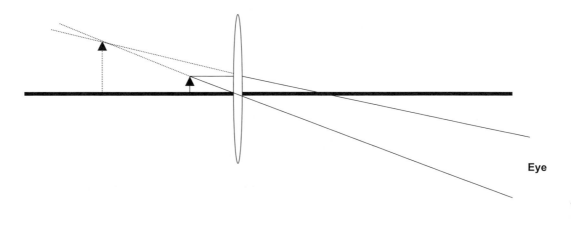

Eye

Reflecting on the Activity and the Challenge

You have explored how convex lenses make real images. You have found these images on a screen by moving a card back and forth until the image was sharp and clear, so you know that they occur at a particular place. Bringing the object near the lens moves the image away from the lens and enlarges the image, but if the object is too close to the lens, there is no real image. Also, these images are reversed left-to-right and are upside-down. You may be able to use this kind of image in your sound and light show. Also, you have projected images of slides on a wall. You may be able to add interest by moving the lens and screen to change the size of these images.

Physics To Go

1. a) What is the focus of a lens?
   b) If the image of an object is at the focus on a lens, where is the object located?
   c) What is the focal length of a lens?
   d) How can you measure the focal length of a lens?

2. a) You set up a lens and screen to make an image of a distant light. Is the image in color?
   b) Is the image right-side-up or upside-down?
   c) Did the lens bend light to make this image? How can you tell?
   d) A distant light source begins moving toward a lens. What must you do to keep the image sharp?

3. a) You make an image of a light bulb. What can you do to make the image smaller than the light bulb?
   b) What can you do to make the image larger than the light bulb?

4. a) You have two lights, a lens, and a screen, as shown. One light is at a great distance from the lens. The other light is much closer. If you see a sharp image of the distant light, describe the image of the closer light.
   b) If you see a sharp image of the closer light, describe the image of the more distant light.

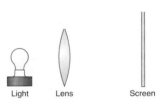

Light   Light   Lens   Screen

c) Could you see a sharp image of both lights at the same time? Explain how you found your answer.

5. Research how a camera works. Find out where the image is located. Also find out how the lens changes so that you can photograph a distant landscape and also photograph people close-up.

Stretching Exercises

1. To investigate how the image position depends on the object position, find a convex lens, a white card, and a light source. Find the image of the light source, and measure the image and object distance from the lens. Make these measurements for as wide a range of object distances as you can. In addition, make an image of an object outside, like a tree. Estimate the distance to the tree. The image of a distant object, like the tree, is located very near the focus of the lens. Draw a graph of the results. Compare the graph with the equation

$$\frac{1}{f} = \frac{1}{D_o} + \frac{1}{D_i}$$

2. Find a camera with a shutter that you can keep open (with a bulb or time setting). Place a piece of wax paper or a piece of a plastic bag behind the lens, where the film would be if you took a picture. Find the image and compare it to the images you made in this activity. Focus the lens for objects at different distances. Investigate how well the object and image location fit the lens equation $\frac{1}{f} = \frac{1}{D_o} + \frac{1}{D_i}$.

Remember that the focal length of the lens is typically printed on the lens.

3. Research how the concept of "depth of field" is important in photography. Report to the class on what you learn.

Activity 9   Color

GOALS

In this activity you will:

- Analyze shadow patterns.
- Explain the size of shadows.
- Predict pattern of colored shadows.
- Observe combinations of colored lights.

What Do You Think?

When a painter mixes red and green paint, the result is a dull brown. But when a lighting designer in a theater shines a red and a green light on an actress, the actress' skin looks bright yellow.

- **How could these two results be so different?**

- **How are the colors you see produced?**

Record your ideas about these questions in your *Active Physics* log. Be prepared to discuss your responses with your small group and with your class.

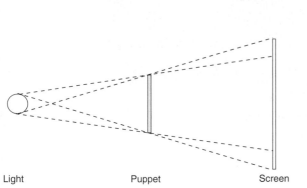

Light   Puppet   Screen

⚠ **Caution:**
Lamps get very hot. Be careful not to touch the bulb or housing surrounding the bulb.

For You To Do

1. Carefully cut out a cardboard puppet that you will use to make shadows.

2. Turn on a white light bulb only. Move the puppet around and observe the shadow.

  🖎 a) Describe the shadow you see.

  🖎 b) What happens to the shadow if you move the puppet sideways or up-and-down?

  🖎 c) What happens to the shadow if you move the puppet close to the screen?

  🖎 d) What happens to the shadow if you move the puppet close to the bulb?

3. Look at the drawing. It shows a top view of a puppet halfway between the light and the screen.

  🖎 a) Make a copy of this drawing in your log. Draw light rays going from the light to the screen. (Light rays will go in straight lines in all directions from all parts of the light.)

  🖎 b) Use the top-view drawing you drew to answer these questions: Which part of the screen receives light? Which part receives no light? Which part receives some light?

  🖎 c) Is the shadow larger or smaller than the puppet? Explain how you found your answer.

  🖎 d) Now copy the other two top-view drawings and show the path of the light rays.

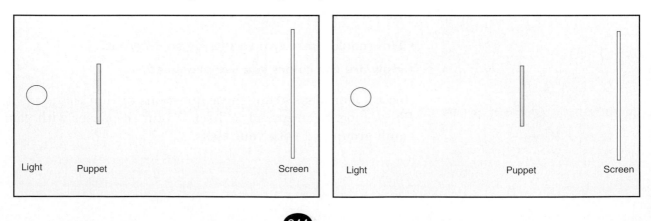

Active Physics

e) On your drawings, show which part of the screen does receive light and which part does not receive light and which part receives some light.

f) For each of these two drawings, tell if the shadow is larger or smaller than the puppet. For each one, explain how you found your answer.

4. Turn off the white bulb. Turn on the red and green bulbs. They should be aimed right at the center of the screen.

a) What color do you see on the screen?

b) Predict what color the shadows will be if you bring your puppet between the bulbs and the screen. Record your prediction, and give a reason for it.

c) Make a top-view drawing to show the path of the light rays from the red and green bulbs.

d) On your drawing, label the color you will see on each part of the screen.

5. Turn off the green bulb and turn on the blue one. Repeat what you did in the previous **Step 4**, but with the blue and red bulbs lit.

6. Turn off the red bulb and turn on the green one. Repeat what you did in **Step 4**, but with the blue and green bulbs lit.

7. Turn on the red bulb so all three—red, blue, and green—are lit. Repeat what you did in **Steps 5** and **6**.

Reflecting on the Activity and the Challenge

Different colored lights can combine to make white light. When an object blocks all light it creates a dark shadow. Since some light comes from all parts of the bulb, there are places where the shadow is black (no light) and places where the shadow is gray (some light reaches this area.) An object illuminated by different colored lights can create shadows which prevent certain colors from reaching the wall and allowing other colors to pass by.

In your light show creation, you may choose to use the ideas of colored shadows to show how lights can add to produce interesting combinations of colors. By moving the object or the lights during the show, you may be able to produce some interesting effects. Lighting design is used in all theater productions. It requires a knowledge and understanding of how lights work, as well as an aesthetic sense of what creates an enjoyable display.

Physics To Go

1. Show how a shadow is created.

2. How can moving the light, the object, and the screen all produce the effect of enlarging the shadow?

3. Explain why a gray halo surrounds a dark shadow made by a light bulb and an object.

4. a) Why is your shadow different at different times of the day?
   b) What is the position of the. Sun when your shadow is the longest? The shortest?

5. Why is the gray halo about your shadow so thin when you are illuminated by the Sun?

6. a) Suppose you shine a red light on a screen in a dark room. The result is a disk of red light. Now you turn on a green light and a blue light. The three disks of light overlap as shown. Copy the diagram into your journal. Label the color you will see in each part of the diagram.

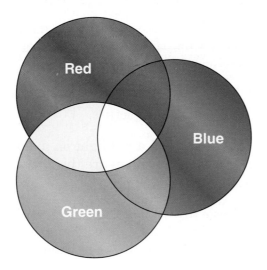

b) Add the labels "bright", "brighter", and "brightest" to describe what you would see in each part of your diagram.

7. a) Make a drawing of an object in red light. The object casts a shadow on the screen. Label the color of the shadow and the rest of the screen.

   b) Repeat **Part (a)** for an object in green light.

   c) Now make a copy of your drawing for **Part (b)**. Add a red light, as in **Part (a)**. Label the color of all the shadows.

8. List some imaginative ways that you can add colors to your light show.

Stretching Exercises

1. With the room completely dark, shine a red light on various colored objects. Compare the way they look in red light with the way they look in ordinary room light.

2. View 3-D pictures with red and blue glasses. Explain how each eye sees a different picture.

3. Shine a white light and a red light on a small object in front of a screen. What colors are the shadows? How is this surprising?

4. Prepare a large drawing of the American flag but with blue-green in the place of red, and yellow in the place of blue. Stare at the drawing for 30 s and then look at a white surface.

Alicja and Dennis Phipps

Alicja Phipps has always been interested in electronics. As a child she wanted to be a television repair person. She now works along with her husband, Dennis Phipps, in their company Light & Sound Entertainment which designs original content programming in a variety of areas—from rock concerts to the Olympics.

Light & Sound Entertainment got its name because Dennis believes strongly that the two are, and should be linked. "It's terrible when the music of a production does not match what you are seeing," he says. "More and more theaters have lighting specialists come in and set up the theater with everything preset on a computerized lighting board. There will be a setting for 'outdoor lighting' and 'nighttime' or 'sunset'. The problem with that is that every production will look the same when in reality nighttime in Canada looks very different from nighttime in Florida. There are also different lighting considerations depending on your audience. A production in front of a live audience needs different lighting than one being recorded on video. For instance, the human eye picks up shadows a lot better than a camera will. If a production is intended for both a live audience and video, lighting needs to be arranged accordingly."

"The sound of a production is only as good as its setup," he continues, "and nothing can replace the actual setting. The Red Rocks Theater in Colorado is terrific, for example, because stone has a very high reverberation rate which is great for guitars. A huge wooden room like Carnegie Hall also provides a unique sound. However these spaces and materials are not readily available." The hardest projects, Dennis says, are those in which you cannot control the elements. "Sound elements include the size and shape of the space, reverberation, feedback, and temperature."

"New media," explains Alicja who oversees the conversion of live events into various other formats such as CD-ROMs, virtual reality, and web sites, "has its own set of challenges. We have to think about how much information (sound and image) we will be able to fit on a disc or on to a web page and how long it will take to load. If it takes too long no one will ever see or hear what we've done."

"We enjoy the creative process of every production," claim Alicja and Dennis, "each one is a unique challenge."

Chapter 4 Assessment

With what you learned about sound and light in this chapter you are now ready to dazzle the world. However, you have neither the funds nor the technology available to professionals. All sounds you use to capture the interest of the class must come from musical instruments that you build yourself, or from human voices. Some of these sounds may be prerecorded and then played in your show. If your teacher has a laser and is willing to allow you to use it, you may do so. All other light must come from conventional household lamps. Gather with your committee to design a two- to four-minute sound and light show to entertain other students your age.

Review the criteria by which you decided that your show will be evaluated. The following suggestions were provided at the beginning of the chapter:

1. The variety and number of physics concepts used to produce the light and sound effects.

2. Your understanding of the physics concepts:
   a) Name the physics concepts that you used.
   b) Explain each concept.
   c) Give an example of something that each concept explains or an example of how each concept is used.
   d) Explain why each concept is important.

3. Entertainment value.

At this time you may wish to propose changes in the criteria. Also, decide as a class if you wish to modify or keep the point value you established at the beginning of the chapter.

Enjoy the sound and light productions!

Physics You Learned

Compressional and transverse waves

Wave speed = wavelength × frequency

Standing waves

Pitch and frequency

Sound production in pipes and vibrating strings

Controlling frequency of sounds produced electronically

Angle of incidence and angle of reflection

Location of image in plane and curved mirrors

$$\frac{1}{f} = \frac{1}{D_o} + \frac{1}{D_i} \text{ in curved mirrors}$$

Real images

Angle of incidence and angle of refraction

Lenses and image formation

$$\frac{1}{f} = \frac{1}{D_o} + \frac{1}{D_i} \text{ in lenses}$$

Color addition

$$n = \frac{\sin\angle i}{\sin\angle R}$$

Chapter 5

5

Long-Distance Communication

Scenario

You are always communicating with others. You talk to your friends at school. You call them on the telephone. You may show photographs of special events or people to them. You may send letters or e-mail, to those who have moved away. Or, you may have made new friends, many miles distant, by communicating through the Internet.

No matter how you communicate, you require a code. Language and pictures are codes you learn from an early age. Talking may feel as natural to you as breathing. But many years ago you had to learn to translate your thoughts and feelings into a code that those close to you could understand. In order to communicate with others you are continually translating your thoughts from one code to another. Code and communication are forever linked.

Challenge

1. You are a member of a team of engineers who is developing a communications system. The system must communicate from one room to the next. Since this system is a model for long-distance communication, assume that the other room is far away. Yelling and waving will not work. The requirement is that you are able to send and receive a message. You will have to divide your team into senders and receivers, with the receivers in the other room. You will have about five minutes to set up your system before you test it to meet the requirement. During the test, you must measure the speed of transmission of your system.

In this test, the message you will communicate will be simple and brief and may include either text, picture, music, or a combination of these.

After a successful test, each team member will submit a written report about the system. This report will have the following parts:

a) the design of the system;
b) how your method of communication is better for this challenge than the other methods you investigated in this chapter;
c) the physics of your system;
d) your measurement of the speed of transmission in words per minute, symbols per minute, or notes per minute.

2. Every day you hear about the Internet. It seems every business and many people have Web pages and e-mail accounts. You can buy books, CDs, or plane tickets on the Internet. You can even bank and buy and sell stocks on the Internet. The Internet is a busy place with a lot of money changing hands. Write an essay that deals with either of the following concerns:

a) As more people use the Internet for shopping, banking, and business, criminals may use the Internet too. What kind of crime might happen on the Internet? What can be done to prevent people from "listening in" or from stealing information? Who should prevent it?
b) Society has decided that some books and movies are not right for children. There are no such restrictions on the Internet. Should children use the Internet as they wish, without any limits? Or should they be restricted in some way? How could these limits be set up? Who should decide?

Criteria

As a class, discuss how you wish your work to be evaluated. You can use the following criteria, with suggested point values, as a starting point in your discussion.

Your communication system will be graded in two ways:

A grade will be assigned to the speed and quality of the transmission. You can determine the speed and quality by recording how much of the message was correctly transmitted.   40 points

The quality of your written report will also be graded.   60 points

a) explanation of design (including drawings)   15 points
b) how your method is better than others you thought of   15 points
c) the physics of your system   25 points
d) your measurement of the speed of transmission of your system   5 points

Your essay will be graded mainly on how well you present the social issues. If you add helpful technical information about the Internet, that can earn additional credit. With your class members, decide on a marking scheme for your essay.

Activity 1 Using Waves to Communicate

GOALS

In this activity you will:

- Observe water waves.
- Observe transmitted and reflected pulse on a spring.
- Transmit vocal sounds over stretched spring.
- Send a message in code.
- Predict how far a message can be sent.

What Do You Think?

A substantial prize was offered fifty years ago for the first person who could develop a new language. Nobody has yet been able to claim that prize.

- **How are animals able to communicate?**
- **Would their communication satisfy your definition of language?**

Record your ideas about these questions in your *Active Physics* log. Be prepared to discuss your responses with your small group and with your class.

For You To Do

1. Fill a styrofoam cup with water to about 5 cm of the top. Add a few drops of food coloring and mix. Float a tiny piece of paper in the styrofoam cup. When the water is calm, touch the center of the water surface with the tip of a pen or pencil. Observe the pulse and the piece of paper.

a) What is the shape of the pulse?

b) What happens to the piece of paper as the pulse passes by?

2. With a partner, stretch out a Slinky on a cleared area of the floor. Have your partner hold the other end of the Slinky firmly, so it cannot move. Make a pulse by snapping your end of the spring back and forth along the floor, like cracking a whip.

a) What happens to the pulse when it reaches the other end of the spring?

b) How is the reflected pulse similar to the original pulse? How is it different?

c) Which way does the pulse move?

d) Imagine you put a small piece of tape on one part of the spring. How does the tape move as the pulse goes by?

e) Once the wave has passed, what has happened to the Slinky? How has it changed from before the pulse went by?

3. With your partner, figure out a way to send a message on the Slinky. The message can be as simple as "yes" or "no," or "0" or "1." It can be as complex as an idea or an emotion. You may need to make a code to deliver your message.

a) State the message you are going to send.

b) Give the message in the code you use.

c) Describe how the message is transmitted.

d) Tell how the receiver converts the code to the message.

e) What is difficult about sending the message?

f) Measure the time required to send the message.

4. To try another way to send a message, make cup phones. Take two plastic cups and a 4-m long string. Carefully punch a small hole in the bottom of each cup and push one end of the string through the hole. Tie a knot in each end of the string.

5. Walk away from your partner until the string is tight. Hold your hands around the cup so your partner can't hear you directly.

✎ a) When you talk, what does your partner hear through the cup phone held up to their ear?

6. Now create a message and try to send it with the cup phone. Take turns talking and listening.

✎ a) Are you able to hear the message?

✎ b) How well is the message transmitted?

✎ c) How does changing the string tension change the quality of the transmission?

✎ d) Do soft sounds transmit as well as loud sounds?

✎ e) If you coded your message, describe the code.

✎ f) Try to modify the cup phone to improve the quality of the transmission.

✎ g) Measure the time required to send your message.

7. Make a code for your cup phone so you can send a message without using your voice. Compare communication using the code with communication using voice.

✎ a) How does communicating using a code differ?

✎ b) How far could a cup phone transmit a message? Make a prediction. Record what you think will happen.

8. Test your prediction from **Step 7**.

✎ a) Record the result.

9. Use a third cup and string to eavesdrop on a message that is being transmitted on the cup phone.

✎ a) How well does the third cup work?

✎ b) Can the receiver and sender detect if their call is being monitored?

Reflecting on the Activity and the Challenge

In this activity you were able to invent a code and transmit messages using that code. In transmitting the code along the Slinky, you observed that the Slinky remained in the same place after the message was transmitted. In the cup phone, you used an existing code, language, and transmitted the message. Once again, the cup phone remained in the same place while the message traveled from one cup to another. You also investigated the properties of Slinkys and cup phones in order to find out how to optimize their performance. Finally, you tried to eavesdrop using a third cup.

In the **Chapter Challenge** you will be required to send a message from one room to another. The Slinky or cup phone may work with modification. As you learn other techniques for transmitting messages, you will begin to understand when Slinkys and cup phones are the best technology. The challenge also requires you to write an essay about secrecy on the Internet. Your experience with eavesdropping in a cup phone may provide some help with this essay.

Physics To Go

1. a) You are wading in a river and watching water waves washing over your feet. If one wave washes over your feet every two seconds, what is the number of the waves per second?

   b) You watch the waves out on the river before they hit your feet. The distance from one wave crest to the next crest is 5 m. Predict the speed of this wave.

2. a) In **For You To Do**, you made a pulse on the Slinky. What happened to the pulse when it reflected from one end of the Slinky?

   b) Predict how a water wave would reflect if the wave hit a sea wall.

   c) Run a little water in a bathtub. Push the water to make a "pulse," and watch what happens when the pulse hits the end of the tub. How does your prediction compare to what happened?

   d) Does the water pulse reflect in the same way as the Slinky pulse?

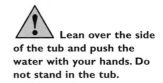

Lean over the side of the tub and push the water with your hands. Do not stand in the tub.

Integrated Coordinated Science for the 21st Century

3. When the Slinky pulse moved past a point on the Slinky, the spring moved from its normal position and then returned. Compare this movement of the spring with the movement of water when a wave passes by.

4. Compare the cup phone to a telephone. How are they similar? How are they different?

5. Predict what would happen if you changed the size of the cup on the cup phone. How could you test your prediction?

6. You may have heard of a washtub bass. In this instrument, a metal washtub sits upside down on the ground. A single metal string is fastened to the top of a metal washtub. The performer plucks this string. How is a washtub bass similar to a cup phone? How is it different?

7. Compare your code for the Slinky with your speech for the cup phone. Describe two advantages for each code.

8. What limits the speed of sending code through the Slinky? How can you improve the speed?

9. When the "eavesdropping" cup was added to the cup phone, was this apparent to the other people? Is there a way to prevent this type of eavesdropping with cup phones?

10. a) Do you think that people eavesdrop on your telephone calls? Why or why not?
    b) What should be the penalty for eavesdropping?

11. Military secrets are sent from one place to another. How do you think that the military code their signal so that nobody will be able to eavesdrop on the message?

Stretching Exercises

What would happen if you used the cup phone outside and an owl perched on the string? Make a model of a perched owl. Predict the effect this model will have on cup phone communication. Then test your prediction.

Activity 2

Signals and Noise

GOALS

In this activity you will:

• Visualize a design.

• Communicate a design in words.

What Do You Think?

It has been suggested that 95% of human communication happens without words.

• **When you talk with adults, why don't they always understand you?**

• **Do your friends always understand what you say? Why or why not?**

• **What happens when you try to exchange ideas with someone who doesn't speak your language?**

Record your ideas about these questions in your *Active Physics* log. Be prepared to discuss your responses with your small group and with your class.

For You To Do

1. Imagine the great Pharaoh of Egypt in his palace. He has just approved a model of a stone monument that his architect has designed. They both want to begin work as soon as possible. His building supervisor is already in the desert, ready to begin work. Bringing the building supervisor back to the palace would waste too much time. How can the Pharaoh and his architect communicate the plan to the building supervisor? Assume some sort of "telephone" hook-up between the architect and the building supervisor. With a partner, assume the roles of Pharaoh's architect and building supervisor.

2. Divide a set of building bricks so you each have an identical set of bricks. Set up a curtain of books or cardboard between you and your partner.

3. The architect constructs a model of the monument, but without allowing the building supervisor to see the model. The model should be an original design. Do not simply build a pyramid. The architect then gives verbal directions to the builder over the curtain between them. The supervisor builds a model based on these directions. The supervisor can ask questions, but neither the architect nor the supervisor can see each other's model.

4. When you have completed the exercise, compare the builder's model to the architect's model. Add up the total number of correctly placed blocks. Also add up the total number of blocks in the architect's model. To get one number that describes the success of the communication, find the fraction of correctly placed blocks:

$$\frac{\text{number of correctly placed blocks}}{\text{total number of blocks}}$$

a) Write the fraction as a decimal number.

5. Play a game like "Wheel of Fortune." Your teacher will make up a phrase or expression and put spaces for each letter on the board. Take turns choosing letters that might be in the phrase.

6. Before you begin the next game, record the total number of spaces for the letters in a table like the one shown. Notice the column in the table labeled "Number of letters showing." At the beginning of the game, this number is zero. At the end of the game, all the letters are showing.

Number of letters showing	Prediction of number of students who can guess the phrase	Number of students who can guess the phrase

✎ a) Fill in the "Number of letters showing" column up to the total number of letters in the phrase. Predict how many students will guess the phrase when each number of letters is showing. Of course, when the number is zero, no letters are showing, and probably no one in the class will be able to guess the phrase. When all the letters are showing, everyone in the class can read the phrase.

7. As you play this time, continue to choose letters out loud. But do not guess the phrase out loud.

✎ a) In your log, write down the blanks for the letters. Each time you make a guess, record the guess and the number of letters. Circle the number of letters that were showing when you guessed correctly.

8. Make a class graph on the board. Your teacher will ask, "Who got the answer after the first letter? After the second letter? . . ." The graph will show the number of letters as the independent variable (on the horizontal axis). The dependent variable (on the vertical axis) is the total number of students who have correctly guessed the phrase.

✎ a) Make a copy of the graph for your log.

Reflecting on the Activity and the Challenge

Communicating an image with words can be quite difficult as you have observed in the architect-builder exercise. With practice, you would probably improve your ability to describe shapes with words. A picture, though, would always be more efficient. Some people can express themselves with images and create paintings to communicate their ideas. If they could express those ideas in words, perhaps we might not need art. But as you've seen, substituting words for images leads to lots of problems.

You also tried to communicate a word message without all of the letters. Some people are better at this than others. The success of this depends on a shared knowledge between the sender and receiver of the knowledge. A person could probably communicate the name Elvis Presley with only the first five letters if both people know the singer. If one has never heard of the singer, the entire name would have to be spelled out.

When you try to communicate your message in the **Chapter Challenge**, you may have to decide whether a picture or words are easier to send. You may also have to decide if there is a common experience that would allow you to send the message more efficiently. Common experiences may also be a way of ensuring that you have privacy. If you both know certain things that others do not know, you can use this to hide information and maintain secrecy. This could help you with your essay about privacy on the Internet.

Physics To Go

1. a) Identify the mistakes in communication between the architect and the building supervisor that your group made.
   b) Explain how each mistake happened.
   c) Suggest an improvement to the communication system you used. Explain how this change would prevent the mistake.

2. a) Give an example of a mistake in communication between you and another person.
   b) Explain how the mistake happened.
   c) Suggest an improvement to the communication system you and the other person used. Explain how the change would prevent the mistake.

3. Suppose the architect had given the building supervisor a drawing, but the two could not speak to each other. How well would they have communicated? Explain your answer.

4. a) Repeat the first part of **Activity Two** at home. Instead of a design of blocks, limit the design to stacks of pennies, nickels, and dimes.
   b) Is this activity easier or more difficult than the Pharaoh activity? Tell why.
   c) Could you communicate even better if you and your partner had agreed on a code in advance?

5. a) Suppose the Pharaoh's architect and building supervisor had agreed on a code in advance. How would that have changed the communication?
   b) If the building supervisor was blind, how would that have changed the communication? How could you change the activity to improve the communication?
   c) If the building supervisor was deaf, how would that have changed the communication? How could you change the activity to improve the communication?

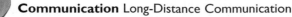
Activity 3

The Electricity and Magnetism Connection

GOALS

In this activity you will:

• Observe induced currents.

• Observe magnetism of a current-carrying wire.

• Infer the importance of relative motion.

• Build an electromagnet.

• Investigate variables in an electromagnet.

What Do You Think?

Earth's north pole has not always been in the same place. In fact, over many millions of years, the poles have actually reversed many times. The magnetic north pole has been near the geographic south pole.

• **How does a compass show which way is north?**

Record your ideas about this question in your *Active Physics* log. Be prepared to discuss your responses with your small group and with your class.

For You To Do

1. Place a compass on the table. Wait until the needle stops moving. Bring a small magnet near the compass.

⬤ a) Record your observations.

2. Move the magnet around slowly.

⬤ a) What happens to the compass?

3. Create a code so that someone looking at the compass can read the code. The person reading the code can manipulate the compass from under a piece of paper.

⬤ a) How fast can you send the code?

4. Remove the magnet. Place a magnet wire on top of the compass, as shown. Briefly touch the ends of the wire to the ends of the battery.

⬤ a) What happens to the compass needle?

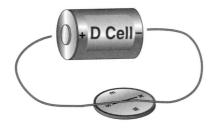

5. Create a setup where the magnet wire is placed on the compass and the presence of a current creates a code. The code can then be read by observation of the compass.

⬤ a) How fast can you send this code?
⬤ b) Does this code have any advantages over the code in **Step 3**?

6. Turn the wire to a different direction and repeat **Step 4**.

⬤ a) What happens this time? Try several different directions.

7. Obtain a 5-m length of magnet wire and a cardboard tube. *Carefully* strip 1 cm of insulation from each end of the wire. Wrap the wire around the cardboard tube, with all turns going in the same direction. Before you start, leave about 30 cm on each end for making connections. Tape the coil of wire in place.

8. Connect the ends of the wire to a meter that measures small currents. This type of meter is called a *galvanometer*.

9. Push a bar magnet into the cardboard tube, as shown.

   a) What happens?

   b) Pull the magnet out of the tube. What happens?

   c) Move the magnet in and out rapidly. What happens?

   d) Hold the magnet still and move the coil back and forth. What happens?

   e) Was a current produced when the magnet moved through the tube?

   f) Was a current produced when the magnet was at rest inside the tube?

   g) How was the direction that the magnet moved important?

   h) Did it matter if the coil moved or if the magnet moved? Explain your answer.

10. Create a code that can be read by someone observing the current meter in **Step 8**.

   a) How fast can you send this code?

   b) Does this code have any advantage over the codes used in **Steps 3** and **5**?

11. Make electromagnets by wrapping wire around nails. Be sure the last few centimeters of insulation is sanded off each end of each wire. You will investigate the effect of the number of turns of wire. Wind each piece of wire tightly around a separate nail. For each nail, wind a different number of turns. Leave enough unwrapped wire at each end to connect to a cell. Tape each coil of wire in place.

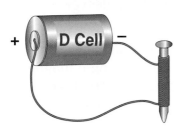

12. Hook up one coil to a battery as shown in the drawing. Figure out a way to measure the strength of your electromagnet. Hint: You can count how many paper clips or washers the electromagnet will pick up. Leave the battery connected for as short a time as possible to limit the battery's energy loss.

13. Connect several batteries together end-to-end, as in a flashlight. Make an electromagnet with these batteries.

a) How does using several batteries change the strength of your electromagnet?

14. A **digital** code is a set of ones and zeroes. An **analog** code is a continuous set of numbers, like the number line in mathematics, between zero and one.

a) Which of the methods you investigated in this activity can be used for digital coding?

b) Which of the methods you investigated in this activity can be used for analog coding?

c) Which of the methods can be used for both?

d) What advantage would digital coding have over analog coding?

e) What advantage would analog coding have over digital coding?

Physics Words

digital: description of data that is stored or transmitted as a sequence of discrete symbols; usually this means binary data (1s and 0s) represented using electronic or electromagnetic signals

analog: a description of a continuously variable signal or a circuit; an analog signal can be represented as a series of waves

Reflecting on the Activity and the Challenge

You have investigated a relationship between magnetism and electricity. A magnet affects a compass as does an electric current. You have also created electricity by moving a magnet past a coil of wire. Finally, you have made an electromagnet by using current to create the magnet. Each of these mechanisms was then used by you to code a message. Some of these approaches were limited to digital codes while others could be digital or analog codes.

In setting up your communication system for the **Chapter Challenge**, you may decide to use one of these techniques. You will have to decide whether your code should be digital or analog. You may also view one of these methods as a way to prevent a message from being transmitted. This may be important in maintaining secrecy in the second part of your challenge.

Physics To Go

1. a) If you place a compass on the table, which way does the compass needle point?
   b) What happened to the compass needle when an electric current ran through the wire?
   c) Does the current in the wire make the compass point in a particular direction? Can you identify that direction?
   d) In **Step 6**, you turned the wire in many different directions. Was there one direction where the electric current did not change the compass? Provide an explanation for this.
   e) In **Step 12** you connected together several batteries end-to-end and investigated their effect on the electromagnet. Predict what would have happened if you had done that in the activity with the wire and the compass.

2. a) Make a drawing to show a compass under a wire.
   b) Draw the compass when the wires are connected to a battery.
   c) Draw the compass when the wires in **Part (b)** are reversed.

3. a) In this activity, you made a coil to investigate how a moving magnet can produce electric current. What would have happened if you had just used a straight wire?

   b) In **Step 3**, you ran a current through a straight wire to investigate the effect on a compass. Predict what would have happened if you had used a much longer wire and wound it into a coil.

4. Predict what would happen if you brought the compass near the electromagnet.

5. a) List the variables that affect the strength of an electromagnet.

   b) Briefly, tell how you would investigate each variable.

6. Review the steps in this activity where you used a coil of wire. What effect did the coil of wire have in each case?

7. a) Locate the circuit breaker box or fuse box in your home.

   b) With the help of an adult, find out how the switches, fuses, or breakers work.

8. a) Sketch your electric meter, including the readings on the dials and the positions of the hands. Date your sketch.

   b) One week later, sketch the meter and the readings again.

   c) Figure out how much electricity you used in that week.

Stretching Exercises

1. Investigate the effect of wrapping a coil around a compass and running current through the coil. Find out the effect of changing the number of turns in the coil. Also find out the effect of adding a second coil with the same number of turns as the first.

2. Build a compass by magnetizing a paper clip and floating it on water. Find out what happens when you bring a coil of wire near the compass and using a battery run current through the coil.

3. Investigate how an electromagnet affects a compass. Also, investigate how two electromagnets affect each other, and how two compasses affect each other. Write a summary of everything you have discovered.

Activity 4

Making the Connection

GOALS

In this activity you will:

- Apply basic physics to build a telegraph.
- Test, improve, and re-test the design.
- Record the design in a drawing.

What Do You Think?

The first telegraph sent messages along a wire.

- **How do you think this telegraph worked?**
- **How do you think it was improved?**

Record your ideas about these questions in your *Active Physics* log. Be prepared to discuss your responses with your small group and with your class.

For You To Do

Design Your Own Investigation

1. You are going to design and build a telegraph. Two people operate a telegraph—the sender and the receiver. The sender opens and closes a switch. The receiver, some distance away, observes whether a second switch opens or closes. Your telegraph must include both a sender and a receiver. Examine the list of materials that you can use.

> magnet wire (10 m)
> steel nails
> sandpaper
> wire cutter/stripper
> batteries (with a total of 6 V)
> plastic or flexible clips for connecting wires
> alligator clips for connecting wires
> key or normally open push-button switch
> mounting board for transmitter and receiver
> small nuts and bolts

2. Work with your partner to make a plan.

a) Make a drawing of your design.

3. With your teacher's approval, build your system and test it.

a) How well did your system work?

b) How could you improve your system? Remember that engineers and inventors are hardly ever satisfied with their first designs.

4. Improve your system and re-test it.

a) Make a careful drawing of your system. Be sure to list all the materials you use.

b) Explain how you improved your system over your first design.

5. Practice sending messages in Morse code. Part of the code is shown.

● is a dot; — is a dash

A	● —	N	— ●	1	● — — — —
B	— ● ● ●	O	— — —	2	● ● — — —
C	— ● — ●	P	● — — ●	3	● ● ● — —
D	— ● ●	Q	— — ● —	4	● ● ● ● —
E	●	R	● — ●	5	● ● ● ● ●
F	● ● — ●	S	● ● ●	6	— ● ● ● ●
G	— — ●	T	—	7	— — ● ● ●
H	● ● ● ●	U	● ● —	8	— — — ● ●
I	● ●	V	● ● ● —	9	— — — — ●
J	● — — —	W	● — —	0	— — — — —
K	— ● —	X	— ● ● —	.	● — ● — ● —
L	● — ● ●	Y	— ● — —	?	● ● — — ● ●
M	— —	Z	— — ● ●		

6. Measure the time it takes to send a short message using the Morse code.

a) Calculate the time needed to send one letter of the alphabet.

b) How long do you think it would take to send 500 words by telegraph using the Morse code?

Reflecting on the Activity and the Challenge

You have designed and built a working telegraph. You may want to build a telegraph to meet the **Chapter Challenge**. Since you have made a careful drawing of your design, you can easily reassemble it. Or you may want to modify your design. Perhaps you will have additional materials when you meet the challenge, and you can change your design to use these materials.

Physics To Go

1. a) Explain in a few sentences how your telegraph works.
   b) Review the earlier activities in this chapter. How does what you learned in these activities help you explain the physics of the telegraph?

2. a) What would you like to improve about your telegraph design?
   b) If you had any materials you wanted, how could you improve your design?

3. a) Telegraph lines were first run along railroad tracks. Why was this a good place for the lines?
   b) Why was it good for the railroads to have the telegraph lines run along the railroad tracks?

4. a) Write a simple message.
   b) Write your message in Morse code.
   c) What are the advantages of Morse code?
   d) What are the disadvantages of Morse code?
   e) If you had to design a system to send messages with Morse code, how could you speed up the communication?

5. a) If you sent a message in Morse code, how would you show that a sentence had ended?
   b) How would you show that the whole message had ended?

6. a) You may know that computers work with binary numbers. In the binary number system, the only possible digits are zero and one. How is the binary number system similar to Morse code?

b) The following are the binary numbers from 0 to 9:

0	0
1	1
2	10
3	11
4	100
5	101
6	110
7	111
8	1000
9	1001

Write the binary numbers for 10 to 20.

7. Could the telegraph information be stolen? How could someone tap into the line and pick up your secret communication?

Stretching Exercises

Go to the library and look up how a telegraph key works. Also find out how a telegraph receiver works. Make a brief presentation to the class. Explain how this telegraph is an improvement over your telegraph.

Activity 5

Voice Signals

GOALS

In this activity you will:

• Build a speaker/microphone.

• Identify energy conversion.

• Send a coded message.

What Do You Think?

You can send your voice over a telephone line. You can also send computer information using a telephone and a modem. Using a fax machine and a telephone you can send images. You can even send video images using a telephone line.

• **How does a telephone work?**

Record your ideas about this question in your *Active Physics* log. Be prepared to discuss your responses with your small group and with your class.

Integrated Coordinated Science for the 21st Century

Caution:
Soldering irons are
very hot and can
easily burn you.

For You To Do

1. Check the ends of a 1-m long piece of magnet wire. Be sure that the last few centimeters have been sanded. Notice that the copper metal of the wire itself is a slightly different color than the orange insulation painted on the wire.

2. Make a coil with the magnet wire. The diameter should be about 2 cm. If a cardboard tube is available, wind the coil around the tube. Be sure to leave about 5 cm free at each end. Tape the coil together so it will not unwind.

3. Find the headphone plug with two wires coming out. Check to see that each end has an alligator clip.

4. Connect the alligator clips with the headphone plug to the ends of the coil. Be sure the coil wires are sanded at the point where the alligator clips make contact.

5. Tape the coil to the bottom of a styrofoam cup, as shown.

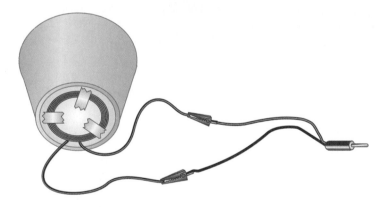

6. Turn on a personal stereo and tune the radio to a station. Push the plug into the earphone jack. Hold a magnet up to the coil. What do you hear?

  a) Record your observations in your log.

  b) Remove the magnet. What happens? Record the result.

7. If you have an amplified speaker, insert the plug into the amplified speaker jack. After turning the amplifier on, speak into the cup. What do you hear?

a) Record your results in your log. Try it with and without the magnet near the coil. If your words come out of the speaker, your cup has become a microphone.

8. Find the solar cell and earphone plug. Connect the solar cell leads to the earphone plug leads, with the alligator clips, as shown.

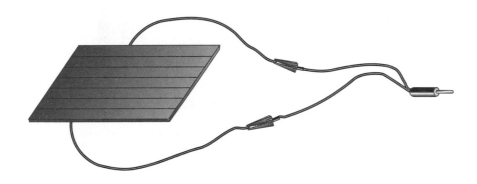

9. Insert the plug into the input of the amplifier/speaker, and turn the amplifier on. Point the solar cell toward the room lights. What do you hear?

a) Record your observations. The solar cell is converting light into electricity.

10. Shine a flashlight beam at the solar cell. Move the beam off and on the cell. Try to send a short message in Morse code to your partner.

a) What was the result?
b) How far can you send a message this way?

FOR YOU TO READ

Speakers and Microphones

The radio sends a small amount of current through the earphone jack to the coil. This current changes thousands of times each second. The speaker moves when the charge flows, if the magnet is in place inside the speaker. The changing current makes the bottom of the cup vibrate, and this vibration produces sound. A microphone has the same design as a speaker. In the microphone, the vibration of your voice moves a coil of wire. Since there is a magnet next to the coil, this movement makes an electric current in the coil. That current becomes the signal that is sent through the wire.

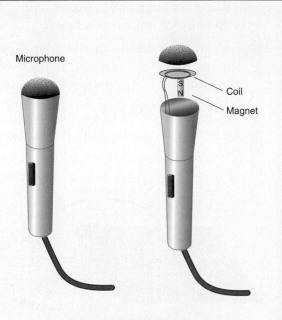
Microphone

Coil
Magnet

Speaker

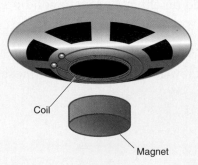
Coil
Magnet

Active Physics

Reflecting on the Activity and the Challenge

You have made a speaker and a microphone. You have learned that a speaker contains a coil of wire with a magnet very close by. When the electric charge from the radio flowed through this coil, the coil vibrated and made sound. A solar cell is able to convert light into electricity. By varying the amount of light, you were able to change the current and make a sound.

Part of your **Chapter Challenge** is to build a communications system. You may want to design and build a speaker for your communications system or use solar cells as part of the equipment. You can also use your understanding of the speaker when you describe the physics of your communications system.

Physics To Go

1. a) When you plugged the wires from your cup into the personal stereo, what kind of energy entered the cup through the wires?
   b) When you spoke into the cup and heard your voice on the amplifier/speaker, what kind of energy left the cup?

2. How well would your earphone have worked if you only had a 0.1-m wire to wind into a coil (instead of a 1-m wire)? Give a reason for your answer.

3. a) What are the variables that affect the performance of the earphone you built?
   b) If you had whatever materials you wanted and plenty of time, how could you improve the performance of the earphone you built?

4. a) How can a magnet and a coil of wire produce a current?
   b) How can a current and a coil of wire make a magnet?
   c) Use your answer to either **Part (a)** or **(b)** to explain how a speaker works.
   d) Use your answer to either **Part (a)** or **(b)** to explain how a microphone works.

5. a) In the activity, you aimed the solar cell at the room lights. If they were fluorescent, you probably heard a hum. What can you conclude about the light that comes from the fluorescent tube?

   b) When you kept the flashlight beam aimed at the solar cell, what did you hear?

   c) What can you conclude about the light that comes from the flashlight?

6. a) Think of the solar cell as a device that transforms energy. What kind of energy was the input energy?

   b) What kind of energy was the output energy?

7. a) Imagine you have a laser instead of the flashlight. How would you set up a communications system like the one in this activity?

   b) Which light source—a laser, a flashlight, or a bulb and convex lens—would enable you to communicate over the greatest distance? Give a reason for your answer.

Stretching Exercises

1. Take apart an old loudspeaker. Report to the class on what you find inside.

2. Feed the output of the solar cell to an oscilloscope. Observe the wave form for various light sources.

Activity 6

Sending a Message with Light

GOALS

In this activity you will:

- Build an electrical circuit.
- Transmit a message with light.
- Observe energy conversion.
- Make and test a prediction.

What Do You Think?

Before long, local telephone lines will be made of tiny glass fibers, and the telephone signals will be sent on light beams. Light has a very high frequency and a short wavelength.

- **How might these properties be important in sending messages?**

Record your ideas about this question in your *Active Physics* log. Be prepared to discuss your responses with your small group and with your class.

Integrated Coordinated Science for the 21st Century

For You To Do

1. Obtain an LED, as shown in the diagram. Note that one of the wires from the LED is longer than the other. Also, notice that part of the LED base is flat, not curved. This flat part is next to the shorter wire.

2. Connect the positive side of a battery to the long lead of the LED. If you have wires with alligator clips on each end, you can make this connection with one of those wires. Otherwise, twist the leads together.

3. Obtain a resistor. It is a cylinder with four colored bands. You can connect the resistor in either direction. Connect one end of the resistor to the short lead of the LED. Use a lead with two alligator clips, if you have them.

LED

Flat

Flat

4. Touch the other end of the resistor to the negative side of the battery. What happens?

    a) Record your observations.

    b) Reverse the battery connections. What happens now?

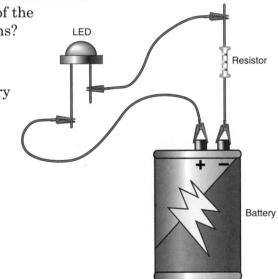

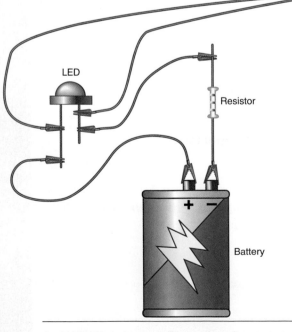

5. Set up the circuit as it was in the first part of **Step 4**. Connect the wires from the plug to the LED leads, as shown. If you do not have wires with alligator clips, *carefully* solder the connections in the circuit. Tape the electrical connections to keep them from touching each other.

282

6. Tune the radio to a station. Insert the earphone plug into the earphone jack of the radio.

7. Find a solar cell, with wires to a plug. Turn on the amplifier/speaker. Insert the solar cell plug into the amplifier/speaker's input jack. You will use this circuit as a receiver.

8. The circuit with the LED, which you completed in **Step 5**, will be the transmitter. Point the LED at the solar cell. Move them close together.

a) With the radio on, what do you hear?

b) How would you describe the sound quality?

9. Predict what will happen if you place a file card between the LED and the solar cell.

a) Record your prediction.

b) Now try it. What happened?

c) From your observations what can you conclude about how the signal is transmitted from the LED to the solar cell.

10. Increase the separation between the solar cell and the LED.

a) What happens to the quality of the transmission?

Reflecting on the Activity and the Challenge

You have transmitted music by converting an electrical signal in a wire into light. The LED made the light. When this light reached the solar cell, the solar cell makes another electrical signal. When the speaker/amplifier amplified this signal, you could hear it. If you could shine a beam of light over a long distance, you could use this system for communication. Think of how you might build a communications system with a light source and a solar cell to meet the **Chapter Challenge**.

Physics To Go

1. When you transmitted music in this activity, energy changed forms several times. List each change and where it occurred. Hint: When the music is recorded, the microphones change sound energy into electrical energy.

2. a) Compare what you did in this activity with what you did in **Activity 4** when you built a telegraph. Which method would you choose to transmit a "yes" or "no" answer? Why?

   b) Which method would you choose to transmit a speech? Why?

   c) Which method would you choose to transmit a simple message 10 m? Why?

3. a) Identify some of the problems with the music transmitter that you built in this activity.

   b) Tell how you might solve these problems. Assume you can get whatever materials you need.

4. a) What effect do you think the room light had on your transmission system?

   b) How could you reduce the effect of room light?

5. a) Do you think the solar cell is designed for bright light or dim light? Explain your answer.

   b) Compared to sunlight, is the light from the LED bright or dim?

   c) Do you think the solar cell is well matched to the LED? Explain your answer.

6. How could you include a laser in your music-transmission system?

Stretching Exercise

Obtain a length of optical fiber. Set up the transmission system you built in this activity, but keep the LED away from the solar cell. Put one end of the optical fiber up against the LED and the other end up against the solar cell. Report to the class on how you transmitted music through the optical fiber.

Activity 7   Just the Fax

GOALS

In this activity you will:

- Assemble a fax image from a stream of data.

- Observe how a fax image is made of pixels.

- Compute the number of pixels in an image.

- Compare a fax to a newspaper photo.

What Do You Think?

A fax is a picture sent by telephone. Faxes are remarkably detailed. If you drew a thin line across a page, a typical fax would represent each centimeter of that line by 100 tiny dots.

- **How does the fax machine store and send all the information for each picture?**

Record your ideas about this question in your *Active Physics* log. Be prepared to discuss your responses with your small group and with your class.

285

For You To Do

1. Look at the data shown. It is a stream of zeroes and ones. These numbers are the code for an image. The image is made up of tiny squares. For each square on the image, a one tells that the square is darkened, a zero indicates that the square is light. A coordinate system enables you to match the ones and zeroes to their location in the image.

```
000000001100000110000101001100000000000000000000000111
000110001010010000000000000000011110000100001000100010100
100000000000000000000011110110001101101001000000000000000

00000001111111111110110101100001110000000000111111111
11111111111111111110000000000000011111111111111111111
11110000000000000000011111111000000000000001111111111100000

01111011111100000000000000011111111000000000011111111
0000000000000000111111100000000000001111110000000000000
00011111111100000000000111100000000000000000011111110000

01111111111000110000000000000111111100000000000111101
1111000000000000011111111100000000011110000001000111110
0001110011000000111111111100110000000000011001110001100

11110011111001110000011101001111000110000000111111100
0001000011110000111110001100000111111000010001001110
000111111001110001001110000100001000110000111111110011

01100111110001000000000010001111111110001100110111111
1000000100000011111111001001101100111001100000010000
11111111110010000100111000010000011111001111111100010000

00100111100000110111111110011111111101100001000111111111
00111111100101011110100000000001101111001001111100001
11111100100000000010001110001011100000011111111001100

0000100001100001111111111111111111110000000000000011110
0000000000000111111101100000000000001111110000000011
11111001110000000000111110110000111111111111111110011000

0000011111100010110011111111110110000000000111111100
0000000111111111100110000000000111111110000000000111111
1110100010000000111111111111101100111111111001100000000

1111111111101010111111111111110010000000001111111111111
0101001111111111001000000000111111111111110101001111111
1110000000000011111111111111101010011111111111111000000000
```

2. On a piece of graph paper, write the numbers 1 to 40 across the top, and the numbers 1 to 40 down the left side, as shown.

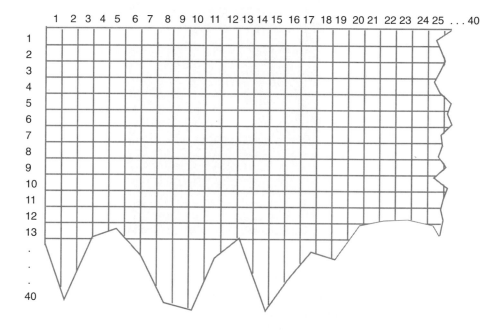

3. Now translate the data you are assigned onto your graph paper. As you begin reading ones and zeroes from the top left, move across the first row of the data from the top left to the top right. When you reach the right side of a row of data, drop down to the next row and begin reading again from left to right. When you reach the right side of the row on the graph paper, drop down to the second row of graph paper and keep on going. Rows of data do not correspond to rows of the graph paper.

✎ a) Record the data on your graph paper.

4. Your teacher will assign each group a section of the image. Within your group, decide how to prepare your part of the image. When you are done, cut out your group's part of the image and glue it to the "master" image that your teacher will give you.

5. Look at the finished image from a distance. The white and dark squares on the graph paper are called *pixels*.

✎ a) In your log record what you see. Where have you seen this picture before?

287

6. Look at the picture below. Hold this picture at reading distance.

✎ a) Record what you see.

✎ b) Step back several paces. How is what you see different from what you saw in **Part (a)**.

✎ c) Write a brief explanation in your log of what happened. Be sure to discuss what happened to the pixels.

7. Examine the fax through your magnifier.

✎ a) How many pixels high is the fax image?

✎ b) How many pixels wide is the fax image?

✎ c) What is the total number of pixels in the fax image?

8. Examine a newspaper photograph.

Kingsbridge crash

a) How is it similar to a fax?

b) How is it different from a fax?

c) Estimate the number of dots in a typical newspaper
photograph.

Reflecting on the Activity and the Challenge

You now understand that data sent over telephone lines is a
series of ones and zeroes. Each one or zero describes one pixel
of the image. You also understand that when you look at the
fax picture close-up, you see the individual pixels. When you
back away, the individual pixels disappear and you see the
image as a whole. This set of data can be sent over a telephone
line to transmit a picture. To meet the **Chapter Challenge**,
you might want to send a picture. You can use what you have
learned in the other activities to send a series of ones and
zeroes. The pattern of pixels you construct from could be in a
code that contains the message.

Physics To Go

1. How large is the pixel size for a typical fax? Hint: See **What
Do You Think?** in this activity.

2. a) Look at a computer screen or TV screen. Use a magnifier
to get a good view. Describe what you see.

   b) Compare what you see to what you see when you look at a
fax through a magnifier.

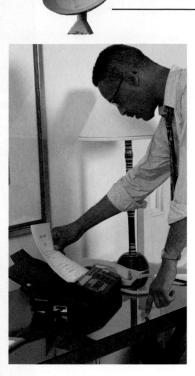

3. A fax of a page of text requires approximately 30 s to transmit. Estimate the amount of dots which must be sent in the page of text by counting the number of lines of information and the number of dots horizontally and vertically in each letter. Calculate the transmission rate of the fax.

4. Compare Morse code to a fax.

5. Japanese is a different language than English. Why was the fax so important for transmitting information in Japanese? Hint: You may need to look up information about how Japanese is written.

6. How are pictures sent back to Earth from space?

7. A small fax machine has only ten pixels in each row. On a piece of graph paper, create the image from the data stream below.

```
00000000000010010000000100
10000001111110000000111010
00001110100000101010000001
01000000010100000000000000
```

Rows of data do not correspond to rows of the fax.

8. The image you make in this activity had only two kinds of pixels—white or black. Making pixels in shades of gray can increase the detail shown in the image. If you could use five different shades (white, three shades of gray, and black), how many ones and zeroes would you need to transmit the picture?

Stretching Exercises

1. Look at a newspaper photograph and a black-and-white photographic print through a microscope. Research the concept of "grain" in a photographic print. Use your research to understand what you see in the microscope. Report to the class on what you find.

2. Research the painter Georges Seurat. Find out how Seurat's painting is related to the fax and newspaper pictures that you studied in this activity.

Activity 8   Bar Codes

GOALS

In this activity you will:

• Read a code.

• Translate a number into code.

What Do You Think?

A bar code mail sorter can read 30,000 envelope addresses per hour.

• **How does the red light scan products you buy?**

• **How does the bar code work?**

Record your ideas about these questions in your *Active Physics* log. Be prepared to discuss your responses with your small group and with your class.

For You To Do

1. Look at the postal bar code on the next page.

a) What does the bar code consist of?

`10010/2007` `|₁₁|||||₁₁||₁₁||₁₁₁₁₁||||₁₁|₁|`

| 1 | 2 | 3 | 4 | 5 | 6 | 7 | 8 | 9 | 5 |

Example
7 4 2 1 0

`ı||ıı`

4+2=6

2. The bars are organized into groups of five. Each bar location has a value. Reading from left to right in a group, the values are 7, 4, 2, 1 and 0, as shown in the drawing of the bar code key.

a) In each group of five, how many bars are long, and how many are short?

b) Look at the representation of the number 6 which is enlarged from the bar code key. The second and third bars are long. They correspond to the values 4 and 2. Since 4 + 2 = 6, this is the way 6 is represented. What digit is represented by each of the following bar codes?

`₁₁||` `₁|₁₁|` `|₁₁|₁`

c) Draw the bar codes for the digits 2 and 7.

d) Is there any digit from zero to nine that cannot be represented using the above rules?

e) If the first two bars are long, the ZIP digit is zero. Make the bar code for the digit zero.

3. Look at a whole ZIP code. There are nine digits in a ZIP code. But when the ZIP code is translated into a bar code, there are ten bar groups. The first nine groups give the nine digits in the code. The last group of five bars is a check digit. It helps catch any mistakes in either printing or reading the code.

ZIP Code: 52847-2014

`|₁|₁|₁₁|₁||₁₁|₁|₁₁|₁₁|₁|₁||₁₁₁₁₁₁||₁|₁||₁₁₁||`

| 5 | 2 | 8 | 4 | 7 | 2 | 0 | 1 | 4 | ? |

To find the check digit, you first perform several steps.

• Add up the first nine digits in the code.

• Find the next higher multiple of ten.

• Subtract the sum from the next multiple of ten.

• The result of the subtraction is the check digit.

a) What is the check digit for the ZIP code shown to the left?

4. The very first bar and the very last bar are not part of the code. These bars are called "frame bits." They show the beginning and the end of the code. Find the frame bits in the code above.

292

✎ a) Record in your log how to read a ZIP code.

5. Use what you have learned to "crack the code." Notice that you must separate the bars into groups of five yourself. Remember that the first and last bars are the "frame bits."

✎ a) ||₁₁|||||₁₁|₁|₁||₁₁₁|₁|₁₁₁|||₁₁|₁||₁|₁|₁|||₁₁|

✎ b) Write the ZIP codes for

Nowhere, USA 01234-9876

Somewhere, USA 56789-0001

✎ c) Write the bar code for your birthday.
✎ d) Write the bar code for your height.

Reflecting on the Activity and the Challenge

You have learned how to write a bar code for a number. You have learned how each group of five bars represents one digit and how the bars are read to form a ZIP code. You could use this code to help meet the **Chapter Challenge.** You could send a message with a ZIP code if you can find a way to transmit the bars from one room to another. Think about how you might do this. If the message was a sentence, you would have to convert each letter to a number.

Physics To Go

1. a) What is special about the first and last bars in the ZIP code?
   b) Are the first and last bars long or short?

2. How are zeroes represented by bars in the ZIP code?

3. Write the ZIP code for this bar code. |||₁₁₁₁|₁|₁₁₁₁||₁₁|₁|₁||₁₁₁|₁|₁|₁₁₁|||₁₁₁₁₁|₁₁|₁|

4. Write the bar code for this ZIP code: 08420-1670

5. Show how two long bars produce each digit from one to nine. Hint: Use the bar code key. For example, to produce 5, you will add 4 and 1. The long bars would be under the 4 and the 1, and the other bars would be short.

6. The code for zero is made with two bars, but it does not follow the same code as the other eight digits. Why is zero an exception? Hint: Using the bar code key, look for two numbers that add up to zero.

7. Why does using a bar code for the ZIP code make mail sorting easier?

8. a) What information do you think is put on the bar codes at a supermarket?
   b) How is the use of the bar codes helpful in running a supermarket?

Stretching Exercises

1. A remote control from a TV sends a signal that is like a bar code. The signal is sent with infrared radiation, which is similar to light. We cannot see infrared, but a video camera can record it. Aim a video camera at the TV remote. Shoot a video while someone pushes the remote buttons. The camera responds to the infrared from the remote. What do you see on the video?

2. Explore the effect a magnet has on iron filings. Now put the magnet far away. Sprinkle some filings on a credit card. Gently tap the card to remove the larger filings. Examine the card with a magnifier. What do you see? How do you think information is coded on the card? When you are finished, be sure to gently wipe off all the filings.

3. What type of bar codes are used in supermarkets? Investigate the following:

   How are products coded at the manufacturer?

   How are products coded at the supermarket?

   How do manufacturers and the supermarkets use the bar codes?

PHYSICS AT WORK

Dale Hatfield

Webster's *New World Dictionary* defines a hobby as "something that one likes to do or study in one's spare time." A career is defined as "a profession or occupation which one trains for and pursues as a lifework." In fact, for Dale Hatfield, the Chief of the Office of Engineering and Technology at the Federal Communications Commission (FCC), his hobby has become his career.

As a child he liked communications technology. "When I was 12 years old I built my own ham radio," says Dale, "and I soon realized there was an important connection between radio technology, math, and science."

At the FCC his most important responsibility is to manage the radio spectrum and decide what frequencies should be used for what purposes. Sounds easy enough until you realize just how many things need their own radio frequency. There are radio stations, television stations, amateur radio stations, police and fire departments, airports, and satellites. There are also cellular phones, pagers, cordless telephones, baby monitors, keyless entry systems, and many other personal devices which necessitate enough frequencies so that their many users do not collide with each other. "You can't have a taxicab on the same frequency as NBC," explains Dale.

"One of the tricks to finding additional space is to use higher and higher frequencies, but at a certain point radio waves begin to work like light waves and reflect off buildings, snow, and rain. They are then no longer effective."

In addition to managing wireless communication, the FCC is responsible for regulating long-distance "wired" communication. The latest and greatest advance in this area is fiber optics. In contrast to traditional phone lines, fiber optic lines are made of glass with a reflective property to keep the light waves intact and traveling without resistance. "A tremendous amount of information can be sent more efficiently through fiber optic lines," Dale explains, "and the technology is still advancing."

As technology continues to advance, so does the need for lifelong experts like Dale Hatfield. In 1997, after 18 years of service with the United States government, Dale was thinking about retiring. But the FCC offered him his current position and "it sounded like fun" so he took it and has not looked back. Why retire when your life's work is your favorite pastime?

Chapter 5 Assessment

1. Now that you have completed this chapter, you are ready to engineer a communication system. You and your team may already have a good idea of the type of system you wish to develop, and the type of message you wish to send.

   During the test of your system, you must measure the speed of transmission of your system. After a successful test, each team member will submit a written report about the system. This report will have the following parts:

   a) the design of the system;
   b) how your method of communication is better for this challenge than the other methods you investigated in this chapter;
   c) the physics of your system, and
   d) your measurement of the speed of transmission in words per minute, symbols per minute, or notes per minute.

2. Some of the activities in this chapter also focused on privacy and confidentiality in a communication system.
   You can now write an essay about the stealing of information on the Internet.

   Or, perhaps you have formed opinions about restricting Internet access to young children, and may wish to write an essay about that.

   Review the criteria you and your classmates established at the beginning of the chapter for grading your work. Now that you have completed the chapter you may wish to make additional alterations to the suggested scheme.

A grade will be assigned to the speed and quality of the transmission.	40 points
The quality of your written report will also be graded:	60 points
a) explanation of design (including drawings)	15 points
b) how your method is better than others	15 points
c) the physics of your system	25 points
d) your measurement of the speed of transmission of your system	5 points

You may also wish to develop a detailed grading scheme for your essay.

Physics You Learned

An electric current can produce magnetism.

A moving magnet can produce electricity.

The current and number of turns are important variables in the electromagnet.

A speaker contains a moving coil and a magnet.

A telegraph contains an electromagnet.

Light can be transformed into electricity.

Electricity can be transformed into light.

Messages can be sent with spring waves, a tight string, light, and electricity.

A series of ones and zeroes can be a code for an image.

A series of bars can be a code for a digit.

Chapter 6

IS ANYONE OUT THERE?

Is Anyone Out There?

Scenario

Science has provided you with an enormous amount of knowledge about the world. Most of that knowledge has come from direct experience with objects that you can hold in your hands. You do experiments in a laboratory. Science experiments are also conducted on land, in the oceans, in the air and in space. Since these experiments are designed to test ideas about how things work, scientists have developed a relatively good understanding of the Earth and the life on it.

By comparison, almost nothing is known about life outside the Earth. Scientists estimate that there should be a huge number of planets with conditions that can support life. These planets would have about the same range of temperatures and the same kind of atmosphere as Earth. Throughout the universe, there ought to be millions of possible locations for life to evolve. But if there is life out there, it may not be very advanced. And even if it were advanced, how would it be possible to communicate over such tremendous distances?

Some scientists have dedicated their life's work to the effort of finding extraterrestrial life. They have identified stars that might have planets with conditions similar to Earth. They observe the sky closely for possible signals from advanced civilizations. When they think about communication with other life forms, they use both science and language. The search for extraterrestrial life is expensive. Is it sensible to fund this type of research?

Challenge

1. Outline a plan to look for and listen for extraterrestrial life. Develop methods that are based on sound scientific principles. In this part of the challenge, you will show *how* you would communicate with any life forms you discover.

2. Decide *what* to say to extraterrestrial beings. Remember that you might make contact with a civilization that is more or less technologically advanced than that on Earth. Certainly they will not speak English. The message must:

- use science and mathematics that the extraterrestrial beings can understand, and
- present important information about human life and the Earth.

3. Write an essay describing what could be learned from contact with extraterrestrial beings.

4. Hold a mock hearing of the Space Committee of the United States Senate. Some of the students will be senators. Some will be scientists who would like to begin a search for extraterrestrial life. The scientists are requesting $3 billion for the project. They must convince the Senate Committee that the money will be well spent. Many of the Committee members are skeptical, so the scientists must be persuasive.

Criteria

Most of your grade will be based on how well you apply the physics you will learn in this chapter to the challenge. Part of your grade will be determined by your imagination and creativity.

As a class discuss the questions below as you develop your grading system for this challenge.

- Should you do every part of the challenge? Or, should you select one or two of the parts?
- How can you assess your creativity?

When you have answered these two questions, you can create the grading system. Here is an example of one way to grade the first two parts of the challenge:

Part 1:

Choice of methods
to communicate: 40 points

Explanation of the science:

   correct statement of
   science concepts: 25 points

   how **Chapter 6** activities
   present these concepts: 35 points

Part 2:

Choice of language for communication; discussion of how extraterrestrials will be able to understand the science:

   correct statement
   of science used in
   communication: 25 points

   how extraterrestrials
   might use the science
   in a message: 25 points

Choice of
message content: 25 points

Description of how
the content is
important: 25 points

Activity 1   Lenses and Ray Optics

GOALS

In this activity you will:

- Observe real and virtual images.

- Calculate image distance.

- Relate magnification to focal length.

- Make a real image on a screen.

- Summarize experimental results.

- Predict the image distance.

What Do You Think?

- **What do a camera, photocopier, and slide projector have in common?**

- **How do they function?**

Record your ideas about these questions in your *Active Physics* log. Be prepared to discuss your responses with your small group and with your class.

For You To Do

1. A **convex** (or **converging**) **lens** is thicker in the middle and thinner at the edges, as shown. Use a convex lens, a bright light bulb, and a white screen to simulate a photocopier. Move the lens and the screen until the image of the bulb is sharp, and the same size as the actual bulb. An image on a screen is called a **real image.**

   ✏ a) Describe what you see.

   ✏ b) Measure and record the distance of the bulb (object) from the lens and the image from the lens.

⚠ **Do not use lenses with chipped edges. Mount lenses securely in a holder.**

2. Use the convex lens, bulb, and screen to construct a simulation of a slide projector. Make the image twice the size of the object.

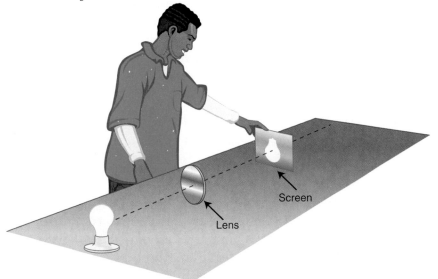

Screen

Lens

Physics Words

convex lens: a lens that causes parallel light rays to converge; a lens that is thinner at its edges than in the center

real image: an image that will project on a screen or on the film of a camera; the rays of light actually pass through the image

   ✏ a) Measure and record the distance of the object from the lens and the image from the lens.

3. Use the lens, bulb, and screen to simulate a camera. Make the image size one-quarter the size of the object.

   ✏ a) Measure and record the distance of the object from the lens and the image.

4. Obtain a second convex lens, and repeat **Step 1**.

🖎 a) Measure and record the distance of the object from the lens and the image from the lens for the second convex lens.

🖎 b) How do these distances compare with those you measured in **Step 1**?

🖎 c) What do you think makes one convex lens different from another?

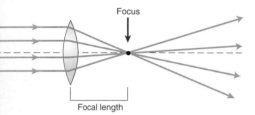

Focus

Focal length

5. Use the first convex lens. Measure the image distance when the object is very far away, like a tree outside the lab window.

🖎 a) Record this distance.

🖎 b) Repeat **Step 5** for a second convex lens. Record this distance.

🖎 c) The distance between the lens and the image of a distant object is called the *focal length*. The position of the image is at the *focus* of the lens, as shown. From your results of **Parts (a)** and **(b)**, give the focal length of each lens.

🖎 d) How does the focal length of each lens compare with the image distance you found in **Steps 1** and **4** (image size equals object size)?

Physics Words

concave lens: a lens that causes parallel light rays to diverge; a lens that is thicker at its edges than in the center

6. Look directly through each convex lens at a distant object and through each convex lens at an object only a few centimeters away.

🖎 a) Record what you see in each case.

🖎 b) How is what you saw with each lens different?

🖎 c) How does the magnifying power of each lens compare with its focal length? Write a general statement about the relationship between the focal length and how much the convex lens magnifies.

7. A **concave lens** is thinner in the middle and thicker at the edges, as shown. Using a concave lens and a bright light bulb try to make an image on a white screen.

🖎 a) Could you make an image on the screen?

8. Look directly through the concave lens at a variety of objects around you.

🖎 a) Record what you see.

🖎 b) How is what you saw with the concave lens different from what you saw using the convex lens?

Active Physics

PHYSICS TALK

These are the equations that describe relationships in a convex lens.

$$\frac{1}{f} = \frac{1}{D_o} + \frac{1}{D_i}$$

$$\frac{S_o}{S_i} = \frac{D_o}{D_i}$$

where f is the focal length of the lens

D_o is the object distance

D_i is the image distance

S_o is the object size

S_i is the image size

If the rays of light actually converge to a point, the image

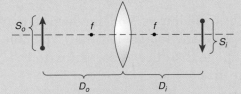

is a *real image*. A real image can be projected on a screen. If the light only appears to come together, the image is a **virtual image** and cannot be projected on a screen.

Physics Words

virtual image: an image from which rays of reflected or refracted light appear to diverge, as from an image seen in a plane mirror; no light comes directly from or passes through the image

Reflecting on the Activity and the Challenge

You have learned that a convex lens makes an image on a screen and can be used as a magnifying glass. You have also learned that concave lenses cannot form an image on a screen and do not magnify. Also, you have learned about the focal length, which is a most important property of a lens. To meet the **Chapter Challenge**, you must make a plan to look and listen for life in space. Your plan can include observations made through telescopes, and your understanding of lenses is essential to understanding how the telescope works. Your next activity will deal with telescopes.

Physics To Go

1. a) Copy the drawing on your paper.

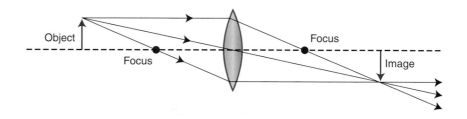

   b) Label the object distance and the image distance.
   c) If you move the object further away from the lens, what happens to the image distance?
   d) If you move the object closer to the lens, what happens to the image distance?

2. Many optical devices use lenses. For the devices listed below, describe the object and the image. Estimate the object distance and the image distance. Also, estimate the object size and the image size.

   a) slide projector
   b) camera
   c) telescope
   d) photocopy machine
   e) the human eye
   f) magnifying glass

3. a) Your lab partner holds a bright light at night. You set up a convex lens and a white screen to make a sharp image of the light. Now your lab partner begins to walk away from you. What must you do to keep the image sharp?

   b) Now your lab partner begins to walk toward you. What must you do to keep the image sharp?

4. For each of the optical devices listed in **Question 2** above, tell whether the image is real or virtual and if real, the location of the "screen."

5. a) Give an example of how a convex lens makes a real image.

   b) Give an example of how a convex lens makes a virtual image.

   c) Give an example of how a concave lens makes a virtual image.

6. a) Tell how to measure the focal length of a lens.

   b) If you had two lenses with different focal lengths, which would make the stronger magnifier?

   c) Look at the two drawings of lens (i) and lens (ii). Which lens has the shorter focal length? How could you tell?

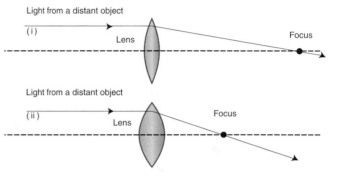

Light from a distant object
(i)   Lens   Focus

Light from a distant object
(ii)   Lens   Focus

7. A convex lens with a focal length of 0.05 m makes an image that is 3 m away from the lens. Where is the object?

8. a) If the distance from the image to the convex lens and the distance from the object to the convex lens are both 0.2 m, what is the focal length of the lens?

   b) Suppose the image and object are both the same distance from the convex lens. Make a general statement about how this distance is related to the focal length.

9. a) A convex lens has a focal length of 0.08 m. Where is the image of an object that is 1 m away?

   b) Where is the image of an object that is 5 m away?

   c) Where is the image of an object that is 20 m away?

   d) If the object is extremely far from the lens, how is the focal length related to the image distance?

   e) Show how the equation in **Physics Talk** predicts your answer to **Part (d)**.

Stretching Exercises

Find a convex lens and measure its focal length. Now make an image of a light bulb on a screen. Investigate how the image distance changes as you change the object distance. Make a graph of the object distance and the image distance. See if your results agree with the prediction of the lens equation given in **Physics Talk**.

Activity 2 The Telescope

GOALS

In this activity you will:

• Observe the image in a telescope.

• Align a system of lenses.

• Calculate magnification.

• Measure focal length.

• Make and test a prediction.

What Do You Think?

One of Einstein's most famous predictions was that light can be bent by gravity. Astronomers tested this idea during an eclipse of the Sun. They aimed their telescope at stars right at the edge of the Sun. The positions of the stars were shifted just as Einstein predicted they would be.

• **How does a telescope work?**

• **How could a telescope be improved?**

Record your ideas about these questions in your *Active Physics* log. Be prepared to discuss your responses with your small group and with your class.

For You To Do

1. Obtain two convex lenses. One with a very small focal length, and one with a much longer focal length. Measure the focal length of each lens.

✎ a) Record the focal length of each lens in your log.

2. Mount the lens with the shorter focal length on one end of a meter stick. When you use the telescope you will assemble, you will look through this lens. It is called the eyepiece.

3. The other lens is called the objective. To find out where to place the objective lens, add the two focal lengths that you measured in **Step 1**. This sum is the distance between the two lenses. When you have found this distance, mount the objective, as shown in the diagram.

✎ a) In your log, make a drawing similar to the one shown. Label the distance between the two lenses.

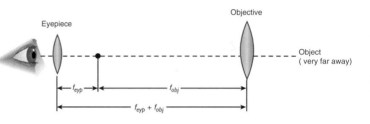

4. Observe a distant object outside. Be sure that light from this object travels through both lenses to your eye.

✎ a) What do you see? Make a drawing for your log.

✎ b) Record how the object appeared through your telescope.

5. An astronomical telescope magnifies objects. The objects look larger through the telescope than they do through the "naked eye." The magnification M tells how much larger the object appears. M is simply the ratio of the two focal lengths:

$$M = \frac{f_{obj}}{f_{eyp}}$$

where f_{obj} = focal length of the objective lens
f_{eyp} = focal length of the eyepiece

✎ a) Using the focal lengths of the two lenses in your telescope, predict the magnification.

6. Obtain two other lenses that will give a different magnification. Measure their focal lengths.

✎ a) Record the focal lengths in your log.

✎ b) Calculate the magnification for these two lenses.

✎ c) Predict how what you see through these lenses will be different from what you saw in **Step 4**. Record your prediction.

307

7. Set up the two lenses as you did in **Step 3**. Observe a distant object.

✏ a) Record how the object appears through this telescope. Make a drawing for your log.

✏ b) Compare the results with those you obtained in **Step 4**, and with the prediction you made in **Step 6**. How do the results compare with your prediction?

FOR YOU TO READ

Refracting and Reflecting Telescopes

You have made a simple **refracting telescope**. In a refractor, the light enters the telescope through the objective lens. The focal length of this lens is an important characteristic of the telescope. The longer the focal length, the larger the image. A telescope that observes details of the surfaces of planets, or that measures the parallax of nearby stars, has an objective with a very long focal length. The focal length of the objective lens of the refractor at Yerkes Observatory is 18 m. Imagine building a mount to aim a telescope that long!

Unfortunately, in a large image, the light is spread out so much that the image becomes very dim. To make a brighter image requires more light. That means the objective lens must be larger in diameter, to let in more light. The refractor at the Yerkes Observatory has a diameter of about 1.0 m. Imagine making a lens that large!

The difficulty of making large lenses led to the need for the **reflecting telescope**. In a reflector, a large concave mirror makes an image. The astronomer observes the image through an eyepiece lens. Modern astronomical telescopes are reflectors.

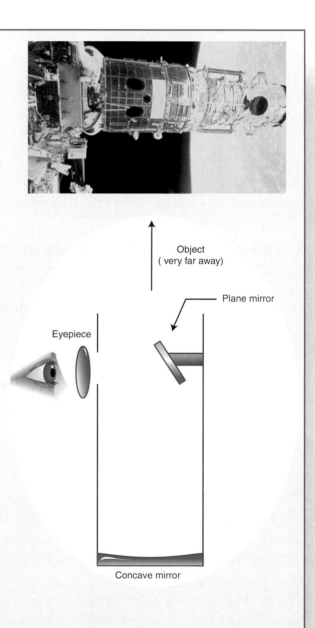

Reflecting on the Activity and the Challenge

You have learned how to make a telescope. You have seen that a telescope contains two lenses, and that the focal length of the objective is much longer than the focal length of the eyepiece. You have learned that it is essential to line up these lenses carefully, so both point right at the object. You can use what you have learned to meet the **Chapter Challenge**, since one way to look for life in space is to look through telescopes. From your work in this activity, you will be able to explain and demonstrate how a telescope works.

Physics To Go

1. Describe the lenses that can be used to make a telescope.

2. a) You are observing a distant light bulb through your telescope. If you held a card between the eyepiece and objective, could you make an image of the light bulb on the card?

   b) Where would this image appear?
   c) You look at this image through a convex eyepiece. Then you switch to a concave eyepiece. Which eyepiece would give the larger image? Why?

3. a) The longer the focal length of the objective, the greater the magnification. If the focal length of the objective increases, what happens to the length of the telescope? Explain your answer.

   b) If you wanted to increase the magnification of a telescope, why couldn't you simply get an objective lens with a much longer focal length and make the telescope much longer? What would happen if you did? Hint: The real image from the objective lens will be much larger. But the same amount of light will be spread over a much larger image.

4. Explain how a telescope lets you see a magnified image.

5. a) How is the diameter of the objective lens important in a telescope?

   b) The Mt. Palomar telescope has a mirror to collect the light. The mirror is 200 inches across. Why are telescopes made with such large openings?

Physics Words

refracting telescope: an optical device that uses lenses to gather light and make distant objects appear larger

refraction: the change in direction (bending) of a light beam as it passes obliquely from one medium to a different one

reflecting telescope: an optical device that uses a concave mirror to gather light and make distant objects appear larger

6. You are looking at an image of a distant object in a telescope. How can you calculate the magnification of the telescope?

7. a) In old pirate movies, the captain of the ship would take a small device out of his pocket and pull on the ends to make it longer. Then the captain would use this device to view distant objects. What is this device?

   b) How does it work?
   c) Draw a diagram of what you think is inside.

8. Write an advertisement to sell telescopes in the 1600s.

9. Part of the search for extraterrestrial life is the search for planets that could support life. Planets, like Earth, shine only with reflected light, so they are not very bright. Also, they are usually small. A planet moving around a star would probably be lost in all the light the star gives off. But as the planet circles the star, it pulls the star itself back and forth. In 1995 astronomers observed this kind of back-and-forth motion of a star. They concluded that the star had a planet! Since then, many more stars with planets have been identified. Discuss how these observations might aid the search for extraterrestrial life.

Stretching Exercises

1. Different kinds of telescopes can be used in observing "invisible" signals, such as ultraviolet, infrared, microwave, and radio waves. Research one of these devices to learn what information they provide.

2. Research the Hubble Space Telescope. You can get plenty of information at the NASA site on the world-wide web.

   • Find out why the Hubble is more capable than ground-based telescopes.
   • Describe some important discoveries that have been made with the Hubble telescope.

Activity 3   Digital Imaging

GOALS

In this activity you will:

- Decode a stream of digital data.
- Design a digital representation.
- Build an image on a rectangular grid.
- Observe pixels and other image units.

What Do You Think?

The digital sound of the CD revolutionized the audio recording industry. The digital picture of High Density Television (HDTV) is about to revolutionize the television industry.

- **What is analog?**
- **What is digital?**
- **How does each work?**

Record your ideas about these questions in your *Active Physics* log. Be prepared to discuss your responses with your small group and with your class.

Integrated Coordinated Science for the 21st Century

For You To Do

1. The "3" in the diagram is represented by a pattern of pixels. The pattern is nine pixels high by five pixels wide.

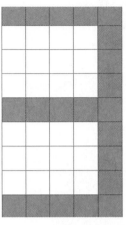

✎ a) On graph paper, make similar pixel patterns to represent the other numbers from zero to nine.

✎ b) On a piece of graph paper, repeat **Part (a)** but with more pixels in the same space. Make the pixels smaller, so you have 27 pixels high and 15 pixels wide. Notice that the total area of the pixels is the same as in **Part (a),** where the pattern was 9 pixels high by 5 pixels wide.

✎ c) If you had more pixels available, how would that affect the quality of the figure? Explain why.

2. You are an engineer who has to design a way to represent numbers from zero to nine. Your display must contain as few pixels as possible, but it still must be easy-to-read.

✎ a) What is the minimum number of pixels you can use? Explain how you found your answer.

Digital Representation

```
1 1 1 1 1
0 0 0 0 1
0 0 0 0 1
0 0 0 0 1
1 1 1 1 1
0 0 0 0 1
0 0 0 0 1
0 0 0 0 1
1 1 1 1 1
```

3. You can use the numbers one and zero to represent numbers, in the same way you used pixels above. A one means the pixel is on, so the pixel is black. A zero means the pixel is off, so the pixel is white, like the rest of the page. Look at the "3" made with zeroes and ones. This is called a digital representation.

✎ a) Choose two other one-digit numbers. On a piece of graph paper, represent these numbers digitally (make a picture with zeroes and ones).

✎ b) See if your lab partners can decode your picture and identify the number.

Active Physics

4. Turn on a computer. Examine the screen closely with a magnifier. Pay special attention to numbers and letters.

✎ a) Describe what you see.

✎ b) How does the existence of letters complicate the digital representation of numbers?

✎ c) Could you tell letters apart with an array of nine by five pixels? If not, how many pixels would you need?

5. Examine a newspaper photo with a magnifying glass.

✎ a) Can you see the individual dots of ink?

✎ b) Look at the individual dots. How many different levels of light, dark, and gray can you find?

✎ c) Examine a black-and-white magazine photo with a magnifier. Compare the dots in the newspaper and magazine photos.

FOR YOU TO READ

Digital Images

As you have seen, an image on a computer monitor is made up of tiny lighted dots. Inside the computer, the image is stored digitally. It is stored as a series of ones and zeroes. These numbers tell whether each dot on the monitor screen is lighted or dark. The dots are all arranged on a grid, which is a rectangular coordinate system. This grid covers the whole screen.

A dot matrix printer makes images in the same way. The dot is either printed or it is not. When you see the dots, your eye and brain combine them to make a letter, number, or picture.

A modern telescope also uses pixels. The astronomer sits in front of a computer monitor. The monitor displays a black-and-white image of the stars. Each pixel can typically display eight different levels of brightness.

In a color computer monitor, each pixel can light up in different colors. A pixel could be red, blue, green, or any combination of the three. And each of these three colors can be shown in many different levels of brightness. That's why making color computer images uses up so much computer memory.

Reflecting on the Activity and the Challenge

You have learned how digital images are made. You have made numbers with patterns of dots, and you have represented the dots with ones and zeroes. You can use what you have learned to create a message for an extraterrestrial. If your message is a picture, you now know how to represent it in a way that can be stored in a computer.

Physics To Go

1. a) Examine a black-and-white print (on photographic paper) with a magnifier. How is this print different from a digital image?

   b) If you scan the print into a computer, you turn it into a digital image. If you printed out the image from the computer, how would it look different from the original print?

   c) Why would some astronomers prefer photographic slides over computer images?

2. a) Suppose you want to buy a printer. A store has two different models. One has 80 dots per centimeter, and the other has 240 dots per centimeter. If the cost and features were similar, which would you choose and why?

   b) Would the extra number of dots per centimeter be more important for representing numbers or letters?

3. a) A standard TV screen has about 400 horizontal lines and about 500 vertical lines. What is the total number of pixels on the screen?

   b) Look at the screen with a magnifying glass. Can you count the lines?

   c) Look at a modern computer video screen with a magnifying glass. Compare the computer image with the TV image.

   d) What makes a modern computer image better than a standard TV image?

4. a) Many computer monitors are available today. Some have more pixels per centimeter than others. Why is the number of pixels per centimeter important?

   b) Would you prefer a monitor with more pixels per centimeter or with fewer? Explain why.

5. a) Suppose you observe a still black-and-white picture on a computer screen. The screen has about half a million pixels. Each of those pixels is stored inside the computer as a one or a zero. Now the picture suddenly bursts into color. Which image requires more memory? How much more? Explain your answer.

   b) Now the picture comes to life as full-motion color video. Which requires more memory, the still image or the video? Explain your answer.

6. a) A traveling spaceship can send back binary messages. Describe how these messages might be made into an image.

   b) If you could send one image to an extraterrestrial, which image would you choose?
   c) How would you transmit it?
   d) What would the extraterrestrial have to know to turn your digital message back into the picture?

7. a) How much time would it take to transmit a digital picture?

   b) Estimate the number of zeroes and ones that you would need.
   c) Select a total time for transmitting the picture.
   d) Estimate the rate of transmission (in zeroes and ones per second) that you would need to send the message in this time.

Stretching Exercises

Find some images from the Hubble Space Telescope. These images can be found at the NASA site on the world-wide web. The original image from the telescope was recorded digitally. It was transmitted to Earth digitally. Sometimes these images are processed by a computer to make them look smoother. Find a smoothed image that you can compare with the original image. Describe the differences.

Activity 4

The Electromagnetic Spectrum

GOALS

In this activity you will:

• Estimate wavelengths.

• Infer distance from travel time.

• Calculate wave frequencies.

What Do You Think?

News reports are often sent from reporters at a distant location to network headquarters by satellite. The report goes from Earth to a satellite and then back to Earth. When you watch the news, you can observe a delay between the end of a question from the anchor and the beginning of the reporter's answer.

• **What causes this delay?**

Record your ideas about this question in your *Active Physics* log. Be prepared to discuss your responses with your small group and with your class.

For You To Do

1. The table lists three different kinds of electromagnetic radiation. Next to each is the antenna, detector, or enclosure for that kind of radiation. Estimate the size of each of the three devices mentioned.

✎ a) Record your estimate in the appropriate column in a table in your log.

Kind of electromagnetic wave	Antenna/ enclosure	Size of antenna/ enclosure	Estimated wavelength	Estimated frequency
Radar	Radar gun			
Microwave	Microwave oven			
Radio	Telescoping antenna			

2. Assume that the wavelength of the electromagnetic radiation is about the same size as the antenna or enclosure given in the table. Make an estimate of each wavelength.

✎ a) Record your estimate in the table.

3. Wave speed, frequency, and wavelength are related by this equation

   speed = frequency × wavelength

In mathematical language:

$$v = f\lambda$$

where v = speed

   f = frequency

   λ = wavelength

✎ a) Solve this equation for the frequency (f). Record this equation in your log.

✎ b) Find the frequency (f) for each of the three kinds of radiation. You will need the speed of light, which is $c = 3.0 \times 10^8$ m/s. Record your result in the table. See the sample calculation for FM radio on the next page.

Example:

An FM radio antenna on a car is approximately 1 m long. Therefore, assume that FM radio waves have a wavelength of 1 m.

$$f = \frac{v}{\lambda}$$

$$f = \frac{3.0 \times 10^8 \text{ ms}}{1 \text{ m}}$$

$$f = 3.0 \times 10^8 \text{ Hz}$$

4. Listen to a recording of communication between the Apollo astronauts on the moon and Mission Control on Earth. Listen closely when someone asks a question and then receives an answer. This communication took place with radio waves. The question traveled by radio from Earth to the moon. After it reached the moon, the astronauts gave the answer. The answer traveled by radio to Earth. On Earth, there was a delay observed between the end of the question and the beginning of the answer. Estimate this time delay.

a) Make several estimates, record each, and take the average.

b) From the time delay you found in **Part (a)**, calculate the distance the radio waves traveled. The speed of light is 3.0×10^8 m/s. You can find the distance using this equation:

$$\text{Distance} = \text{speed} \times \text{time}$$

$$d = vt$$

In this case:

d = the distance the radio waves travel

v = the speed of the radio waves

t = the time of the delay

c) The distance you calculated is the round-trip distance of the radio waves. Calculate the one-way distance (the distance between the Earth and the moon).

d) When the Voyager spacecraft was on its journey to Jupiter, there was a ninety-minute delay between sending a signal from Earth and receiving a response. How far away was the spacecraft?

FOR YOU TO READ

Calculating the Speed of Light

About 400 years ago, Galileo tried to measure the speed of light. He had no instruments, not even a clock. Galileo stood on a hilltop. He uncovered a lantern and began counting. When his assistant on a distant hilltop saw the light from Galileo's lantern, the assistant uncovered his lantern. When Galileo saw the assistant's lantern, he stopped counting. Galileo realized immediately that the speed of light was too large to measure in this way.

Although Galileo did not succeed in measuring the speed of light, he did recognize that light takes time to move from one place to another. That meant light has a speed. Galileo inspired others to try this measurement. Roemer succeeded about seventy years later. He viewed Jupiter's moons. By making observations at two different positions of the Earth's orbit, he was able to increase the total time the light traveled. He measured this larger time accurately. An American, Albert Michelson, made an accurate measurement with rotating mirrors. For his work he won the Nobel prize, the first ever awarded to an American scientist.

PHYSICS TALK

Electromagnetic Waves

Electromagnetic waves include radio, television, microwaves, infrared, visible, ultraviolet, X-rays, gamma rays and radar. They share many properties. All can travel through a vacuum. All travel at the same incredible speed, 3.0×10^8 m/s (186,000 mi. per sec.). This is so fast that if you could set up mirrors in New York and Los Angeles, and bounce a light beam back and forth, it would make 30 round trips in just one second!

319

Reflecting on the Activity and the Challenge

In this activity you have learned about the **electromagnetic spectrum.** Scientists have learned about the universe through observations of electromagnetic waves. You have been told that all the different kinds of electromagnetic waves have the same speed. You have also learned about the speed of light. The most likely way to communicate with extraterrestrial life is through sending and receiving electromagnetic radiation. You can use what you have learned in this activity when you design a plan to look and listen for life in space.

Physics To Go

1. Explain why Galileo was unable to make a measurement of the speed of light.

2. a) In **Step 2** of the activity, you assumed that the detector of electromagnetic radiation is about the same size as the wavelength of the radiation. The light-sensitive cells in the eye have a diameter of about 1.0×10^{-6} m. From this diameter, estimate the wavelength of visible light.

   b) From your answer to **Part (a)**, estimate the frequency of visible light.

3. a) Look at the list of electromagnetic waves.

Physics Words

electromagnetic spectrum: the entire range of radiation extending in frequency from approximately 10^{23} hertz to 0 hertz; this includes gamma rays, x-rays, ultraviolet radiation, visible light, infrared radiation, microwaves, and radio waves

Type of Wave	Typical Frequency
AM radio	1 MHz (10^6 Hz)
FM radio/commercial TV	100 MHz
radar	1 GHz (10^9 Hz)
microwaves	10 GHz
infrared radiation	10^{12} Hz
light	6×10^{14} Hz
ultraviolet radiation	10^{16} Hz
X-rays	10^{18} Hz
gamma rays	10^{21} Hz

   b) Calculate the wavelength of each type of wave.

4. a) The table shows some astronomical distances in meters. For each distance, calculate how long it takes light to go that distance.

From—To	Distance (meters)
Earth to moon	3.8×10^8
Earth to Sun	1.5×10^{11}
Sun to Pluto	5.9×10^{12}
Sun to nearest star	4.1×10^{16}

b) You can use the travel time of light as a unit of distance. For instance, the distance from the Earth to the moon is 1.3 light-seconds. Convert the distance from the Earth to the Sun to light-minutes. To do this, find the number of minutes it takes light to reach the Earth from the Sun.

c) Convert the distance from the Sun to Pluto to light-hours. You need to divide the time in your table by the number of seconds in an hour.

d) Large astronomical distances are measured in **light-years**. This is the distance light travels in one year. Convert the distance from the Sun to the next-nearest star to light-years.

e) If a spacecraft could go almost as fast as the speed of light, how much time would it take to travel to the next-nearest star?

Physics Words

light-year: the distance that light travels in one year (9.46×10^{12} km)

5. a) Think back to how Galileo attempted to measure the speed of light. How much time did it take the light to travel from one hilltop to the other? Assume that the hill was 5 km away.

b) Could Galileo have measured the speed of light with this method? Explain your answer.

6. Do you think that an extraterrestrial would be able to "see" with the same light that you do? If you learned that extraterrestrials could see microwaves, what might that tell you about their "eyes?" Draw an extraterrestrial who can see microwaves. Also draw one that can see radio waves.

7. How could you choose a frequency that beings on a planet in a distant galaxy might be listening to? How would you know?

Stretching Exercises

1. You can measure the speed of sound in the same way that Galileo tried to measure the speed of light. Remember, though, that sound is not part of the electromagnetic spectrum. You and your partner will need a pair of cymbals and a stopwatch. Stand as far apart as possible. Time how long it takes for the sound of the crash of the cymbals to travel the distance between you and your partner. Remember that you can see the crash.

2. Ultraviolet radiation from the Sun can be dangerous to your skin and eyes. Research this problem and make a report to the class.

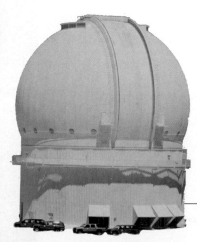

Activity 5

Interference and Spectra

GOALS

In this activity you will:

- Measure the wavelength of light.
- Make a spectroscope.
- Observe spectral lines.

What Do You Think?

All the nuclei (atomic) in your body were created in the stars.

- **How can astronomers figure out what kind of atoms are in stars?**

Record your ideas about this question in your *Active Physics* log. Be prepared to discuss your responses with your small group and with your class.

For You To Do

1. View a white light through a diffraction grating. Repeat the experiment for a different grating. The grating contains very fine parallel lines. Try to view these lines under a microscope.

323

✎ a) Draw a sketch in your log of the patterns produced by your grating.

2. Mount the grating in the laser beam. Mount the screen several meters away from the grating, as shown below. Observe the pattern of spots on the screen.

✎ a) Measure and record the separation between one spot and the next, x.

✎ b) Measure and record the distance from the grating to the screen, L, the hypotenuse of the right triangle, the measurement to be taken.

✎ c) Measure and record the spacing between the lines of the grating, d. Alternately, you can use the spacing given by the manufacturer.

3. From your measurements, find the wavelength of the light. You will use the following equation

$$\lambda = \frac{d\,x}{L}$$

. where λ is the wavelength of laser light

   L is the distance from the grating to the spot on the screen
   x is the separation between the spots
   d is the spacing between lines in the grating

✎ a) Show your calculations in your log.

 **Never look directly at a laser beam or shine a laser beam into someone's eyes. Always work above the plane of the beam and beware of reflections from shiny surfaces.**

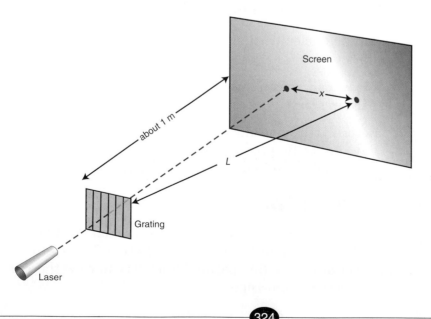

Active Physics

4. Set aside the laser. Fasten the grating to the end of a cardboard tube or film can. Place a slit at the other end, as shown. Be sure the slit lines up with the grating. You have made a spectroscope.

5. Aim your spectroscope at a white light source with the grating toward your eye. What you see is called a *spectrum*.

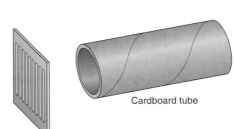

Grating (vertical lines) Cardboard tube Vertical slit

a) Sketch the spectrum you see.

b) White light makes a continuous spectrum. "Continuous" means going on smoothly without a break. How well does "continuous" describe what you see? Explain your answer.

6. With your spectroscope, view the light of several spectrum tubes (hydrogen, mercury, neon, and helium).

a) Sketch what you see for each element.

Spectrum tube

b) What do all these spectra have in common? How is each spectrum different?

7. Measure the wavelength of two of the lines you see in your spectroscope. You will view the spectrum by looking through the grating. Stand about one meter from the tube. Have your partner stand beside the spectrum tube and face you. Be sure you can see the spectrum tube. Your partner will move a finger of one hand outward until it lines up with one of the spectral lines.

a) Measure and record the distance between your partner's finger and the spectrum tube. This will be the value of *x* you will use in the equation:

$$\lambda = \frac{d\,x}{L}$$

325

b) Measure and record the distance between the grating and the spectral line. This will be the value of L you will use in the equation.

c) Calculate the value of the wavelength of this spectral line.

d) Repeat the above calculation for another spectral line.

8. Bite into a wintergreen mint, cracking it into pieces, while your lab partners watch for flashes of light. These mints have the interesting property of giving off flashes of light when they are crushed. The molecules themselves break up, and as they do, they give off light. The light is characteristic of the molecule.

FOR YOU TO READ

Spectra: The Fingerprints of Elements

You have observed the bright spectral lines of hydrogen. Hydrogen can give off light of these colors. Hydrogen can also absorb light of these colors. In that case, you would observe the entire spectrum with thin black lines missing. Either way, these specific colors are evidence of hydrogen.

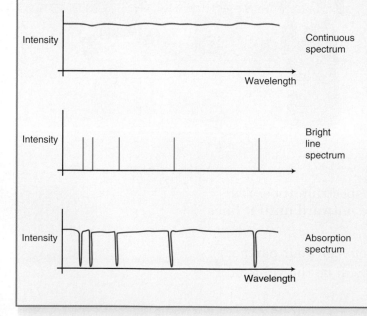

Each different gas gives off a particular kind of light. The spectroscope creates a line spectrum, which shows groups of lines of different wavelengths. The pattern of the lines is a fingerprint for the kind of atom that produced the light. No two people have the same fingerprints, and no two unlike atoms have the same set of spectral lines.

Astronomers use this spectrum to identify those chemical elements present in the outer part of the star. The elements astronomers have identified in stars are the same elements known on Earth. When astronomers analyzed the spectrum of the Sun, they found a set of lines from hydrogen. But there was another set of lines that was a puzzler, because these lines had never been observed on Earth. These lines came from the element helium, and at that time helium had not yet been discovered on Earth. The new element was named after Helios, the Greek Sun god. Of course, scientists soon discovered that helium was indeed present on the Earth as well.

Reflecting on the Activity and the Challenge

In this activity, you have learned how a diffraction grating separates white light into light of all the colors of the rainbow. You have learned that scientists use gratings to reveal the characteristic spectral lines of gases. These lines enable astronomers to identify the gases that are present on stars. You have also learned that there are two different types of spectra—emission spectra and absorption spectra. Emission spectra consist of bright lines, the kind you saw through the spectroscope. Absorption spectra consist of dark lines, the kind in the spectrum of a star. The spectral lines would be known by any advanced civilization and could be the basis of a common language. You can use what you have learned to plan communication with extraterrestrial life

Physics To Go

1. a) Take your spectroscope home and use it to view the spectra of any and all lights or colors you might see. Street lights and lighted signs in store windows are highly recommended.

   b) Some colors are rather "washed out," while others are very "pure" (saturated). Can you explain the difference with the data you obtain from your spectrometer?

2. How might spectra be used to communicate with an extraterrestrial?

3. a) How might spectra be used for receiving communication from an extraterrestrial?

   b) Would spectra information be a common "language" for two civilizations?

4. a) Many spectral lines are not in the visible light range. How are such lines detected and measured?

   b) In communicating with an extraterrestrial, which spectral lines would you send?

   c) If the spectral lines you received from an extraterrestrial were in the infrared, what might this tell you about the intelligent life form?

5. All elements and compounds have their own characteristic spectra. Spectra can identify which element or compound is present, even when very little is present. For instance, tiny amounts of substances that are dissolved in water cannot be detected by chemical tests. But scientists can analyze the spectra of the solution to find out what is in the solution. For example, spectra can be used to investigate:

- toxins in food

- chemical spills in a river

- a drug overdose in an unconscious victim

How could the information from the spectra be used in each case?

6. a) The Delaney clause in the Pure Food and Water Act states that no food can be sold that contains any carcinogen (cancer-causing chemical). It doesn't matter how small the amount of the chemical is, even if it is only a trace. In fact, trace amounts (tiny concentrations) of carcinogens are believed to be harmless. At the time this act was passed, there was no way to test for trace substances, since the spectral analysis had not yet been developed. But now, with spectra, these tiny concentrations can be identified. So because of this law, food could be taken off the market, even though scientists believe it is perfectly safe. Discuss how the government should deal with this conflict.

b) The Delaney clause was changed in 1996! Research this change and describe some of the foods affected by the change. Do you think they are safe to eat?

Stretching Exercises

1. Set up two identical loudspeakers about 1 m apart. Send the same 1000 Hz sine wave from an oscillator to each speaker. Walk around and investigate the changes in loudness. The places where the sound is loud corresponds to the bright spots when using light. This experiment is the audio version of the interference experiment you performed in this activity.

2. Research the field of electronic noise cancellation. Make a report to the class on how it works.

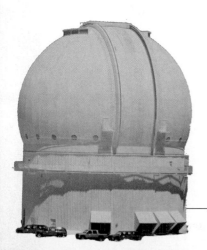

Activity 6

Send Them a Recording

GOALS

In this activity you will:

- Measure small distances with interference.
- Contrast analog and digital recordings.
- Estimate length.
- Convert units.

What Do You Think?

Today you can buy an entire encyclopedia on a compact disc.

- **Is there any limit to how much can be stored on a single disc?**

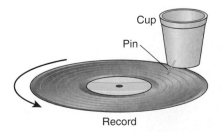

329

For You To Do

1. Carefully place a pin through the bottom of a Styrofoam® cup. Gently let the pin ride in the groove of a long-playing record, as shown in the drawing.

2. Examine the grooves of the record with a magnifier.

   ✍ a) In your log, make a sketch of what you see.

   ✍ b) How do you think the grooves represent the sound?

3. Place a centimeter ruler on the record, so the ruler extends out from the center. Estimate the grooves in one centimeter of the record.

   ✍ a) Record your estimate in your log.

4. Another way to estimate the number of grooves in a centimeter of record is by timing how long it takes to play a one-centimeter band of the record. Read the example below.

   ✍ a) Use this method to make an estimate for your record.

Example:

The number of revolutions per minute is $33\frac{1}{3}$. (This was determined by the manufacturer of the record.)

$$\text{Number of revolutions/second} = \left(\frac{\text{number of revolutions}}{\text{min}}\right)\left(\frac{1\text{ min}}{60\text{ s}}\right)$$

$$= \left(\frac{33\frac{1}{3}\text{ rev}}{\text{min}}\right)\left(\frac{1\text{ min}}{60\text{ s}}\right)$$

$$= 0.56\ \frac{\text{rev}}{\text{s}}$$

Suppose the time to play 1 cm is 150 s.

$$\text{Number of revolutions in 1 cm} = 0.56\text{ rev/s} \times 150\text{ s}$$

$$= 84\text{ rev}$$

The number of grooves per centimeter is about 84.

---

5. There is a third way to find the number of grooves per centimeter. This way uses interference of light, which you investigated in **Activity 5**. You will need a laser pointer. Tape a white piece of paper to a wall to be the screen. Mount a $33\frac{1}{3}$ rpm record 100 cm from the screen as shown in the diagram. You can lean the record against a stack of books.

6. Mount the laser pointer on books so the beam hits the record and is reflected to the screen.

✎ a) What do you see on the screen?

✎ b) Measure and record the distance between two of the central dots.

7. Use the example below.

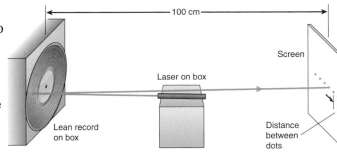

100 cm

Screen

Laser on box

Lean record on box

Distance between dots

Example:

The distance d between the grooves can be found by using the equation:

$$\lambda = \frac{d\,x}{L} \quad \text{or} \quad d = \frac{\lambda L}{x}$$

where $\lambda = 6.7 \times 10^{-5}$ cm

$L = 100$ cm

$x = $ distance between the dots

Assume that $x = 0.5$ cm

Then $d = \dfrac{6.7 \times 10^{-5} \text{ cm} \times 100 \text{ cm}}{0.5 \text{ cm}}$

$= 0.0134$ cm

$\text{Number of grooves/cm} = \dfrac{1}{d} = \dfrac{1}{0.0134} = 75$

✎ a) Calculate the number of grooves per centimeter using this method.

✎ b) How does this calculated value compare with what you found using the first two methods?

8. Suppose you unwound all the grooves in the 1-cm band you have been investigating so you had a groove that made a straight line, as shown.

✎ a) Estimate how long this groove would be.

✎ b) You have already found the number of grooves in the band. If you can find the distance around a typical groove (its circumference), then you can find the total length of the groove. Use the equation for circumference: $C = \pi d$

9. Examine a CD. Observe the surface with a magnifier.

✎ a) What do you see? Do you see grooves?

10. Set up the laser pointer, screen, and CD as you did with the

Never look directly at a laser beam or shine a laser beam into someone's eyes. Always work above the plane of the beam and beware of reflections from shiny surfaces.

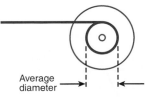

Average diameter

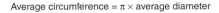

Average circumference = π × average diameter

331

record. You will need a much wider screen this time. Be sure that the CD is 100 cm from the screen.

a) Measure and record the distance between the dots.

b) Calculate the number of grooves per centimeter.

c) How does your number of grooves per centimeter for the CD compare with what you found for the long-playing record? How many times larger is it?

11. Edison made the first grooved recording in 1877. It had about 25 grooves/cm and was a cylinder. In 1887 the record was a disk, played at 78 rpm, and had about 60 grooves/cm. Around 1950 the $33\frac{1}{3}$ rpm and 45 rpm records had about 80 grooves/cm. In 1958, stereo records appeared with about 110 grooves/cm. In 1982 came the first CD, with over 5000 grooves/cm.

a) Graph this data, with time on the horizontal axis.

b) Look at the graph and think about how compressed recordings will become in the future. What do you think will happen?

FOR YOU TO READ

Analog and Digital Representation of Sound

The CD uses a completely different technology to store information than does the long-playing record. The long-playing record contained waves in its grooves. These grooves vibrate a needle and produce sound. When the music is loud, the wave amplitude is large. This is an *analog* representation of sound. The result is a smooth, continuous signal, like the one shown.

The CD provides a *digital* representation. The sound is represented by tiny black pits. A laser beam is aimed at the surface of the CD. If the pit is present, there is no reflection. If there is no pit, the beam is reflected. In the binary system, reflection produces a one. No reflection produces a zero. When the CD is originally recorded, an electronic device samples the sound about 40,000 times each second. These values are converted to binary numbers. They are then recorded on the CD as a stream of pits. The resulting signal looks like the one shown under the diagram.

When the CD plays, the player creates a long string of ones and zeroes. Computer technology in the CD player turns this stream of data into very high-quality audio signals.

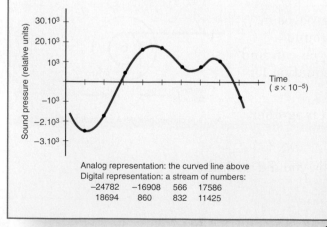

Analog representation: the curved line above
Digital representation: a stream of numbers:

| −24782 | −16908 | 566 | 17586 |
| 18694 | 860 | 832 | 11425 |

Reflecting on the Activity and the Challenge

In this activity you have learned about the way information is stored on long-playing records and compact disks. You have explored three different methods to calculate the number of grooves per centimeter on the long-playing record. You have learned that the analog recording on a long-playing record uses a smooth, continuous groove to represent the vibrations of the sound. The CD, on the other hand, is a record of a sampling of the sound. The samples are stored as tiny pits, which provide a digital recording. You have discovered that there are far more grooves per centimeter in the CD than in the long-playing record. You can use what you have learned to plan a recording to send into space to communicate with extraterrestrials. You can decide if the recording should be analog or digital, and you can explain the physics behind your decision.

Physics To Go

1. a) Explain how sound is stored on a long-playing record.
   b) Explain how sound is stored on a CD.

2. a) What is analog recording?
   b) What is digital recording?
   c) Explain how a long-playing record is an analog recording.
   d) Explain how a CD is a digital recording.

3. a) Is a clock with hands analog or digital? Give a reason for your answer.

   b) Is a clock with only numbers analog or digital? Give a reason for your answer.

4. a) Estimate the length of a popular song in seconds.
   b) A CD samples the sound 40,000 times a second. How many samples are in a popular song?
   c) Each sample represents the loudness at that instant. Eight ones or zeroes are needed to represent the loudness. How many ones and zeroes are needed to represent the whole song?

5. a) The drawing shows the waveform of a note on a guitar. Is this waveform an analog or a digital representation of the sound? Explain how you found your answer.

Sound
pressure

Time

b) How would you make a digital representation of this sound?

6. a) When a CD is made, the sound is sampled 40,000 times per second. How long is the time between samples?

b) What is the frequency range of human hearing?

c) What is the highest frequency that you think would be recorded on a CD?

d) What is the period of this frequency? Hint: The period is the time for one cycle of the sound.

e) If the sampling rate is 40,000 times per second, will that give an accurate representation of this high-frequency sound? Explain your reasoning.

7. When you play a CD, 40,000 sound samples per second come out of the speaker. Why doesn't the music sound choppy?

8. a) What advantages do CDs have over long-playing records?

b) Do records have any advantages over CDs?

9. If a groove on a record is damaged, the needle skips and the sound is distorted. What can go wrong with a CD?

10. What advances in CD technology do you expect in the next ten years?

11. a) You are in charge of creating a recording about our civilization. The recording will be sent into space. How much information can you include on such a record?

b) What information might you include?

c) How would you provide instructions for using the record player or CD player?

Stretching Exercises

Go to the NASA web site and search for information about the Voyager program. Report to the class on the records that were placed aboard the Voyager spacecraft.

Activity 7

The Size of Space

GOALS

In this activity you will:

- Make a scale drawing.
- Measure distances with parallax.
- Apply parallax to astronomical measurements.

What Do You Think?

If you have normal eyesight, your eyes can read a book or see across a stadium.

- **How do your eyes and brain estimate distances in order to focus properly?**

Record your ideas about this question in your *Active Physics* log. Be prepared to discuss your responses with your small group and with your class.

For You To Do

1. Hold your index finger out at arm's length. With one eye closed or covered, line up your index finger with a distant object. You are "sighting" the object. Without moving your index finger, close or cover the other eye instead. What happens to your view of the distant object?

✎ a) In your log explain what happened.

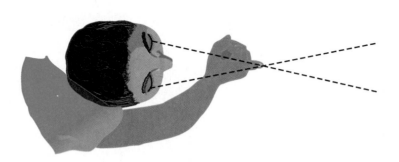

You sighted your finger first from one eye and then from the other. This shift in the position of your finger compared to the distant object is called *parallax*.

Physics Words

parallax: the apparent difference of position of an object as seen from two different places, or points of view

2. You can use **parallax** to find the distance to an object in your lab. You will sight an object from two different places, just as you did in **Step 1**. Find an object on a wall, and stand as far back from it as possible. Mark the place where you are standing. As you sight this object, put a little tape on the floor to show the direction of the object.

3. Now move five meters sideways (that is, parallel to the wall). Again, mark the place where you are standing. Sight the object, and again put tape on the floor to show the direction you are sighting. The line between the two sighting places is called the baseline.

4. Measure the angles between the baseline and the two sight lines, which you marked with tape.

✎ a) Make a scale drawing on graph paper of the triangle made by the baseline and the two sight lines. Hint: First make a rough sketch of the triangle. This sketch will help you select a scale that will show the whole triangle on your graph paper.

5. Find the sides of the triangle from the scale drawing. Then measure the lengths of these sides directly.

✎ a) Record your measurements in your log. How accurate was your parallax measurement?

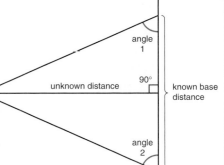

6. If possible, go outside to perform the same activity. This time, stand about 100 m from the object in an area free of traffic. Make the baseline at least 20 m. As before, measure the distance using parallax. Then measure the distance directly and compare your results.

✎ a) Record your measurements and results in your log.

PHYSICS TALK

Astronomers use parallax to measure the distances to nearby stars. The baseline is the diameter of the Earth's orbit, which is 3.0×10^{11} m. As the drawing shows, a telescope makes two sightings of the star. The sightings are six months apart, so the Earth will have moved halfway around the Sun between the sightings.

The star is observed against the background of much more distant stars. From one sighting to the next, the star shifts slightly. This shift is very tiny, even though the baseline is so large.

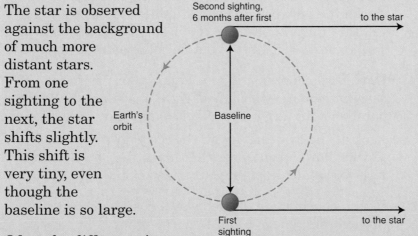

Often the difference in the two angles is only a few thousandths of a degree. With these angles, astronomers in essence construct a triangle by using trigonometry to find the distance with parallax, just as you did in this activity. The star with the greatest parallax shift is the nearest star, Proxima Centauri, which is 4.3 light-years away (or 4.1×10^{16} m) away.

337

Reflecting on the Activity and the Challenge

You have learned how astronomers measure the distances to nearby stars. These distances are important because you would have to travel at least that far to find extraterrestrial life. You can also use these distances in describing how you could communicate with light or radio, which travel at the speed of light. To reach the nearest star, a light beam or radio wave would require 4.3 years.

Physics To Go

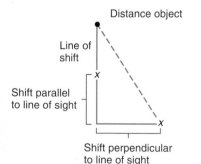

1. a) Explain the concept of parallax.

   b) If you shift the position of your view, why does the position of a nearby object seem to shift?

   c) If you shift the position of your view, why does the position of a very distant object not seem to shift?

   d) Explain why astronomers cannot use parallax to calculate the distance to stars that are very far away.

   e) When you observed parallax in your lab, you observed how something nearby seemed to shift its position compared to an object on a distant wall. When an astronomer observes the shift in the position of a star, how can the astronomer tell that the star shifted? You used an object on a distant wall to observe a shift. What does the astronomer use?

2. a) Look at the drawing. If you change your position *perpendicular* to your line of sight, does that make the parallax shift large or small? Explain your answer.

   b) Look at the drawing. If you change your position *parallel* to your line of sight, does that make the parallax shift large or small? Explain your answer.

Distance object

Line of shift

x

Shift parallel to line of sight

x

Shift perpendicular to line of sight

3. a) Hold a pencil about 20 cm away. Look at the pencil through first one eye and then the other.

   b) What happens to the position of the pencil when you change from one eye to the other?

   c) Make a drawing to explain what happens.

   d) What happens if you look at the pencil through both eyes? What can you see with both eyes that you cannot see with just one?

   e) If you held the pencil twice as far away, what would change? Try it and see.

Pencil

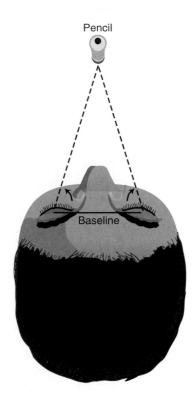

4. a) In **Question 3**, your baseline was the distance between your eyes. Approximately what is this distance?

b) Make a top-view drawing like the one shown. The drawing shows the pencil and your baseline. Also show the object you are sighting.

c) Now double the pencil distance. Make a drawing for this larger distance. On your drawing, show the angle between the line-of-sight from your left eye and the line-of-sight from your right eye.

d) Double the distance again, and again make a drawing. Show the angle between the two lines-of-sight.

e) Make a general statement about how the distance of the object affects the angle between the two lines-of-sight.

5. a) Depth perception is the ability to see how far away something is. Do you need both eyes for depth perception?

b) Have someone hold a pencil about 30 cm in front of you. Cover or close one eye. Reach out and touch the pencil.

c) Now look with both eyes. Reach out and touch the pencil.

d) Was it easier to touch the pencil when you looked with both eyes or only with one? Tell why.

6. a) The speed of light is about 186,000 miles per second. About how many miles are in a light-year (i.e., the distance light travels in one year)? Hint: You will need to find the number of seconds in a year.

b) If you could run five miles per hour, about how long would it take you to run a light-year?

c) The speed of light is about 3×10^8 m/s. About how many meters are in a light-year?

Stretching Exercises

Visit a camera store that sells used cameras. Ask the salesperson to show you how a rangefinder camera works. Research rangefinders in the library and report what you have learned to your class.

Activity 8

The Doppler Effect

GOALS

In this activity you will:

- Describe red shift.
- Sketch a graph.
- Observe changes in pitch.
- Calculate with a formula.

What Do You Think?

You have probably heard the sound of a fast-moving car passing by you.

- **Why is there a change in tone as the car moves by?**

Record your ideas about this question in your *Active Physics* log. Be prepared to discuss your responses with your small group and with your class.

For You To Do

1. Listen to a small battery-powered oscillator. It makes a steady tone with just one frequency. The oscillator is fastened inside a Nerf™ ball for protection.

340

2. Stand about 3 m away from your partner. Toss the oscillator back and forth between you. Listen to the pitch as the oscillator moves. As you listen, observe how the pitch changes as the oscillator moves.

a) How is the oscillator moving when the pitch is the highest?

b) How is the oscillator moving when the pitch is the lowest?

3. Stop the oscillator so you can listen to its "at rest" pitch.

a) With the oscillator moving, record how the pitch has changed compared to the "at rest" pitch. How has the pitch changed when the oscillator is moving toward you?

b) How has the pitch changed when the oscillator is moving away from you?

4. Look at the graph axes shown. The axes show pitch vs. velocity. When the velocity is positive, the oscillator is moving away from you. When the velocity is negative, the oscillator is moving toward you.

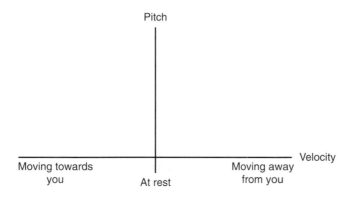

a) On a similar set of axes in your log, sketch a graph of your pitch observations. Explain your graph to the other members of your group.

5. You can do an outdoor Doppler lab using the horn of a moving car as the wave source. Tape-record the horn when the car is at rest next to the tape recorder. Then, with the driver of the car maintaining an agreed-upon speed, tape the sound of the horn as the car passes. Have the driver blow the horn continuously, both as the car approaches and as it moves away. Be very careful to stay away from the path of the car.

341

6. You can determine the observed frequency by matching the recorded tone to the output of an oscillator and loudspeaker. Use this formula:

$$f = f_0\left(\frac{s}{(s-v)}\right)$$

f_0 = frequency when car is at rest

v = speed of the car

s = speed of sound = 340 m/s

 a) When the car is moving toward you, v is positive. When the car is moving away from you, v is negative. Use the equation to calculate the speed of the car from the data you collected.

FOR YOU TO READ

Measuring Distances Using the Doppler Effect

Astronomers measure distances to stars in two different ways. One way is with parallax, but this method works only for the nearest stars. For all other stars astronomers use the Doppler shift of spectral lines. The next-nearest galaxy is Andromeda, more than a million light-years away. Astronomers have observed galaxies at far greater distances, up to about 12 billion light-years away. These incredible distances are measured by observation of the absorption lines, which you investigated in **Activity 5**. These lines are consistently Doppler-shifted toward the red end of the spectrum, and the result is called the "red shift."

All the lines are shifted toward longer wavelengths. Since this is a shift toward lower frequencies, the galaxies are moving away from us. By measuring the size of the shift, astronomers find the speed of distant galaxies. Different galaxies move away at different speeds, but with a clear pattern. The farther away the galaxy, the faster it is moving away, as shown in the graph.

Astronomers explain this result with the Big Bang theory, which says that the universe began in an explosion about 15 billion years ago. After the explosion, the matter in the galaxy continued to move apart, even after the galaxies formed.

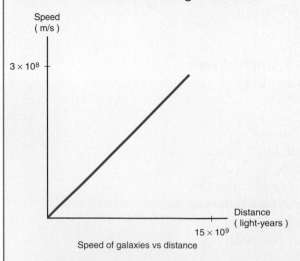
Speed of galaxies vs distance

Reflecting on the Activity and the Challenge

You now have learned how astronomers measure distances in the universe. They use parallax for nearby stars, and they use the **Doppler Effect** for distant galaxies. Since there may be life in the distant galaxies, it is important to understand how far away they are. Since even the closest galaxy is more than a million light-years away, communicating with life from another galaxy will be a great challenge. You can use what you have learned to meet the **Chapter Challenge**, because you now can explain how the distances to galaxies are measured.

Physics To Go

1. a) If a sound source is moving toward an observer, what happens to the pitch the observer hears?

   b) If a sound source is moving toward an observer, what happens to the sound frequency the observer measures?

2. a) If a sound source is moving away from an observer, what happens to the pitch the observer hears?

   b) If a sound source is moving away from an observer, what happens to the sound frequency the observer measures?

3. a) If you watch an auto race on television, what do you hear as the cars go by the camera and microphone?

   b) Sketch a graph of the pitch you hear vs. time. Make the horizontal axis of your graph the time, and the vertical axis the pitch. Hint: Don't put any numbers on your axes. Label the time when the car is going right by you.

   c) Sketch a graph of the frequency you observe vs. time. As in **Part (b)**, label the time when the car is going right by you. Hint: Don't put any numbers on your axes.

4. a) In **Question 3** above, what would happen to your graphs if the speed of the racing car doubled? Make a sketch to show the change.

   b) What would happen to your graphs if the speed of the racing car was cut in half? Make a sketch to show the change.

Physics Words

Doppler effect: a change in the observed frequency of a wave when the source and an observer are in motion relative to each other; the frequency increases when the source or observer approach each other and decreases when they move apart

5. a) Red light has a longer wavelength than blue light. Which light has the lower frequency? You will need the equation:

wave speed = wavelength × frequency

Show how you found your answer.

b) When the oscillator moved away from you, was the pitch you heard lower or higher?

c) When the oscillator moved away from you, was the frequency you heard lower or higher?

d) If light from a distant galaxy is shifted toward the red, is it shifted to a lower or a higher frequency?

e) If the light is shifted toward the red, is the galaxy moving away from Earth or toward Earth?

Stretching Exercises

Watch a broadcast of an auto race. Listen closely to the cars as they zoom past the microphone. Use the Doppler Effect to explain your observations.

Activity 9   Communication Through Space

GOALS

In this activity you will:

- Calculate time delays in radio communications.
- Express distances in light travel-time.
- Solve distance-rate-time problems with the speed of light.

What Do You Think?

In 1865, Jules Verne wrote *From the Earth to the Moon*. In this book, a team of three astronauts were shot to the moon from a cannon in Florida. They returned by landing in the ocean. Verne correctly anticipated many of the details of the Apollo missions.

- **How well do you think *Star Trek* predicts the future?**

Record your ideas about this question in your *Active Physics* log. Be prepared to discuss your responses with your small group and with your class.

For You To Do

1. Alexander Graham Bell's grandson suggested a simple way to talk to Europe long-distance. He recommended placing a long air tube across the bottom of the Atlantic Ocean. He believed that if someone spoke into one end of the tube, someone else at the other end would hear what was said.

   a) Do you think this is practical? Give reasons for your answer.

   b) If the sound could be heard in Europe, how long would it take to send a message? Hint: The distance to Europe is about 5000 km, and the speed of sound is about 340 m/s.

   c) Compare this time with the time to communicate with extraterrestrials in the next galaxy using light. The nearest galaxy is Andromeda, which is about two million light-years away. (It takes light about two million years to get from Earth to Andromeda.)

2. The highest speed ever observed is the speed of light, 3.0×10^8 m/s. In addition, a basic idea of Einstein's Theory of Relativity is that no material body can move faster than light. Radio waves also travel at the speed of light. If Einstein is correct, there are serious limitations on communication with extraterrestrials. Look at the table of distances below. These are distances from the Earth.

to the Sun:	1.5×10^{11} m
to Jupiter:	8.0×10^{11} m
to Pluto:	6.0×10^{12} m
to the nearest star:	4.0×10^{16} m
to the center of our galaxy:	2.2×10^{20} m
to the Andromeda galaxy:	2.1×10^{22} m
to the edge of the observable universe:	1.5×10^{26} m

   a) How long would it take to send a message using radio waves to each place?

   b) How long would it take to send this message and get an answer back?

3. A real-life problem occurred when the Voyager spacecraft was passing the outer planets. NASA sent instructions to the spacecraft but had to wait a long time to find out what happened. The ship had to receive the instructions, take data, and send the data back home.

 a) If the spacecraft was at Jupiter, how long would it take for the message to travel back-and-forth?

 b) If this spacecraft was at Pluto, how long would it take for the message to travel back-and-forth?

4. Make a time-line of Earth history. For the scale of your time-line, make six evenly spaced marks.

 a) Label the time-line like the one shown.

100 million years ago   50 million years ago   Present

 b) On your time-line, label interesting events in Earth's history that occurred during these times. Possibilities include the end of the last Ice Age (10,000 years ago), the evolution of the modern horse (50 million years ago), the evolution of humans (3 million years ago), the Iron Age (1000 BC), the Stone Age (8000 BC), the Middle Ages in Europe (13th century), the beginning of civilization (3000 BC), and the spread of mammals over the Earth (50 million years ago).(Dates given are approximations.)

5. Many scientists believe that intelligent life would most likely be thousands or millions of light-years away.

 a) How would this affect two-way communication?

 b) If you asked a question, how long would it be before a response came back? Would you be able to receive the response?

 c) What questions would you ask? (Note: Think about the distances involved.)

 d) What kind of answers might you expect?

 e) What changes have occurred on Earth over this time period?

 f) What changes would you expect on Earth before the answer came?

 g) Is two-way communication possible over such distances? Is it practical? Is it likely?

Reflecting on the Activity and the Challenge

This activity has prepared you for at least two of the **Chapter Challenges**. You can now describe how the large distances in space would make communication difficult. You now know that you might not live long enough to receive any answer. What you have learned will be valuable for planning a way to communicate over a long period of time. Also, you have begun to think about what kind of message to send to another life form.

Physics To Go

1. a) The speed of sound is about 340 m/s in air. You and another student take gongs outside about 200 m apart. You hit the gong. After hearing the sound of your gong, the other student hits the other gong. How long is it before you hear the sound of the other gong?
   b) How is this experiment similar to the problem of communicating with extraterrestrial life?

2. a) If extraterrestrial life is probably 1000 light-years away, would it be within this galaxy?
   b) If extraterrestrial life is likely probably several million light-years away, would that be within this galaxy? Could it be in the Andromeda galaxy? (Note: This galaxy has over 100 billion stars.)

3. a) The moon is 3.8×10^8 m from the Earth. How long does it take a radio wave to travel from the moon to the Earth?
   b) The Sun is 1.5×10^{11} m from the Earth. How long does it take a light wave to travel from the Sun to the Earth?
   c) Pluto is about 6×10^{12} m from the Sun. How long does it take a light wave to travel from the Sun to Pluto?
   d) The nearest star is 4.3 light-years away from Earth. How long does it take a radio wave to travel from Earth to the nearest star?
   e) This galaxy is about 100,000 light-years across. How long does it take light to go all the way across our galaxy?
   f) The nearest galaxy is more than a million light-years away. How long does it take light to reach us from this galaxy?
   g) The universe is about 15 billion light-years across. How long does it take light to cross the universe?

4. a) In *Star Trek*, the spaceship can move at "warp speed." This speed is faster than the speed of light. How is "warp speed" important for space travel?

   b) Do you think "warp drive" is likely to be developed? Is it possible? Explain your answers.

5. Suppose your job is to make a plan to send people in space ships to explore nearby galaxies. How would the distances in space affect your plan?

6. a) How would you choose a language for communication with extraterrestrials?

   b) Many scientists suggest that a good starting point is to describe the periodic table of the elements. Do you agree? Explain your answer.

   c) Is there any evidence that extraterrestrials would observe the same elements, with the same properties, that you observe? Tell what the evidence is.

   d) Do you think another advanced civilization would have already discovered the periodic table? Tell why or why not.

   e) How would you start to create a language?

   f) How would you begin communication?

7. a) Suppose that intelligent extraterrestrial beings exist. Suppose that you are able to communicate with them. Why would you want to?

   b) Should you be afraid of extraterrestrial beings?

   c) Is it more likely that they would help Earth or enslave Earth? (Note: Consider the distances involved.)

8. a) What is known of the Earth of 2000 years ago?

   b) It takes 2000 years for a spaceship to travel to a star. When the travelers arrive at the star, would their information about the Earth be up-to-date? Explain why or why not.

   c) If the trip to another star took 10,000 years, would such a trip be worthwhile? Explain why or why not.

9. A record was sent into space in an effort to communicate with extraterrestrials.

   a) If you were on the team designing the record, what music would you include?
   b) What photographs would you include?
   c) What drawings would you include?
   d) Have you fairly represented the majority of the world with your choices?

10. a) Make a list of movies, books, and TV shows that involve trips to other parts of the galaxy or extraterrestrials visiting the Earth.
    b) Very briefly describe the plot of the story.
    c) How accurately is science represented?

Stretching Exercises

1. Read the Carl Sagan book, *Contact*, or watch the movie. What features of the book and movie have you considered in this chapter? What features have been ignored?

2. Look up the messages that were placed on the Pioneer and Voyager spacecraft. Make a report to the class on how this plaque communicated information about humans.

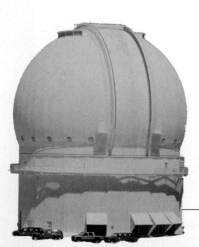

Dr. Neil Tyson

Is there another planet out there with beings looking for us?

"Nearly all scientists agree there is a strong likelihood that there is life on other planets," says Dr. Neil Tyson, the director of the Hayden Planetarium at the Museum of Natural History in New York City and an astrophysicist at Princeton University. "Although communication with extraterrestrial life is not the research focus of most astrophysicists, discovering a planet with any life—simple algae even—would be exciting."

His focus has been to determine the "structure of our galaxy," a task which he compares to "an unborn child trying to figure out what his mother looks like." Dr. Tyson and his colleagues must look past The Milky Way, at other galaxies hundreds of light-years away in an effort to understand by comparison.

The effort to understand other galaxies and other planets may one day allow us to affect what happens on earth. "We look at Venus, a planet similar in size to Earth" says Dr. Tyson. "Why is it so hot? Well, there was a runaway greenhouse effect. Why is there no water on Mars? There is evidence that there was water there at one time. What happened?" These are questions that astrophysicists will continue to explore by "pushing the limits of technology."

"We now know of more planets outside of our solar system than inside and they have all been discovered in this decade," claims Dr. Tyson. "When searching for a planet we look for the Doppler Effect in the host star," he continues. "A planet and a star orbit around a common center of gravity and we notice the presence of the planet by the jiggling of the host star. This concept, and others, has been predicted for some time but only substantiated in this decade with the development of both high-powered telescopes and sensitive detectors."

As for communication with extraterrestrial life, Dr. Tyson describes it as "an interesting challenge." One of the most interesting parts of the challenge is the language in which to communicate. "Certainly not English," he says. "Science is something that would appear the most universal. The periodic table of elements, for instance. The symbols may be different but the organization may be something we have in common. Nothing, of course, is certain. It is literally a shot in the dark."

351

Chapter 6 Assessment

All the activities you have done in this chapter were designed to give you the information, knowledge, and understanding to complete the chapter challenge. With what you have learned, you will be able to:

Outline a plan for how you would communicate with extraterrestrial life forms you might discover.

Decide what to say to extraterrestrial beings using science that they can understand and presenting them with important information about human life and Earth.

Write an essay describing what could be learned from contact with extraterrestrial beings.

Participate in a mock hearing of the Space Committee of the United States Senate regarding a request from scientists for $3 billion for a project to search for extraterrestrial life forms.

What do you think? Is there anyone out there listening to your communication?

Review the criteria for grading which you and your class developed at the beginning of this chapter. Do you wish to further modify the suggested grading scheme?

Part 1:

Choice of methods
to communicate: 40 points

Explanation of the science:

   correct statement of
   science concepts: 25 points

   how **Chapter 6** activities
   present these concepts: 35 points

Part 2:

Choice of language for communication; discussion of how extraterrestrials will be able to understand the science:

   correct statement
   of science used in
   communication: 25 points

   how extraterrestrials
   might use the science
   in a message: 25 points

   Choice of
   message content: 25 points

Description of how
the content is important: 25 points

Physics You Learned

Distances in the universe

Communication with extraterrestrial life

Light-years

Electromagnetic radiation

Interference of light

Spectra

Doppler shift

Red shift

Concave and convex lenses

Real and virtual images

Focal length

Telescopes

Analog and digital recordings

Digital images

Information storage

Unit 3

Active Chemistry™

Making Connections

You are now going to start a unit of *Active Chemistry*. You investigate the world of chemistry every time you cook a meal. You mix chemicals together, heat them, and new chemicals appear. There are many different foods. How many different chemicals are there? In the *Active Physics* unit you learned about the properties of light waves and sound waves. Now you will explore properties of chemicals and try to make your complex world simpler to understand.

The laws of physics are also the laws of chemistry. In chemistry, you will continue to study forces, energy, and atomic structure. You will learn about these laws of nature from a new perspective.

What Do You Think?

• How do you think that colors are created on the atomic level?

• How is sugar different from salt?

• What makes some chemicals nutritious and others dangerous to eat?

Record your ideas about this in your log. Be prepared to discuss your response with your small group and the class.

For You To Try

• Look up a recipe for making a cake. When do you think that chemical reactions are taking place?

• Compare the labels on a box of cereal and a cleaning fluid. What similarities and differences are apparent?

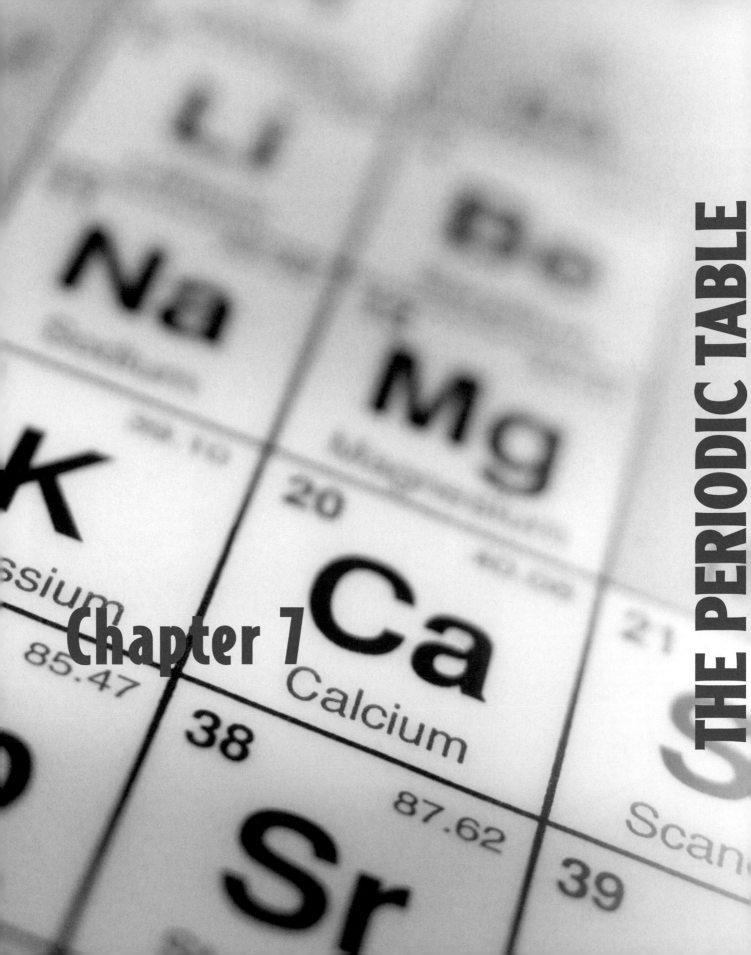

Chapter 7

THE PERIODIC TABLE

The Periodic Table

Scenario

Every time you say you like or don't like something, you are putting it into a category. You have probably developed categories for many things in your life. You may have categories for food you eat for breakfast, as opposed to dinner, or for clothes you wear to school, as opposed to at home. Can you imagine what your life would be like if nothing were sorted into categories? What if you went shopping in a supermarket that displayed milk next to shoe polish, next to oranges, next to oatmeal, next to hams, next to orange juice, next to detergent? Where would you look for yogurt, shoelaces, corn flakes, ground beef, lemonade, and soap?

That kind of supermarket display pretty much describes the state of chemistry in the mid-19th century. By then chemists had identified and isolated a large number of chemical elements, but they needed a way to sort them into categories—much as a  supermarket groups milk with yogurt, shoe polish with shoe laces, oatmeal with corn flakes, ham with ground beef, orange juice with lemonade, and detergent with soap.

Like similar items in a supermarket, some chemical elements were recognized to share similar chemical properties. The first chemist to arrange these elements successfully into a pattern according to their properties was the Russian, Dimitri Mendeleev.

One of the things Mendeleev did was to write down everything that was known about each element on a small card. Then he moved the cards around until he got an arrangement that showed the groups of elements with similar properties.

Dimitri Mendeleev

In Mendeleev's time the periodic table was developed as a way to arrange elements according to their chemical behavior. Surprisingly, it then revealed information about the structure of the atoms of those elements as well.

By writing the properties of the elements onto separate cards and arranging them, Mendeleev created a puzzle, and he solved that puzzle when he arranged the first version of what is now known as the Periodic Table of the Elements. The table was independently created at the same time by the German, Julius Lothar Meyer.

Chapter Challenge

Your challenge in this chapter is to develop a game related to Mendeleev's Periodic Table of the Elements.

How the game is played, whether on a table, with cards, on a computer, or with equipment that only you might choose, is up to you. You might even choose to emphasize some aspects of the periodic table over others, or to focus on some types of information presented by the table rather than others. However, you need to keep in mind the criteria you and your teacher establish.

Criteria

How will your game be graded? What qualities should a good game have? Discuss these issues in small groups and with your class. You may decide that some or all of the following qualities should be graded:

- how well the game shows your understanding of the periodic table;

- how well the game enables players to learn about the periodic table;

- how interesting the game is to play;

- how long the game takes to play;

- whether the game is sequential or can be continued.

Once you have determined the list of qualities for evaluating the game, you and your class should also decide how many points should be given for each criterion. Make sure that you understand all the criteria as well as you can before you begin. Your teacher may provide you with a sample rubric to help you get started.

Activity 1 Organizing a Store

GOALS

In this activity you will:

• Plan the arrangement of the items for sale in a store.

• Analyze trends in the arrangement of the store.

• Relate the arrangement of items in the store to the arrangement of elements in the periodic table.

What Do You Think?

Some supermarkets now sell books, flowers, and prescription drugs in addition to eggs, meat, and cereal.

• How many different items do you think that a supermarket has in its inventory?

Record your ideas about this question in your *Active Chemistry* log. Be prepared to discuss your responses with your small group and the class.

Investigate

1. Suppose that you decided to go into the business of opening and running a supermarket grocery store. In your group, brainstorm a list of between 50 and 100 items you would sell at your supermarket.

   A member of your group should volunteer to record the items suggested by all members of the group. Everyone, including the person serving as recorder, should participate in suggesting items to be sold.

   a) Make a map showing the locations of all of the items in your store. Give some thought to what will be at the front of each aisle, and what will be at the back, and how the store will be arranged from left to right.

b) Keep in mind which items you want shoppers to see as they enter the store and which should be near as they approach the cash register. Would either of these factors alter your arrangement?

c) Consider the arrangement of items going from left to right across your store. Why did you choose to arrange the items that way?

Reflecting on the Activity and the Challenge

Organizing 50 to 100 items in your store is not unlike the problem faced by Mendeleev when he organized about the same number of chemical elements into the periodic table. In the following activities you will learn about the properties of chemical elements that led Mendeleev to arrange the elements the way he did and the information about them provided by the periodic table. This activity, in which you were asked to organize a group of items familiar in your everyday experience, was designed to acquaint you with some of the problems Mendeleev faced in the hope that you can better appreciate what he did. You may wish to build this experience into the game you design.

Chemistry to Go

1. What is the pattern or arrangement in your store's aisles?

2. Choose one aisle in your store. Describe the arrangement of items going from the front of the store to the back of the store. What is the trend (or general drift) in that aisle?

3. A new item is brought into the store — chocolate covered peanuts. Where would you place this item? Provide an explanation for your decision.

4. Your store decides to sell napkins, plates, and other decorations for Thanksgiving. How will you adapt your store arrangement to accommodate these items?

5. You would like people to purchase a certain item because it gives you a big profit. Where would you place it in your store and why?

6. One of the characteristics of Mendeleev's original periodic table was a series of blank spots. Since As and Se didn't have anything in common with Al and Si, but do with P and S, Mendeleev decided there must be a couple of other elements yet to be discovered. He left spaces for them and put As under P and Se under S where they belong. What would such a "blank" correspond to in your store?

Activity 2

Elements and Their Properties

GOALS

In this activity you will:

- Apply ancient definitions of elements to materials you believe are elements.

- Test some properties of several common chemical elements.

- Classify elements as metals, nonmetals or neither.

- Learn to differentiate between chemical and physical properties of materials.

- Organize a table of the elements you tested based on their properties.

- Practice safe handling of corrosive chemicals in the laboratory.

What Do You Think?

Throughout the ages of history, philosophers and scientists have talked about "the elements." Reference to elements is most frequent today in the field of chemistry.

- What is a chemical element?

Record your ideas about this question in your *Active Chemistry* log. Be prepared to discuss your responses with your small group and the class.

Investigate

1. Work individually first and then in your group.

   a) Make a list of four or more substances you use or encounter in your everyday experience that meet your definition of element.

2. The ancient Greeks believed that the four elements were: earth, air, fire, and water.

   The alchemists of the early Renaissance identified three elements: mercury, sulfur, and salt.

   a) Does each of the above "elements" satisfy your definition of an element? Why or why not?

3. Your teacher will provide a series of jars containing several common chemical elements: aluminum, copper, iodine, iron, magnesium, silicon, sulfur, and zinc.

You will investigate the properties of these elements. By observing common properties, you may gain an insight into how an organizational chart can be created for all of the known elements. Observe the sample of the chemical element in each jar (without removing any).

on the apparatus goes on, that means that a complete circuit is created, and an electric current is passing through both the light bulb and the sample of the element in the jar.

It is important to make sure that the part of the apparatus immersed into the elements stays dry and is not contaminated by any of the other elements it has been immersed in. Also, use steel wool to polish the metal strips before you test them.

Safety goggles and a lab apron must be worn during this activity.

Element	Initial observations	Conducts electricity	Reacts with HCl	Metal or nonmetal
aluminum				
copper				
iodine				
iron				
magnesium				
silicon				
sulfur				
zinc				

a) Record your observations in a table. You may wish to use a table similar to the above to record your observations in this activity.

4. One of the properties of the chemical elements on Mendeleev's cards was the ability of the element to conduct electric current.

Insert the terminals of the electrical conductivity apparatus into the jar containing each element. If the light

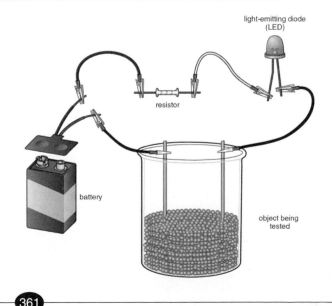

light-emitting diode (LED)

resistor

battery

object being tested

a) Test the samples of each element with the electrical conductivity apparatus and record whether they conduct electric current (yes) or not (no).

5. Another of the properties of each chemical element known to Mendeleev was how it reacts with acid.

   You must still be wearing your safety goggles. Pour 5 mL of 1 M hydrochloric acid into each of eight small test tubes. Use a chemical scoop or tongs to remove a small portion of each element from the jar and add it to the hydrochloric acid. It is important to add the hydrochloric acid to the test tube first so that you will not be surprised by a reaction by

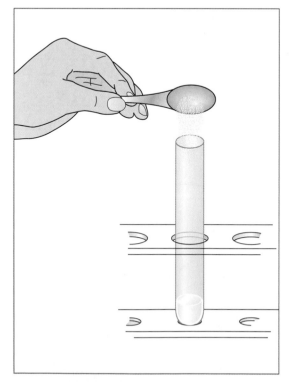

pouring acid over a reactive chemical element. Place a piece of white paper in the background behind the test tube and observe the reaction between the element and hydrochloric acid by looking through the side of the test tube.

a) Test small samples of each element for their reaction with hydrochloric acid and record whether they react with the acid (yes) or not (no).

b) For those that do react, try to determine whether all exhibit the same type of reaction (do they all do the same thing?) and compare the relative vigor of the reactions. If the reaction is vigorous, include a + sign next to your "yes." If the reaction is weak, place a − sign next to your "yes."

6. Dispose of the contents of the test tubes and clean the test tubes as directed by your teacher. Wash your hands.

7. A metal is generally a solid that is shiny, malleable, and a good conductor of heat and electricity. A nonmetal is generally dull, brittle, and is a poor conductor of heat and electricity.

   Classify each of the elements you observed as either a metal or nonmetal.

a) Record your observations in the table in your *Active Chemistry* log.

8. Create index cards for each of the elements and find a way to sort them

based on their properties. You may try arranging them and/or color coding them. Your method of sorting will be successful if you can quickly find an element and know from its position whether it:

- conducts electricity;
- reacts with HCl;
- is metallic or nonmetallic.

a) Record your method of sorting the cards in your *Active Chemistry* log.

Chem Talk

PHYSICAL AND CHEMICAL PROPERTIES

Classifying Elements Using Properties

You began this activity by trying to define the meaning of a chemical element. The ancient Greek philosopher Aristotle defined an element as "a body into which other bodies may be analyzed ... and not itself divisible into bodies different in form." The first modern definition of chemical element, which is not much different, is from Robert Boyle: "Bodies, which not being made of any other bodies, or of one another, are the ingredients of which all those ... mixed bodies are ... compounded." We now state that an element is any material that cannot be broken down by chemical means into simpler materials.

Before the mid-19th century, scientists were preoccupied with discovering elements and observing and recording their properties. Then they tried to organize the elements they had discovered in a useful way. At first, they listed the elements alphabetically. However, every time a new element was discovered, the whole list had to be changed. They tried other methods. Could elements be organized by properties like state, color, or taste? None of these methods appeared practical or safe! However, chemists worldwide were sure that elements existed in families that had similar physical and chemical properties. To the Russian scientist, Dimitri Mendeleev (1843 - 1907), the development of a tool to organize the elements began the same way that so much of science inquiry begins, with a simple question. The question Mendeleev wanted answered was: "What is the relationship of the elements to one another and to the chemical families to which

→

Checking Up

1. Define a chemical element.

2. What question did Mendeleev use to guide his science inquiry?

3. In your own words, describe the difference between a physical and a chemical property.

they belong?" At that time there were 63 known elements. To help him with his organization, he developed a card game, much the same as you did in this activity. He wrote the properties of each known element on a different card and then spent many hours arranging and rearranging the cards. He was looking for patterns or trends in the data in front of him. Mendeleev, however, had more information on his cards than you presently have. In the following activities, you will look at additional properties of elements that will help you organize your game.

Physical and Chemical Properties

In this activity you observed several properties of the elements you were provided. You probably initially observed the color and the state of the element. You then investigated whether or not the chemical element conducted electricity. You could have also observed the luster, measured the density or the strength, or determined the malleability of each element. In each case, you would not have changed the element itself. In this investigation the element still looked the same in the jar after you removed the electrical conductivity apparatus as it did when you initially inserted it. If measuring a property of a substance does not change the chemical identity of one substance, it is called a **physical property**.

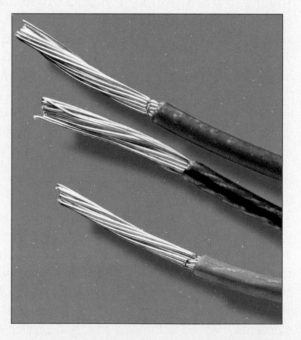

Chem Words

physical property: a property that can be measured without causing a change in the substance's chemical composition

chemical property: a characteristic that a substance undergoes in a chemical reaction that produces new substance(s)

On the other hand, when you observed whether the chemical element reacted with hydrochloric acid, the element clearly changed. A **chemical property** is the kind of reaction that a substance undergoes. Measuring chemical properties changes the chemical composition of a substance.

Reflecting on the Activity and the Challenge

In this activity you learned not only the definition of a chemical element but also some of the properties of chemical elements. Measuring these properties not only enabled Mendeleev to place the elements in his periodic table but also allowed other chemists to identify the elements. You have tried to sort the cards of elements in the same way that Mendeleev did. Perhaps your periodic table game can have sorting cards as one part of the strategy.

Chemistry to Go

1. Make a list of three more physical properties of a chemical element that you could observe.

2. Make a list of three more chemical properties of a chemical element that you could measure.

3. Why did you want the metals to be clean or polished before you tested them for electrical conductivity?

4. What criteria did you use to differentiate metals from nonmetals in this investigation?

   a) Is this a valid statement of a trend you saw: as the color of the element becomes darker, the element is less metallic? Support your assessment of this statement with evidence that you observed in your investigation.

   b) Is this a valid statement of a trend you saw: the elements react with hydrochloric acid more as you move down a list of the elements listed in alphabetical order? Support your assessment of this statement with evidence that you observed in your investigation.

Preparing for the Chapter Challenge

Prepare a set of index cards for each of the elements with which you are familiar. Record as many properties of each element you know on the card. Use your observations in the following activities and any research you complete on your own to add information to each card.

Activity 3   Atoms and Their Masses

GOALS

In this activity you will:

- Explore the idea of atoms by trying to isolate a single atom.

- Measure how many times greater mass a copper atom has than an aluminum atom.

- Practice careful laboratory technique with measuring masses and filtration.

- Locate sources of the variation in the class's experimental results.

- Compare Dalton's experimental results to the masses of atoms known today.

- See that atoms react in definite proportions of mass when forming a compound.

- Relate the mole concept to real quantities.

- Use scientific notation in calculations.

What Do You Think?

Atoms are the smallest, indivisible part of an element.

- When did you first hear of atoms? What did they mean to you then, and what do they mean to you now?

- Use the following headings: Things I Know about Atoms, Things I Think I Know about Atoms, Things I Would Like to Know about Atoms. Include at least one entry under each heading.

Record your ideas in your *Active Chemistry* log. Be prepared to discuss your responses with your small group and the class.

Investigate

1. One way to think about an atom is to imagine trying to isolate a single atom from a large number of atoms.

   Take a piece of aluminum foil and cut it in half. Take one of the resulting pieces and cut it in half again. Repeat this process with each successive half until you cannot make another cut.

   a) In your *Active Chemistry* log, record how many cuts you were able to make. How does the size of the smallest piece of aluminum compare to the size of the original piece? Does the smallest piece of aluminum have the same properties as the original piece of aluminum foil?

2. An atom is the smallest part of an element. Since you can still cut the aluminum in pieces, you have not reached the size of a single atom.

Now imagine that there may be a way to cut the smallest piece of aluminum you have into even smaller and smaller pieces.

a) How small can the smallest piece be and still retain the properties of aluminum? Could you cut the piece in half and half again 10 more times? 100 more times? 1000 more times?

Using your imagination of cutting and cutting, you will eventually get to one atom of aluminum.

3. Chemists combine elements to form new substances. By measuring the amounts of elements used and substances formed, they are able to draw conclusions about the properties of the elements involved. You will study the reaction between aluminum metal and a solution of copper (II) chloride.

Read through the procedure below.

a) Make a table in your *Active Chemistry* log for the data you will be collecting. You will need room for measurements (mass) and observations. You can use a table similar to the one provided below.

4. Check your balance to make sure that it reads zero with nothing on it. Then measure the mass of a 50-mL beaker.

a) Record the mass in your *Active Chemistry* log.

Safety goggles and a lab apron must be worn during this activity.

Finding the mass of aluminum	
1. Mass of empty 50-mL beaker	g
2. Mass of beaker and aluminum foil	g
3. Calculate the mass of aluminum from 1 and 2 above.	g
Finding the mass of copper (II) chloride	
4. Mass of weighing paper	g
5. Mass of paper and copper (II) chloride	g
6. Calculate the mass of copper (II) chloride from 4 and 5 above.	g
Finding the mass of the product	
7. Mass of dry filter paper	g
8. Mass of filter paper with product, after drying	g
9. Calculate the mass of the product material from 7 and 8 above.	g

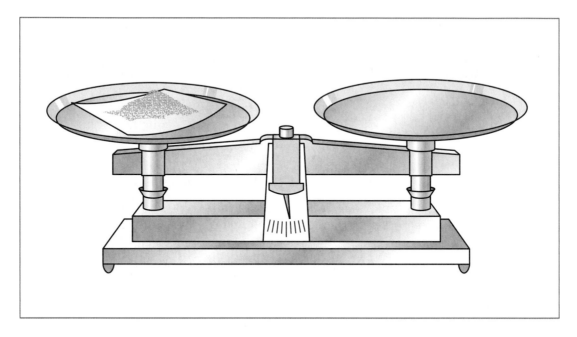

5. Measure out approximately 0.20 g of aluminum foil into the empty beaker. Try to get your mass measurement close to the assigned value.

   If you have a centigram balance, you'll need to adjust the balance to read 0.20 more grams than the beaker alone. Then add pieces of aluminum foil until it rebalances.

   If you have an electronic balance, simply add pieces of aluminum foil until the display indicates 0.20 g more than the empty beaker.

   a) Record the value that you obtain, even though you might not hit the target value.

6. Measure the mass of a piece of weighing paper.

   Place approximately 2.00 g of copper (II) chloride on the weighing paper. (The chemical elements you would expect to find in copper (II) chloride

Wipe up any spills immediately.

are copper and chlorine.) Again, remember that your target value is 2.00 g and that you may be slightly over or under this value.

   a) Record the masses in your *Active Chemistry* log.

7. Add the copper (II) chloride to the beaker.

   Next add water to the beaker until it is approximately half full.

   a) Record your observations in your *Active Chemistry* log. Consider including the following: how the beaker feels when you touch it; what you hear when you listen closely to the beaker; what you see happening in the beaker.

   b) What color forms on the aluminum foil? What do you think is responsible for this color? Where is the color coming from?

8. You will now need to find the mass of the substance formed in the chemical reaction. You can filter out this substance and then find its mass.

First measure the mass of a piece of dry, clean filter paper.

a) Record the mass in your *Active Chemistry* log.

9. Set up a filtration system, as shown in the diagram below.

10. Wait until you no longer see or hear any reaction between the aluminum foil and copper (II) chloride and the liquid begins to clear up. Pour the contents of the 50-mL beaker into the funnel. You should rinse the beaker a couple of times with some water to be sure that all of the contents of the beaker are transferred.

Remove the filter from the funnel and place it on a piece of folded paper towel and allow it to dry overnight. Label the paper towel so that you can identify your filter paper.

Clean and put away your equipment and dispose of your chemicals as directed by your teacher. Wash your hands.

11. When the filter paper is dry, measure the mass of the filter paper and its contents. Dispose of the filter paper and its contents as directed by your teacher. Wash your hands.

a) Record the mass in your *Active Chemistry* log. Determine and record the mass of the contents of the filter paper.

b) What element is inside the filter paper?

12. The reaction you witnessed is called a **single-displacement reaction**. In this reaction, a single element (aluminum) replaces another element (copper) in its combined form (copper (II) chloride). As a result of this reaction, the copper leaves its combined form to become an uncombined, or free element. The aluminum leaves its uncombined form to join with the chlorine to form a new compound. It's time to look at your data and see if you can make some sense of the numbers.

a) How many grams of aluminum did you start with? How many grams of copper did you end up with (contents of the dry filter paper)?

b) How many times as great is the mass of the copper as compared

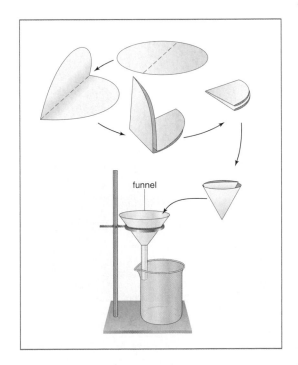

funnel

to the mass of aluminum you originally used? (What is the ratio of mass of copper to mass of aluminum?)

c) If one atom of copper is released for each atom of aluminum that becomes combined (with chlorine), the masses of copper and aluminum determined in (a) should contain the same number of atoms. What does this tell you about the relative masses of copper and aluminum atoms? The number of atoms in 0.20 g of aluminum EQUALS the number of atoms in 0.71 g of copper. How many times more massive is a copper atom than an aluminum atom? (You may wish to compare

objects that you are familiar with: a dozen bowling balls of mass 60.0 kg can be compared to a dozen eggs of mass 2.4 kg. Since there are a dozen bowling balls and a dozen eggs, you can find that the bowling balls are 25 times as heavy as the eggs (60.0 kg/2.4 kg).

13. Recall that every group in your class reacted the same mass of aluminum with the same mass of copper (II) chloride. Discuss the similarities and differences in the data and calculations among the groups in the class.

a) Record your thoughts on how and why the results are similar and/or different.

Chem Talk

ATOMIC MASS

Atoms

In **Activity 2**, you defined the term element and explored the properties of some common elements. In this activity, you focused on atoms. An **atom** is the smallest representative part of an element. The ancient Greek philosopher Aristotle did not believe in the existence of atoms. In his thinking, if atoms did exist, there would have to be empty space between them.

Aristotle

Chem Words

atom: the smallest representative part of an element

Aristotle did not believe it was possible to have empty space. Not everyone agreed with Aristotle. Another ancient Greek named Democritus believed that matter was made up of tiny particles that could not be broken down further. He called the particles atoms, from the Greek word *atomos*, meaning indivisible.

If you could have continued cutting the aluminum foil until it could no longer be cut, by any means, you would have reached one atom of aluminum. A mind-expanding fact is that if you started with 27 g of aluminum, you would find that there are 6.02×10^{23} atoms of aluminum. Nobody has ever counted this nor could they. Scientists have determined this number by other means and are very confident that it is correct.

Masses of Elements and Compounds in a Reaction

By the turn of the 19th century, chemists were combining elements to form new substances. The new substance was called a **compound**, because the atoms of the elements were believed to combine to form what they called a compound atom. The chemists were also particularly interested in measuring the amounts of elements used and substances formed. Their first attempts in determining masses were wrong, possibly due to the equipment that they had available at that time.

John Dalton, an early 19th century chemist who did much to advance the belief in the existence of atoms, expected that atoms combined in the simplest possible relationship. He reported that seven pounds of oxygen reacted with one

John Dalton

Chem Words

compound: a material that consists of two or more elements united together in definite proportion

pound of hydrogen to form water. Accurate modern experiments give eight pounds to one. We will use modern values rather than historical ones to avoid confusion. Dalton reported that five pounds of nitrogen reacted with one pound of hydrogen to form ammonia. He also reported that seven pounds of oxygen reacted with five pounds of nitrogen to form a compound he called nitrous gas.

In 1809, Joseph Gay-Lussac reported that the hydrogen reacting with oxygen to form water occupied twice as much volume as the oxygen. He also noted that the hydrogen reacting with nitrogen to form ammonia occupied three times as much volume as the nitrogen. Furthermore, he found that equal volumes of nitrogen and oxygen reacted to form nitrous gas (now known as nitric oxide or nitrogen monoxide, NO).

Gay-Lussac's data was inconsistent with Dalton's assumption that water, ammonia, and nitrous gas are formed from one atom of each of the combining elements. This inconsistency was subsequently resolved by Amadeo Avogadro, who furthered the understanding of the correct chemical formulas and atomic masses.

Relative Mass of Atoms

Chem Words

atomic mass unit (amu): a unit of mass defined as one-twelfth of the mass of a carbon-12 atom

atomic mass: atomic mass is determined by the mass of the protons and neutrons of the atom

law of definite proportions: the composition of a pure substance is always the same or the elements of the compound always combine in the same proportion by mass

Eventually, chemists determined a scale of relative masses of atoms through the systematic study of chemical reactions. By measuring the masses of two elements reacting with each other and knowing the formula for the compound that was formed, the relative mass of the two elements was determined. In this way, chemists were able to determine, for example, that one element has twice the mass of a second element. Relative mass does not tell you the exact mass measured in kilograms. It does provide a relative scale. Comparison of many reactions resulted in a scale of relative masses. Atoms of carbon were found to have a mass 12 times greater than the mass of hydrogen atoms, whereas oxygen atoms were found to have a mass 16 times greater than the mass of hydrogen. The units for this scale are called **atomic mass units**, defined in such a way that the mass of one type of carbon (carbon-12) is exactly 12 atomic mass units. The average mass of an atom of a given element in atomic mass units is known as the **atomic mass**. Atoms of hydrogen have an atomic mass of one unit. In addition to the physical and chemical properties of

Element	Relative atomic mass
Aluminum	26.98
Copper	63.55
Iodine	126.90
Iron	55.85
Magnesium	24.31
Silicon	28.09
Sulfur	32.06
Zinc	65.38

elements, the relative mass (incorrectly called weight) of each element was known and used by Mendeleev as he organized his table. The atomic mass is still one of the most prominent pieces of information provided for each element on the periodic table. The table gives the relative atomic masses of the eight elements that you observed in **Activity 2**.

Checking Up

1. What is the difference between an element and a compound?
2. What is an atom?
3. How is an atomic mass unit defined?
4. How can the existence of atoms help to explain the Law of Definite Proportions?

The Law of Definite Proportions

Chemists at the beginning of the 19th century noted that eight pounds of oxygen always reacted with one pound of hydrogen to form nine pounds of water. This observation is an example of **The Law of Definite Proportions**. This law, first articulated by Joseph Proust in 1799, states that whenever two elements combine to form a compound, they do so in a definite proportion by mass. Proust based this statement on his observations that 100 pounds of copper, dissolved in nitric acid and precipitated by carbonates of soda (sodium) or potash (potassium), invariably gave 180 pounds of green carbonate. The Law of Definite Proportions is not direct proof of the existence of atoms. However, if you believe in the existence of atoms it

does make it easier to explain why the Law of Definite Proportions should hold. The existence of atoms can also help explain why a given mass of aluminum reacting with sufficient copper (II) chloride in solution should always produce the same mass of copper.

Reflecting on the Activity and the Challenge

In this activity you learned how chemists measured elements in chemical reactions to determine the relative masses of atoms and how these masses were assembled into a scale of atomic masses. The atomic mass is one of the most important pieces of information listed for each element on the periodic table. How will you incorporate it into your game about the periodic table? Will you test players' ability to simply identify the atomic mass from a periodic table, or will you require that players understand how the relative scale was determined?

Chemistry to Go

1. John Dalton believed that water was formed from the simplest combination of hydrogen and oxygen atoms—one of each. Observations today show that eight pounds of oxygen react with one pound of hydrogen to form water. We now know that Dalton's values were wrong but his attempt was based on the data that he had available at the time.

   a) Based on these two statements, what conclusion could Dalton draw about the relative masses of oxygen and hydrogen atoms? How many times more massive is an oxygen atom than a hydrogen atom?

   b) The atomic mass of oxygen is 16 and the atomic mass of hydrogen is 1. How do the current atomic masses of oxygen and hydrogen compare to Dalton's?

   c) You know that water molecules are not made from one atom of hydrogen and one atom of oxygen. A water molecule is made up of 2 atoms of hydrogen and one atom of oxygen. If the pound of hydrogen reacting with eight pounds of oxygen is due to twice as many hydrogen atoms as there are oxygen atoms, how many times more massive is an oxygen atom than a hydrogen atom?

   d) Are the values of these revised masses closer to the current atomic masses of oxygen and hydrogen atoms?

2. In Dalton's time, ammonia was observed to be formed when nitrogen reacted with hydrogen. Today's values show that fourteen pounds of nitrogen react with three pounds of hydrogen.

   a) If ammonia were formed from Dalton's simplest formula of one atom of each element, what would he have concluded about the relative masses of nitrogen and hydrogen atoms?

   b) Ammonia molecules are made not from one atom each of hydrogen and nitrogen but from three atoms of hydrogen and one atom of nitrogen. If the three pounds of hydrogen reacting with fourteen pounds of nitrogen is due to three times as many hydrogen atoms as there are nitrogen atoms, how many times more massive is a nitrogen atom than a hydrogen atom?

3. A student uses magnesium instead of aluminum in this activity and obtains the following data:

Mass of beaker: 30.20 g

Mass of beaker + magnesium strip: 30.40 g

Mass of beaker + magnesium + copper (II) chloride: 32.40 g

Mass of beaker + magnesium + copper (II) chloride + water: 57.40 g

Mass of dry filter paper: 0.67 g

Mass of new beaker: 30.50 g

Mass of beaker + wet filter and residue + solution: 58.37 g

Mass of dry filter + residue: 1.19 g

a) How many grams of magnesium did the student use in this experiment?

b) How many grams of copper did the student measure in the dry filter paper?

c) How many times as great is the mass of the copper as the mass of magnesium the student originally used? (What is the ratio of mass of copper to mass of aluminum?)

d) If one atom of copper was released for each atom of magnesium that becomes combined (with chlorine), the masses of copper and magnesium determined in (a) and (b) should contain the same number of atoms. What does this tell you about the relative masses of copper and magnesium atoms? How many times more massive is a copper atom than a magnesium atom?

4. Look at the table in the **ChemTalk** reading section that gives the atomic masses of the eight elements that you observed in **Activity Two**. Add this data to your element cards. Can you now improve upon the way you sorted the cards in the previous activity taking this new information about relative masses into account?

Preparing for the Chapter Challenge

In a paragraph, explain how the relative scale of atomic masses is determined.

Inquiring Further

Avogadro's number and a mole

Chemists are interested in keeping track of quantities of particles. However, the particles are very small so chemists use a particular quantity that is convenient for counting particles. The quantity is called a **mole**. The quantity of particles in a mole is 602,000,000,000,000,000,000,000. The mole can be represented more easily in scientific notation as 6.02×10^{23}. This is a very large number because many, many small particles (atoms or molecules) make up a mole. The number 6.02×10^{23} is sometimes called Avogadro's number.

Research to find the significance of Avogadro's number and a mole. Record your findings in your *Active Chemistry* log.

Then, to appreciate how huge a mole is, answer the following question:

Imagine you have 7 billion people (7×10^9 people, which is approximately the human population of the world) and they are given the task of dropping $1-bills once every second into a large hole. How long will it take 7×10^9 people to drop 1 mole of dollar bills into the hole? How old will you be when they complete this task?

Activity 4 — Are Atoms Indivisible?

GOALS

In this activity you will:

- Observe the behavior of a cathode ray in the presence of a magnet.

- Discuss Thomson's conclusions from 1897 about cathode rays.

- Simulate an experiment from 1911 by Rutherford in which he learned more about the structure of atoms.

- Organize your understanding of some of the different particles that comprise matter.

What Do You Think?

Ever since Democritus from ancient Greece hypothesized the existence of atoms, a major question was how atoms of different elements were different.

- If you could observe a single atom of gold and a single atom of lead, how do you think they would be different? How could they have something in common?

Record your ideas about these questions in your *Active Chemistry* log. Be prepared to discuss your responses with your small group and the class.

Investigate

1. Your teacher will demonstrate the behavior of what were called cathode rays a hundred years ago. They were called cathode rays because they were emitted from the negative terminal, or cathode of what was known as a cathode-ray tube, a forerunner of the television or the computer monitor tube.

⚠️ Do not to try to see the effect of a magnet on an actual television or computer monitor; you may damage the monitor.

a) What happens to the path of the cathode rays when a horseshoe magnet is placed near the tube? Record your observation in your *Active Chemistry* log.

b) Record what you think will happen to the path of the cathode rays when the orientation of the horseshoe magnet is reversed.

c) Observe the path of the cathode rays as your teacher reverses the magnet. Record what does happen.

2. Magnets exert a force on moving electrically charged particles. The effect of the magnet on the cathode rays therefore shows that these rays are moving electrically charged particles. Cathode rays, which have a negative electric charge, are made up of electrons. In 1897, Joseph John (J. J.) Thomson showed that identical rays (electrons) were emitted from the cathode of a cathode-ray tube, regardless of the metal of which the cathode was made.

Discovery of electrons emerging from the atoms of the cathode gave scientists new information about the atom. The atom is not indivisible. It has internal parts, one of which is the electron.

a) In a sentence or two, describe the relationship between cathode rays, the electron, and the structure of atoms.

3. In order to investigate the other components of an atom, you will take part in the following simulation, similar to the game *Battleship*. You will work with a partner for this activity.

You and your classmate should each construct a grid of squares, 8 by 10. Without letting your classmate see your grid, color in a section of ten squares. The squares must touch each other. To make the simulation relatively simple, begin with a fairly compact design. This shape (colored region) represents your target.

You and your partner will try to guess the shape of each other's targets by sending "missiles" onto any of the 80 squares in this array. For the purpose of this description, designate one person to be Player X and the other person to be Player Y. To begin, Player X will tell Player Y the destination (number and letter) of

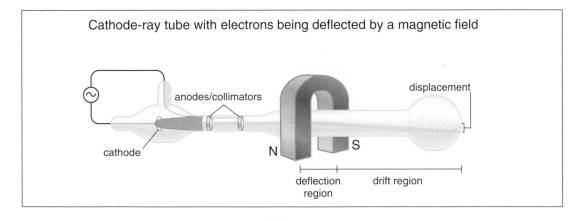

Cathode-ray tube with electrons being deflected by a magnetic field

anodes/collimators

cathode

N   S

displacement

deflection region   drift region

	A	B	C	D	E	F	G	H	I	J
1										
2										
3										
4										
5										
6										
7										
8										

the missile being sent. Player Y will respond, indicating that the missile "hit" or "missed" the target shape. Player X will make note of the response. Then Player Y sends the next missile, noting the response. Continue this process until one player identifies the other player's target.

a) Record the number of turns taken to complete the game.

b) Repeat the game with a target of only 2 adjacent squares. Record the number of turns taken.

4. Now do a thought experiment. The same-size game grid is divided into smaller squares—100 squares across and 100 squares down. There are now 10,000 squares in the same size board as before. A target of only one square is chosen.

a) Record an estimate of how many turns will be required to identify the target square amongst the 10,000 squares in the game grid.

5. Now modify the thought experiment. The same-size grid is now 1000 rows across and 1000 squares down. That is a total of 1,000,000 squares.

a) Record an estimate of how many turns will be required to identify the target square among the 1,000,000 squares in the game grid.

6. An experiment similar to your game of "*Battleship*" was carried out in 1911 by Lord Ernest Rutherford. Rutherford sought to learn something about the structure of the atom by bombarding gold atoms with energetic particles given off by certain atoms.

In Rutherford's game of "*Battleship*," it seemed that he was required to send an incredible number of missiles to get a "hit." He concluded that the grid of the atom must be composed of tiny, tiny cells and only one cell contains all of the positive charge of the atom.

a) Explain why you think he concluded this.

379

ChemTalk

THE CHANGING MODEL OF AN ATOM

J.J. Thomson's Model of an Atom

As you noted in this activity, in the late 1800s J.J. Thomson, an English physicist, found evidence for the existence of negatively charged particles that could be removed from atoms. He called these subatomic particles with a negative charge **electrons.** Using this new information, Thomson then proposed a model of an atom that was a positive sphere, with electrons evenly

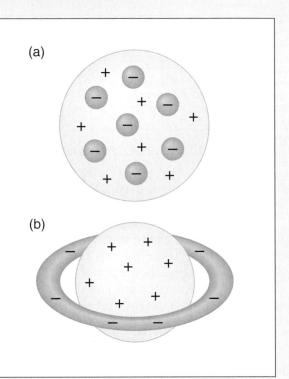

distributed and embedded in it, as shown in the diagram. Using the same evidence, H. Nagaoka, a Japanese scientist, modeled the atom as a large positively charged sphere surrounded by a ring of negative electrons.

Chem Words

electron: a subatomic particle that occurs outside of the nucleus and has a charge of –1 and mass of 9.109×10^{-28}g

Rutherford's Discovery of the Nucleus

For several years there was no evidence to contradict either Thomson's or Nagaoka's atomic models. However, in the early 1900s, Ernest Rutherford, a New Zealand-born scientist, designed experiments to test the current model of an atom. In Rutherford's experiment, alpha particles were sent as "missiles" toward a thin sheet of gold. Gold was used because it is malleable and could be hammered into a thin, thin sheet. Most of the alpha particles went through the sheet and were not deflected. It is as if they missed the target. This was expected since it was assumed that the atom's charge and mass

Ernest Rutherford

was spread evenly throughout the gold. Occasionally one of the alpha particles that "hit" the gold sheet bounced back. This was the big surprise. The conclusion: there must be tiny places containing lots of charge and mass. Since the bouncing back was so unusual, it was assumed that the places where all the charge and mass were concentrated were only 1/100,000 of the area of the gold. Rutherford concluded that almost all the mass and all of the positive charge of the atom is concentrated in an extremely small part at the center, which he called the **nucleus**. He also coined the term **proton** to name the smallest unit of positive charge in the nucleus.

The story of Rutherford's discovery of the atomic nucleus is best told by Rutherford himself. Examining the deflection of high-speed alpha particles as they passed through sheets of gold foil, Rutherford and his student Hans Geiger noticed that some particles were scattered through larger angles than predicted by the existing theory of atomic structure. Fascinated, Rutherford asked Geiger's research student Ernest Marsden to search for more large-angle alpha scattering. Rutherford did not think that any of the alpha particles in his experiment would actually bounce backward. "Then I remember two or three days later Geiger coming to me in great excitement and saying, 'We have been able to get some of the alpha particles coming backwards ...' It was quite the most incredible event that has ever happened to me in my life. It was almost as incredible as if you fired a 15-inch shell at a piece of tissue paper and it came back and hit you."

Chem Words

nucleus: the very dense core of the atom that contains the neutrons and protons

proton: a positively charged subatomic particle contained in the nucleus of an atom. The mass of a proton is 1.673×10^{-24}g and it has a charge of $+1$

381

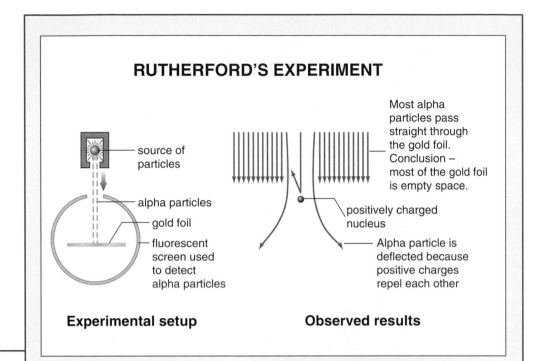

RUTHERFORD'S EXPERIMENT

source of particles

alpha particles

gold foil

fluorescent screen used to detect alpha particles

Most alpha particles pass straight through the gold foil. Conclusion – most of the gold foil is empty space.

positively charged nucleus

Alpha particle is deflected because positive charges repel each other

Experimental setup

Observed results

Checking Up

1. What is an electron?

2. Thomson's model of an atom is sometimes referred to as the "plum-pudding" model. (A plum pudding is a heavy pudding with raisins mixed into it.) Explain why this is an appropriate comparison.

3. Why was Rutherford surprised that some alpha particles bounced back from the gold foil?

4. What is the nucleus of an atom?

A Physics Connection

What was responsible for the wide-angle scattering of the alpha particles and their bouncing back? The force between the positive nucleus and the positive alpha particle is the coulomb force. Positive charges repel one another according to the coulomb force law.

$$F = \frac{kq_1 q_2}{d^2}$$

where k is Coulomb's constant
   ($k = 9.0 \times 10^9 \text{ N m}^2/\text{C}^2$),
   q is the charge in coulombs, and
   d is the distance between the charges.

The closer the alpha particle gets to the nucleus, the larger the force and the larger the deflection of the alpha particle.

Reflecting on the Activity and the Challenge

In this activity you learned of evidence that atoms are made of a positively charged nucleus and negatively charged electrons. The nucleus contains most of the atom's mass and its positive charge is balanced by the combined negative charge of the electrons, resulting in an atom that is electrically neutral. The number of protons of the neutral atom plays a very important role in the periodic table. Called the atomic number, it supports the order in which Mendeleev arranged the elements in his periodic table, long before anything was known about the structure of the atom or atomic number. How will your game reflect your new knowledge about atomic structure and its relationship to the periodic table?

Chemistry to Go

1. Since the electron has a negative electric charge and the nucleus has a positive electric charge, where would you expect to find electrons in atoms?

2. Are atoms indivisible? Support your answer using information from this activity.

3. Construct a chart or diagram to summarize what you have learned in this activity about the particles that make up an atom. Include electric charge and location of the particles.

4. Lead has an atomic number of 82; iron has an atomic number of 26; and copper has an atomic number of 29. How do the charges of the nuclei of these three elements compare?

5. The element chlorine has an atomic number of 17. How many electrons does chlorine have? Support your answer with a logical explanation of how you could arrive at this answer.

6. Sketch the outline of three grids. Pretend that each grid has 100,000 squares.

   a) If the target was 50,000 squares, draw the target.

   b) If the target was 25,000 squares, draw the target.

   c) If the target was only 1 square, draw the target.

   Which grid most closely relates to Rutherford's experiment? Explain your answer.

Inquiring Further

1. An atomic timeline

Construct a timeline that reflects how scientists' views of the atom have changed through the ages. Identify significant scientists, their beliefs, and experimental findings as mentioned in this chapter. You may also wish to consult other resources. Add information to your timeline as you continue to work through this chapter.

2. John Dalton's Atomic Theory

John Dalton, an English scientist, developed his atomic theory in the early 1800s. This theory was based on the Greek concept of atoms and the studies of Joseph Proust's Law of Definite Proportions or Law of Constant Composition. Dalton's atomic theory contained a series of postulates based on the data of his time and his observations:

• Matter consists of small particles called atoms.

• Atoms of one particular element are identical and the properties are identical.

• Atoms are indestructible. In chemical reactions, the atoms rearrange or combine, but they are not destroyed.

• Atoms of different elements have a different set of properties.

• When atoms of different elements combine to form compounds, they combine in a fixed numerical ratio.

From his postulates, the Law of Conservation of Mass would be supported. Since his postulates state that atoms cannot be destroyed but they can be moved around and combine with other atoms to form compounds, then the mass of the compound must be the sum of the atoms of the compound. This law still exists with a slight modification for nuclear reactions. So, you can conclude that if water has a certain mass today, it will have the same mass any other day (unless evaporation occurs).

Investigate whether all of Dalton's postulates are presently accepted or describe how some have been modified based on our current understanding.

Joseph Proust

Activity 5   The Chemical Behavior of Atoms

GOALS

In this activity you will:

• View the spectrum of hydrogen.

• Interpret changes in electron energies in the hydrogen atom to develop an explanation for where the colored light in the hydrogen spectrum comes from.

• Use Bohr's model of the atom to predict parts of the hydrogen atom spectrum.

• Calculate and compare the wavelengths, energies, and frequencies of light of different colors.

• Identify regions in the electromagnetic spectrum.

What Do You Think?

A neon sign uses electricity and a gas-filled tube to produce a colored light. A fluorescent bulb uses electricity, a gas-filled tube and a phosphor coating to produce white light.

• How is the color produced in a neon sign?

Record your ideas about this question in your *Active Chemistry* log. Be prepared to discuss your response with your small group and the class.

Investigate

1. In order to directly observe the behavior of atoms, you can observe the spectrum of light given off when atoms are excited by a high-voltage, electric-power supply. You probably have already seen this effect in the familiar red color of neon signs.

   For this demonstration, your teacher will set up a tube of hydrogen gas connected to a high-voltage power supply. This light can be viewed through a spectroscope or a diffraction grating lens, as shown in the diagram on the next page. When the slit at the end of the spectroscope is aimed toward the light, the colors of the spectrum appear separately off to the sides of the slit.

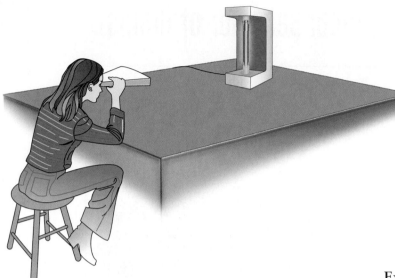

a) What colors do you see in the spectrum of light given off by hydrogen gas?

b) Make a colored diagram in your *Active Chemistry* log of what you see inside the spectroscope. Make sure to draw the colors with the order and spacing between them that you observe.

2. When you observed the spectrum of light given off by hydrogen gas, you probably saw three or four distinct lines, each having a different color. The color of light is determined by its frequency; the greater the energy in the light, the greater the frequency.

The diagram on the right shows the visible lines of the line spectrum of hydrogen.

The wavelengths are measured in nanometers (nm). The prefix *nano*

means 10^{-9}. Thus, 656.5 nm is 656.5×10^{-9} m. The frequency of each line can be determined using the equation:

$$f = \frac{c}{\lambda}$$

where,

f is the frequency (waves/s or cycles/s or hertz),

c is the speed of light and is a constant (2.998×10^8 m/s), and

λ is the wavelength measured in nanometers.

Example:

Given red light with a wavelength $\lambda = 656.5 \times 10^{-9}$ m and the speed of light $c = 2.998 \times 10^8$ m/s, calculate the corresponding frequency and energy of the light.

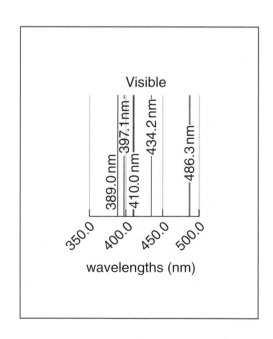

First calculate the frequency.

$$f = \frac{c}{\lambda}$$

$$= \frac{2.998 \times 10^8 \text{ m/s}}{656.5 \times 10^{-9} \text{ m}}$$

$$= 4.567 \times 10^{14} \text{ cycles/s (or Hz)}$$

$$= 4.567 \times 10^{14} \text{ Hz (Hertz)}$$

To calculate the corresponding energy of a photon of light, you can use an equation called Planck's equation that relates the frequency to the energy. A photon is a tiny, indivisible packet of light. Planck's constant is h and has the value of 6.63×10^{-34} J•s.

$$E = hf$$

$$= (6.63 \times 10^{-34} \text{ J•s})$$
$$\quad (4.567 \times 10^{14} \text{ cycles/s})$$

$$= 3.03 \times 10^{-19} \text{ J}$$

a) Calculate the frequencies and energies for the other visible wavelengths of light in the hydrogen spectra. Complete a table like the one below in your *Active Chemistry* log.

3. In 1913, Niels Bohr, a Danish physicist, tried to explain the line spectrum of hydrogen by hypothesizing that the electron in the hydrogen atom is allowed to have only certain amounts of energy. Bohr believed that an electron in a higher energy level would give off light when it fell to a lower energy level, and the amount of energy in the light would be the difference in these energy levels. Bohr pictured the atom to be similar to the Solar System, with electrons orbiting around the nucleus in the way that planets orbit around the Sun. If you picture the electron to be in orbit about the nucleus of the hydrogen atom, as Bohr did, allowing the electron to have only certain amounts of energy would mean that the electron could be allowed in orbits of only certain distance from the nucleus. As the electron "jumps" from one energy level to another, it behaves something like a ball falling down a flight of stairs. It's allowed to rest only on one of the steps, nowhere in between.

The light was the result of electron energy jumps. These jumps should be able to produce the corresponding energies of the light. Bohr calculated the lowest energy level to be -2.18×10^{-18} J. Each of the other

Wavelength λ (nm)	Frequency f (cycles/s or Hz)	Energy E
410.3		
434.2		
486.3		
656.5	4.567×10^{14}	3.03×10^{-19} J

Niels Bohr

energy levels can be computed from this first one with the equation:

$$E_n = \frac{1}{n^2} E_1$$

The second energy level:

$$E_2 = \frac{1}{2^2} E_1$$

$$= \frac{1}{4} (-2.18 \times 10^{-18} \text{ J})$$

$$= -5.45 \times 10^{-19} \text{ J}$$

The third energy level:

$$E_3 = \frac{1}{3^2} E_1$$

$$= \frac{1}{9} (-2.18 \times 10^{-18} \text{ J})$$

$$= -2.42 \times 10^{-19} \text{ J}$$

a) Calculate the energy levels for the fourth, fifth, and sixth levels and record all these values in your log.

4. In Bohr's model, the electrons jump from E_3 to E_2 and give off light with that energy.

$$E_3 - E_2 = (-2.42 \times 10^{-19} \text{ J}) - (-5.45 \times 10^{-19} \text{ J})$$

$$= 3.03 \times 10^{-19} \text{ J}$$

This is equivalent to the energy of the red light. The model is successful, so far.

a) Calculate the energy of light when the electron of hydrogen jumps from:

E_4 to E_2

E_5 to E_2

E_6 to E_2

b) Do these energies correspond to the energies of the light that is emitted from hydrogen that you calculated earlier?

c) If the model is a truly good model, it should be able to predict something unknown. Bohr's model does just this. Calculate the energy of light when the electron of hydrogen jumps from E_2 to E_1.

The light corresponding to this transition was not observed because it is not in the visible range of light. It is in the ultraviolet spectrum. When an ultraviolet detector is used, the wavelength of the ultraviolet light is just as predicted by Bohr's model. The light emitted from transitions of E_3 to E_1 and E_4 to E1 are also in the ultraviolet.

When the electron jumps from a higher energy level to a lower energy level, light is emitted. The light emitted from a neon sign is based on this phenomenon.

The opposite can also occur. If the electron absorbs light of just the right energy, the electron can jump up to a higher energy level. For instance, an electron in the E_2 energy level can absorb light of 3.02×10^{-19} J and jump up to the E_3 energy level. If enough energy is applied to the hydrogen atom, the electron can be totally removed. This is commonly called the ionization energy; for one electron of hydrogen, the ionization energy is 2.18×10^{-19} J. If the electron in the E_1 level absorbs light of energy 2.18×10^{-19} J, then its new energy will be 0 J. This means that it is no longer bound to the hydrogen nucleus. The atom is ionized (the electron has been removed).

Chem Talk

BOHR'S MODEL OF AN ATOM

The Electromagnetic Spectrum

Visible light is only one part of the **electromagnetic spectrum**. You've probably heard of some of the other parts including ultraviolet, infrared, x-rays, gamma rays, microwaves, and radio waves. As you demonstrated in calculations using Bohr's model, the light from some of the transitions is in the ultraviolet. Infrared light is also emitted as the electron jumps from E_4 to E_3 and E_5 to E_3 and other higher energy levels.

Many people do not think of radio waves as being light waves, but they are part of the electromagnetic spectrum. The problem is that you can only see a

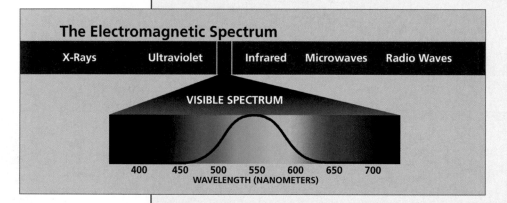

The Electromagnetic Spectrum

X-Rays   Ultraviolet   Infrared   Microwaves   Radio Waves

VISIBLE SPECTRUM

400   450   500   550   600   650   700
WAVELENGTH (NANOMETERS)

Chem Words

electromagnetic spectrum: the complete spectrum of electromagnetic radiation, such as radio waves, microwaves, infrared, visible, ultraviolet, x-rays, and gamma rays

frequency: the number of waves per second or cycles per second or hertz (Hz)

wavelength: the distance measured from crest to crest of one complete wave or cycle

very small part of the electromagnetic spectrum. Often, you hear radio announcers say that they are broadcasting at a certain **frequency**. Your FM radio dial may have MHz (megahertz) printed on the side. This tells you that the numbers correspond to frequencies in units of MHz or 10^6 Hz. Frequency tells you the number of cycles or waves that are being produced per second. The unit for frequency is a hertz (Hz). 1 Hz = 1 cycle/s = 1 s^{-1}. Normally, frequency is read as per second and the cycles are dropped from the terminology.

Wavelength (λ), where λ is the Greek letter *lambda*, is the distance from crest to crest of a wave. All light waves travel at the same speed. The speed of electromagnetic radiation is constant and it is called the speed of light (c), $c = 2.998 \times 10^8$ m/s or 3.00×10^8 m/s. From this information you can calculate the frequency of light of a given wavelength. The equation that is used for this is:

$$f = \frac{c}{\lambda}$$

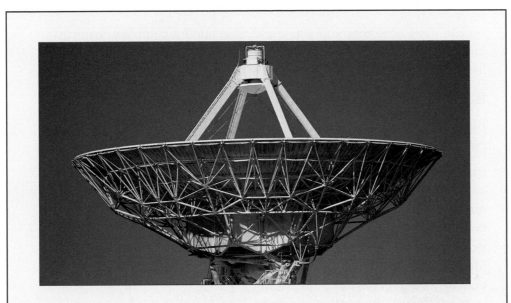

As an example, if the wavelength is 434.2 nm, then the frequency is:

$$f = \frac{2.998 \times 10^8 \text{ m/s}}{434.2 \times 10^{-9} \text{ m}}$$

$$= 6.905 \times 10^{14} \text{ cycles/s or } 6.905 \times 10^{14} \text{ Hz.}$$

As you go across the electromagnetic spectrum you should note that the wavelength continues to get smaller as the frequency increases. Also, you should understand that the energy of the spectrum increases as you go from radio waves to x-rays or gamma rays. Max Planck, a German physicist, found that the energy of a wavelength could be calculated. The equation that he developed was based on measuring the change in energy from one level to another level like you did in the **Investigate** section. The equation he developed is

$E = hf$,

where h is Planck's constant and is 6.63×10^{-34} J · s
and f is the frequency.

The corresponding energy of the red light above would be:

$$E = hf$$

$$= (6.63 \times 10^{-34} \text{ J} \cdot \text{s}) (4.567 \times 10^{14} \text{ Hz})$$

$$= 3.03 \times 10^{-19} \text{ J.}$$

→

391

So the next time that you are standing around a campfire, you can inform your fellow campers that red light has less energy than blue light and you can also tell them how to calculate these values. ☺

Bohr's Atomic Theory

Niels Bohr, a brilliant Danish physicist, was aware that his theory of electron jumps had incredible success but also raised some problems.

Bohr proposed a "planetary" model of the atom. He theorized that electrons travel in nearly circular paths, called **orbits**, around the nucleus. Each electron orbit has a definite amount of energy, and the farther away the electron is from the nucleus, the greater is its energy. Bohr suggested the revolutionary idea that electrons "jump" between energy levels (orbits) in a quantum fashion. That is, they can never exist in an in-between state. Thus, when an atom absorbs or gives off energy (as in light or heat), the electron jumps to higher or lower orbits. Electrons are the most stable when they are at lower energy levels closer to the nucleus. Bohr's theory could only account for the spectrum of hydrogen and not for the spectra of any other element. Bohr's theory could not explain why only certain orbits were allowed, nor how the electron could jump from one orbit to another. Other scientists improved on Bohr's model as they discovered more about the atom and quantum mechanics.

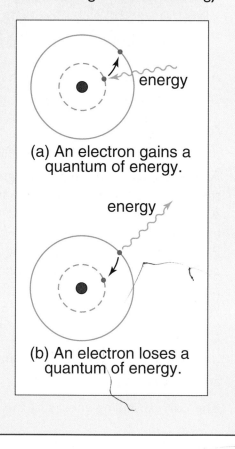

(a) An electron gains a quantum of energy.

(b) An electron loses a quantum of energy.

Chem Words

orbit: the path of the electron in its motion around the nucleus of Bohr's hydrogen atom

Checking Up

1. How are visible light, ultraviolet light, infrared light, x-rays, gamma rays, microwaves, and radio waves related?

2. Explain the meaning of wavelength.

3. Why is "planetary" model an appropriate name for Bohr's model of the atom?

4. How do the energy levels of different electron orbits compare?

5. Why do elements produce certain color light when heated?

Reflecting on the Activity and the Challenge

In this activity, you've recognized that it is the electrons in an atom that are responsible for the colors of light emitted. Bohr explained the spectrum of light given off by excited hydrogen atoms by hypothesizing that each hydrogen atom's electron was allowed in only certain energy levels. Although Mendeleev knew nothing about electrons or energy levels when he first developed the periodic table (though he did live long enough to know of the electron's discovery by Thomson), the periodic table today is seen as a reflection of the number of electrons in an atom of each element and the energy levels those electrons occupy. Many versions of the periodic table today list the energy levels occupied by each electron in an atom of a given element. You will learn more about this in **Activity 6**. The periodic table is a way of organizing information and knowledge about the atom. Electron structure is a crucial part of that knowledge. Continue to think about how this information could be included in the game you are designing.

Chemistry to Go

1. In this activity you were told that light with greater energy has greater frequency.

   a) Which color in the visible spectrum of hydrogen has the greatest energy? The least energy?

   b) Which color in the visible spectrum of hydrogen has the highest frequency? The lowest frequency?

2. If an electron were to fall down to the E_1 level from the E_3 level, how would its energy compare to one that fell to the E_2 level? Explain.

3. What is the difference measured in energy when an electron falls from E_3 to E_1? How many times greater is this value as compared to the difference of the electron falling from E_3 to E_2?

4. A wavelength of light is 389.0 nm and its frequency is 7.707×10^{14} Hz. Show how this frequency value was calculated.

5. Show that the wavelength of 389.0 nm has an energy of 5.11×10^{-19} J.

6. a) Microwave radiation is absorbed by the water in food. As the heat is absorbed by the water it causes the food to get hot. If the λ of a microwave is 10 cm, calculate the frequency of the microwave and the energy of each photon.

b) The red light you observed in the hydrogen spectrum produced a $\lambda = 656.5$ nm. The energy of the red light was 3.02×10^{-19} J. How many times greater is this value when compared to the energy value that you found for the microwave energy?

Inquiring Further

Balmer, Lyman, and Paschen series

In this activity, you learned that the visible light emitted by the hydrogen lamp resulted when an electron moved from a higher energy level to the second lowest energy level in Bohr's scheme. This series of visible spectral lines is said to comprise the **Balmer series.**

What do you think happens when an electron in a hydrogen atom moves from a higher energy level to the lowest level? This series is known as the **Lyman series** (ultraviolet light).

What if a transition from a higher energy level leads to an electron in the third lowest energy level in Bohr's scheme? How do these energy levels compare with visible light? This series is known as the **Paschen series** (infrared light).

Activity 6   Atoms with More than One Electron

GOALS

In this activity you will:

- View the spectra of various materials.

- Graphically analyze patterns in the amounts of energy required to remove electrons from different kinds of atoms.

- Compare trends in stability of atoms in the periodic table.

- Compare the structure of the periodic table with the patterns of levels and sublevels to which electrons can be assigned.

- Develop a shorthand notation to describe the configuration of electrons in an atom.

What Do You Think?

In **Activity 5** you learned that Niels Bohr was able to explain the spectrum of light emitted by hydrogen using a model that assigned the electron to specific energy levels. Bohr was awarded a Nobel Prize in 1922 for expanding the understanding of atomic structure. He worked with hydrogen, the simplest atom, which contains only one electron. However, the atoms of other elements contain more than one electron.

- How do you think an increase in the number of electrons would impact the spectrum of an atom?

- What modifications in Bohr's model would need to take place to accommodate the extra electrons?

Record your ideas about these questions in your *Active Chemistry* log. Be prepared to discuss your responses with your small group and the class.

395

Investigate

1. In **Activity 5** you observed the spectrum of hydrogen gas as its electron moved from a higher energy level to a lower energy level. You also explored a model that used Bohr's theory to explain this spectrum. Now it's time to look at the spectra of some other elements.

   a) Your teacher will connect a tube containing an element other than hydrogen to a high voltage supply. Record the name of the element in your *Active Chemistry* log. Look at the spectrum of light of this element through the spectroscope.

   b) What colors do you see? Make a diagram in your log of the spectrum (pattern of colors) you see inside the spectroscope.

   c) Record how this spectrum is similar to and different from the hydrogen spectrum you observed in **Activity 5**.

   d) Repeat **Steps (a)**, **(b)**, and **(c)** for as many samples as your teacher demonstrates.

2. Although the spectra of such elements as helium and neon are very beautiful, they cannot be explained by Bohr's simple theory for the single electron in the hydrogen atom. The basic idea is still true—light is emitted when electrons jump from a higher energy level to a lower energy level. The energy levels, however, are more complex if there are additional electrons. A more elaborate labeling of electron energy levels is necessary. In this activity you will explore the pattern of electron energy levels in

Atomic Number	Element (Symbol)	1st Ionization Energy J (x10⁻¹⁹)	2nd Ionization Energy J (x10⁻¹⁹)
1	H	21.8	
2	He	39.4	87.2
3	Li	8.6	121.2
4	Be	14.9	29.2
5	B	13.3	40.3
6	C	18.0	39.1
7	N	23.3	47.4
8	O	21.8	56.3
9	F	27.9	56.0
10	Ne	34.6	65.6
11	Na	8.2	75.8
12	Mg	12.3	24.1
13	Al	9.6	30.2
14	Si	13.1	26.2
15	P	16.8	31.7
16	S	16.6	37.4
17	Cl	20.8	38.2
18	Ar	25.2	44.3
19	K	7.0	50.7
20	Ca	9.8	19.0
21	Sc	10.5	20.5
22	Ti	10.9	21.8
23	V	10.8	23.5
24	Cr	10.8	26.4
25	Mn	11.9	25.1
26	Fe	12.7	25.9
27	Co	12.6	27.3
28	Ni	12.2	29.1
29	Cu	12.4	32.5
30	Zn	15.1	28.8
31	Ga	9.6	32.9
32	Ge	12.7	25.5
33	As	15.7	29.9
34	Se	15.6	34.0
35	Br	18.9	34.9
36	Kr	22.4	39.0

atoms containing more than one electron.

When multiple electrons are present, some are easier (i.e., require less energy) to remove from the atoms than others. The chart on the left provides information about the amount of energy required to remove the electrons in the two highest energy levels. These are the electrons that are easiest to remove. These energies are called the 1st and 2nd ionization energies, and are given in units of joules. Notice that all values are multiplied by 10^{-19}.

a) Make a graph that shows how the ionization energies vary with atomic number. Since the atomic numbers range from 1 to 36, label the x-axis with atomic numbers from 1 to 36. Since the ionization energies range from 7 to 122, label the y-axis with ionization energies from 0 to 130. Plot the first ionization energy data from the chart in one color, connecting the data points as you go along.

b) Plot the values for the second ionization energies in a different color.

c) Include a title and legend on your graph.

3. Look at the graph of the first ionization energies and answer the following questions:

a) What kinds of patterns do you see? How could you quickly relate the shape of the graph to someone who had not seen it?

b) Where are the ionization energies the largest? The smallest?

c) What happens to the ionization energies as the atomic number increases?

d) Group the elements by their ionization energies into four consecutive "periods." List the range of atomic numbers in each group.

e) Is there any interruption in the general trend of ionization energies as the atomic number increases for a "period"? If so, describe it.

4. Look at the second colored graph line you drew.

a) Describe how the two graphs are alike and/or different. Do you see similarities between the two graphs?

5. If a large amount of energy is needed to remove an electron from an atom, the arrangement of electrons in that atom is considered to be especially stable. Thus, a high first ionization energy means that a lot of energy must be supplied to remove an electron from an atom and that the electron arrangement in that atom is especially stable. Any element that has a larger first ionization energy than its neighboring elements has an electron arrangement in its atoms that is more stable than its neighboring elements.

a) Which element in the first period (atomic numbers 1 and 2) has the most stable arrangements of electrons in its atoms? (Remember, you are looking for elements that have larger ionization energies than their neighbors. In reality you are looking for peaks in your

397

graph, not just those elements with higher values.)

b) Which elements in the second period (atomic numbers 3 through 10) of the periodic table have the most stable arrangements of electrons in their atoms?

c) Which elements in the third period (atomic numbers 11 through 18) of the periodic table have the most stable arrangements of electrons in their atoms?

d) Which elements in the fourth period (atomic numbers 19 through 36) of the periodic table have the most stable arrangements of electrons in their atoms?

6. As mentioned earlier, the Bohr model was not able to account for the spectrum of an element containing more than one electron. A more elaborate model was needed. In this new model, the energy levels are broken down into sublevels. When

these sublevels are filled, the atom exhibits a higher degree of stability. In this model, the sublevels are designated by the four letters s, p, d, and f.

The periodic table shows the atomic number, the chemical symbol, and how many electrons in an atom of each element are in each sublevel. The total number of electrons is equal to the atomic number of the element. This is because the atoms are neutral and therefore have a number of electrons equivalent to the number of protons. This arrangement of the electrons in each sublevel will be referred to as the electron assignment or electron configuration of the element. Use this periodic table to answer the following questions:

a) In what sublevel (include number and letter) are the electrons in hydrogen (1 electron) and helium (2 electrons) found?

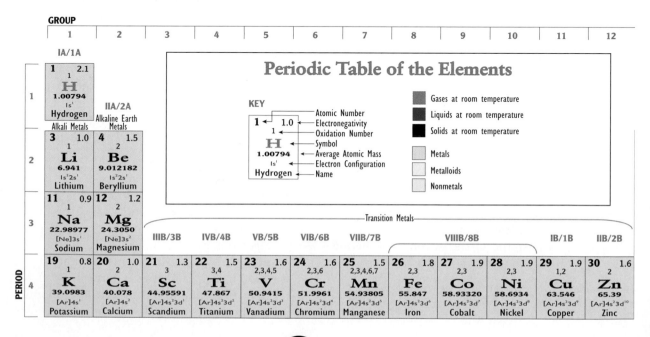

As you move to the second period (second row on the periodic table) each new element has one more proton in its nucleus and one more electron. The electrons must find a place to reside — an energy level and a sublevel within that energy level.

As you move along in the periodic table to increasing atomic numbers, you see that the additional electrons fill the sublevel. A completed sublevel is one that is holding the maximum number of electrons allowed to it before electrons must be placed in the next higher sublevel.

b) In what region of the periodic table are electrons added in an *s* sublevel? What is the greatest number of electrons found in any *s* sublevel?

c) In what region of the periodic table are electrons added in a *p* sublevel? What is the greatest number of electrons found in any *p* sublevel?

d) In what region of the periodic table are electrons added in a *d* sublevel? What is the greatest number of electrons found in any *d* sublevel?

e) In what region of the periodic table are electrons added to an *f* sublevel? What is the greatest number of electrons found in any *f* sublevel?

f) Select a column in the periodic table. (A column of elements on the periodic table is called a family or group.) Look at the electron configuration for each element within the column. Take special note of the last entry, the sublevel to which the last electron in an atom of each element in that column is added. What do all of these sublevels have in common? How many electrons are in these particular sublevels?

g) Mendeleev assigned elements to the same column of the periodic table because the elements had similar properties, both physical and chemical. How, then, does the number and location of the electrons in the outermost sublevel relate to chemical properties? We can now acknowledge that electrons (as opposed to the nucleus) are the key to the chemical properties of elements.

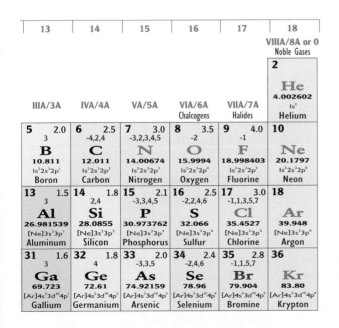

Chem Talk

A PERIODIC TABLE REVEALED

Ions and Ionization Energy

Chem Words

ionization energy: the energy required to remove an electron from a gaseous atom at ground state

ion: an electrically charged atom or group of atoms that has acquired a net charge, either negative or positive

electron configuration: the distribution of electrons in an atom's energy levels

In the table in the **Investigate** section the amount of energy required to remove an electron from an atom was called **ionization energy**. Atoms are neutral. That is, the number of electrons is equivalent to the number of protons. However, atoms can gain or lose electrons. Atoms that have lost or gained electrons are called **ions** and thus the energy used to remove the electrons is known as the ionization energy. The energy required to remove a single electron from the highest occupied energy level is called the first ionization energy, and the energy needed to remove a second electron from the same atom, after the first one has already been removed, is called the second ionization energy.

Electron Configuration and Energy Levels

As you discovered, the Bohr model was not able to account for the spectrum of an element containing more than one electron. In the new model you investigated, the energy levels are broken down into sublevels. This arrangement of the electrons in each sublevel is called the electron assignment or **electron configuration** of the element. When these sublevels are filled, the atom exhibits a higher degree of stability. The sublevels are designated by the four letters s, p, d, and f. The letters come from the words, *sharp*, *principal*, *diffuse*, and *fundamental*. The early scientists used these words to describe some of the observed features of the line spectra. They are governed by the following rules:

(i)   The first energy level (corresponding to E_1 in **Activity 5**) has only one type of orbital, labeled $1s$, where 1 identifies the energy level and s identifies the orbital.

(ii) The second energy level (corresponding to E_2 in **Activity 5**) has two types of orbitals (an s orbital and three p orbitals) and are labeled as the $2s$ and $2p$ orbitals.

(iii) The third energy level (corresponding to E_3 in **Activity 5**) has three types of orbitals, (an s orbital, three p orbitals, and five d orbitals) and are labeled as the $3s$, $3p$, and $3d$ orbitals.

(iv) The number of orbitals corresponds to the energy level you are considering. For example: E_4 has four types of orbitals (s, p, d, and f); E_5 has five types of orbitals (s, p, d, f, and g).

(v) The maximum number of electrons that can be contained in an orbital is two. Three p orbitals could contain a maximum of six electrons. The number of the type of electrons is indicated by superscript following the orbital designation. For example, $2p^5$ means five electrons in the $2p$ orbitals.

Stability is an important feature for all matter. Remember the excited electron of the hydrogen atom? If the electron were in energy level 3, it would drop down to energy level 2 and give off a specific wavelength of light. Alternatively, the electron in energy level 3, could drop down to energy level 1 and give off a different, specific wavelength of light. The word "excited" is used to describe an electron that has been promoted to a higher energy level, before it falls back down to its original state. The electron in the excited state was unstable and lost energy to go to a more stable form. Particles arranged in an unstable way will move to a more stable arrangement.

The Periodic Table

In previous activities you tried to organize elements by their properties and then by their atomic number. When elements are arranged according to their atomic numbers a pattern emerges in which similar properties occur regularly. This is the periodic law. The horizontal rows of elements in the periodic table are called **periods**. The set of elements in the same vertical column in the periodic table is called a **chemical group**. As you discovered, elements in a group share similar physical and chemical properties. They also form similar kinds of compounds when they combine with other elements. This behavior is due to the fact that elements in one chemical group have the same number of electrons in their outer energy levels and tend to form ions by gaining or losing the same number of electrons.

Chem Words

period: a horizontal row of elements in the periodic table

chemical group: a family of elements in the periodic table that have similar electron configurations

Checking Up

1. What is an ion?
2. What is ionization energy?
3. What are the horizontal rows of the periodic table called?
4. Explain the term chemical group.
5. Name three elements in a chemical group.

401

Reflecting on the Activity and the Challenge

In this activity you learned that electrons in atoms are assigned not only to energy levels but also to sublevels, labeled *s*, *p*, *d*, and *f*. You have also learned that the electron configuration of atoms of all elements in the same column of the periodic table end with the same sublevel and number of electrons in that sublevel. Mendeleev organized elements into columns based on similar chemical properties. Thus, electron energy sublevels are clearly associated with chemical properties of elements and their position on the periodic table. How will you incorporate the information about electron configuration in your game to meet the **Chapter Challenge**?

1. Write the complete sequence of electron energy levels, from 1*s* to 4*f*.

2. Consider the element boron (B) as an example.

   a) What is boron's atomic number?

   b) How many electrons does boron have?

   c) What is the complete electron sequence for boron? (Be sure to include the number and letter of the appropriate sublevels, as well as the number of electrons in each sublevel.)

3. Answer the following questions for the element zinc:

   a) What is zinc's atomic number?

   b) How many electrons does zinc have?

   c) What is the complete electron sequence for zinc? (Be sure to include the number and letter of the appropriate sublevels, as well as the number of electrons in each sublevel.)

   d) What is the last sublevel (number and letter, please) to which electrons are added? How many electrons are in this sublevel?

   e) Where would you expect to find zinc on the periodic table? Support your prediction with your answers from (d).

   f) What other elements might you expect to have chemical properties similar to zinc? Explain your choices.

4. Answer the following questions for the element calcium:

   a) What is calcium's atomic number?

   b) How many electrons does calcium have?

c) What is the complete electron sequence for calcium? (Be sure to include the number and letter of the appropriate sublevels, as well as the number of electrons in each sublevel.)

d) What is the last sublevel (number and letter, please) to which electrons are added? How many electrons are in this sublevel?

e) Where would you expect to find calcium on the periodic table? Support your prediction with your answers from (d).

f) What other elements would you expect to have chemical properties similar to calcium? Explain your choices.

5. A chemist has synthesized a heavy element in the laboratory and found that it had an electron configuration:

$1s^2 2s^2 2p^6 3s^2 3p^6 4s^2 3d^{10} 4p^6 5s^2 4d^{10} 5p^6 6s^2 4f^{14} 5d^{10} 6p^6 7s^2 5f^{14} 6d^8$.

a) What is the number of electrons in this element?

b) What is the atomic number?

c) What might you predict about this element?

6. If the electron configuration is given you should be able to determine what element it is. Identify the following element from its electron configuration:

$1s^2 2s^2 2p^6 3s^2 3p^6 4s^2 3d^6$.

Preparing for the Chapter Challenge

Write a sentence or two to explain in words the pattern you noticed between any group and the electron configurations of the elements belonging to that group.

Inquiring Further

1. Determining electron configuration

In this activity, you were able to look at the electron configuration for a given element provided in the periodic table. Research other ways that the electron configuration can be determined.

Activity 7

How Electrons Determine Chemical Behavior

THE SODIUM CHLORIDE ROMANCE

GOALS

In this activity you will:

- Investigate more patterns in the electron arrangements of atoms.

- Relate the positions of elements on the periodic table, their electron arrangements, and their distances from the nearest noble gas, to chemical properties of the elements.

- Relate electron arrangements to ionization energies.

- Assign valence numbers to elements and organize the periodic table according to valence numbers.

What Do You Think?

You have learned that electron configurations determine an atom's chemical behavior. You have also learned how these electrons are labeled according to a series of energy sublevels.

- How does the arrangement of electrons in an atom determine its chemical behavior?

Record your ideas about this question in your *Active Chemistry* log. Be prepared to discuss your responses with your small group and the class.

Investigate

1. In **Activity 6** you learned that elements with relatively high ionization energies have stable arrangements of electrons. One particular group of elements, located in the column at the extreme right of the table, exhibit high ionization energies and therefore have stable arrangements of electrons. They are called the noble gases.

Look at the periodic table on the inside back cover for the assignment of electrons to energy sublevels for atoms of each of these elements. Focus on the sublevel at the end of the electron arrangement where the last electron is assigned.

a) Make and complete a chart like the one below in your *Active Chemistry* log. An example has been provided for you.

Element	**Column A** Energy level (number) to which the last electron is assigned	**Column B** Sublevel (letter) to which the last electron is assigned	**Column C** Number of electrons in the sublevel to which the last electron is assigned	**Column D** Total number of all electrons of the energy level in Column A
Helium				
Neon				
Argon	3	p	6	8
Krypton				
Xenon				
Radon				

b) Look at the numbers in Column A in your chart. How are these numbers related to the respective rows of the periodic table in which each of the elements is located?

c) What pattern do you notice in Columns B and C?

d) What pattern do you notice in Column D?

2. The chemical behavior of an element can be understood by looking at the electron assignment of an atom of the element as compared to the electron assignments of neighboring noble gas atoms. The chemical inactivity of noble gas atoms reflects the stable arrangement of their electrons, one which other atoms cannot easily disturb. In the following questions you will compare the electron assignments in atoms with those of noble gases.

a) Make and complete a chart like the following one in your *Active Chemistry* log. In this chart you will compare the electron assignments of lithium, beryllium, and boron to the electron assignment of helium ($1s^2$), the closest noble gas. An example has been provided for you.

Element being compared	Number of electrons more than those found in closest noble gas (He)	Energy level (number) to which the last electron is assigned	Energy sublevel (letter) to which the last electron is assigned	Location of element (row) in the periodic table	Location of element (column) in the periodic table
Lithium	1	2	s	Row 2	Column 1
Beryllium					
Boron					

b) Make and complete another chart like the one above in your *Active Chemistry* log. This time you will compare the electron assignments of sodium, magnesium, and aluminum to the electron assignment of neon ($1s^2 2s^2 2p^6$), the closest noble gas.

Element being compared	Number of electrons more than those found in closest noble gas (Ne)	Energy level (number) to which the last electron is assigned	Energy sublevel (letter) to which the last electron is assigned	Location of element (row) in the periodic table	Location of element (column) in the periodic table
Sodium					
Magnesium					
Aluminum					

c) Describe any patterns you notice in the charts in 2(a) and/or 2(b) above.

d) Make and complete a chart like the one at the top of the next page in your *Active Chemistry* log. In this chart you will compare the electron assignments of nitrogen, oxygen, and fluorine to the electron assignment of neon ($1s^2 2s^2 2p^6$), the closest noble gas. An example has been provided for you.

e) Make and complete another chart like the one at the top of the next page in your *Active Chemistry* log. This time you will compare the electron assignments of phosphorus, sulfur, and chlorine to the electron assignment of argon ($1s^2 2s^2 2p^6 3s^2 3p^6$), the closest noble gas.

Element being compared	Number of electrons more than those found in closest noble gas (Ne)	Energy level (number) to which the last electron is assigned	Energy sublevel (letter) to which the last electron is assigned	Location of element (row) in the periodic table	Location of element (column) in the periodic table
Nitrogen	3	2	p	Row 2	Column 5
Oxygen					
Fluorine					

Element being compared	Number of electrons more than those found in closest noble gas (Ar)	Energy level (number) to which the last electron is assigned	Energy sublevel (letter) to which the last electron is assigned	Location of element (row) in the periodic table	Location of element (column) in the periodic table
Phosphorus					
Sulfur					
Chlorine					

f) Describe any patterns you notice in the charts 2 (d) and/or 2(e) above.

3. In your *Active Chemistry* log, draw a simplified periodic table that contains only the first three rows of the periodic table. Your table should have 3 rows and 8 columns, and should contain the elements with atomic numbers 1 through 18.

a) Write the symbol for each element in each appropriate box.

b) In the columns headed by lithium, beryllium, and boron, indicate how many more electrons are found in atoms of those elements than in an atom of the nearest noble gas. Place a plus sign in front of these numbers to indicate that these elements contain more electrons than their nearest noble gas element.

c) In the columns headed by nitrogen, oxygen, and fluorine, indicate how many fewer electrons are found in atoms of those elements than in an atom of the nearest noble gas. Place a minus sign in front of these numbers to indicate that these elements contain fewer electrons than their nearest noble gas element.

d) The carbon column was not listed in the table. How many fewer electrons are found in atoms of these elements than in an atom of the nearest noble gas? How many more electrons are found in atoms of these elements than in an atom of the last noble gas? What can you conclude about the position of the carbon column in respect to the other columns that you have examined?

407

4. The questions in **Step 2** asked you to compare the electron assignments in atoms of the second and third rows with the electron assignments of the noble gas that was closest in atomic number to those elements. You noted that electrons are added to the *s* and *p* sublevels of the energy level whose number is the same as the row of the periodic table the elements are found in. For instance, lithium has one more electron than its closest noble gas element. That additional electron is added to the *s* sublevel of the second energy level, corresponding to the second row, where lithium is located.

The number of an electron energy level is significant, because the higher the number, the greater the average distance between the nucleus and the electron. The electrons in the energy levels with the highest number are, on average, the farthest from the nucleus. Because differences in electrons located in the outermost level distinguish an atom from its nearest noble gas, these are the electrons responsible for the atom's chemical behavior. These electrons are often called valence electrons. The general definition of valence electrons are those electrons found in the outermost energy level *s* and *p* orbitals. The maximum number of valence electrons that you can have is 8 for the representative elements (2 in the *s* and 6 in *p* sublevel). For example, sodium contains one valence electron since its outermost level is 3 and sublevel is *s*. It does not

have any electrons in the *p* sublevel. Bromine would have seven valence electrons, since its outermost energy level is 4 and it contains 2 electrons in *s* sublevel and 5 electrons in *p* sublevel. Use the assignment of electrons to energy sublevels in the periodic table on the inside back cover and your answers to the questions in **Steps 1** and **2** to answer the following questions:

a) How many valence electrons are in an atom of helium? Neon? Argon? Krypton? Xenon? Radon?

b) How many valence electrons are in an atom of lithium? Sodium? Potassium? Rubidium? Cesium? This family of elements is known as the alkali metals.

c) How many valence electrons are in an atom of beryllium? Magnesium? Calcium? Strontium? Barium? This family of elements is known as the alkaline earth metals.

d) How many valence electrons are in an atom of boron? Aluminum?

e) How many valence electrons are in an atom of carbon? Silicon?

f) How many valence electrons are in an atom of nitrogen? Phosphorus?

g) How many valence electrons are in an atom of oxygen? Sulfur?

h) How many valence electrons are in an atom of fluorine? Chlorine? Bromine? Iodine? This family of elements is known as the halogens.

Chem Talk

THE NOBLE GASES

The Discovery of Argon

Imagine that you prepared two samples of nitrogen, each one liter in volume, and found one to have a mass of 1.250 g (grams) and the other a mass of 1.257 g. You might be tempted to attribute the difference to experimental error. Lord Rayleigh didn't! In 1892 he decomposed ammonia to generate one liter of nitrogen with a mass of 1.250 g. In another preparation method, he isolated one liter of nitrogen with a mass of 1.257 g by removing what he thought were all the other gases from a sample of air.

What accounted for the difference in masses of the two liter samples? Could there be yet another gas in the air that Rayleigh didn't know about? William Ramsay, a colleague of Rayleigh, looked to the experiments conducted by Henry Cavendish a hundred years earlier. Henry Cavendish (the discoverer of hydrogen) had been puzzled by a small bubble of gas remaining after he had chemically absorbed all of a sample of nitrogen he had similarly extracted from the atmosphere.

As Cavendish had done, Ramsay extracted a sample of nitrogen from the atmosphere and then chemically absorbed all of the nitrogen in that sample. He looked at the spectrum of the remaining bubble of gas, just as you have looked at the spectra of various gases in **Activity 4** and **5**. The new spectral lines of color he saw showed him that the bubble of gas was a new element, which today we know as argon. It had previously escaped notice because of its rarity and lack of chemical activity.

A New Family

When Mendeleev formulated the first periodic table argon had not been discovered, and therefore it had not been placed in the periodic table. There was no obvious place for argon. A new column was created. A prediction was therefore made that there would be other elements with similar properties to argon. The other elements of this family (He, Ne, Kr) were subsequently discovered by the end of the 19th century.

Checking Up

1. Why did one liter of nitrogen prepared by Lord Rayleigh appear to have a greater mass than the other liter prepared by a different method?

2. What are two reasons that the noble gases had escaped notice?

Chem Words

noble gas (also rare or inert gas): a family of elements (Group 18 or VIIIA) of the periodic table

Unlike atoms of the other chemical elements, atoms of elements in this column are so stable that they either do not react at all, or they react only in unusual circumstances, with other elements. For this reason, this family has been known as **rare** gases (because they are rare in abundance), **inert** gases (because they are not chemically reactive), or **noble** gases.

Reflecting on the Activity and the Challenge

In this activity you have learned that the electrons in the energy sublevels with the highest number are, on the average, the farthest from the nucleus of an atom. These electrons, also known as valence electrons, determine the atom's chemical behavior. This chemical behavior is best understood in relationship to the arrangement of electrons in energy sublevels in atoms of noble gases, which, by virtue of their chemical inactivity, have a stability which is unmatched by other chemical elements. The key is an atom's excess or deficiency of electrons compared to an atom of the nearest noble gas on the periodic table. This excess or deficiency is readily indicated by the position of an element on the periodic table. How will you include this in your game about the periodic table?

Chemistry to Go

1. From the periodic table on the back inside cover, identify the excess or deficiency of electrons in an atom of a given element relative to an atom of the closest noble gas. Be sure to indicate both the number of electrons and a sign (plus or minus) to indicate whether the electrons are in excess or deficiency.

   a) calcium   b) arsenic
   c) potassium   d) iodine

2. Listed below are groups of three elements. For each group determine which two elements have more in common in terms of electron arrangement and therefore exhibit more similar chemical behavior. Give a reason for your selection.

   a) carbon, nitrogen, silicon   b) fluorine, chlorine, neon
   c) sulfur, bromine, oxygen   d) sodium, magnesium, sulfur
   e) helium, neon, hydrogen

3. Listed below are pairs of elements. For each pair determine which of the two has the most stable arrangement of electrons. You may refer to the table of first ionization energies in **Activity 6** and the periodic table on the back inside cover. Provide a statement explaining your choice in terms of ionization energy and electron arrangement.

   a) helium and lithium
   b) lithium and beryllium
   c) magnesium and chlorine
   d) magnesium and argon
   e) neon and krypton

4. a) Write the electron configuration for magnesium.

   b) Determine how many valence electrons magnesium contains.

   c) Write the electron configuration for barium.

   d) Determine how many valence electrons barium contains.

   e) How do the number of valence electrons of magnesium compare to the number of valence electrons of barium?

   f) What general statement can you make about the number of valence electrons of each element of the alkaline earth metals?

5. a) Write the electron configuration for cobalt.

   b) How many valence electrons does cobalt contain?

Inquiring Further

1. Valence electron of transition elements

How many valence electrons are there in an atom of iron (Fe, atomic number 26 and called a transition element)? When you look at the periodic table on the back inside cover, you see that iron has all the electrons in an atom of calcium plus six additional electrons in the $3d$ sublevel. Relative to the 2 electrons in the $4s$ sublevel in calcium, do these $3d$ electrons qualify as valence electrons? Explain your thinking. What can you say about the number of valence electrons in the other transition elements, from scandium to copper?

2. Ionization energies of beryllium (Be) atoms

The first three ionization energies of beryllium atoms are as follows:

1st $= 1.49 \times 10^{-18}$ J

2nd $= 2.92 \times 10^{-18}$ J

3rd $= 2.47 \times 10^{-17}$ J

Explain the magnitudes of the energies in terms of electron configurations and from this information determine how many valence electrons are contained in beryllium.

411

Activity 8

How Atoms Interact with Each Other

GOALS

In this activity you will:

• Relate patterns in ionization energies of elements to patterns in electron arrangements.

• Use your knowledge of electron arrangements and valence electrons to predict formulas for compounds formed by two elements.

• Contrast ionic bonding and covalent bonding.

• Draw electron-dot diagrams for simple molecules with covalent bonding.

What Do You Think?

You have learned that the chemical behavior of an atom is determined by the arrangement of the atom's electrons, specifically the valence electrons. The salt that you put on your food is chemically referred to as NaCl—sodium chloride.

• How might the valence electrons of sodium (Na) and chlorine (Cl) interact to create this bond?

Record your ideas about this question in your *Active Chemistry* log. Be prepared to discuss your responses with your small group and the class.

Investigate

1. In **Activity 3** you read that John Dalton assumed that chemical compounds formed from two elements combined in the simplest possible combination—one atom of each element. In **Activity 6** you began to see that an atom's chemical behavior reflects its excess or deficiency of electrons relative to an atom of the closest noble gas on the periodic table. Use the list of ionization energies in **Activity 6** to answer the following questions:

a) Which atoms have the smallest values for first ionization energies? (Remember, the first ionization energy is the amount of energy required to remove the first electron.)

Where are these atoms located on the periodic table?

b) What do you observe about the amount of energy required to remove the second electron from atoms of the elements identified in (a) above?

c) Use your understanding of the arrangement of electrons in this group of elements to suggest a reason for the pattern you noted in (b).

d) Which atoms have the smallest values for second ionization energies? Where are these atoms located on the periodic table?

e) Use your understanding of the arrangement of electrons in this group of elements to suggest a reason for the pattern you noted in (d).

2. Once you recognize the role of an atom's electron arrangement—especially the valence electrons—in an atom's chemical activity, you can often predict formulas for compounds formed by two chemical elements. (Recall that valence electrons are the electrons located in the highest energy level, the levels designated by the sublevel having the highest numbers.)

Sodium (Na) has one valence electron in the 3s sublevel. By losing that electron, the sodium atom becomes a sodium ion and it has the same stable electron arrangement as neon. What is the electric charge on the resulting Na ion?

Consider a chlorine atom.

a) How many valence electrons does a chlorine atom have?

b) How many electrons does a chlorine atom need to gain to have the same number of electrons as an argon atom?

c) When a chlorine atom gains an electron, a chloride ion is formed. Since the original chlorine atom was electrically neutral and it gained a negative electron to form the ion, what is the electric charge (sign and value) on the resulting ion?

d) Each chlorine atom is capable of accepting one electron. Describe how you think the compound sodium chloride (NaCl) is formed?

3. Consider the reaction between aluminum and zinc chloride (similar to the reaction in Activity 3). The zinc atoms in zinc chloride have two valence electrons located in the 4s sublevel. You can note the two valence electrons in the electron arrangement marked on the periodic table.

In order to acquire the electron configuration of argon atoms a rather stable arrangement, the zinc atoms give up their two valence electrons to form zinc ions. Since the original zinc atom was electrically neutral and it lost two negative electrons to form the ion, the resulting ion has a positive charge with a magnitude two times the charge on the electron. It has a plus two charge.

a) Each chlorine atom is capable of accepting one electron. How many chlorine atoms are needed to accept the 2 electrons that zinc atoms have to give?

b) When writing the formula for a compound, the number of atoms necessary to balance the loss and gain of electrons can be designated through the use of a subscript, such as the 2 in H_2O. How would you write the formula for the compound zinc chloride?

4. In a reaction between aluminum and zinc chloride, aluminum replaces the zinc in the zinc chloride, forming aluminum chloride and zinc.

a) Consider an atom of aluminum. How many valence electrons does an aluminum atom have?

b) How many electrons does an aluminum atom need to give up to reach the same chemical stability as a neon atom?

c) What are aluminum atoms called after they give up their valence electrons? What is their electric charge (sign and value)?

d) How many chlorine atoms are needed to accept the electrons given up by an aluminum atom?

e) How would you write the formula for the compound aluminum chloride?

Chem Talk

FORMING COMPOUNDS

The Octet Rule

In this activity, you explained the formation of the compounds that you investigated by how the electrons are transferred or shared between atoms. Some scientists explain these observations using the octet rule. The octet rule works well with the representative elements and is stated as follows: atoms tend to gain or lose electrons during chemical reactions so that the atoms have an outer shell configuration of 8 electrons. The exceptions to this are the transition elements. They can form compounds that do not have 8 electrons in their outer shell. For example, when chlorine, one of the **halogens** (Group 17), gains one electron it now has 8 electrons in its outermost *s* and *p* sublevels (octet of electrons). Also, you should note that the name of all of the compounds that you have studied always started with the name of the metal and then followed with the nonmetal part. The second thing that you should note is that all of these compounds are binary (meaning two parts). **Binary compounds** always end with the suffix *ide* (except for a few compounds with common names like water and ammonia).

Chem Words

halogens: group VIIA (17) on the periodic table consisting of fluorine, chlorine, bromine, iodine, and astatine

binary compound: a compound, formed from the combining of two different elements

ionic bond: the attraction between oppositely charged ions

covalent bond: when two atoms combine and share their paired electrons with each other

Covalent and Ionic Bonds

You may have noticed that the column headed by carbon in the periodic table has not received a lot of attention so far. In **Activity 7** you learned that atoms of these elements contain 4 valence electrons. Atoms with a small number of valence electrons give up electrons, and atoms with a large number of valence electrons gain additional electrons to have the same electron arrangement as an atom of the nearest noble gas. Except for helium, with 2 valence electrons, the noble gases each have 8 valence electrons. What do atoms of carbon do: give up their 4 valence electrons, or gain 4 more?

In actuality, atoms of carbon do neither. Instead of giving or taking electrons, carbon atoms share electrons with atoms of other elements. Instead of giving or taking electrons to form what are called **ionic bonds**, carbon atoms share electrons with atoms of other elements to form what are called **covalent bonds**. In fact, all nonmetallic elements whose atoms have four or more valence electrons can form covalent bonds by sharing electrons. This sharing results in a situation in which each atom is associated with 8 valence electrons, as is characteristic of an atom of a noble gas.

Covalent bonding can be illustrated using electron-dot diagrams, in which each valence electron is indicated by a dot (or other appropriate symbol) around the chemical symbol for the element in question. Consider the following covalent compound illustrations:

hydrogen chloride contains one hydrogen atom and one atom of chlorine:	water contains 2 hydrogen atoms and one oxygen atom:	and carbon dioxide contains one atom of carbon and 2 oxygen atoms:
H : C̈l :	H : Ö : H	Ö :: C :: Ö

You can count 8 electrons around the chlorine in hydrogen chloride (note that hydrogen can only have 2 electrons). In water the oxygen has 8 electrons around it and hydrogen again has only 2 electrons. Carbon dioxide shows that oxygen contains 8 electrons and carbon has 8 electrons as well. These shared electrons in these examples all produce stable covalent compounds.

Checking Up

1. When naming a binary compound, which element is named first, the metal or the nonmetal? Give an example to explain your answer.

2. Explain the difference between an ionic and a covalent bond.

3. Draw electron-dot diagrams showing covalent bonding in the following compounds:

   a) water (two atoms of hydrogen, one atom of oxygen). Note: Since the noble gas nearest hydrogen is helium, with only two valence electrons, hydrogen atoms need be associated with only two valence electrons.

   b) methane (four atoms of hydrogen, one atom of carbon).

   c) ammonia (three atoms of hydrogen, one atom of nitrogen).

   d) carbon tetrachloride (four atoms of chlorine, one atom of carbon).

Reflecting on the Activity and the Challenge

In this activity you learned that atoms of two chemical elements will interact with each other in order to achieve a stable electron arrangement like that of nearby noble gases. The way in which atoms interact is based on their excess or deficiency of electrons relative to atoms of the closest noble gas on the periodic table. An atom's excess or deficiency of electrons relative to the closest noble gas is readily indicated by the position of an element on the periodic table. In this way the periodic table can be used to predict the chemical formulas when two elements interact to form a compound. This information can be deduced from the periodic table. Perhaps you can invent a way to make this more explicit as you create your periodic table game. How might you incorporate this information into your game to meet the **Chapter Challenge?**

1. From the periodic table on the back inside cover, identify the excess or deficiency of electrons in an atom of each of the following pairs of elements relative to an atom of the closest noble gas, and then predict the formula of the compound formed when these elements interact:

   a) sodium and oxygen (to form sodium oxide),

   b) magnesium and chlorine (to form magnesium chloride),

   c) aluminum and oxygen (to form aluminum oxide).

2. a) In your *Active Chemistry* log, draw a simplified periodic table that contains only the first three rows of the periodic table. Your table should have 3 rows and 8 columns, and should contain the elements with atomic numbers 1 through 18.

   b) In the box for each element, write the symbol for the element.

   c) In the columns headed by lithium, beryllium, and boron, indicate the charge (sign and value) of the ion formed when atoms of these elements give up electrons to attain a more stable electron arrangement.

   d) In the columns headed by nitrogen, oxygen, and fluorine, indicate how many electrons are gained by atoms of those elements to attain a more stable electron arrangement.

3. You know the formula for sodium chloride (NaCl) and from this knowledge you can also write the formula for potassium chloride, cesium bromide, lithium iodide and sodium fluoride.

a) What tool makes it possible for you to do this, even though you may have never investigated these compounds?

b) Using the periodic table, explain what information you used to help explain how you arrived at the formulas.

4. The formula for calcium chloride is $CaCl_2$ and from this knowledge you should be able to write the formulas of the alkaline earth metals (Group 2) and halogens combining.

a) Write the formula for magnesium bromide, strontium iodide, beryllium fluoride, barium chloride and calcium iodide.

b) What information from the periodic table did you use to support your writing the formulas of these compounds?

5. A compound that was used previously is aluminum chloride ($AlCl_3$). Use your understanding of why elements are grouped together and are called a family, to write the formula for each of the following compounds:

a) boron fluoride,   b) aluminum bromide,

c) gallium iodide,   d) indium (III) chloride,

e) thallium (III) bromide.

6. You have explored how the alkali, alkaline earth metals, and IIIA group (boron, aluminum, gallium, indium, and thallium) combine with the halogens, but how do these metals combine with the group VIA elements (oxygen, sulfur, selenium, tellurium, and polonium)? Look at a few compounds such as sodium oxide that has a formula of Na_2O. Alkali metals like sodium "want" to lose one electron. Oxygen "wants" to gain 2 electrons. Therefore, when the alkali metals combine with oxygen or other elements of group VIA, they should have a similar formula.

a) Write the formula for each of the following compounds:

   i) potassium sulfide   ii) rubidium selenide

   iii) lithium telluride   iv) sodium sulfide

   v) cesium oxide

   You can do the same thing with the alkaline earth metals combining with the group VIA elements. Calcium oxide has the formula CaO. The alkaline earth metals want to lose 2 electrons and the group VIA elements want to gain 2 electrons. They will combine in a 1:1 ratio.

b) Write the formula for each of the following compounds:

   i) magnesium sulfide   ii) strontium selenide

   iii) barium oxide   iv) beryllium telluride

   v) calcium sulfide

Magnification of sulfur crystal

Finally, look at the group IIIA elements combining with the group VIA elements. Aluminum oxide has the formula Al_2O_3. The group IIIA elements want to lose 3 electrons and the group VIA elements want to gain 2 electrons. In order to make a whole number exchange 6 electrons must be transferred. (Remember to make sure that your formula has the correct number of electrons being transferred.)

c) Write the formula for the following compounds:

    i) boron sulfide   ii) aluminum selenide

    iii) gallium telluride   iv) indium (III) oxide

    v) thallium (III) sulfide

Inquiring Further

Creating compounds with "inert" gases

For a long period of time the noble gases were called the inert elements, because it was assumed that they were non-reactive and did not want to gain or lose electrons. Research to find out if compounds can be formed with the noble gases. Record your finding in your *Active Chemistry* log. If time permits, share your findings with the class.

Activity 9

What Determines and Limits an Atom's Mass?

GOALS

In this activity you will:

- Investigate the composition of the atom's nucleus.

- Explain why the atomic masses of some elements are not whole numbers.

- Use symbols to represent different isotopes of an element.

- Determine the composition of the nucleus of an atom from its isotope symbol.

- Calculate the average atomic mass of an element from the percent abundance of its isotopes.

What Do You Think?

In **Activity 4** you learned that the structure of an atom includes a nucleus surrounded by electrons. Most of the mass of an atom is concentrated in the small nucleus that has a positive electric charge equal in magnitude to the negative charge of all the electrons surrounding the nucleus.

- What do you think makes up the nucleus of the atom?

Record your ideas about this question in your *Active Chemistry* log. Be prepared to discuss your responses with your small group and the class.

Investigate

Part A: What's in the Nucleus?

1. Atomic mass is the average mass of atoms of each element. Atomic number indicates the number of electrons in the atom and the number of protons located in the nucleus needed to produce an electrically neutral atom. Refer to the periodic table to answer the following questions:

Integrated Coordinated Science for the 21st Century

a) How many protons are there in a hydrogen atom?

b) To the nearest whole number, what is the atomic mass of a hydrogen atom?

c) How many protons are there in a helium atom?

d) Since the mass of an electron is negligible, compared to the nucleus, what would you expect the atomic mass of a helium atom to be? Explain your answer.

e) To the nearest whole number, what is the atomic mass of a helium atom?

2. In **Step 1**, you found that the helium atom has a mass that is four times the mass of a hydrogen atom, while the electric charge on the helium nucleus is only twice that of the hydrogen atom. This suggests the presence of another particle in the nucleus, with about the same mass as the proton but no electric charge. This particle is called a neutron.

Sample:

Boron has atomic number 5. This informs you that there are 5 electrons and that the nucleus contains 5 protons. The average atomic mass of boron is 10.811 atomic mass units. Most boron has 11 atomic mass units and some has 10 atom mass units. Since the mass is the sum of the protons and the neutrons (electrons have very, very little mass) then you can conclude that most boron nuclides have 5 protons and 6 neutrons in the nucleus.

Refer to your table of atomic numbers and atomic masses to answer the following questions:

a) How many protons would you expect to find in the nucleus of a helium atom? (Recall that the number of protons needs to balance the number of electrons.)

b) How many neutrons would you expect to find? (The atomic mass is a combination of the mass of the protons and the mass of the neutrons.)

c) How many protons and neutrons would you expect to find in the nucleus of an atom of each of the following elements:

- lithium
- beryllium
- boron
- carbon
- nitrogen
- oxygen
- fluorine
- neon

3. Refer again to the periodic table.

a) What are the atomic masses of magnesium and chlorine? What are the atomic masses of sodium and fluorine? Which set is closer to whole numbers?

b) We expect protons and neutrons to exist in whole numbers. You cannot have part of a proton in the nucleus. What would you expect the atomic masses of most magnesium, chlorine, sodium, and fluorine atoms to be? Explain your answer.

4. The fact that some atomic masses are not close to whole number multiples of the atomic mass of hydrogen is now explained by the fact that the number of neutrons is not the same in all atoms of a given element. Only the number of protons, the atomic number, is the same in all atoms of a

given element. Atoms of the same element with different number of neutrons in the nucleus are known as isotopes (meaning "same number of protons"). Isotopes are identified by their mass number, the sum of the number of neutrons plus protons.

Sample:

Lithium has an atomic number of 3 and an average atomic mass of 6.941. All lithium atoms have 3 protons in the nucleus. A neutral atom of lithium always has 3 electrons to balance the charge of the three protons. The average atomic mass of a lithium atom is 6.941 atomic mass units, indicating that some lithium atoms have 3 neutrons, to make a total atomic mass of 6 and other lithium atoms have 4 neutrons, to make a total atomic mass of 7. These 2 isotopes are designated lithium-6 and lithium-7. Since there are so many more lithium-7 atoms, the average of all of the atoms is very close to 7.

Refer to your list of atomic masses to answer the following questions:

a) What isotopes (as indicated by their mass numbers) do you expect to account for the known atomic masses of the following elements?

- carbon (carbon-12 atoms with 6 neutrons and carbon-13 atoms with 7 neutrons; more carbon-12 atoms)

- hydrogen
- boron
- magnesium
- beryllium
- sodium

b) In the notation below, the mass number is written at the upper left of the chemical symbol of the element. The atomic number is written at the lower left of the chemical symbol of the element. How many neutrons and protons are present in the following isotopes?

i) $^{3}_{2}\text{He}$ and $^{4}_{2}\text{He}$

ii) $^{6}_{3}\text{Li}$ and $^{7}_{3}\text{Li}$

iii) $^{12}_{6}\text{C}$ and $^{13}_{6}\text{C}$

iv) $^{14}_{7}\text{N}$ and $^{15}_{7}\text{N}$

Part B: Forces within the Atom

1. There are two very different forces acting on the electrons, protons, and neutrons in the atom. In order to better understand the atom, you must first understand these forces.

Cut two strips of transparent tape about 12 cm long. Bend one end of each strip under to form a tab. Place one strip sticky-side down on a table and label the tab "B," for "bottom." Place the other strip sticky-side down

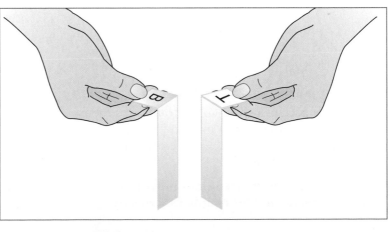

on top of the first strip and label the tab "T," for "top."

Peel off the top strip, using the tab, with one hand and then pick up the bottom strip with the other hand. Hold both strips apart, allowing them to hang down.

Slowly bring the hanging strips toward each other, but do not let them touch.

a) Record your observations.

b) If the strips accelerated toward or away from each other, Newton's Second Law tells you that there must be a force. Is the force between the two strips of tape attractive or repulsive?

2. Make a second set of strips as in **Step 1**.

a) Predict what you think will happen if the two top strips are picked up, one from each set and brought toward each other. Record your prediction in your *Active Chemistry* log.

Pick up the two top strips by the tabs, allowing both strips to hang down. Slowly bring them toward each other.

b) Record your observations.

c) Was the force attractive or repulsive? Explain.

d) Predict what you think will happen if the two bottom strips of tape are picked up and brought toward each other. Record your prediction.

Pick up the two bottom strips by the tabs, allowing both strips to

hang down. Slowly bring them toward each other.

e) Record your observations.

f) Was the force attractive or repulsive? Explain.

3. The two different strips of tape have different charges. The top strips have a positive electric charge. They have lost some of their electrons. Since the number of protons has remained the same, the strips are positive. The bottom strips have a negative charge. The bottom strips have gained some electrons. Since the number of protons has remained the same, the strips are negative. The force between the strips is called the electric force.

a) Is the force between two positive strips repulsive or attractive? Use evidence to justify your answer.

b) Is the force between two negative strips repulsive or attractive? Use evidence to justify your answer.

c) When a positive and a negative strip come near each other, is the force attractive or repulsive? Justify your answer.

4. The nucleus has a positive charge due to all of the protons there. The electrons surrounding the nucleus have negative charges.

a) What kind of electric force (attractive or repulsive) exists between the nucleus of an atom and any one of the atom's electrons?

b) What kind of electric force (attraction or repulsion) exists between pairs of protons in the nucleus?

5. The nucleus is a very crowded place. The protons in the nucleus are very close to one another. If these protons are repelling each other by an electrostatic force (and they are!), there must be another force, an attractive force, that keeps them there. The attractive force is the nuclear force, also called the strong force. This force is much stronger than the electric force. It acts between pairs of protons, pairs of neutrons, and protons and neutrons. The electron is not affected by the nuclear force.

   a) Copy and complete the table below in your *Active Chemistry* log. The first row has been completed for you.

6. If the nucleus were too large, the protons on one side of the nucleus are too far away to attract the protons on the other side of the nucleus. The protons can still repel one another since the coulomb electrostatic force is long-range. The repulsive electrostatic force wins and the nucleus won't form.

   A large nucleus will break apart when the electrostatic repulsion between the protons is too great.

The repulsion pushes the fragments of the nucleus apart, releasing a great amount of energy. This process of splitting an atom into smaller atoms is called fission. It occurs in uranium when an additional neutron is added and causes instability.

One example of the fission process can be represented as follows:

$$_{92}^{235}U + _{0}^{1}n \rightarrow _{36}^{94}Kr + _{56}^{139}Ba + 3\ _{0}^{1}n + energy$$

a) Is the mass number conserved on both sides of the reaction? What is the total mass number on each side?

b) Is the atomic number conserved on both sides of the reaction? What is the total atomic number on each side?

c) Why does the neutron have a mass number of 1?

d) Why is the atomic number of a neutron equal to 0?

   Small nuclei can also combine to form a larger nucleus and release energy. This process is called fusion.

Particles	Coulomb electrostatic force	Strong, nuclear force
electron-proton	*attractive*	*none*
electron-neutron		
proton-proton		
proton-neutron		
neutron-neutron		

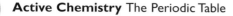

THE NUCLEUS OF AN ATOM

Discovery of the Neutron

The average atomic masses of some elements were known in Mendeleev's time, even though scientists didn't know much about the actual structure of an atom. In **Part A** of this activity you explored the idea of how the atomic mass relates to the atomic number. Mendeleev began organizing his periodic table by listing all the known elements in order of atomic mass. However, he found that organizing the elements in this way did not always make sense in terms of the behavior of the elements. He concluded that his measurements of atomic mass were incorrect and in those situations used the properties of the elements to place them in the table.

As it turned out, Mendeleev's measurements were not necessarily flawed. Although early models of the nucleus included the **proton**, the proton alone could not account for the fact that the mass of a helium atom is four times the mass of a hydrogen atom while the electric charge on the helium nucleus is only twice that of the hydrogen atom. Lord Rutherford (after discovering that atoms had a nucleus) addressed this problem when he suggested that another particle was present in the nucleus, with about the same mass as the proton but no electric charge. He named this particle the **neutron**.

The neutron was actually discovered in 1932 (by Chadwick, a British physicist), adding a great deal to the understanding of the nucleus of the atom. This discovery did not solve all of the mysteries concerning the atomic masses of some elements. Scientists today refer to protons and neutrons as nucleons since they reside in the nucleus and are almost identical in mass. The mass number tells us the number of nucleons.

Isotopes

In **Part A** of this activity you also investigated why the atomic mass of an element is not a whole number. Not all atoms of a given element have the same number of neutrons in the nucleus. Only the number of protons, the atomic number, is the same in all atoms of a given element. Atoms of the same element with different number of

Chem Words

proton: a positively charged subatomic particle contained in the nucleus of an atom. The mass of a proton is 1.673×10^{-24}g and has a charge of $+1$

neutron: neutral subatomic particle with a mass of 1.675×10^{-24}g located in the nuclei of the atom

neutrons in the nucleus are known as **isotopes** (meaning "same number of protons"). Isotopes are identified by their mass number, the sum of the number of neutrons plus protons.

You can refer to an element by its name (chlorine), by its atomic symbol (Cl), or by its atomic number (17). All three identifications are equivalent and used interchangeably in chemistry. The same element can have a different number of neutrons in the nucleus. Chlorine, which must have 17 protons in the nucleus, can have 18 or 20 neutrons. Chlorine with 20 neutrons and chlorine with 18 neutrons are the isotopes of chlorine (^{35}Cl and ^{37}Cl).

Electrostatic and Nuclear Forces

In **Part B** of this activity, when you brought the two positive strips near each other, they experienced a repulsive force. This was true for two negative strips as well. When a positive and a negative strip were brought close together, the force was attractive. As you have heard, "opposites attract!"

Inside the nucleus, the protons are repelling one another. Every pair of protons has a repulsive force between them. The force is very large because the distances within the nucleus are very small. The nucleus is between 10,000 and 100,000 times smaller than the atom. The electrical force can be described mathematically.

$$F = \frac{kq_1q_2}{d^2}$$

where F is the force,

k is Coulomb's constant
(a number $= 9 \times 10^9$ N m^2/C^2),

q_1 and q_2 are the charges, and
d is the distance between the charges.

As the distance between the charges increases the force weakens. Since the distance in the denominator is squared, if the distance triples the electrical force is 9 times (3^2) weaker or one-ninth as strong.

isotope: atoms of the same element but different atomic masses due to different number of neutrons

The question then becomes, what holds the protons together in the nucleus? The protons do have an electrical force pushing them apart but they have the larger nuclear force holding them together. The nuclear force is strong at short range. Anywhere beyond a distance of approximately 10^{-14} m (that's less than one 10 millionth of one 10 millionth of a meter), the nuclear force is zero. Neutrons in the nucleus are also attracted to each other and to protons with the nuclear force. Electrons are not affected by the nuclear force. Electrons belong to a different class of particles than protons and neutrons and do not interact with the strong nuclear force.

The nucleus is held together by a new force—the strong nuclear force. The nuclear force:

- is very, very strong at small distances;
- acts only between nucleons (proton-proton, proton-neutron, neutron-neutron);
- is always attractive;
- is very short range (if nucleons are more than 10^{-14} m apart, the nuclear force is zero).

The atom is held together by the electrostatic coulomb force. The electrostatic force:

- is strong at small distances, weak at large distances;
- acts only between charged particles (proton-proton, electron-electron, proton-electron);
- is attractive or repulsive;
- is long range (the force gets weaker at large distances).

All the nucleons are attracted by the nuclear force. The electrostatic force repelling protons in the nucleus is overwhelmed by the attractive nuclear force between these protons.

Unstable Atoms

You might expect to find nuclei of atoms with all sorts of combinations of neutrons and protons. Yet the quantity of isotopes for each element is rather small, and the number of elements is also limited. Moreover, elements do not occur in nature with atomic number greater than 92, and the highest atomic number for an atom created in the laboratory is 117.

There are two stable masses of chlorine, chlorine-35 and chlorine-37. The key word in this statement is "stable." There are other isotopes of chlorine, both heavier and lighter than chlorine-35 and chlorine-37, but they are not stable. The unstable isotopes can convert to a more stable combination of neutrons and protons, and they do so according to a systematic pattern in time. These other isotopes of chlorine are said to be **radioactive**. Understanding why certain elements are radioactive requires a deeper understanding of the structure of the nucleus. Scientists are still trying to fully understand stability of the elements.

If the nucleus of an atom is too large, the protons on one side of the nucleus are too far away to attract the protons on the other side of the nucleus. The protons can still repel one another since the coulomb electrostatic force is long-range. The interaction between the repulsive electrostatic force and the attractive nuclear force is one determining factor on the maximum size of a nucleus.

The stability of an atom varies with the elements. Light elements become more stable as the atomic mass (the number of nucleons) increases. The most stable element is iron (atomic number 26) with an atomic mass of 56. Elements with larger atomic masses become less stable.

In general, elements with nuclear mass much, much less than 56 can combine to gain mass, become more stable, and give off energy. This process is called **fusion**. Elements with nuclear mass much, much greater than 56 can break apart to lose mass, become more stable, and give off energy. This process is called **fission**.

Fusion is the process of small nuclei combining to increase their mass. The best example of fusion processes is what occurs in the Sun and other stars. The fusion process is ideal for supplying safe energy because it releases very large amounts of energy without leaving much dangerous radioactive residue. However, it is very difficult to accomplish this on an industrial level at the present time. In the future we hope scientists will figure out how to harness the energy of nuclear fusion, because it would be an excellent source of energy for society.

The process of splitting an atom into smaller atoms is called fission. This is the process that is used to produce nuclear energy. It is used to power nuclear submarines and to produce electrical energy in nuclear power plants all over the world.

Chem Words

radioactive: an atom that has an unstable nuclei and will emit alpha, positron, or beta particles in order to achieve more stable nuclei

fusion: nuclei of lighter atoms combining to form nuclei with greater mass and release of a large amount of energy

fission: the process of breaking apart nuclei into smaller nuclei and with the release of a large amount of energy

Checking Up

1. Explain the difference between atomic mass and atomic number.

2. What two forces are at work in the nucleus of an atom? Explain how each works.

3. What is an isotope?

4. Why are some isotopes unstable?

5. Construct a table or diagram to compare and contrast the nuclear processes of fission and fusion.

The use of nuclear energy for the production of electricity is quite apparent as you look at the numerous states that depend on nuclear energy. For example, over 40% of Illinois' electricity is produced by nuclear energy. Nuclear fission does create some major problems: (1) Security, (2) Radiation, (3) Removal of spent rods, and (4) Disposal of waste. With these problems, there is a need for continued research. Numerous universities and government facilities are trying to improve the efficiency of nuclear fission and at the same time, trying to develop nuclear fusion for commercial use.

This ongoing research is expensive and depends on the government, industry, and other organizations to continue supporting this research. If we can learn how to harness nuclear fusion we can alleviate our nation's electrical problems while decreasing pollution. The field of nuclear science is going to continue to grow and the future will provide great opportunities for a young scientist like you to get involved.

Reflecting on the Activity and the Challenge

In **Part A** of this activity you learned that the mass of an atom, concentrated in the nucleus, is due to two types of particles, the proton and the neutron. Elements are identified by their atomic number, the number of protons in the nucleus. The atomic mass, the average mass of an atom of a given element, listed on the periodic table is a reflection of the variety of isotopes of a given element that exist. How will you incorporate your expanded understanding of the contents of an atom's nucleus, average atomic masses and isotopes into your game about the periodic table?

In **Part B** of this activity you also learned that only some combinations of neutrons and protons in a nucleus are stable, depending on the balance between the strong force holding the nuclear particles together and the electric force pushing them apart. The nuclear force is a short-range force. Beyond a distance of approximately 10^{-14} m, the nuclear force has no strength. Within that distance, this force between protons and protons, protons and neutrons, and neutrons and neutrons is quite strong. Recognizing the interplay between the electric force in the nucleus and the strong, attractive nuclear force provides an insight into the size of nuclei and the maximum size of a nucleus. These insights can be incorporated into your periodic table game in a creative way.

Chemistry to Go

1. If lithium loses an electron to become Li+, what is the average atomic mass of the lithium ion? Explain how you arrived at your answer.

2. Hydrogen has 3 isotopes with mass numbers of 1, 2, and 3. Write the complete chemical symbol for each isotope.

3. Give the complete chemical symbol for the element that contains 16 protons, 16 electrons, and 17 neutrons.

4. Complete the table below: (Use the periodic table.)

Chemical symbol	$^{39}_{19}$K			
Atomic number		9		
Number of protons			15	
Number of electrons				53
Number of neutrons		10	16	
Atomic mass				127

5. Neutrons can be used to bombard the nucleus of an atom like uranium. Why would it be more difficult to inject the nucleus of uranium with a proton?

6. Complete the following reaction: $^{215}_{92}U + ^{1}_{0}n \rightarrow ^{94}_{38}Sr +$ _____ $+ 2\,^{1}_{0}n$

7. Radon is a threat to the well-being of people in their homes because it emits radioactive particles at a significant rate. Complete the following radioactive decay equation:

   $^{222}_{86}Rn \rightarrow ^{218}_{84}Po +$ _____

8. Explain why a helium atom is able to exist. What keeps the 2 electrons, 2 protons, and 2 neutrons together?

Inquiring Further

Calculating average atomic mass

If you know the percentages of abundance for the isotopes of a chemical element and the known masses of those isotopes, you can calculate the average atomic mass of that element. The process is similar to calculating the average age of students in your class — add up each person's age and divide by the number of students in your class. However, if you had to average the age of all of the students in your high school, you might choose another route. It would be easier to find out how many students are fourteen, how many are fifteen, and so on. Then you could multiply the number of students in each age group by that age. Then you would add these subsets together and divide by the total number of students.

A similar process is used to average the masses of different isotopes of an element. Consider the element chlorine. There are two stable isotopes of chlorine, chlorine-35 and chlorine-37. Of all the chlorine atoms on Earth, 75.77% of them are the isotope chlorine-35, each having a mass of 34.96885. The other 24.23% of stable chlorine atoms are the isotope chlorine-37, each having a mass of 36.96590. This means that 75.77 out of 100 chlorine atoms have a mass of 34.96885 and 24.23 have a mass of 36.96590. To find the average mass, the number of each isotope is multiplied by that isotope's mass. Then the products are added together. The sum is divided by 100, since the information pertained to 100 chlorine atoms. The result is an average atomic mass of 35.45 for chlorine, the same value stated in the periodic table. The math is shown below:

Chlorine-35 $34.96885 \times 75.77 = 2649.6$

Chlorine-37 $36.96590 \times 24.23 = 895.7$
$3545.3 \div 100 = 35.453$

Magnesium, another isotope you investigated, has three stable isotopes as follows:

mass number	isotopic mass	% abundance
24	23.98504	78.99
25	24.98594	10.00
26	25.98259	11.01

Calculate the average atomic mass for magnesium. Describe how you arrived at your answer. You may use the process described above or challenge yourself to develop your own process.

The Periodic Table Assessment

Your Chapter Challenge is to develop a game related to Mendeleev's Periodic Table of the Elements. The game should be interesting, entertaining and informative. It should demonstrate your understanding of the periodic table while it helps other students learn about the periodic table. When people begin your game, they may have no knowledge of chemistry or the periodic table. After they complete the game, they should be able to report on chemistry principles which are reflected in the periodic table.

You can begin work on the **Chapter Challenge** by reviewing the important features of the periodic table that you want to include in your game. Choose a small section of the periodic table and list what you know about each element including its atomic number, atomic mass, chemical properties, electron configuration, nuclear structure and where and why it is placed where it is in the periodic table. Next to each of these items, you may wish to describe how we know some of these details (e.g., describe the Rutherford scattering experiment for evidence of the nucleus; Law of Definite Proportions for evidence of atoms). You should review the nine activities in the chapter to add to your list. You should pay particular attention to the section **Reflecting on the Activity and the Challenge.** You should also compare your list with that given in the **Chemistry You Learned** summary.

You now have to create the game which will highlight the chemistry principles that you have investigated in the past few weeks. There are a wide variety of games. There are traditional board games like Monopoly, Parcheesi, Clue and Risk. There are card games like gin rummy, hearts, solitaire, poker and bridge. There are TV games like *Jeopardy, Wheel of Fortune* and *The Price is Right.* There are video games like SimCity, PacMan and Space Invaders. There are also word games like crossword puzzles and anagrams. You have lots of experience with many different kinds of games. The first hurdle for your team will be to decide on the type of game that you will use as the format for communicating your knowledge of the periodic table. Your game should not merely be a periodic table test. It should be an entertaining approach to learning about the periodic table as well as displaying knowledge.

Once you decide and agree upon a game format, you will have to generate a set of rules. These rules will include whether people work individually or in groups, how one earns points or wins, how to get help during the game and suggested strategies for the game.

After the rules of the game are set, you must integrate your expert knowledge of the periodic table into the game. How will people playing the game learn that the atomic number corresponds to the number of protons and electrons in the neutral atom? How will players learn that isotopes of chlorine affect the stated mass? How will players get credit for remembering that the electron configurations are responsible for chemical behavior. The list of chemistry principles that you first completed can now be expanded so that each principle becomes the basis for a part of the game.

After the game structure is completed, you may have to design a board or some computer application so that the game can be played. Some careful preparation here can make a big difference in how well your game is accepted by others.

You should now practice the game as if you and your team members are playing it for the first time. Carefully critique your own game and edit the rules, approaches and chemistry principles so that the game is truly entertaining and educational. Review all of the criteria listed at the beginning of the chapter and the grading criteria agreed to by your teacher and class. Create a checklist and perform a final review of your checklist. Grade yourself before the presentation of your game to ensure that your team is heading for a great grade.

Chemistry You Learned

Elements' chemical and physical properties	Protons	The spectral lines classified as Balmer series, Lyman series, and Paschen series	Group chemical behavior
Atoms	Line spectrums produced by different elements		Noble gas electron configuration and stability
Single-displacement reactions	Energy, frequency, and wavelength produced by the excitation of electrons	Ionization potential of atom's electron	Valence electrons Ionic compounds and ionic bonding
Double-displacement reactions		Periodicity of the elements	Covalent compounds and covalent bonds
Atomic mass	Electromagnetic spectrum	Atom's energy level and the sublevel energy of the outermost electron	Chemical formula
Compound	Bohr's Atomic Theory		Neutrons
Law of Definite Proportions	Orbits of electrons	Electron configuration	Nuclear stability
Avogadro's number and a mole		Family or chemical groups on the periodic table	Isotopes
Electrons			Fission
Nucleus			Fusion
			Electrostatic force
			Strong, nuclear force

Chapter 8

Cool Chemistry Show

8

Scenario

The fourth- and fifth-grade students at a local elementary school have been studying chemistry in their classes. Because of the students' overwhelming interest, their teachers have asked your class to present a chemistry science show to their students. The elementary teachers have requested that the show be both interesting and informative.

For the chemistry science show, the fourth-grade teachers are asking your class to include demonstrations and explanations about chemical and physical properties and changes. The fifth-grade teacher wants the students to learn more about acids and bases, and about chemical reactions that involve color changes

Chapter Challenge

You and your classmates are being challenged to present an entertaining and informative chemistry science show to fourth- and fifth-grade students.

- The content of the show should meet the needs and interest of your audience. Remember that the fourth-grade teacher has specifically requested that the show address chemical and physical properties and changes. The fifth-grade teacher wants the students to learn more about acids and bases, and about chemical reactions that involve color changes. Your class may choose to add other presentations to enhance the show.

- All presentations must include a demonstration and an audience-appropriate explanation of the chemistry concepts involved.

- You must provide the teachers with a written summary including directions for your chemistry show with explanations of the chemistry.

- As always, safety is a top priority. You and your classmates will wear safety gear, including safety goggles, appropriate to the presentation being conducted. Presentations including flammable or explosive reactions are not appropriate for the elementary audience and may not be included in the show.

- adherence to assigned time limits
- showmanship
- creativity
- clarity
- organization
- appeal
- written summary
- directions for experiment
- explanation of chemistry
- appropriateness for an elementary school teacher with limited chemistry background
- statements concerning safety needs

The class, as a whole, is responsible for putting on this Cool Chemistry Show. You will need to coordinate your selection of presentations to provide a show that addresses a variety of chemistry concepts in an entertaining and informative manner.

Criteria

How will your involvement in the Cool Chemistry Show be graded? What qualities should a good presentation have? Discuss these issues in small groups and with your class. You may decide that some or all of the following qualities of your presentation should be graded:

- Chemistry content
  - accuracy
  - meets teacher needs (fourth or fifth grade)
  - number of concepts addressed
- Demonstration
  - carefully planned
  - safety
  - explanation (age-appropriate)

Once your class has determined the list of criteria for judging the presentations, you should also decide how many points should be given for each criterion. Determining grading criteria in advance will help you focus your time and effort on the various aspects of the presentation. How many points should be assigned to the content and how many should be assigned to the actual presentation? Will each high school student be involved in only one presentation, or more? For each criterion, you should decide on how excellence is defined and how it compares to a satisfactory effort.

Since you will be working with other students in small groups, you will need to determine grading criteria that reward each individual in the group for his or her contribution and also reward the group for the final presentation. You should discuss different strategies and choose the one that is best suited to your situation. Your teacher may provide you with a sample rubric to help you get started.

Activity 1

Chemical and Physical Changes

GOALS

In this activity you will:

• Learn to differentiate between chemical and physical changes.

• Make observations and cite evidence to identify changes as chemical or physical.

• Explore the new properties exhibited when new materials are made from combinations of two or more original materials.

• Design an experiment to test properties of different combinations of materials.

What Do You Think?

There are two basic types of changes that matter can undergo: chemical change and physical change. Consider two wooden matches. One is broken in half and the other is ignited by striking it along the side of the matchbox. In both of these instances matter has changed.

• Which match has undergone a chemical change and which has undergone a physical change? Give specific reasons to support your answer.

Record your ideas about this question in your *Active Chemistry* log. Be prepared to discuss your responses with your small group and with the class.

Investigate

1. Listed on the following page are 15 opportunities for you to observe changes in matter. Your teacher may choose to do some or all of these as a demonstration or set up stations for you to visit. Notice that the directions call for small amounts of substances.

Safety goggles and a lab apron must be worn during this activity.

Make a data table to organize your observations of the matter before and after any change(s) that may occur. Be detailed in your observations.

- Heat an ice cube in a beaker.

- Boil a small amount of water.

- Melt a small amount of candle wax. Then allow the melted wax to cool.

- Break a wooden splint into several pieces.

- Hold a wooden splint in a flame.

- Add a few drops of lemon juice to a small amount of milk.

- Add a few drops of vinegar to a small amount of baking soda ($NaHCO_3$).

- Add a small amount of table salt to water; stir; boil the solution to dryness; cool and record the result.

- Add several drops of iodine solution to a small amount of starch.

- Add a small piece of zinc to a small amount of hydrochloric acid (0.1 M HCl).

- Add a drop of phenolphthalein indicator solution to a solution of sodium hydroxide (0.1 M NaOH).

- Add two drops of sodium carbonate (0.1 M Na_2CO_3) to two drops of sodium hydrogen sulfate (0.1 M $NaHSO_4$).

- Add a few drops of household ammonia to a small amount of a copper (II) sulfate (0.1 M $CuSO_4$) solution.

- Add a few drops of vinegar to a small piece of chalk.

- Sharpen a pencil and collect the shavings.

Dispose of the materials as directed by your teacher. Clean up your workstation and then wash your hands.

2. Organize the information in your data table.

a) Prepare and complete a chart that organizes your observations into separate columns — one that includes the situations where color changes occurred, one that notes the formation of precipitates (sometimes visible as a cloudy solution), one that includes gas formation (fizz), one to note other changes, and one where no visible change occurred.

3. A physical change involves changes in the appearance of the material but does not involve creation of new materials. A chemical change involves the formation of new materials. Chemical reactions are characterized by a number of changes, including color changes and the formation of a precipitate or gas.

a) Which of the interactions you observed were chemical changes? Explain your answer.

b) Which of the interactions you observed were physical changes? Explain your answer.

c) When you placed the wooden splint into a flame, what other evidence (besides the color change) indicated that a chemical change took place?

d) Imagine a situation where two colorless solutions are mixed together. There is no color change, no precipitate is formed, and no gas is released. However, heat is released as the solutions are mixed. Is this an example of a chemical or physical change? Explain your choice.

4. Each group will be given a piece of disposable diaper. Place the piece in a beaker.

   a) Predict how much liquid the diaper will be able to hold. Record your prediction in your log.

   b) Design an investigation to measure the amount of liquid that the diaper can absorb. Record your procedure in your log.

   c) With the approval of your teacher, carry out your investigation. Record your results.

d) Explain how your prediction compared with your observations.

e) The diaper is made of a material called sodium polyacrylate. When it absorbs water, is this a physical or chemical change? Explain your answer.

5. Your teacher will show you a solution of sodium acetate in a 250-mL flask. Observe the solution carefully.

   a) Record your observations in your *Active Chemistry* log.

   Your teacher will then add one crystal of sodium acetate to the flask.

   b) What happens? Record your observations in your log.

   c) Was this a chemical or physical change?

6. In a large throwaway glass jar, mix 100 mL of sodium silicate (sometimes called water-glass solution) and 400 mL of water.

   Carefully drop solid-colored crystal compounds of cobalt, copper, nickel, iron, and/or manganese in different locations inside the jar.

   a) Is there evidence of a change immediately? In several minutes? In several hours? In several days? In your *Active Chemistry* log, describe the results.

   b) Is the phenomenon you see the result of a physical or a chemical change? Explain your answer.

ChemTalk

CHANGES IN MATTER

Physical and Chemical Changes

In this activity you observed a number of situations that involved changes in matter, both physical and chemical. A **physical change** involves changes in the appearance of the material but does not involve creation of new materials. A change of a solid to a liquid is a physical change. When the candle wax melted it may have appeared different, but it was still wax. After it solidified, it had a similar appearance to the initial product. Dissolving is also a physical change. When you added the salt to the water, the salt crystals seemed to disappear as they dissolved in the water. However, they had only spread out into a solution. A **solution** is a homogeneous mixture of at least two different materials. The material being dissolved is called the **solute**, and the material present in the largest amount is called the **solvent**. When you boiled away the solvent, water, the solute, the salt crystals, remained the same as they were originally.

A **chemical change** involves the formation of new materials. The new materials are called **products** and the starting materials are

Chem Words

physical change: a change that involves changes in the state or form of a substance but does not cause any change in chemical composition

solution: a homogeneous mixture of two or more substances

solute: the substance that dissolves in a solvent to form a solution

solvent: the substance in which a solute dissolves to form a solution

chemical change: a change that converts the chemical composition of a substance into different substance(s) with different chemical composition

product: the substance(s) produced in a chemical reaction

Chem Words

reactants: the starting materials in a chemical reaction

chemical reaction: a process in which new substance(s) are formed from starting substance(s)

precipitate: an insoluble solid formed in a liquid solution as a result of some chemical reactions

concentration: a measure of the composition of a solution, often given in terms of moles of solute per liter of solution

saturated solution: a maximum amount of solute that can be dissolved at a given temperature and pressure

polymer: a substance that is a macromolecule consisting of many similar small molecules (monomers) linked together in long chains

called **reactants**. The process that brings about a chemical change is called a **chemical reaction**. Chemical reactions are characterized by a number of changes, including color changes, the formation of a **precipitate** or gas, a release of heat or light. Chemical changes are usually not easy to reverse. When you burned the wooden splint you could not put the charcoal together to form the original splint as you could when you simply broke the splint into pieces.

Saturated and Supersaturated Solutions

The solution your teacher used in the demonstration was a supersaturated solution of sodium acetate. Solutions are commonly described in terms of **concentration**. The concentration of a solution is the ratio of the quantity of solute to the quantity of solution. A dilute solution has fewer solute molecules per volume than a concentrated solution. However, in both the dilute and concentrated solutions more solute can dissolve in the solvent. These solutions are unsaturated.

You probably recognize the term "saturated." When something is saturated, it is full. A saturated sponge is full of water; it can't hold any more. A **saturated solution** is one in which no more solute will dissolve under the given conditions. To say that the sodium acetate solution is supersaturated means that it is "over full." A supersaturated solution contains more solute

particles than it normally would under the given conditions. A supersaturated solution can be made using some solutes. If a saturated solution at a high temperature is allowed to cool undisturbed, all the solute may remain dissolved at the lower temperature. The solution is then supersaturated. As you observed in the activity, such solutions are unstable. By introducing a "seed" crystal the extra solute particles "joined" the crystal and came out of the solution.

Polymers

The chemical material that you were working with when you investigated the absorbency of the diaper was sodium polyacrylate. It is a chemical compound called a **polymer**. It is made up of many (poly) repeating units of a smaller group of elements (the monomer called acrylate). This particular polymer has a unique property. It will absorb more than 800 times its own mass in distilled water. The fascinating ability of this polymer (sodium polyacrylate) to absorb large amounts of water has led to its use in a number of commercial endeavors.

Checking Up

1. What is a physical change? Provide two examples.

2. Explain the meaning of a solution, a solute, and a solvent.

3. What is a chemical change? Provide two examples.

4. What "clues" can you look for to determine if a chemical change has occurred?

5. How do you describe the concentration of a solution?

6. Explain the difference between a saturated and a supersaturated solution.

Reflecting on the Activity and the Challenge

Recall that the fourth-grade teacher has specifically requested that your chemistry show addresses chemical and physical properties and changes. You are right on track for the fourth graders. The fifth-grade teacher wants the students to learn more about chemical reactions that involve color changes. You have seen a few of those, too. If you had to conduct the show based on your experiences so far, which activity would you use? What additional information would you need to be able to explain the chemistry to fourth- and fifth-grade students?

Chemistry to Go

1. Which of the following are chemical changes and why?

   a) Toast turns black after being in the toaster too long.

   b) Water condenses on the outside of a glass of iced tea.

441

c) Green leaves turn orange, yellow, and red in the fall.

d) Green bananas become yellow.

e) Butter melts on a hot summer day.

2. Think back to a recent lunch or dinner. Describe two physical and two chemical changes that were involved in the meal and explain why you think each was a physical or chemical change.

3. Write a paragraph describing a common activity (such as making a cake or driving a car). Underline the physical changes (use one line) and chemical changes (use two lines) taking place within the activity. Select and describe an activity that is sure to have at least two physical changes and two chemical changes.

4. The following information is obtained for the element aluminum. Identify which are physical (use one line) and which are chemical (use two lines) properties.

Aluminum is a shiny silver metal and melts at 660°C. When a strip of aluminum is placed in hydrochloric acid, hydrogen gas is released. The density of aluminum is 2.70 g/cm^3. When polished aluminum is exposed to oxygen over a period of time it forms aluminum oxide (Al_2O_3) on the surface of the metal.

5. How would you determine whether a clear solution in a beaker is saturated sugar water or just water? Remember, you do not taste samples in the laboratory.

Preparing for the Chapter Challenge

Describe how you would demonstrate the difference between a physical and chemical change in a "cool" way.

Inquiring Further

Factors affecting solubility and the rate of dissolving

Understanding the factors that affect how quickly a solute dissolves in a solvent is important in many practical applications in manufacturing. Design an investigation to determine the factors that affect solubility. Consider the following:

• nature of the solute and solvent;

• temperature;

• agitation (stirring or shaking);

• surface area (for example, try using a sugar cube, granulated sugar, and icing sugar);

• pressure of gases.

Remember that your investigation must be controlled, if your results are to be reliable. What will be your independent and what will be your dependent variables?

Activity 2

More Chemical Changes

GOALS

In this activity you will:

- Observe several typical examples of evidence that a chemical change is occurring.

- Make generalizations about the combinations of materials that result in the same evidence.

- Make generalizations about materials that tend to react with everything and materials that tend not to react with anything.

- Practice careful laboratory techniques, such as avoiding contamination of reactants, to ensure that results observed are repeatable and unambiguous.

What Do You Think?

Mix 1 cup flour, 1/3 cup sugar, 1 teaspoon of baking powder with a cup of milk and 1 egg, well-beaten. Place the mixture in an oven for 30 minutes.

Add two drops of sodium carbonate (0.1 M Na_2CO_3) to two drops of sodium hydrogen sulfate (0.1 M $NaHSO_4$).

- Which of the instructions above will result in a chemical reaction? Why?

- Describe one similarity and one difference in the above instructions.

Record your ideas about these questions in your *Active Chemistry* log. Be prepared to discuss your responses with your small group and with the class.

Investigate

1. Eight solid materials listed on the next page have been dissolved in distilled water to make solutions. You will combine the solutions (one to one) with each other in an organized manner in order to observe their interactions.

!

Safety
goggles and
a lab apron
must be
worn during
this activity.

- barium nitrate Ba(NO$_3$)$_2$
- sodium hydroxide (NaOH)
- sodium hydrogen carbonate (NaHCO$_3$)
- copper (II) sulfate (CuSO$_4$)
- potassium iodide (KI)
- silver nitrate (AgNO$_3$)
- iron (III) nitrate Fe(NO$_3$)$_3$
- hydrochloric acid (HCl)

After mixing two solutions, make notes on your chart of any changes you observe. Don't overlook any color changes, the formation of a precipitate (sometimes observed as a cloudy solution), the formation of a gas (fizzing or bubbles), or a change in temperature.

Using another dropper, continue by adding three drops of the sodium hydrogen carbonate to the second well.

	Ba(NO$_3$)$_2$	NaOH	NaHCO$_3$	4	5	6	7	8
Ba(NO$_3$)$_2$								
NaOH								
NaHCO$_3$								
4								
5								
6								
7								
8								

!

Silver nitrate
will stain
skin and
clothing.
Handle with
care.

a) Begin by making a chart to record your data. Your chart will require an entire page of your notebook. Allow plenty of room to record your observations. A sample chart has been provided. Notice that some of the blocks in this chart are shaded, indicating there is no need to mix those particular chemicals. Why do you suppose those particular blocks are shaded?

2. Now it is time to mix the solutions.

Begin with barium nitrate. Add three drops of the barium nitrate solution to each of seven wells of a well plate. Add three drops of sodium hydroxide solution to the first well.

It is important that you do not allow the tip of the dropper of one solution to come in contact with another solution. Your attention to this detail will prevent contamination of solutions.

Continue by adding copper (II) sulfate to the third well, and so on.

a) After mixing the pairs of solutions, make note on your chart of any changes you observe.

Continue by putting three drops of sodium hydroxide into each of seven wells and adding the other solutions.

After completing your *entire* chart in this fashion and mixing all possible one-to-one combinations of solutions, clean up your workstation. Your teacher will provide disposal information. Wash your hands.

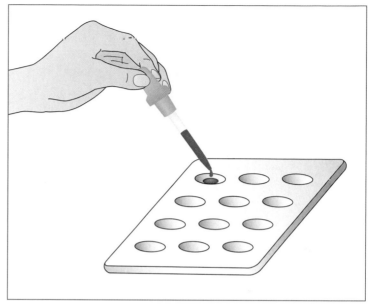

3. Use your chart to answer the following questions:

   a) Which combination of reactants seems to produce no reaction when mixed together?

   b) Which combination of reactants forms a gas? Can you guess which gas is formed? Try to deduce this from the reactants' names and chemical formulas.

   c) Which combination of reactants produces a color change when mixed together?

   d) Which combination of reactants forms precipitates quickly? Slowly?

   e) Which combination of reactants forms a yellow precipitate? A muddy brown precipitate? A white precipitate? A blue precipitate?

   f) Which combination of reactants produces heat? How could you tell?

   g) What evidence indicates that a chemical change is occurring?

4. Place the following chemicals in a quart-size resealable plastic bag with a zipper seal:

   One teaspoon (scoop)(~28 g) of calcium chloride ($CaCl_2$)

   One teaspoon (scoop)(~28 g) baking soda ($NaHCO_3$)

   Seal the bag and mix the powders.

   a) Record your observations in your *Active Chemistry* log. Did a chemical reaction occur?

   Pour 10 mL of phenol red indicator solution into the bag and seal quickly. Make sure the solids come in contact with the indicator solution.

   b) Observe the reaction and, in your *Active Chemistry* log, describe what you see.

   c) Did a chemical reaction occur in the plastic bag? If so, identify all of the evidence of the chemical change.

   d) For this particular reaction, calcium chloride and sodium hydrogen carbonate combined to produce an aqueous solution of sodium chloride and calcium oxide in addition to the carbon dioxide and water.

What are the names of the reactants? What are the names of the products?

5. Your teacher will provide you with a small amount (~25 mL) of limewater, a solution of calcium hydroxide ($Ca(OH)_2$), in a beaker or flask.

Gently blow through a straw into the solution for a minute or so. One end of the straw should be submerged in the solution. You are actually bubbling carbon dioxide through the solution.

a) Did a chemical reaction occur? What is the evidence?

Chem Talk

TESTS FOR CHEMICALS

Chemical Tests for Gases

In this activity you focused on chemical reactions, those processes that result in the formation of new products. You also tested for the presence of some of the new materials. You used **chemical tests** to identify the unknown substances. A chemical test is a form of a diagnostic test. To test for the presence of oxygen, you introduce a glowing splint into a test tube with a small amount of gas. If the splint bursts into a flame, you then know that the gas is oxygen. When you introduce a burning splint into a test tube and heard a loud pop, you assume the gas present to be hydrogen. In this activity you tested for the presence of carbon dioxide. Since carbon dioxide does not burn or support burning, by using a glowing or burning splint, you could not tell if a gas was carbon dioxide.

Chem Words

chemical test: a physical procedure or chemical reaction used to identify a substance

Checking Up

(If the splint is extinguished you can say that the gas is neither oxygen nor hydrogen and therefore could be carbon dioxide.) The test for carbon dioxide uses limewater, a clear, colorless solution of calcium hydroxide in water. When you blew bubbles into the test tube you were actually blowing carbon dioxide from your lungs into the limewater. The carbon dioxide reacted with the calcium hydroxide forming a precipitate. The precipitate caused the limewater to turn cloudy in appearance.

Indicators for Acids and Bases

When acids and bases are involved in a chemical reaction the appearance of the products is often very similar to the appearance of the reactants. (You will learn more about acids and bases in a later activity.) Therefore, indicators are used to determine the presence of an acid or base. Substances that change color when they react with an acid or a base are called **acid-base indicators**. In this activity you used phenol red, an acid-base indicator that turns yellow in the presence of an acid. Chemists use a great variety of acid-base indicators. You may also have used litmus in previous science classes. It is a very common indicator used in school laboratories.

Checking Up

1. What is a chemical test?

2. Describe how you can use a burning or glowing splint to test for hydrogen or oxygen.

3. Why does a glowing splint test not work with carbon dioxide?

4. What test is used to identify the presence of carbon dioxide?

5. What is a precipitate?

6. What are acid-base indicators and how are they useful?

Chem Words

acid-base indicator: a dye that has a certain color in an acid solution and a different color in a base solution

Reflecting on the Activity and the Challenge

In this activity you saw evidence of chemical changes taking place when you observed a color change, a change in temperature, a gas being emitted, a precipitate being formed, or light being produced. Which of these chemical reactions would be an exciting or informative addition to your class's

Cool Chemistry Show? Does your class want to be sure to include a variety of reactions that provide different types of evidence of a chemical reaction, or does your class just want to highlight a few of them? These are decisions your class will need to make as you build your Cool Chemistry Show.

Chemistry to Go

1. In both **Activity 1** and **Activity 2** you gathered evidence for chemical changes. However, this evidence does not always indicate a chemical change. For instance, a change in color can be evidence of a chemical change. However, when you add water to a powdered drink mix, the color often changes, but a chemical change has not taken place.

   In each of the following situations indicate whether the evidence suggests a chemical change or not:

   a) An acid is dissolved in water and heat is released.

   b) A burning match produces light.

   c) A "seed" crystal is placed in a supersaturated solution and the extra solute particles "join" the crystal and come out of the solution.

   d) A bottle of a carbonated beverage is opened and carbon dioxide is released.

   e) The glowing filament of a light bulb produces light.

   f) A small piece of metal is placed into an acid and hydrogen is released.

   g) Solutions of sodium hydroxide and copper (II) sulfate are mixed and a blue precipitate appears.

2. Anhydrous copper (II) sulfate ($CuSO_4$) is a white solid. When it is dissolved in water, the solution becomes blue. Is this a chemical change? Explain how you would defend your answer.

3. If a glass of carbonated soda drink is allowed to sit out for a period of time, you find that the drink seems to be flat. Discuss this observation in terms of whether this is a physical or chemical change.

Preparing for the Chapter Challenge

Select one of the reactions you observed in this activity that you thought was pretty cool. Describe how you might incorporate it into a possible event in the **Cool Chemistry Show** you are designing. Would it meet the needs of the fourth-grade teacher, the fifth-grade teacher, or both? What additional information would you need to be able to explain the chemistry to the audience?

Activity 3 Chemical Names and Formulas

GOALS

In this activity you will:

• Predict the charges of ions of some elements.

• Determine the formulas of ionic compounds.

• Write the conventional names of ionic compounds.

• Make observations to determine whether there is evidence that chemical changes occur on combining two ionic compounds.

What Do You Think?

Chemistry is the study of matter and its interactions. A great contribution to the study of chemistry was the discovery that all of the world is composed of elements and that there are approximately 100 elements in nature. The periodic table provides valuable information about each element.

• What information is provided for the element shown? What significance does this information have?

Record your ideas about these questions in your *Active Chemistry* log. Be prepared to discuss your responses with your small group and the class.

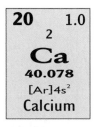

20	1.0
	2
Ca	
40.078	
[Ar]4s^2	
Calcium	

Investigate

1. The periodic table lists the elements in order of their atomic number. The atomic number is the number of protons (positively charged particles) in the nucleus of one atom of that element. For a neutral atom, the number of protons also equals the number of electrons (negatively charged particles).

Electrons are found outside the nucleus. A helium atom, with an atomic number of 2, has 2 protons in the nucleus and 2 electrons surrounding its nucleus.

For each of the following elements, write the symbol for the element and indicate the number of protons an atom of that element would have. (Refer to the periodic table.)

a) copper   b) sulfur

c) zinc   d) gold

e) oxygen   f) carbon

g) silver   h) chlorine

i) nitrogen   j) hydrogen

k) magnesium   l) iodine

m) iron   n) calcium

o) aluminum   p) sodium

q) potassium   r) lead

2. Elements can combine to form compounds. A compound results when two or more different elements bond. Some compounds are comprised of positive and negative ions that are bound by their mutual attraction. An ion is an atom that has lost or gained electrons, and therefore is charged because its protons and electrons no longer balance and cancel each other. For example, when a chlorine atom gains one electron, it becomes a chloride ion with a charge of –1 (remember electrons have negative charge). When a sodium atom loses one electron, it becomes a sodium ion with a charge of +1 (because now there is one more proton than the number of electrons). The resulting compound is sodium chloride (NaCl), which you know as table salt and it is an ionic compound.

a) The chemical formula for the compound of potassium and bromine is KBr. Look at where potassium is located on the periodic table (Group 1) and also where bromine is located (Group 17). Each of these has an ionic charge of 1. Potassium is +1, bromine is –1. List four other compounds that are created from elements in Group 1 combining with elements in Group 17.

b) Magnesium forms an ion with a charge of +2 and oxygen forms an oxide ion with a –2 charge. The chemical formula for magnesium oxide is MgO. List four other compounds that are created from elements in Group 2 combining with elements in Group 16.

3. If the values of the charge on a positive ion and a negative ion are the same, the formula of the resulting compound is simply the chemical symbols of each element. If the values of the charge on a positive ion and a negative ion are not the same, subscripts can be used to balance them. For example, aluminum loses 3 electrons to become an ion with a charge of +3. An iodine atom gains only 1 electron to form an ion with a charge of –1. It takes 3 iodine atoms to accept the 3 electrons given up by aluminum. This is reflected in the formula AlI_3. (Note where the 3 is placed for the 3 iodine atoms.) Another example is $CaCl_2$, where 2 chloride ions (each gaining one electron) and one calcium ion (having lost 2 electrons) combine.

Write the chemical formula and name for the compound formed when the following pairs of elements are combined:

a) calcium and oxygen

b) aluminum and fluorine

c) boron and oxygen

d) strontium and nitrogen

e) barium and selenium

4. Some compounds, like baking soda, sodium hydrogen carbonate ($NaHCO_3$), incorporate polyatomic ions. Polyatomic ions are made up of several elements joined together. In the case of baking soda, the sodium (Na) ion has a charge of $+1$ and the hydrogen carbonate ion (the polyatomic ion HCO_3) has a charge of -1. (Note: hydrogen carbonate ion is also called bicarbonate ion.)

Write the chemical formula for each compound below.

a) potassium nitrate (nitrate: NO_3^{-1})

b) barium sulfate (sulfate: SO_4^{-2})

c) potassium sulfate

d) sodium acetate (acetate: $C_2H_3O_2^{-1}$)

Write the name for each compound below.

e) $(NH_4)_2SO_4$ (ammonium: NH_4^{+1})

f) $Al_2(CO_3)_3$

g) $LiHCO_3$

h) HNO_3

5. You have learned about ionic compounds that are made from positive and negative ions. In another class of compounds, called molecules, the atoms are bound by electrons being mutually attracted to the protons in adjacent atoms. These bonds are called covalent bonds,

because atoms are sharing electrons. It is often useful to imagine, however, that the atoms inside of molecules are charged. These "imagined charges" are called oxidation numbers.

a) The formula for carbon dioxide is CO_2. If you pretend this is an ionic compound, what is the charge (oxidation number) of carbon?

b) Carbon monoxide is CO. What is the oxidation number of carbon now?

You must wear safety goggles and a lab apron.

c) Explain how you arrived at your answers.

6. Do chemical changes occur every time reactants are mixed? Let's find out. Read the directions for this step so you can prepare a data table to record and describe all that you observe.

Put equal amounts of baking soda, crushed Alka-Seltzer™ tablet, and baking powder into three separate test tubes respectively. Be sure to label the test tubes!

Add equal amounts of water to each.

Hold the splint with tongs or wear a heatproof glove. Be sure the mouth of the test tube is pointed away from everyone.

a) Record your observations. (You should now know the chemical formula for baking soda $NaHCO_3$.)

b) Place a glowing splint into the top of each test tube. Make note of what happens. A glowing splint bursts into flames in the presence of oxygen, and a glowing splint is extinguished in the presence of carbon dioxide. Which gases were most likely given off for each reaction?

451

7. When the reactions have stopped completely, your teacher will put three of the test tubes in a beaker of boiling water. Observe what happens.

a) Make a note of the results in your *Active Chemistry* log.

8. Repeat **Steps 6** and **7** using clean test tubes, fresh reagents, and instead of water add

   • vinegar   • ammonia.

9. Your teacher will give you a small amount of a white powdered substance that is either baking soda, Alka-Seltzer, or baking powder.

a) Write down the number of your unknown and determine which of the three substances it is. Provide evidence to support your conclusion.

10. Clean all apparatus and the laboratory bench when you are finished. Dispose of all chemicals as directed by your teacher. Wash your hands.

FORMING COMPOUNDS

Ionic Compounds

There are certainly more than 100 physically different materials in this world. With approximately 100 elements, how is it possible to have such a variety of materials? How is it possible to invent new materials for clothing, building, and food? Elements can combine to form compounds. A **compound** results when two or more different elements bond.

Some compounds are comprised of positive and negative **ions** that are bound by their mutual attraction. An ion is an atom that has lost or gained electrons, and therefore is charged because its protons and electrons no longer balance and cancel each other. For example, when an iodine atom gains one electron, it becomes a iodide ion with a charge of −1 (remember electrons have negative charge). A negatively charged ion is called an **anion**. When a potassium atom loses one electron, it becomes a potassium ion with a charge of +1 (because now there is one more proton than the number of electrons). A positively charged ion is called a **cation**. The resulting **ionic compound** is potassium iodide (KI). Potassium iodide is added to most of the table salt you use. Table salt (NaCl) is another example of an ionic compound.

Chem Words

compound: a material that consists of two or more elements united together in definite proportion

ion: an electrically charged atom or group of atoms that has acquired a net charge, either negative or positive

anion: a negatively charged ion

cation: a positively charged ion

ionic compound: a compound consisting of positive or negative ions

If you refer to a periodic table you will notice that elements that form positive ions are on the left side of the table and elements that form negative ions are on the right side. Metals combine with nonmetals to form ionic compounds. Also, when two elements combine the name given the negative ion will end with -ide, and the compound is named with the metal or positive ion first. This is true for binary compounds, for example: sodium chloride, potassium bromide, and magnesium oxide. When dissolved in water, you would find that ionic compounds conduct electricity. In this activity you also investigated some compounds formed with **polyatomic ions**. Polyatomic ions are made up of several elements joined together. For example, Milk of Magnesia™ incorporates the hydroxide ion (OH^{-1}) with the magnesium ion to form magnesium hydroxide, $Mg(OH)_2$. The following table lists some polyatomic ions and their charges.

Polyatomic Ions		
nitrate	NO_3^{-1}	negative one, -1
sulfate	SO_4^{-2}	negative two, -2
hydroxide	OH^{-1}	negative one, -1
carbonate	CO_3^{-2}	negative two, -2
hydrogen carbonate	HCO_3^{-1}	negative one, -1
acetate	$C_2H_3O_2^{-1}$	negative one, -1
ammonium	NH_4^{+1}	positive one, $+1$

Molecular Compounds

You also learned about **molecular compounds** in this activity. When two atoms of molecular elements come together, neither atom gains nor loses an electron. Instead, the bonding electrons are shared between the two atoms. The mutual attraction of two nuclei for a shared pair of bonding electrons is called a **covalent bond**. Molecular compounds are usually formed by nonmetal-nonmetal combinations. You would find that when dissolved in water, molecular compounds do not conduct electricity.

With covalent bonds you also found that it is often useful to imagine that the atoms inside of molecules are charged. These "imagined →

Chem Words

polyatomic ion: an ion that consists of 2 or more atoms that are covalently bonded and have either a positive or negative charge

molecular compound: two or more atoms bond together by sharing electrons (covalent bond)

covalent bond: a bond formed when two atoms combine and share their paired electrons with each other

Checking Up

1. If there are only about 100 elements in this world, why are there so many different materials?

2. What is an ion?

3. How are ionic compounds formed?

4. What is a polyatomic ion? Provide an example of a compound formed with a polyatomic ion.

5. How are molecular compounds formed?

6. Distinguish between an ionic and a covalent bond.

Chem Words

oxidation number:
a number assigned to an element in a compound designating the number of electrons the element has lost, gained, or shared in forming that compound

charges" are used as a type of bookkeeping and are called **oxidation numbers**. In both ionic compounds and molecular compounds the atoms achieve a stable state, similar to the noble gases.

Reflecting on the Activity and the Challenge

In this activity you have learned how to write the formulas for many compounds and how to name some compounds. You have also investigated both ionic and molecular compounds. As you prepare your presentation for your **Cool Chemistry Show,** you will want to include your knowledge of formulas, the names of compounds,

and the different kinds of compounds. Remember that you will be providing the teacher with an explanation of why you included certain demonstrations, and you will also want to include explanations that are grade-appropriate. Think about how much information you will need to provide for each demonstration.

 **Chemistry to Go**

1. Write the chemical formula and name for the compound formed when the following pairs of elements are combined:

   a) sodium and bromine

   b) potassium and sulfur

   c) magnesium and chlorine

   d) cesium and iodine

   e) aluminum and oxygen

2. Write the chemical formula for each of the following.

   a) hydrogen nitrate (nitric acid)

   b) ammonium hydroxide

   c) calcium carbonate

   d) hydrogen acetate (acetic acid)

3. a) Write the chemical formula for copper (II) sulfate. The (II) indicates that this copper ion has a +2 charge.

   b) Oxygen ions usually have a negative 2 charge (–2). How would formulas for iron (II) oxide differ from iron (III) oxide?

4. You may have noticed that all the elements in the first column of the periodic table (the alkali metals: lithium, sodium, potassium, rubidium, and cesium) have a +1 charge when they combine with negative ions. Another group of positive ions are the alkaline earth metals (beryllium, magnesium, calcium, strontium, and barium), located in the second column of the periodic table. What charge is typical for ions of the alkaline earth metals?

5. The formula for sodium phosphate is Na_3PO_4. What is the charge on the polyatomic phosphate ion? What information did you use to arrive at your answer?

6. When you write the formula for sodium hydroxide, you do not have to put parentheses around the hydroxide polyatomic ion. However, when writing the formula for aluminum hydroxide, you must put parentheses around the hydroxide polyatomic ion.

   a) Write each formula.

   b) Explain why the parentheses are necessary for aluminum hydroxide.

7. a) If the chemical formula for iron (III) chloride is $FeCl_3$, what is the chemical formula for iron (III) nitrate?

   b) If the chemical formula for lead (II) oxide is PbO, what is the chemical formula for lead (II) sulfate?

   c) If the chemical formula for silver chloride is AgCl, what is the chemical formula for silver nitrate?

8. In **Activity 2**, you tested various compounds for chemical changes. (Barium nitrate, sodium hydroxide, sodium hydrogen carbonate, copper (II) sulfate, potassium iodide, silver nitrate, iron (III) nitrate, and hydrochloric acid.) Write the chemical formulas for each of the reactants.

Preparing for the Chapter Challenge

Review any chemical reactions you are considering including in your **Cool Chemistry Show**. Write the formulas of any compounds that you plan to use.

Activity 4 Chemical Equations

GOALS

In this activity you will:

• Represent chemical changes using word equations and chemical equations.

• Distinguish between different classes of chemical reactions.

• Predict the possible products of single-displacement and double-displacement reactions.

• Determine whether a reaction has occurred based on evidence observed.

• Use the principle of conservation of matter to balance chemical reactions.

What Do You Think?

In **Activity 1** you mixed zinc metal and hydrochloric acid. You noticed that a gas was produced from the fizzing that occurred.

• How could you communicate (tell about) the reactants and products of this reaction in a compact way?

Record your ideas about this question in your *Active Chemistry* log. Be prepared to discuss your responses with your small group and with the class.

Investigate

1. Watch closely as your teacher shows you some cool chemistry.

   a) Record your observations in your *Active Chemistry* log.

2. Here's how the cool chemistry was done. Into each of three beakers that appeared empty, your teacher added about 45 mL of 2.0 M ammonium hydroxide solution.

   Before beginning the demonstration, your teacher had also added the following to each beaker:

Beaker One—20 drops of the indicator phenolphthalein solution;

Beaker Two—15 drops of 1 M magnesium sulfate solution;

Beaker Three—15 drops of 1 M copper (II) sulfate solution.

a) Did a chemical reaction take place in each beaker? What evidence do you have to justify your answer?

3. There are many chemical reactions that can occur. You have already observed some of them. Chemists group most of these reactions into four main categories. They are:

• synthesis reactions;

• decomposition reactions;

• single-displacement reactions;

• double-displacement reactions.

a) What do the words synthesis and decomposition mean?

4. In a synthesis reaction two or more chemicals combine to form a compound.

$$A + B \rightarrow AB$$

Here is an example of a synthesis reaction. When magnesium and oxygen react, a white solid, magnesium oxide is formed.

This can be written as a word equation:

Magnesium (solid) and oxygen (gas) produce magnesium oxide (solid).

This can also be written using a chemical equation:

$$?\,Mg + ?\,O_2 \rightarrow ?\,MgO$$

(The subscript communicates the number of atoms in one molecule.

Oxygen is diatomic, that means that it exists as a molecule made up of two atoms.)

a) What do you think are the advantages of writing a reaction using chemical symbols?

Any equation in chemistry must follow scientific laws or principles. The number of atoms of each element must be equal before and after the reaction.

b) In the equation above, how many atoms of oxygen are in the reactants (before the reaction)?

c) How many oxygen atoms are in the product (after the reaction)?

d) What appears to be the problem with the equation? How could you correct this problem?

Write a 2 in front of the MgO.

$$?\,Mg + O_2 \rightarrow 2\,MgO$$

(The number in front of a chemical formula, called a coefficient, communicates the number of molecules or formula units that are involved in the reaction. In this equation there are two molecules of magnesium oxide represented. That is, there is a total of two magnesium atoms and two oxygen atoms.)

e) How many magnesium atoms are now represented in the product?

f) How many reactant atoms of magnesium are shown?

g) What now appears to be the problem with the equation? How could you correct this problem?

Write a two in front of the Mg.

$$2Mg + O_2 \rightarrow 2MgO$$

h) The chemical equation above is now balanced. (The number of magnesium and oxygen atoms in the product is equal to the number in the reactant.) In your own words, explain the meaning of a balanced equation. How does the chemical equation communicate what happened in the reaction, and how does it follow the Law of Conservation of Matter?

When writing a chemical equation the states of the reactants and products are also given. The following symbols are used:

- (s) for solid;
- (l) for liquid;
- (g) for gas;
- (aq) for aqueous, meaning in a water solution.

The complete balanced chemical equation for the reaction of magnesium and oxygen is:

$$2\ Mg_{(s)} + O_{2(g)} \rightarrow 2\ MgO_{(s)}$$

5. Write a word equation and a balanced chemical equation for each of the following synthesis reactions.

Note that there are eight elements that are diatomic, that means that they exist as a molecule comprised of two atoms. They are hydrogen (H_2), nitrogen (N_2), oxygen (O_2), fluorine (F_2), chlorine (Cl_2), bromine (Br_2), iodine (I_2) and astatine (At_2). If you need to include any of these elements in an uncombined state in a chemical equation, don't forget the 2 as a subscript.

a) Solid carbon (C) burns in air (oxygen gas) to form carbon dioxide gas (CO_2).

b) Hydrogen gas reacts with oxygen gas to form liquid water (H_2O).

c) A piece of solid iron (Fe) over time will react with oxygen to form iron (III) oxide (Fe_2O_3).

d) A piece of solid sodium (Na) is dropped into a container of chlorine gas to produce solid sodium chloride (NaCl).

6. Water can be separated into its elements with an input of energy. The equation for this reaction is:

Water (liquid) and energy produces hydrogen (gas) and oxygen (gas).

$$2H_2O_{(l)} + energy \rightarrow 2\ H_{2(g)} + O_{2(g)}$$

a) Is the equation properly balanced? How did you check?

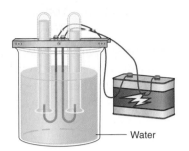

**Decomposition of water
into $H_{2}(g)$ and $O_{2}(g)$ by electrolysis**

When a substance breaks down into its component parts, the process is called a **decomposition** reaction.

form products. Such was the case when solid zinc was dropped into hydrochloric acid in **Activity 1**, forming hydrogen gas and aqueous zinc chloride solution.

The equation for this reaction is:

Zinc (solid) and hydrochloric acid (aqueous) produces hydrogen (gas) and zinc chloride (solution).

$$Zn_{(s)} + 2HCl_{(aq)} \rightarrow H_{2(g)} + ZnCl_{2(aq)}$$

a) Check to ensure that the chemical equation is properly balanced. Complete the following table in your log.

Number of Atoms			
	Before	After	Balanced
Zn	1	1	yes
H			
Cl			

$AB \rightarrow A + B$

Write word and balanced chemical equations for the following decomposition reactions. (Remember that some elements are diatomic $-H_{2}$, N_{2}, etc.):

b) sodium chloride solid ($NaCl_{(s)}$);

c) potassium iodide solid ($KI_{(s)}$);

d) magnesium bromide solid ($MgBr_{2}(s)$).

7. The reactions mentioned above involve elements combining to form compounds or compounds breaking up to form elements.

There are other reactions that involve elements reacting with compounds to

The reaction with zinc and hydrochloric acid is called a single-displacement reaction because zinc replaces the hydrogen in the acid.

$A + BC \rightarrow B + AC$

Write word and chemical equations for the following:

b) A piece of iron (Fe) is added to an aqueous solution of copper (II) sulfate ($CuSO_{4}$) and produces iron sulfate ($FeSO_{4}$) and copper.

c) Solid lead (Pb) is added to an aqueous solution of silver nitrate ($AgNO_{3}$) and produces lead nitrate $Pb(NO_{3})_{2}$ and silver.

Safety goggles and a lab apron must be worn during this activity.

d) Aluminum foil (Al) is placed in a beaker of aqueous copper (II) hydroxide ($Cu(OH)_2$) and produces aluminum hydroxide ($Al(OH)_3$) and copper.

Balance each of the equations, if you have not done so.

8. Another type of reaction is a double-displacement reaction.

$$AB + CD \rightarrow CB + AD$$

Try some double-displacement reactions on your own in your group. Use the chart below to guide your work. The compounds are in water solution.

a) Record your observations of the reactants before you mix them. For example, record your observations of potassium carbonate and silver nitrate before you mix them.

b) Create a chart in your log to record your observations after you mix

the reactants. You may wish to use a chart similar to the one below.

9. Mix three drops of one solution (i.e., potassium carbonate) with three drops of another solution (i.e., silver nitrate), as indicated by the first box on the chart. You can mix these solutions in the well of a spot plate or on a plastic surface. Do not allow the tip of the dropper of one solution to come in contact with another solution. This is important to prevent contamination of solutions.

a) In the chart in your log, record your observations after mixing the reactants.

Continue with the other reactants (i.e., potassium carbonate with copper (II) sulfate; then potassium carbonate with magnesium sulfate; and so on).

b) Record all your observations in your *Active Chemistry* log.

	Silver Nitrate ($AgNO_3$)	Copper (II) Sulfate ($CuSO_4$)	Magnesium Sulfate ($MgSO_4$)	Sodium Hydroxide (NaOH)
Potassium Carbonate (K_2CO_3)	1.	2.	3.	4.
Sodium Hydroxide (NaOH)	5.	6.	7.	8.
Potassium Iodide (KI)	9.	10.	11.	12.
Iron (III) Chloride ($FeCl_3$)	13.	14.	15.	16.

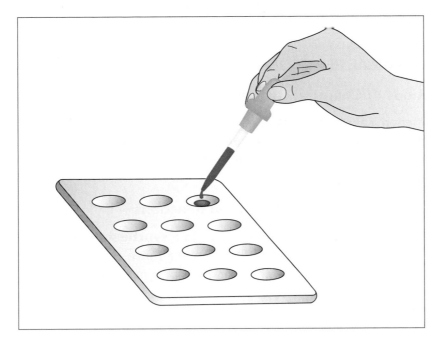

10. Clean all apparatus and the laboratory bench when you are finished. Dispose of all chemicals as directed by your teacher. Wash your hands.

11. Look at the data from the double-displacement reactions that you observed.

    a) Do you think a chemical reaction took place in each case? Explain your answer.

b) Are you able to predict or identify any of the products that were formed? If so, which ones?

c) Write word equations and balanced chemical equations for each reaction that you observed. In all cases, assume only two reactants are used and only two products are formed. Use the following formulas to help you write your equations:

copper (II) carbonate ($CuCO_{3(s)}$);	copper (II) hydroxide ($Cu(OH)_{2(s)}$);
copper (II) iodide ($CuI_{2(s)}$);	iron (III) nitrate ($Fe(NO_3)_{3(s)}$);
iron (III) hydroxide ($Fe(OH)_{3(s)}$);	magnesium carbonate ($MgCO_{3(s)}$);
silver carbonate ($Ag_2CO_{3(s)}$);	silver chloride ($AgCl_{(s)}$);
silver hydroxide ($AgOH_{(s)}$);	potassium nitrate ($KNO_{3(aq)}$);
potassium sulfate ($K_2SO_{4(aq)}$);	magnesium hydroxide ($Mg(OH)_{2(s)}$);
silver iodide ($AgI_{(s)}$);	sodium chloride ($NaCl_{(aq)}$);
sodium nitrate ($NaNO_{3(aq)}$);	sodium sulfate ($Na_2SO_{4(aq)}$);

ChemTalk

CHEMICAL REACTIONS

Kinds of Chemical Reactions

A chemical reaction takes place when starting materials (reactants) change to new materials (products). Synthesis, decomposition, single-displacement, and double-displacement reactions are some common kinds of chemical reactions.

Synthesis and Decomposition Reactions

Synthesis means "putting together." In a **synthesis reaction** two or more elements combine to form one or more compounds. In this activity you investigated the reaction of magnesium in oxygen to form magnesium oxide. The opposite kind of reaction is a **decomposition reaction.** In chemical decomposition a compound is separated into its elements.

Single-displacement Reactions

A **single-displacement reaction** is one in which an element reacts with a compound to produce a new element and an ionic compound. For example, a single-displacement reaction occurs when you put a strip of zinc in a copper (II) sulfate solution. The zinc metal exchanges places with the copper cations. You also observed that the free copper metal atoms now plate on the zinc strip.

Activity Series

If you put copper metal in a zinc sulfate solution you would find that no reaction would take place, as expected. Zinc exchanges places with copper, but copper will not exchange places with zinc. You have learned something about a property of copper and zinc. Zinc is more active than copper. If you were to experiment with different metals and metallic solutions, you should be able to create an activity series of metals. The activity series of metals can be put into a table that you can use to predict if a reaction will take place. The table looks like the one on the following page. The table permits you to determine how a metal will react in a metal solution. A metal that is more active than another will dissolve into the metal solution and plate out the less

Chem Words

synthesis reaction: a chemical reaction in which two or more substances combine to form a compound

decomposition: a chemical reaction in which a single compound reacts to give two or more products

single-displacement reaction: a reaction in which an element displaces or replaces another element in a compound

Activity Series of Metals (Most Active to Least Active)	
1. Lithium ($Li \rightarrow Li^+ + e^-$)	8. Iron ($Fe \rightarrow Fe^{2+} + 2e^-$)
2. Potassium ($K \rightarrow K^+ + e^-$)	9. Lead ($Pb \rightarrow Pb^{2+} + 2e^-$)
3. Calcium ($Ca \rightarrow Ca^{2+} + 2e^-$)	10. Hydrogen ($H_{2(g)} \rightarrow 2H^+ + 2e^-$)
4. Sodium ($Na \rightarrow Na^+ + 1e^-$)	11. Copper ($Cu \rightarrow Cu^{2+} + 2e^-$)
5. Magnesium ($Mg \rightarrow Mg^{2+} + 2e^-$)	12. Mercury ($Hg \rightarrow Hg^{2+} + 2e^-$)
6. Aluminum ($Al \rightarrow Al^{3+} + 3e^-$)	13. Silver ($Ag \rightarrow Ag^+ + e^-$)
7. Zinc ($Zn \rightarrow Zn^{2+} + 2e^-$)	14. Gold ($Au \rightarrow Au^{3+} + 3e^-$)

active metal. Zinc replaced the copper and the copper plated the zinc. For example, let's say that you place a strip of copper in a silver nitrate solution. According to the table, the copper will dissolve into copper ions (Cu^{2+}) and the silver ions will plate out on the copper as silver.

In addition to metals, you will notice that hydrogen gas is also listed in the activity series. In your investigation you found that different metals produced hydrogen gas and metal ions when they reacted with hydrochloric acid. You read above that metals can replace less active metals in metal salt solutions. Metals that are more active than hydrogen can replace the hydrogen from water to form metal hydroxides. As an example, if you were to react potassium metal with water, you would get hydrogen gas and potassium hydroxide solution. The equation is:

$$2K_{(s)} + 2HOH_{(l)} \rightarrow H_{2(g)} + 2KOH_{(aq)}$$

Double-displacement Reactions

Double-displacement reactions are different from single-displacement reactions, in that you start with two aqueous phase solutions and when they react they "switch partners." An example of this type of reaction is:

$$Ba(NO_3)_{2(aq)} + Na_2SO_{4(aq)} \rightarrow 2NaNO_{3(aq)} + BaSO_{4(s)}$$

Note that the cation of the one compound (Ba^{2+}) exchanged places with the cation ($Na+$) of the other compound. The solid $BaSO_4$ is a

Chem Words

double-displacement reaction: a chemical reaction in which two ionic compounds "exchange" cations to produce two new compounds

Chem Words

salts: ionic compounds in which the anion is not a hydroxide ion (OH–) and the cation is not a hydrogen proton (H+)

precipitate. When examining double-displacement reactions, you know that a reaction has taken place if you see:

- a precipitate
- a gas
- water

If none of these are present, then no reaction had occurred.

Solubility Rules

A precipitate will form if the compound is not soluble in water. In the example above, barium sulfate was not soluble in water. This was noted in the equation by referring to it as a solid (s). Chemists have created a set of solubility rules for **salts**. Salts are classified as ionic compounds in which the anion is not a hydroxide ion (OH^-) and the cation is not a hydrogen proton (H^+).

Solubility Rules
1. All salts (defined as ionic compounds) of the alkali (Group 1 on the periodic table) metals and the ammonium ion are soluble in water.
2. All chlorides, bromides, and iodides are soluble with the exception of silver, lead, and mercury halides.
3. All nitrate, chlorate, perchlorate, and acetate salts are soluble.
4. All sulfates are soluble with the exception of calcium, barium, strontium, and lead.
5. All carbonates, phosphates, chromates, hydroxides, and sulfides are insoluble except when they are combined with alkali metals or the ammonium ion.

In the example above, barium sulfate formed a precipitate. Since barium sulfate is insoluble, this agrees with the solubility rules. If you mixed silver nitrate with sodium chloride, would you expect to get a precipitate? The two products that would form are silver chloride and sodium nitrate. The solubility rule #2 tells you that silver chloride is insoluble and solubility rule #3 tells you that sodium nitrate is soluble. Using these rules, you can now predict whether a mixture will produce a precipitate or not.

Checking Up

1. What is a synthesis reaction? Provide an example.

2. What is a decomposition reaction? Provide an example.

3. Distinguish between a single and a double-displacement reaction.

4. What evidence would you look for to determine if a double-displacement reaction has occurred?

5. Will hydrochloric acid react with a clean strip of copper? Explain your answer.

6. Is calcium sulfate soluble in water? Justify your answer.

Reflecting on the Activity and the Challenge

In this activity you have learned about a number of different types of reactions: synthesis, decomposition, single-displacement and double-displacement reactions. Knowing these types of reactions can help you predict the products of some chemical reactions. You'll need to decide if you want the audience for the **Cool Chemistry Show** to learn about these reactions types. You also learned how to write balanced equations for some of the reactions you observed. Think about a creative way of showing how you can explain balancing chemical equation to your elementary school audience. In this activity you have learned how to write the formulas for many compounds and how to name some compounds. You have also investigated both ionic and molecular compounds. As you prepare your presentation for your **Cool Chemistry Show**, you will want to include your knowledge of formulas, the names of compounds, and the different kinds of compounds. Remember that you will be providing the teacher with an explanation of why you included certain demonstrations, and you will also want to include explanations that are grade-appropriate. Think about how much information you will need to provide each.

Chemistry to Go

1. Baking soda ($NaHCO_3$) has been used in several reactions in previous activities. When heat is applied to baking soda, three compounds are produced. Two of the compounds are gases and the other is a solid. If the two gases are water and carbon dioxide, what is the third product? Explain how you arrived at your answer.

2. When solutions of sodium hydroxide and potassium carbonate are mixed together, no apparent reaction takes place. The same is true when you mix sodium hydroxide and potassium iodide together. Explain this observation.

3. If you mix sodium sulfate and barium nitrate solutions together, you get a white precipitate. What is the precipitate that formed? What information did you use to arrive at your answer?

4. There were five combinations that you mixed together that did not form a precipitate. Complete and balance the following equations:

    a) $K_2CO_{3(aq)} + NaOH_{(aq)} \rightarrow$ b) $KI_{(aq)} + MgSO_{4(aq)} \rightarrow$

    c) $KI_{(aq)} + NaOH_{(aq)} \rightarrow$ d) $FeCl_{3(aq)} + CuSO_{4(aq)} \rightarrow$

    e) $FeCl_{3(aq)} + MgSO_{4(aq)} \rightarrow$

5. Use the solubility rules to explain why the products in **Question 4** do not form precipitates.

Activity 5 Chemical Energy

GOALS

In this activity you will:

- Make hot packs and cold packs.

- Observe energy changes when matter changes.

- Determine whether energy changes are endothermic or exothermic from a particular point of reference.

What Do You Think?

Two chemicals at room temperature are mixed together and the temperature cools drastically. You may have used cold packs that work like this when you were injured.

- How do the chemicals in the cold pack lower the temperature?

Record your ideas about this question in your *Active Chemistry* log. Be prepared to discuss your responses with your small group and with the class.

Investigate

1. To make a cold pack, place 10 g of ammonium nitrate in a quart-size, resealable plastic bag. Add 20 mL water to the bag and seal.

   a) Record your observations.

   In an endothermic chemical reaction, energy in the form of heat is absorbed in the process. In an exothermic chemical reaction, energy in the form of heat is given off in the process.

Safety goggles and a lab apron must be worn during this activity.

b) Was the cold pack an example of an exothermic or endothermic chemical reaction?

2. Make a hot pack by placing 20 g of sodium carbonate (or calcium chloride) in a quart-size, resealable plastic bag. Add 20 mL of water to the bag and seal.

a) Record your observations.

b) Was the reaction exothermic (heat generating) or endothermic (heat absorbing)?

3. To a flask containing 16 g of ammonium thiocyanate, add 32 g of barium hydroxide.

Place a rubber stopper in the mouth of the flask. Shake it vigorously.

Put the stoppered flask on a wood board that has been wet down with puddles of water.

a) Record your observations. Cool chemistry!

b) Was the reaction exothermic (heat generating) or endothermic (heat absorbing)?

4. Using a chemical scoop, transfer a few pellets of sodium hydroxide to a test tube half full of water. Carefully feel the side of the test tube.

a) Record your observations.

b) Was the reaction exothermic (heat generating) or endothermic (heat absorbing)?

Be careful when working with the sodium hydroxide pellets. Wear rubber gloves and eye protection. If you should accidentally drop a pellet, do not try to pick it up with your bare hands as it may burn them. Use gloved hands to retrieve the pellets.

Chem Talk

ENDOTHERMIC AND EXOTHERMIC REACTIONS

Chem Words

endothermic change or reaction: a change in which energy in the form of heat is absorbed from the surrounding environment resulting in an increase in the internal energy of the system

exothermic change or reaction: a change in which energy in the form of heat is released from a system resulting in a decrease in the internal energy of the system

A process is described as **endothermic** when heat energy is absorbed, increasing the internal energy of the system. One example of an endothermic reaction is the cold pack you made with ammonium nitrate. Another example is the decomposition of potassium chlorate. In this reaction, energy must be added to the system in order to cause the decomposition of the potassium chlorate to form the products of oxygen gas and potassium chloride. If you touch a container that holds an endothermic process, it will feel cool to the touch.

An **exothermic** process results when heat energy is released, decreasing the internal energy of the system. If you touch a container that holds an exothermic process, it will feel warm or hot to the touch. One example of an exothermic reaction is the hot pack you made with sodium carbonate. Another example was the combining of sodium hydroxide solution with hydrochloric acid. This reaction produces sodium chloride and water and releases energy to the environment. The terms endothermic and exothermic can be used when describing both physical and chemical changes.

Why is energy so important? In order for a chemical reaction to take place, the particles (reactants) involved in the reaction must interact. Not all collisions result in a chemical reaction. The particles involved must have enough energy to enable them to react with each other. The colliding particles must have enough kinetic energy to break the existing bonds in order for new bonds to be formed. The minimum energy required for a chemical reaction is activation energy. Bond breaking is an endothermic process and requires an addition of energy and bond formation is an exothermic process and requires a release of energy. (Physics reminder: Kinetic energy is the energy of motion $KE = \frac{1}{2}mv^2$.)

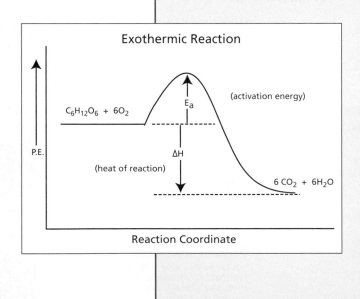

Exothermic Reaction

$C_6H_{12}O_6 + 6O_2$

E_a (activation energy)

P.E.

(heat of reaction) ΔH

$6 CO_2 + 6H_2O$

Reaction Coordinate

When more energy is released as products form than is absorbed to break the bonds in the reactants, the reaction is said to be exothermic, as shown in the graph. A chemical reaction in which energy is released is called exothermic. The prefix *exo* means exit and *thermo* means heat or energy.

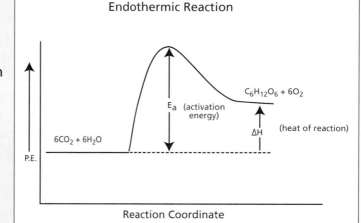

Endothermic Reaction

E_a (activation energy)

$C_6H_{12}O_6 + 6O_2$

$6CO_2 + 6H_2O$

ΔH (heat of reaction)

P.E.

Reaction Coordinate

The cells in your body use glucose to get energy for cellular respiration. Glucose plus oxygen (from breathing) provides you with energy.

$$C_6H_{12}O_6 + 6O_2 \rightarrow 6CO_2 + 6H_2O + energy$$

When more energy is needed to break the bonds in the reactants than is given off by forming the bonds in the products, the reaction is said to be endothermic—a chemical reaction in which energy is absorbed, as shown in the second graph. In some endothermic reactions, energy must be added in order for the reaction to occur.

In the process of photosynthesis, plants use energy from light to break the bonds of carbon dioxide and water in order to form the products glucose and oxygen. The glucose produced makes the plant grow and the reaction also provides animals with oxygen:

$$6CO_2 + 6H_2O + light\ energy \rightarrow$$
$$C_6H_{12}O_6 + 6O_2$$

Conservation of Energy

Energy transfer is an important feature in all chemical changes. Energy is transferred whether the chemical reaction takes place in the human body, like the metabolism of carbohydrates, or in a car, like the combustion of gasoline. In both these cases energy is released into the surroundings.

Checking Up

1. Describe an endothermic reaction.

2. Describe an exothermic reaction.

3. Explain whether each of the following is endothermic or exothermic:

   a) bond breaking

   b) bond forming.

4. Distinguish between heat and temperature.

The photosynthesis that occurs in living plants and the decomposition of water into hydrogen and oxygen both remove energy from the surroundings. According to the Law of Conservation of Energy, the energy absorbed from the surroundings or released to the surroundings is equal to the change in the energy of the system.

Energy is the great organizing principle of all science. The conservation of energy allows you to better understand the world around you. Energy exists as light energy, heat energy, sound energy, nuclear energy, kinetic energy, chemical energy as well as other forms. The total energy in any closed system remains the same. In the simplest physical systems, it is quite easy to describe the energy changes. When a bowling ball falls, its original gravitational potential energy becomes kinetic energy as the ball increases its speed. After the ball hits the ground, this kinetic energy is converted to sound energy (you hear the crash) and heat energy (you can measure a temperature rise of the ball and ground) and the compression and vibrations of the ground. Each of these can be measured and it is always found that the total energy before an event is equal to the total energy after the event. When a human being is involved, you notice other energy interactions. A person is able to eat food and digest the food. The energy released from this slow-burn of the food (metabolism) is able to keep the body at about 37°C. As all non-living things in the room cool down to room temperature, humans are able to stay warm in the 22°C room environment. People also use the food energy that they ingest for moving muscles, keeping the heart pumping and operating all human functions. Living organisms are superb energy conversion systems.

Heat and Temperature

Both heat and **temperature** have been mentioned in this activity. It is important to note that heat and temperature are not the same, although they are related. Heat is one form of energy. When two materials of different temperatures interact, they exchange heat energy until they arrive at the same temperature. Temperature is a number associated with how hot or cold something is. On a molecular level, temperature is related to the average kinetic energy of the atoms in the material. All particles in a material are in a constant state of motion. The temperature of the material is a measurement of this molecular motion. If the kinetic energy of the particles increases, the temperature increases. Temperature can be

Chem Words

temperature: the measure of the average kinetic energy of all the particles of the material

defined as the measure of the average kinetic energy of all the particles of a substance. A thermometer is an instrument that measures temperature. Heat is the transfer of energy, which often results in a change in the kinetic energy of particles—a change in the temperature of the system.

Reflecting on the Activity and the Challenge

Energy is involved in any process that requires the breaking or making of bonds. The process may be a chemical or physical change. Sometimes energy changes are not noticed or measured, but other times an energy change is significant enough to be detected. In this activity you explored both endothermic and exothermic processes. As you select activities to include in the **Cool Chemistry Show**, you must be aware of any heat energy released or absorbed. The audience may be interested to learn about the energy changes that accompany chemical processes. In addition, your awareness will ensure that the presentations are safe for both the presenters and the audience.

Chemistry to Go

1. Identify the following changes as endothermic or exothermic. (Ask yourself whether the reaction requires the addition of heat energy to occur or does it release energy in the form of heat.)

   a) Melting ice.

   b) Lighting a match.

   c) Dry ice subliming into carbon dioxide gas.

   d) Frying an egg.

   e) Burning gasoline.

   f) Explosion of hydrogen gas.

2. The water in a teapot is heated on a stovetop. The temperature of the water increases. Is this an endothermic or exothermic process?

3. If a red-hot piece of iron is dropped into a bucket of water, what type of heat change takes place in reference to the water? What type of heat change takes place in reference to the iron?

4. Explain in terms of energy flow how a cold pack works on a sprained ankle.

5. If ice is at −20°C and you apply some heat by sitting a beaker of the ice on a hot plate, explain why the ice does not appear to be melting.

Preparing for the Chapter Challenge

Review the chemical reactions that you have so far planned to feature in your **Cool Chemistry Show**. Have you included both endothermic and exothermic reactions? In a paragraph describe the difference between the two types of reactions. Be sure to mention why energy transfers are important.

Inquiring Further

1. Commercial cold and hot packs

Research several cold and hot packs. What materials are used in the packs, and how is the chemical reaction activated? You should be aware that there are a variety of commercially available hot and cold packs. In general some are reusable and some are not. Those that are not reusable are typically chemical reactions. Those that are reusable are typically physical changes.

Design a process to make a cold pack, using your research. Have your teacher approve your design before you actually try it out.

2. The colligative property of a solvent

A salt solution will depress the freezing point of water. This is commonly known as the colligative property of the solvent. When you add anti-freeze (ethylene glycol) to water, you find that the freezing point of the water is lowered, which prevents the water in the car radiator from freezing at 0°C. It also elevates the boiling point of the water, which will prevent the water solution from boiling. Design an experiment to demonstrate the colligative property of a solvent. With the approval of your teacher carry out your experiment.

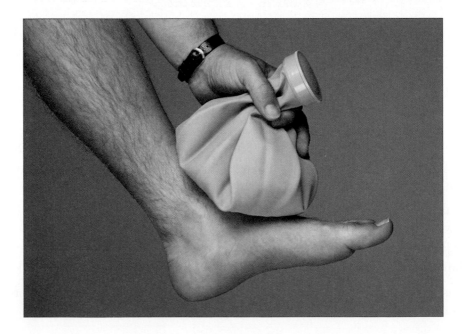

Activity 6   Reaction Rates

GOALS

In this activity you will:

• Discover conditions that make a reaction proceed faster or slower.

• Discuss explanations for why this happens at the molecular level.

What Do You Think?

Have you ever wondered why some chemical reactions, like the burning of a match, take place at a fast rate, while others, like the spoiling of milk, take place slowly? The rate of a chemical reaction is the speed at which the reactants are converted to products.

• What are some factors that influence the rate of a reaction?

• How could you make a reaction take place at a faster rate?

• How could you slow a reaction down?

Record your ideas about these questions in your *Active Chemistry* log. Be prepared to discuss your responses with your small group and with the class.

Investigate

1. One way to study the rate of a reaction is to time the reaction with a stopwatch. Try this!

   Place 20 mL of vinegar into a large test tube.

   To a second test tube, add 10 mL of vinegar and 10 mL of water. Mix well using a stirring rod.

Safety goggles and a lab apron must be worn during this activity.

473

In a third test tube, add 5 mL of vinegar to 15 mL of water. Mix.

Prepare three equal-sized pieces of polished magnesium ribbon. Set your stopwatch so that it is ready to start immediately.

Add a piece of magnesium ribbon to the first test tube, keeping track of the time the reactions take.

a) Record your observations and time on a data table. Repeat for the other two test tubes.

b) In this step, you changed the concentration of one of the reactants (the vinegar). The vinegar was less concentrated (more dilute) in each successive test tube. Did this impact the reaction rate? If so, describe the relationship between the concentration of the reactant and the resulting reaction rate.

2. Repeat the same reaction above using a well plate and smaller amounts of vinegar, water, and magnesium.

a) Record your design. Include the equipment you will need, the amount of reactants, and any safety procedures.

b) With the approval of your teacher, carry out the procedure. Record your data and results.

c) How do the results compare with the reaction in **Step 1**?

3. Place 10 drops of 0.1 M HCl (weak concentration) into one clean well in your well plate and 10 drops of 1.0 M HCl (strong concentration) into a second clean well. Drop a small piece of zinc (equal size) into each well containing HCl.

a) Record your observations.

b) How do these results compare to your earlier results? Do these results support or refute the relationship you stated in **Step 2 (c)** above?

4. Hydrogen peroxide is sold over the counter in pharmacies to be used as a disinfectant for minor injuries. Because hydrogen peroxide decomposes slowly to form oxygen and water, it is also a source of oxygen gas.

$$2H_2O_2(l) + light\ energy \rightarrow O_2(g) + 2H_2O(l)$$

Pour a small amount of hydrogen peroxide (about 15 mL) into each of two test tubes. Add a small amount of manganese dioxide to one of the test tubes.

a) Record your observations.

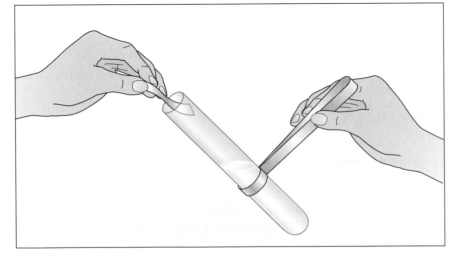

The manganese dioxide did not actually react with the hydrogen peroxide; it simply acted as a catalyst for the decomposition of the hydrogen peroxide. A catalyst is a material that speeds up a reaction without being permanently changed itself. The chemical equation for this reaction is:

$$2H_2O_{2(l)} \xrightarrow{MnO_2} O_{2(g)} + 2\ H_2O_{(l)}$$

5. Design an investigation to prove that the manganese dioxide did not get used up in the reaction.

   Record your design. Include the equipment you will need, the amount of reagents, and any safety procedures.

   a) Record your procedure in your *Active Chemistry* log.

   b) With the approval of your teacher, carry out the experiment.

   c) Record your data and results.

   d) Describe the relationship between the use of a catalyst and the rate of reaction.

6. Pour 200 mL hot water into one beaker and 200 mL ice water into another beaker. Add a tea bag to each.

   a) Record your results.

   b) Repeat the procedure using an Alka-Seltzer tablet in place of the tea bag. Record your observations.

   c) Describe the relationship between temperature and the rate of reaction, based on the two situations you studied.

7. Prepare two beakers, each containing equal amounts (about 200 mL) of room temperature water.

   Obtain two Alka-Seltzer tablets. Crush one and leave the other whole.

   Simultaneously add the crushed table to one beaker and the whole tablet to the other beaker.

   a) Record your observations.

   What factor was being studied in **Step 4 (a)**? Describe the relationship between that factor and the rate of reaction.

8. Use the results of this activity to answer the following:

   a) Describe how you could increase the rate of reaction by altering:

   • concentration   • catalyst

   • temperature   • surface area

9. Dispose of all chemicals as directed by your teacher. Clean and put away any equipment as instructed. Clean up your work station. Wash your hands.

10. Chemical systems that highlight reaction rates can be very interesting. Because time is a factor, these systems are often called clock reactions. Your teacher will do the following reaction as a demonstration.

Your teacher will use the following solutions:

Solution A = 0.1 M potassium iodate (KIO$_3$)

Solution B = 1% starch solution

Solution C = 0.25 M sodium hydrogen sulfite (NaHSO$_3$)

Two rows of five beakers (all the same size!) will be arranged in front of you.

Each of the beakers in the back row contains 100 mL of Solution A,

50 mL of Solution B, and 100 mL of distilled water.

Each beaker in the front row contains 20 mL of Solution C and 130 mL of water.

Your teacher will add the contents of one beaker from the back row to the contents of one of the beakers in the front row.

Use a stopwatch and stop when a color change occurs.

Your teacher will then combine the next set of beakers as you will again use the stopwatch. She or he will continue down the row.

a) Record the time and observations about the change in each case.

Chem Words

surface area: changing the nature of the reactants into smaller particles increases the surface exposed to react. Successful reaction depends on collision and increasing the area of the reactant increases the chance of a successful collision taking place. Lighting a log is more difficult than lighting wood shavings. The shavings have a greater surface area and speed up the reaction

FACTORS AFFECTING THE RATE OF A REACTION

In this activity you investigated several common factors that influence reaction rate. They included surface area, concentration of reactants, temperature, and catalysts. On a molecular level, these factors increase the collision frequency of the particles of the materials involved in the reaction.

Consider **surface area**. In water, a sugar cube dissolves in water at a much slower rate than if the same cube is first crushed. The crushed cube has a greater surface area — more parts of the sugar are in contact with the water. In a fireplace, wood chips burn faster than a pile of logs. In both of these cases, the smaller pieces, with their increased surface area, allow the particles that are reacting to come in

Checking Up

1. List four factors that influence the rate of a reaction.

2. For each of the factors you listed above, describe how the factor increases the collision frequency of the particles of the materials involved in the reaction.

3. How is a catalyst different from the reactants and products of a chemical reaction?

contact with each other more often. This increases the collision frequency.

Another factor that influences reaction rate is the **concentration** of the reactants. An increase in concentration means an increase in the number of particles in the reaction. This results in an increase in the collision frequency. If a chemist wants to increase the rate of a reaction, an increase in the concentration of one or more of the reactants will do the trick.

Altering collision frequency and efficiency can also be accomplished through **temperature** changes. According to the kinetic theory, particles move faster at higher temperatures and slower at lower temperatures. The faster motion of the particles increases the energy of the particles and increases the probability that particles will collide. As a result, the reaction rate increases.

Catalysts play an important role in many chemical reactions. A catalyst is a substance that speeds up a reaction without being permanently changed itself. The catalyst lowers the action energy of the reaction. Many commercial reactions make use of catalysts, because the catalysts can be recovered, regenerated, and reused. You are probably familiar with the term catalytic converter, a device used in automobiles to improve the efficiency of unleaded gasoline engine's combustion exhaust. The catalyst in this converter is platinum.

Chem Words

catalyst: a substance that changes the speed of a chemical reaction without being permanently changed itself

Reflecting on the Activity and the Challenge

In this activity you have observed how different factors affect the rate of a reaction. This knowledge can be applied to the presentations you will make in the **Cool Chemistry Show** demonstrations. If you need to cause a reaction to happen faster or slower, you now know what changes you can make. Of course, it is important for you to check with your teacher before making adjustments to any procedure you might be considering.

Chemistry to Go

1. Explain each of the following in terms of the factors that influence reaction rate:

   a) Which will cook faster: Cookies at 50°C or at 150°C?

   b) A bear (and many other animals) hibernates during the winter months. Scientists claim that the low body temperature slows down the animal's metabolism. Explain.

   c) A sugar cube dissolves slower than the same amount of sugar in granulated form.

   d) Antacid tablets are used to neutralize acid in the stomach. Explain why two tablets are faster than one tablet in neutralizing the acid.

   e) If you tried to burn a sugar cube with a match, you would find it very difficult to get the sugar to burn. However, if you put some cigarette ash on the cube, the cube would then burn when you put a flame to it. Explain the purpose of the cigarette ash in changing the burning of the sugar cube.

   f) Why does powdered aspirin dissolve faster than an aspirin tablet in water?

   g) Sugar dissolves more readily in hot tea than in iced tea. Explain.

2. In most cases, if you increase the temperature, the reaction rate increases. Explain this in terms of the collision theory.

3. Imagine that you purchase a lightstick necklace or wristband at a social event and want to make it last as long as possible. What would you do? Why would it help?

4. Explain why the effervescent antacid tablet did not seem to react as fast when it was put in a more dilute solution of vinegar.

5. Explain in terms of the reaction rate factors that you have studied why it is possible for a person who has been submerged in very cold ice water in some

cases to survive, but individuals who have been submerged in warmer water for the same length of time do not survive.

6. Grain elevators have been known to have explosions because of the production of fine grain powders. Explain in terms of the reaction rate factors that you have studied as to why this could happen.

Preparing for the Chapter Challenge

The factors affecting a reaction can be varied to achieve different reaction rates. How could you use this information in developing a presentation for the **Cool Chemistry Show**? Describe one possible scenario.

Inquiring Further

1. Quantifying the relationship between temperature and reaction rate

You have seen that temperature is a factor that influences the rate of reaction. In general, if the temperature

increases, the reaction rate increases. When the temperature decreases, the reaction rate decreases. Can this relationship be quantified? Is there a mathematical relationship between temperature and reaction time? To answer these questions, explore the reaction between magnesium ($Mg_{(s)}$) and vinegar ($CH_3COOH_{(aq)}$). Design and conduct an investigation that will use this reaction to show the relationship between temperature and reaction time in a quantitative way. Have your teacher approve your design before you begin. Remember — the point of the investigation is to see if the relationship between temperature and reaction time is quantifiable. You'll need to monitor both the temperature and the time carefully. Plot your data on a graph to make the relationship explicit. In your notes, include the chemical equation for this reaction.

Activity 7

Acids, Bases, and Indicators—Colorful Chemistry

GOALS

In this activity you will:

• Identify common household acids and bases.

• Identify characteristic properties of acids and bases, and learn to tell the difference between acids and bases.

• See how strong acids and bases behave differently from weak acids and bases.

• Make neutral solution by combining an acid and a base by titration.

• Determine the pH of various solutions using indicators.

• Categorize solutions based on the pH scale.

• Use the mathematical definition of pH.

What Do You Think?

When red cabbage is chopped up and added to boiling water and the resulting mixture is allowed to cool, a special bluish colored solution is made. After the solution is separated from the cabbage, it can be used to indicate if other substances are acids or bases. When household vinegar, a common acid, is added to the cabbage-juice water, the solution turns red. When household ammonia, a common base, is added to the cabbage-juice water, the solution turns green.

• What are some other properties of acids and bases you know about?

• How can you tell the difference between an acid and a base?

Record your ideas about these questions in your *Active Chemistry* log. Be prepared to discuss your responses with your small group and with the class.

Investigate

1. Your teacher will provide you with samples of some of the materials listed below. Place a small amount of each solution in a separate well of a well plate.

Add a small piece of polished zinc (or magnesium) to each of the solutions.

a) Make a data table to record your observations.

hydrochloric acid (HCl$_{(aq)}$)

lemon or orange juice (citric acid)

vinegar (acetic acid, CH$_3$COOH$_{(aq)}$)

sulfuric acid (H$_2$SO$_{4(aq)}$)

mineral water

carbonated beverage such as Sprite® or Seven Up® (contains H$_2$CO$_{3(aq)}$)

milk

dishwashing solution (Ivory®, Palmolive®, Joy®, etc.)

sodium hydroxide (NaOH$_{(aq)}$)

Milk of Magnesia® (contains Mg(OH)$_{2(aq)}$)

apple juice (malic acid)

potassium hydroxide (KOH$_{(aq)}$)

calcium hydroxide (Ca(OH)$_{2(aq)}$)

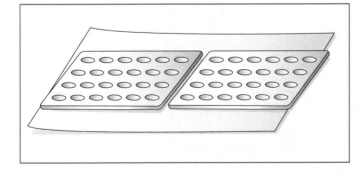

household ammonia (NH$_3$ or NH$_4$OH$_{(aq)}$)

b) Which substances reacted with the metal? How could you tell? What do these substances have in common? (Consider the chemical formulas listed for some of the substances.)

c) Which substances did not react with the metal? What do these substances have in common? (Consider the chemical formulas listed for some of the substances.)

Safety goggles and a lab apron must be worn during this activity.

2. Place small amounts of each solution you used in **Step 1** in a separate well of a well plate.

Test the solutions with one or more common laboratory indicators. (Your teacher will provide acid-base indicators like blue litmus paper, red litmus paper, phenolphthalein, bromothymol blue, methyl red.) Indicator papers are activated simply by dipping a small piece of the paper into the solution and noting any color change. If the indicator is a solution, add a drop or two to the substance being tested and note any color change. You will need to use fresh test solutions if you want to test with more than one indicator solution.

a) Make up a chart and record your observations.

3. Use your observations as well as previous experiences to answer the following.

a) Make a list of some of the observable properties for acids and bases.

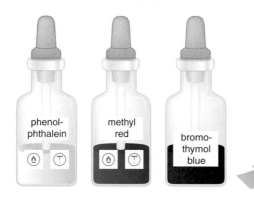

There are a number of ways you can use to measure pH. You will use pH paper and/or a universal indicator solution. Determine the pH of some of the substances you used in **Step 1**.

a) Make a data table that includes the name of the substance, the pH test, and whether the substance is an acid, a base, or a neutral substance.

For example:

- How do substances containing acids or bases taste? You should never taste substances in a lab, but you have probably had the opportunity to taste vinegar or lemon juice at home, or you may have accidentally got soap in your mouth.

- How do acids and bases feel. You must be very cautious when handling chemicals both at home and in the lab. However, you've probably had the experience of touching cleaning materials, such as soaps or floor cleaners. Think about vinegar or citrus fruits. How do they feel on a cut on your skin or a canker sore in your mouth?

4. The pH scale can also be used to describe acids and bases. This number scale ranges from 0 to 14. Acid solutions have a pH less than 7. The more acidic a solution is, the lower the pH. Base solutions have a pH greater than 7. The more basic a solution is, the higher the pH. Neutral solutions have a pH of 7.

b) You may have used both pH paper and universal indicator solution. Both of these are made from a combination of indicators, in order to produce a continuous range of colors throughout the pH scale. Methyl red is a chemical that changes from red to yellow when the pH is between 4.2 and 6.3. Thymolphthalein is a chemical that changes from colorless to blue when the pH is between 9.4 and 10.6. Thymol blue is a chemical that changes from red to yellow when the pH is between 1.2 and 2.8. How could these three chemicals be used to create an indicator scale? What are the limitations of being limited to these three chemicals?

5. Use the pH paper to test additional common household substances in order to determine which are acids and which are bases. (Hint: Try carbonated beverages, tea, coffee, baking powder, mayonnaise, power drinks, pickle juice, window cleaner, stain removers.) Your teacher may give you some pH paper to take home with you.

a) Make a list of common acids and bases found in your school or home. When possible, include both the name and formula for each substance you test.

6. Dispose of all chemicals as directed by your teacher. Clean and put away any equipment as instructed. Clean up your workstation. Wash your hands.

7. Here are two activities that display the characteristics of acids and bases in a colorful way. Your teacher will show you these as demonstrations.

   • Paint a message on a large sheet of paper or poster board using phenolphthalein indicator solution. (How about painting a message announcing your **Cool Chemistry Show**?) Allow the message to dry completely and hang the paper/poster board where everyone can see it. Use a window glass cleaner that contains ammonia water and when you are ready to reveal the message, lightly spray the design with the basic solution. (The secret message can also be revealed with a dilute ammonia solution. As the ammonia evaporates, the secret message that has been revealed will disappear again.)

   • Rinse a small beaker with a strong acid and label it "A." Rinse another small beaker with a strong base and label it "B." Let both beakers air dry. In another beaker (label it "I") add 20 drops of phenolphthalein indicator solution to about 50 mL of distilled water. When you are ready, pour some of the solution from beaker "I" into beaker "A." Then pour the solution from beaker "A" into beaker "B."

a) Record your observations.

b) Account for the observations in each case.

Caution must be used with these sprays, because they can cause eye damage if they get into the eyes.

ChemTalk

ACIDS AND BASES

Arrhenius' Definition of Acids and Bases

Acids and **bases** were first classified according to their characteristic properties. As you've experienced, acids and bases have different, distinct interactions with indicators (substances that change color with changes in the acidic or basic nature of another material). Some acids react with metals, while bases do not. Bases have a characteristic bitter taste and slippery feel, while acids have a characteristic sour taste. In fact, the term, acid, comes from the Latin word, *acidus*, which means sour. Acids and bases are also good conductors of electricity.

Chem Words

acid: a substance that produces hydrogen ions in water, or is a proton donor

base: a substance that releases hydroxide ions (OH⁻) in water, or is a proton acceptor

In the 19th century a chemist named Svante Arrhenius attributed the characteristic properties of acids to their ability to produce hydrogen ions when dissolved in water. If you look at the formulas for many common acids (HCl, H_2CO_3, H_2SO_4), you'll notice that they all have H as a common element. When these acids are added to water, a hydrogen atom can be drawn off into the water solution. The hydrogen atom leaves an electron behind, forming a positive hydrogen ion ($H+$) and a negative ion. Consider the action of hydrochloric acid in solution:

$$HCl_{(g)} \xrightarrow{\text{water}} H^+_{(aq)} + Cl^-_{(aq)}$$

The chemical equation shown above is valuable because of its simplicity. However, in reality, the hydrogen ion (H^+) is simply a proton and readily attaches itself to a water molecule. The result is called a hydronium ion (H_3O^+).

$$\underset{\text{hydrogen ion}}{H^+} + \underset{\text{water}}{H_2O} \rightarrow \underset{\text{hydronium ion}}{H_3O^+_{(aq)}}$$

To be more complete, the chemical equation above could be written as shown below. (Your teacher may allow you to use the simpler form of the equation—using the hydrogen ion as opposed to the hydronium ion).

$$HCl_{(g)} + H_2O \rightarrow H_3O^+_{(aq)} + Cl^-_{(aq)}$$

Arrhenius also addressed bases and their characteristic properties. He defined a base as a substance that produces hydroxide ions (OH^-) when dissolved in water.

Let's look at a base using Arrhenius' definition. When solid sodium hydroxide is dissolved in water, both sodium ions and hydroxide ions are produced, as shown in the chemical equation below:

$$NaOH_{(s)} \xrightarrow{H_2O} Na^+_{(aq)} + OH^-_{(aq)}$$

Over time, scientists have extended their definition of acids and bases beyond Arrhenius' definition to be more inclusive. You will learn more about the contributions of scientists like Johannes Bronsted of Denmark, Thomas Lowry of England, and Gilbert Lewis of the United States in further chemistry courses.

Neutralizing Acids and Bases

When acids and bases react together in solution, the hydrogen ions and hydroxide ions react in a one-to-one ratio to produce water. The remaining ions can join to form a salt. The process of an acid and base reacting to form water and a salt is called **neutralization**. Because the hydrogen ions and hydroxide ions have formed water, the solution is said to be neutral. The process of neutralization is shown in the chemical equations below. The chemical formula for water is actually H_2O. In the equations below the formula is written as HOH, so that you can see where the hydrogen and hydroxide ions end up.

$$H^+_{(aq)} \quad + \quad OH^-_{(aq)} \quad \rightarrow \quad HOH_{(aq)}$$
hydrogen ion   hydroxide ion   water

$$HCl_{(aq)} \quad + \quad NaOH_{(aq)} \quad \rightarrow \quad HOH_{(aq)} \quad + \quad NaCl_{(aq)}$$
acid   base   water   salt

If a suitable indicator is added to the reaction system, it will change colors when neutralization occurs. The point at which the indicator changes color is called the endpoint.

Consider the reaction of a strong acid (HCl) and a strong base (NaOH), as shown in the equation above. These substances are described as "strong" because they ionize completely in solution. For every HCl molecule, one hydrogen ion is released. For every NaOH, one hydroxide ion is released. These two ions then combine in a one-to-one ratio to form a neutral water molecule. Chemists take advantage of the neutralization process to help determine the concentration of solutions of acids or bases.

The pH Scale

In this activity you observed that one way of describing acids and bases is by examining their effects on indicators. Scientists also use the pH scale to express how acidic or basic a solution is. This number scale ranges from 0 to 14. Acid solutions have a pH less than 7. The more acidic a solution is, the lower the pH. Base solutions have a pH greater than 7. The more basic a solution is, the higher the pH. Neutral solutions have a pH of 7. The pH of a substance can be measured using methods like a pH meter or probe, pH paper, or universal indicator solution.

Chem Words

neutralization: the process of an acid and base reacting to form water and salt

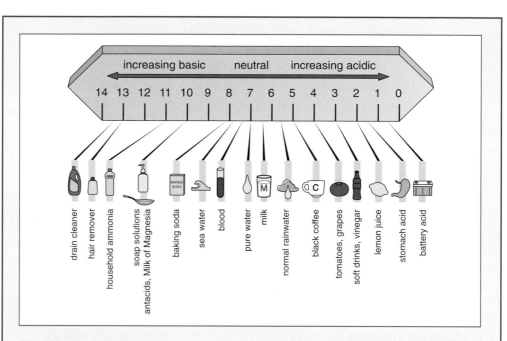

Acid and base indicators are compounds that are sensitive to pH. The color of the indicator changes as the pH of the solution changes. Most indicators are weak acids or weak bases that typically exhibit two different colors under varying pH conditions. The table below shows some common laboratory indicators and the colors they display under different pH conditions.

Common Laboratory Acid-Base Indicators		
Indicator	**Color Change**	**pH Range**
methyl violet	yellow to blue	0.0 to 1.6
thymol blue	red to yellow	1.2 to 2.8
methyl orange	red to yellow	3.2 to 4.4
bromocresol green	orange to violet	3.8 to 6.4
methyl red	red to yellow	4.2 to 6.3
litmus paper	red to blue	5.5 to 8.0
bromothymol blue	yellow to blue	6.0 to 7.6
phenolphthalein	colorless to red	8.2 to 10
thymolphthalein	colorless to blue	9.4 to 10.6
cabbage juice	red to green	2 to 12 (universal)

The pH scale ranges from 0 to 14 and is used to express the concentration of the hydrogen (H+) or hydronium ion (H_3O^+) of a solution at 25°C. Mathematically, it is defined as the negative logarithm of the hydrogen ion concentration. The term **pH** stands for **p**ower of **H**ydrogen ion. It can be written as:

$$pH = -\log_{10}[H^+]$$

where the brackets [ ] stand for "concentration of" (hydrogen ions in solution). Because pH is a logarithmic scale, the concentration of the hydrogen ion [H⁺] actually increases or decreases tenfold for each unit on the scale. An acid with a pH of 2 has a [H⁺] that is 10 times greater than an acid with a pH of 3 and 100 times the concentration of an acid with pH 4. A base with a pH of 10 has a [H⁺] that is 10 times less than a base with a pH of 9.

Chem Words

pH: a quantity used to represent the acidity of a solution based on the concentration of hydrogen ions (pH = – log[H⁺])

Checking Up

1. Use a chart to compare the properties of acids and bases. Be sure to include headings like taste, feel, pH, and reaction with metals.

2. What characteristic property did Arrhenius attribute to acids and bases?

3. Describe the process that occurs when an acid reacts with a base.

4. Why are litmus paper and phenolphthalein particularly useful indicators for distinguishing between acids and bases?

5. What does pH stand for?

6. How much more acidic is a solution of pH 3 than pH 5?

Reflecting on the Activity and the Challenge

In this activity you expanded your knowledge about acids and bases by becoming familiar with many of their characteristics. You learned about Arrhenius' definition of acids and bases. You also learned a bit about pH, another way of expressing the acid or base nature of substances. This information will all come in handy as you plan your presentation for the **Cool Chemistry Show**. Remember that the fifth-grade teacher has specifically asked that your class includes presentations and information about acids and bases.

Chemistry to Go

1. Identify which of the following characteristics relate to acids and which relate to bases:

   a) taste sour

   b) release hydroxide ions ($OH^-_{(aq)}$) when dissolved in water

   c) feel slippery

   d) release hydrogen ions ($H^+_{(aq)}$) when dissolved in water

   e) turn pink in the presence of phenolphthalein

   f) react with metals to produce hydrogen gas

   g) taste bitter

   h) turn red cabbage juice indicator green

2. Use Arrhenius' definition of an acid to help you write a chemical equation that shows the acidic nature of the following:

   a) sulfuric acid (H_2SO_4)

   b) carbonic acid (H_2CO_3)

3. Use Arrhenius' definition of a base to help you write a chemical equation that shows the basic nature of the following:

   a) potassium hydroxide (KOH)

   b) calcium hydroxide ($Ca(OH)_2$)

4. If you prepared the same concentration of two strong acids, sulfuric and hydrochloric, why would the pH of sulfuric be smaller than the hydrochloric acid?

5. Distilled water should have a neutral pH of 7, but water often has a pH less than 7. Suggest a reason for this lowering of the pH.

6. If you bubbled carbon dioxide through water, what would the new pH of the solution be?

7. Lemon juice, curdled milk, vinegar, all taste sour. What other properties would you expect them to have in common?

Preparing for the Chapter Challenge

You have seen a number of interesting color changes using acids, bases, and indicators. Choose one or two different cool activities to demonstrate in your show. Describe the procedure you will use and explain the chemistry involved. You may also wish to include an interesting scenario to accompany your "presto-change-o" demonstrations.

Inquiring Further

1. Titration

Titration is the process whereby a measured amount of solution of known concentration of acid (or base) is added to a known amount of a solution of unknown concentration. Research how chemists perform a titration, and the importance of indicators.

With your teacher's permission, demonstrate titration to your class.

2. The changing definition of an acid and base

The definition of acids and bases has changed through time. You are familiar with the earliest definitions that defined acids and bases in terms of their characteristic properties. The traditional definition has been expanded a number of times to include other substances that behave like acids and bases, but don't fit the traditional definition. Research the expansion through time of the definition of acids and bases. Identify the scientists involved and the changes that were made. Consider researching chemists such as Johannes Bronsted of Denmark, Thomas Lowry of England, or the American chemist Gilbert Lewis.

3. Is it pH balanced?

You may have heard the term "pH balanced" used to describe a shampoo or a deodorant. What does this term mean? What is the pH of most shampoos? Deodorants? Is it important for a shampoo or deodorant to be "pH balanced?" Conduct some research, both in and out of lab, to get answers to these questions. Focus just on shampoos or just on deodorants.

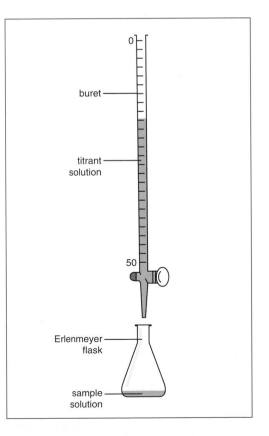

Activity 8

Color Reactions that Involve the Transfer of Electrons

GOALS

In this activity you will:

- Cause different metals to rust by oxidation-reduction (redox) reactions.

- Determine what materials can react with metals, causing the metals to rust.

- Write the word equations and chemical equations for redox reactions.

- Identify the materials that react, and the materials that are simply spectators, in a redox reaction.

- Learn how to impede rusting.

What Do You Think?

What happens to a scratch on a car that is not repaired? What happens to metal barbecue tools that get left out in the rain for a few weeks?

- What is rust and what causes it?

Record your ideas about this question in your *Active Chemistry* log. Be prepared to discuss your responses with your small group and with the class

Investigate

1. Half-fill a test tube with copper (II) sulfate pentahydrate solution ($CuSO_4 \cdot 5H_2O_{(aq)}$). Add a small amount of zinc powder to the test tube. Stopper the test tube, and shake carefully.

   a) Record your observations.

      Dispose of the products as directed by your teacher.

Safety goggles and a lab apron must be worn during this activity.

b) The reaction you just observed was a single-displacement reaction. The zinc displaced the copper. Use this information and your observations to complete the following equations:

zinc + copper (II) sulfate →

_____ + _____

c) Write the word equation as a sentence. Also, explain why this would be classified as a single-displacement reaction. (Refer back to **Activity 4**.)

d) Write the equation using the chemical formulas of the products.

$Zn_{(s)} + CuSO_{4(aq)} →$

_____ + _____

Because the sulfate ion shows on both sides of the equation, it is considered a spectator ion and the equation can be written as shown below:

$Zn_{(s)} + Cu^{2+}_{(aq)} → Cu_{(s)} + Zn^{2+}_{(aq)}$

e) Write a sentence or two describing what happened in the test tube in terms of the zinc and copper.

2. Cut a design or a strip of aluminum from a pie plate or tray. If you cut a strip of aluminum, twist it into an interesting shape.

Place the aluminum in a solution that contains copper (II) ions ($Cu^{2+}_{(aq)}$). Possible solutions include: copper (II) nitrate ($Cu(NO_3)_{2(aq)}$) or copper (II) chloride ($CuCl_{2(aq)}$).

a) Observe and record your results. Dispose of the products as directed by your teacher.

b) What evidence do you have that a chemical reaction occurs? What changes have taken place with the aluminum? With the copper ions?

c) Complete this equation

$Al_{(s)} + Cu^{2+}_{(aq)} →$

_____ + _____

3. Repeat **Step 2** using a different metal such as zinc.

a) Record your observations.

b) Write a chemical equation for the reaction that takes place.

4. Repeat **Step 2** again, this time using a strip of copper in a solution of aluminum nitrate ($Al(NO_3)_{3(aq)}$).

a) Record your observations.

b) Write a chemical equation for the reaction that takes place.

Chem Talk

REDOX REACTIONS

Chem Words

oxidation: the process of a substance losing one or more electrons

reduction: a process in which the substance under consideration gains electron(s)

When zinc solid reacts with copper ions in solution, a change occurs. Atoms of zinc lose electrons to form zinc ions (Zn^{2+}) that dissolve into the solution. Copper ions (Cu^{2+}) gain the electrons from the zinc atoms to form copper atoms that plate out as a solid. Whenever an atom or ion becomes more positively charged in a chemical reaction, as in the case of zinc atoms forming positive zinc ions, the process is called **oxidation**. Oxidation is the process of losing electrons. Whenever an atom or ion becomes less positively charged in a chemical reaction, as in the case of the copper ions forming copper atoms, the process is called **reduction**. Reduction involves a gain of electrons. The processes of oxidation and reduction happen together and as such are commonly referred to as "redox" reactions. An easy way to remember which is oxidation and which is reduction is by remembering "LiOn GRrr,"— Lose electrons Oxidation; Gain electrons Reduction.

The formation of rust is a redox process. Water and oxygen are necessary for the iron metal to corrode (rust). Iron atoms lose electrons to form mostly Fe^{3+} ions with the help of the moisture in the air and the heat of the Sun. Because the atoms have given up electrons to become more positively charged, oxidation of iron has taken place. Molecules of oxygen gain electrons to form O^{2-} ions. The oxygen has accepted electrons and is said to have been reduced. Corrosion can be prevented by painting a surface of iron to prevent moisture and air from coming in contact with the metal. Let's summarize what you have learned about atoms and ions:

The term atom means that the element is neutral; this means that it has the same number of protons and electrons.

Ions mean that the atom (or ion) has gained or lost electron(s). Examples are:

$Na \rightarrow Na^+ + e^-$ (Sodium atom loses 1 electron and now has a net charge of +1.)

$Cl_2 + 2\ e^- \rightarrow 2\ Cl^-$ (The two chlorine atoms gain 1 electron each and the net charge is −1 for each chloride ion.)

Polyatomic ions like the sulfate ion (SO_4^{2-}) imply that there are 2 more electrons than protons in the entire structure.

In some cases you will find that an ion can gain or lose an electron and form a new ion. An example of this type is: $Fe^{2+} \rightarrow Fe^{3+} + e^-$ (The iron in the 2+ state loses 1 more electron and now will be in a 3+ state.)

Reflecting on the Activity and the Challenge

Although many colorful chemical reactions involve the use of acids and bases with indicators, there is an entire group of chemical reactions that produce colorful results through the transfer of electrons. In this activity you became familiar with some of the simple concepts behind redox reactions, and you saw several examples of the color changes they can produce. You and/or your classmates may decide to include some redox reactions in the **Cool Chemistry Show**.

Chemistry to Go

1. Aluminum metal can react to form an ion with a charge of $+3$. Does the aluminum atom gain or lose electrons to form the Al^{+3} ion?

2. A copper ion with a charge of $+2$ can react to form an atom of copper. Does the copper ion have to gain or lose electrons in this reaction?

3. The element iron can form two different ions. The iron (II) ion (Fe^{+2}) is commonly called a ferrous ion while the iron (III) ion (Fe^{+3}) is called a ferric ion. When ferrous ions undergo a chemical change to become ferric ions, what process has taken place, oxidation or reduction? Explain your answer.

4. In the reaction you did with zinc metal reacting with copper ions, which substance gains electrons? Which loses electrons?

5. What must take place for copper metal to be oxidized?

6. Galvanized iron nails are used to fasten materials that will be exposed to the outdoors. A galvanized nail is a regular iron nail that is coated with zinc.

   a) Why would a zinc coating be an advantage here? What do you think is the purpose of the zinc?

   b) What two reactants could you use to test this in the laboratory? What results would you expect if you were right about the purpose of the zinc?

Inquiring Further

1. The Statue of Liberty

In the 1980s the Statue of Liberty in New York harbor underwent extensive renovation. Research the involvement of oxidation-reduction reactions in this renovation. Identify what the problem was and its solution.

Cool Chemistry Show Assessment

Your Chapter Challenge is to present an entertaining and informative chemistry science show to fourth- and fifth-grade students. The show for fourth graders should address chemical and physical properties and changes. The show for fifth graders should help students learn about acids and bases, and about chemical reactions that involve color changes. All presentations must include a demonstration and an audience appropriate explanation of the chemistry concepts involved. Finally, the teachers of the fourth- and fifth-grade students need written directions for your chemistry show with explanations of the chemistry concepts included in the show.

Your team should review the activities that you completed. A useful way of completing this review would be to list the activities, the cool chemistry demonstrations that you can perform, whether these demonstrations would be most appropriate for the fourth- or fifth-grade show and the chemistry concepts of the demonstration. You should pay particular attention to the section **Reflecting on the Activity and the Challenge.** You should also compare your list with that given in the **Chemistry You Learned** summary.

Your team's next step would then be to decide on which demonstrations are best suited to your interests and can be the most interesting, informative, creative and entertaining

for the elementary students. Your teacher may wish you to share your decision with the class as a whole so that the full cool chemistry program is not repetitious.

Each demonstration that you plan on producing will be judged along specific criteria. Each demonstration should be carefully planned, should adhere to all safety considerations, should be completed within the assigned time limits and should exhibit showmanship, creativity, clarity and appeal. As you plan and practice your demonstration, you should use these criteria as a checklist to ensure high quality.

Each demonstration must also be accompanied with an explanation of chemistry concepts. You should rehearse your explanation so that it complements the demonstration itself. You may choose to have one team member producing the demonstration, another team member explaining the manipulations and focusing the audience attention on specific observations and a third team member explaining the chemistry concepts. You should decide if your presentation would be strengthened by having some of the chemistry concepts described prior to the demonstration of if the explanation should follow the demonstration.

Your final responsibility is to provide detailed instructions to the fourth- and fifth-grade teachers so that the teacher could repeat the demonstration. This will require a list of materials, step-by-step directions, notes on what should be happening and safety considerations. You must also provide a written explanation of the chemistry concepts illustrated in the **Cool Chemistry Show**. Your chemistry concepts should be more thorough than the oral presentation during the show. Your explanation of chemistry concepts is now targeted to teachers rather than elementary students. You can include more formulas, more background and provide additional experiments which clarify the chemistry concepts.

Your class should generate a grading rubric. The rubric will assign points to the demonstration, the chemistry content and the written summary. It will also assign points to specific aspects of each major category. For instance, how many additional points will be afforded for additional concepts introduced in the demonstration? How many points will be assigned for creativity, showmanship and adherence to time limits of the cool chemistry demonstration? This rubric can be a useful tool for your team to check the quality of your work and to ensure that you have included all necessary parts of the project.

Chemistry You Learned

Chemical and physical changes of matter	Cations and anions	Decomposition reactions	Reaction rates
Solute, solvent and solution	Polyatomic ions	Metal activity series	Factors that affect the reaction rate:
Saturated and supersaturated solution	Ionic compounds and formulas	Endothermic and exothermic reactions	• Concentration
Precipitate	Molecular compounds	Conservation energy	• Catalyst
Solubility of compounds in water	Chemical equations	Kinetic and potential energy	• Temperature
pH indicators for acids and bases	Synthesis reactions	Heat energy	• Surface area or nature of the material
	Single- and double-displacement reactions	Colligative properties	Acids and bases
			Titration
			Oxidation and reduction

Marc Pollack

President, Flix FX

"Everyone talks about 'Movie Magic,'" says Marc Pollack, president of the prestigious Hollywood special effects company Flix FX. "So I guess that makes me a magician." But Pollack is clearly more comedian than magician. The 'magic' he creates for movies like *Blackhawk Down*, *Men In Black* and *Cast Away*, in addition to scores of television commercials, museum installments and Las Vegas casinos, is the product not of mysterious hocus-pocus but rather fundamental principles of science. "One of the most important aspects of our work," he continues, "is to push the limits of how chemicals are designed to be used." Among other things, Pollack and his crew at Flix FX use vacuum-forming thermoplastics to make tin-based silicon molds for everything from prehistoric creatures to futuristic robots. Through a combination of trial and error experimentation and traditional research science, they've perfected the process. "Silicon is what we call an R.T.V.," Pollack explains. "That stands for room temperature vulcanization. So depending on the type and amount of catalyst we use, the mold will cure at different rates and with slightly differing properties." By manipulating the ratio of silicon to catalysts they can make strong, realistic molds in the most efficient way possible. "Increasing the amount of catalyst will speed up the curing process but too much catalyst will shorten the life of the mold," he says. "Every job is different so determining that balance is one of our many challenges."

Pollack, who is now a master in the art of using chemicals like silicon, polypropylene, urethane and urethane elastimers, is not a chemist by trade. He actually graduated from film school at SUNY Purchase in the hopes of becoming "the next Steven Spielberg." Then, through a twist of fate, he became a special effects nut and eventually founded Flix FX in 1990. "Now," Pollack says, "Spielberg may one day come to me."

Special effects — Pollack creates both mechanical and physical — is an industry in a constant state of transformation. "The industry is always trying new stuff and that's exciting," Pollack says. "For instance, someone just developed a great water-based breakaway glass for stunts called Smash Glass. It's similar to fiberglass without the dangerous elements associated with that material and can be made to break into either large chunks or tiny little pieces. I can't wait to get my hands on it and break it over someone's head. That's part of my job these days and I love it."

Unit 4

Active Biology™

Making Connections

At this point you have come to the last unit in your *Integrated Coordinated Science for the 21st Century* course. In the first unit on Earth Science, you learned that the Earth is a set of closely linked systems. You related what was happening in the geosphere to its effects on all the other systems. You are now going to take a closer look at the biosphere, the part of Earth where living organisms are found.

You have spent much of your time in this course studying nonliving things. What is the difference between living and nonliving things? Historically, this has always been a real puzzle for scientists. Some scientists believed that living things could come from nonliving things. Another group believed that life had a vital force that was neither chemical nor physical.

What Do You Think?

• Is there a difference between the elements found in living things and nonliving things?

• What is the difference between an organic and inorganic chemical?

Record your ideas about this in your log. Be prepared to discuss your response with your small group and the class.

For You To Try

• Research and report to your class about a career that requires a knowledge of both chemistry and biology.

• What is biophysics? How might what you learned in physics be related to biology? Research and report to your class the connection between physics and biology.

SAVE THE TREES

Chapter 9

SAVE OUR JOBS

We need our jobs!

PROTECT THE ENVIRONMENT

Protect our environment

A VOTE FOR ECOLOGY

A Vote for Ecology

Scenario

Many Americans have begun to realize the importance of ecological issues. Americans now care about problems that were almost unknown a few years ago. Land and water management, pollution, biodiversity, invasive species, and many more concerns are on people's minds.

However, ecological issues cannot be considered on their own. They must be included in the economic and social spheres. The hidden costs of environmental programs are sometimes forgotten. It is necessary to develop a balanced solution to problems. This is the only reasonable way to sustain the environment.

For example, fishing provides food, income, and employment for millions of people. However, fishing has environmental costs. Rare species may be threatened. Marine ecosystems can be disturbed. Also, it is questionable how long the resource will last. Aquaculture presently offers an alternative. It provides a chance to expand the food supply from freshwater or the sea. However, aquaculture can also be ecologically unsound. Natural habitats are lost. The introduction of alien species in an area can pose a threat to the existing ecosystems. The spread of disease from farmed to wild populations is also a concern.

The League of Concerned Voters in your area recognizes the importance of preserving the environment. However, they are also aware that a lack of information about ecological issues could lead to conflict rather than constructive action. That is why they have decided to commission the development of a series of booklets. These booklets are intended to introduce the scientific facts behind current issues.

Chapter Challenge

Your challenge is to create a booklet addressing one current issue. These booklets will be provided to the public. The League hopes that this will produce an informed public, who is better able to decide how to vote on any given issue. Before you begin, you will need to decide which audience you are targeting. You may choose to write your booklet geared to adult voters, teenagers, or a child. Regardless of which you choose, it is assumed that the readers will be non-specialists and the text should be written with this in mind. The booklets should be easily understood by your target audience.

In producing your booklet, you should:

- identify and research one current issue that threats the environment;
- provide the relevant data on the issue;
- draw attention to areas where data may be weak or lacking;
- interpret the data and indicate the limits of the interpretation.

In providing the science behind the issue, you should:

- identify the roles and importance of consumers, producers, and decomposers in an ecosystem;
- explain how matter is cycled and energy flows through ecosystems;
- provide the meaning and the importance of biodiversity;
- describe how changes in an ecosystem are determined and how they can be analyzed;
- tell how fluctuations in size of a population are determined by birth, death, immigration, and emigration.

Criteria

How will your booklet be graded? What qualities should a good booklet have? Discuss these matters with your small group and with your class. You may decide some or all of the following qualities are important:

- significance of the issue identified;
- completeness and accuracy of the ecology principles presented;
- merit of the interpretations suggested;
- readability of the booklet;
- design and layout of the booklet.

You may have additional qualities that you would like to include. Once you have determined the criteria that you wish to use, you will need to decide on how many points should be given to each criterion. Your teacher may wish to provide you with a sample rubric to help you get started.

Activity 1   Diversity in Living Things

GOALS

In this activity you will:

• Observe a group of diverse organisms.

• Relate the structure of an organism to its adaptation to the environment.

• Describe the organization of the biosphere.

• Define biodiversity and explain its importance.

• Explain the effects of human activity on biodiversity.

• Read about the effects of extinction.

• Practice safe laboratory techniques for handling living organisms.

What Do You Think?

It is estimated that 4% of all living species are found in Costa Rica, even though this country comprises only 0.01% of the area of the Earth.

• How many species do you think are found in Costa Rica? How many species are found globally?

• Why do you think that Costa Rica has such a large number of species?

Write your answers to these questions in your *Active Biology* log. Be prepared to discuss your ideas with your small group and other members of your class.

For You To Do

This activity provides you with an opportunity to view several very different species of organisms. It should give you an appreciation of the huge diversity of life that fills your world.

Part A: Observing Animal Diversity

1. With your teacher, review the guidelines concerning the proper handling of laboratory animals. Follow these guidelines carefully.

2. In your *Active Biology* log make an enlarged copy of the table shown below. The table should extend across two facing pages. Each of the 13 spaces should allow for several lines of writing.

3. In the *Characteristics* column, copy the words in italics from each of the following questions. The 13th space is for any other observations you make. All the specimens of one animal species and the materials and equipment needed for observing them are arranged at the station. Each team will have a turn at each station. Record only your observations, not what you have read or heard about the organism.

   1 What is the *habitat* of the animal? Does it live in water, on land, or both?

2 Is *body symmetry* radial (symmetry about a center) or bilateral (the left and the right sides of the body are mirror images)?

3 Does the animal have a *skeleton* (a structure that supports the organism's body)? If it does, is it an endoskeleton (on the inside) or an exoskeleton (on the outside)?

4 Is the animal's body *segmented* (divided into sections) or is it *unsegmented*?

Several of the activities that follow involve the use of organisms in water. The water that the organisms are in should be considered a contaminant. Tables, equipment, and hands should be washed carefully so that germs are not inadvertently passed to people.

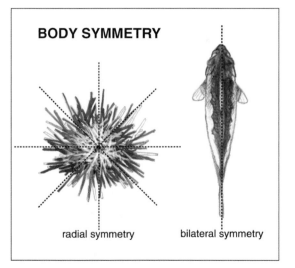

BODY SYMMETRY

radial symmetry   bilateral symmetry

Comparing Animals					
Characteristics	Hydra	Planarian	Earthworm	Hermit Crab	Frog
1					
2					
3					
13					

5 Which type of *digestive cavity* does the animal have, a sac (only one opening) or a tube (open at both ends)?

6 Does it have *paired appendages*? Are the limbs (arms, legs, fins, wings) found in pairs?

7 How does the animal *obtain oxygen*? Through lungs, gills, skin, or a combination of these?

8 Are any *sense organs* visible? If so, what types and where?

9 How does the animal *move* from one place to another?

10 Does it make any types of *movement* while it remains more or less in one spot?

11 How does the animal *capture* and take in *food*?

12 How does it react when *touched* lightly with a small brush?

Station 1: Observing Hydras

1. Place a single hydra in a small watch glass with some of the same water in

which it has been living. Wait until the animal attaches itself to the dish and extends its tentacles. Then slowly add a few drops of a daphnia culture with a dropping pipette.

2. Touch the hydra gently with a soft brush. Observe its reactions.

3. Examine a prepared slide of a lengthwise (longitudinal) section of a hydra under a compound microscope. Try to determine the presence or absence of a skeleton and of a digestive system.

Station 2: Observing Planarians

1. Place one or two planarians in a watch glass containing pond or aquarium water. Add a small piece of fresh raw liver. Observe using a stereomicroscope or hand lens.

As you move among the stations, keep your hands away from your mouth and eyes. Wash your hands well after the activity.

2. Use a compound microscope to examine cross sections of a planarian. Examine whole mounts with a stereomicroscope. Determine the presence or absence of a skeleton and a digestive system.

Station 3: Observing Earthworms

1. Pick up a live earthworm and hold it gently between your thumb and forefinger. Observe its movements. Do any regions on the body surface feel rough? If so, examine them with a hand lens.

2. Place a worm on a damp paper towel. Watch it crawl until you determine its anterior (front) and posterior (back) ends. Use a hand lens to see how the ends differ. Describe.

If you are observing a live crab in your classroom, keep your fingers away from the crab's pincers.

2. Place a small piece of food from the food dish in with the hermit crab. Observe how the hermit crab eats.

Station 5: Observing Frogs

1. Observe the breathing movements of a frog while it is not moving.

2. Observe the variety of movements of a live frog.

3. If possible, observe a frog capturing its food and feeding.

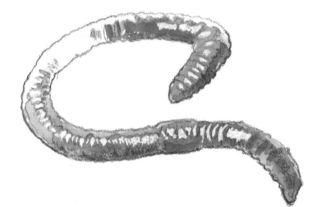

3. Place an earthworm on loose soil and observe its movements as it burrows.

4. Examine a model or a diagram of a cross section and lengthwise section of the earthworm's body.

Station 4: Observing Hermit Crabs

1. Observe the movements of the appendages and the pattern of locomotion (movement from one place to another) of a living land hermit crab. Observe the antennae. Touch them gently with a soft brush. Note the animal's reaction.

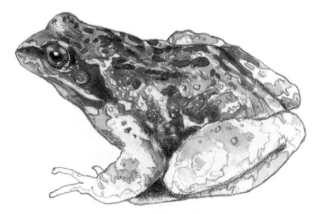

Wash your hands thoroughly before leaving the laboratory.

If you are handling a live frog in the classroom, do not rub your eyes. Wash your hands immediately after handling.

Part B: Animal Adaptations to the Environment

1. Review what you have learned about each of the organisms in **Part A**. By reading across the table, you should be able to compare and contrast the characteristics of the five animals you have studied.

a) For each animal, select two functions it performs as part of its way of life. Describe how its structure enables it to perform these functions.

BIODIVERSITY

Organization in the Biosphere

The **biosphere** is the area on Earth where living organisms can be found. Most are found in a narrow band where the atmosphere meets the surface of the land and water. Life forms are referred to as the **biotic**, or living, component of the biosphere. The **abiotic**, or nonliving, component is made up of items like rocks, soil, minerals, and factors like temperature and weather.

Bio Words

biosphere: the area on Earth where living organisms can be found

biotic: the living components of an ecosystem

abiotic: the nonliving components of an ecosystem

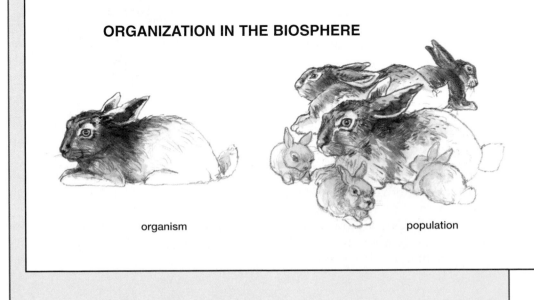

ORGANIZATION IN THE BIOSPHERE

organism   population

Just as you did in this activity, ecologists begin their studies with the **organism**. Their investigations are designed to explore how the individual interacts with its biotic and abiotic environment. However, an organism does not live on its own. It tends to form a group with others of the same **species**. (A species is a group of organisms that can reproduce successfully only with others of the same type.) These groups of species are called **populations**. When more than one population occupies an area, a **community** of organisms is created. The abiotic component as well as the community form a functional unit known as an **ecosystem**.

The Importance of Biodiversity and the Human Threat

In this activity you looked at some very different species of organisms. Scientists have discovered and named close to two million species. That would mean looking at a lot of different organisms. Yet, it may be less than 20 percent of the species that exist! There are thousands of organisms in the world that scientists know very little about. More than 750,000 species of insects have been identified. Yet, it is thought that at least twice that many exist. Biological diversity, or **biodiversity**, is the sum of all the different types of organisms living on Earth.

Bio Words

organism: an individual living thing

species: a group of organisms that can interbreed under natural conditions and produce fertile offspring

population: a group of organisms of the same species occupying a given area

community: all the populations of organisms occupying a given area

ecosystem: a community and the physical environment that it occupies

biodiversity: the sum of all the different types of organisms living on Earth

community   ecosystem

Unfortunately, many organisms are disappearing. This is partly due to alterations of habitats. The result is a decrease in biodiversity. Ecosystems with a large number of different types of organisms are quite stable. Ecosystems with a small number of different organisms are less stable. Humans are partly responsible for this change. As the human population grows it occupies more land. This infringes on or destroys the habitats of many organisms.

The smog created by automobiles and industry is killing many types of trees over a wide area of southern California. The needles of ponderosa pines, for example, gradually turn brown. The tops of palm trees have only small tufts. When this happens, photosynthesis is greatly reduced. The plants die. The Everglades National Park in southern Florida depends on a slowly moving sheet of water. The water flows from north to south. Drainage ditches built at the northern edge of the Everglades have decreased the flow of water over the entire area. As a result, many alligator holes have dried up. These holes helped to contain fires in the Everglades. Now, destructive fires are more frequent in this national park.

Smog is also hazardous to people. This is especially true of those with respiratory problems, the elderly, and children. People have died from the effects of smog.

Tropical rainforests are the most diverse ecosystems on Earth. They are home for many different species. Two-thirds of the world's species are located in the tropics and subtropics. The cutting of trees in the rainforests today has grown at a rapid rate. The trees are cut for lumber, grazing land, and other uses. This loss of habitat is destroying many species every day. Nearly half of the Earth's species of plants, animals, and microorganisms will become extinct, be gone forever, or be severely threatened, during the next 25 years.

To find a similar rate of **extinction** (loss of species), you need to go back 65 million years. That was the end of the Cretaceous period when dinosaurs and other organisms disappeared. Because there are more

Bio Words

extinction: the permanent disappearance of a species from Earth

species today than there were then, the absolute number of species lost will be greater now. Hundreds of species of plants and animals are threatened today. They include the whooping crane and some rare pitcher plants. Extinction is a natural process. However, the process has been speeded up because humans have changed whole ecosystems.

In tropical regions, humans are cutting down, burning, or otherwise damaging the rainforests. Extinction of many species as well as change in global climate are some of the effects of this deforestation.

Why is biodiversity important? Why does it matter if whooping cranes and pitcher plants become extinct? One argument comes from genetics. In a field of crop plants planted by humans, all the plants are genetically similar. They have all inherited the same characteristics.

About 90% of the world's food comes from 15 species of plants. Three of them are corn, wheat, and rice. However, there are over 10,000 known species of cereals.

509

If one individual gets a disease, all the plants may die. In a wild population a vast pool of genetic characteristics are available. This means that some of the plants could resist the disease. Therefore, not all the plants would be destroyed. The extinction of each wild population erases genetic material that could mean healthy crops and animals. Once extinction occurs, the genetic material is gone forever.

A second argument is related to the fact that simple ecosystems are unstable. Think of a field of corn as a simplified ecosystem. Suppose all the corn dies. This means that the whole ecosystem would collapse. The simpler the ecosystem, the easier it is to disrupt its balance. The fewer the species, the easier it is to upset an ecosystem. New species are evolving all the time. However, the process is very slow compared to the rate at which humans are able to cause species to become extinct. Each time a species becomes extinct, the biosphere is simplified a little more. It becomes more difficult to maintain the stable biosphere on which all life depends.

A third argument comes from research on plants. The island of Madagascar, off the east coast of Africa, is the only known habitat of the Madagascar periwinkle. This plant produces two chemicals not produced by other plants. Both of these chemicals are used to fight Hodgkin's disease, a leukemia-like disease. As the human population on Madagascar grew, the habitat for the periwinkle shrank. The periwinkle almost became extinct. Fortunately, botanists collected and grew some of these plants before they were gone forever. The medicines made from the Madagascar periwinkle are worth millions of dollars each year. They also help many people with Hodgkin's disease to live longer. These medicines never would have been known if the plant had become extinct.

Extinction Can Cause a "Domino Effect"

Every organism in an ecosystem is connected to all the other organisms. The reduction in biodiversity caused by the extinction of a single species can cause a "domino effect." The removal of one part from an ecosystem, like the removal of a moving part from a car, can cause the collapse of an entire food chain. If a species acts as a predator, it keeps the population of its prey in check. If a species is prey, it provides an important food source.

For example, sea otters were over-hunted along the Pacific coasts of Asia and North America. This removed the main predator of the sea urchin. Predictably, the number of sea urchins grew rapidly. Sea urchins eat kelp, a form of seaweed. As the number of sea urchins grew, the amount of kelp declined. As a result, the fish that relied on the kelp for habitat and food were reduced in number.

Sea otters very nearly became extinct due to hunting pressure. For humans, killing the sea otters for their fur resulted in a decline in a valuable fishery. Where the sea otter has been reintroduced, sea urchin populations have fallen, kelp beds are being re-established, and the number of fish is increasing.

Restoring the Balance Is a Difficult Task

Introducing the sea otter to the Pacific northwest is an example of an attempt to restore a natural balance. It is not always easy to do. Conservationists have also tried to restore the whooping crane. In spring, whooping cranes fly north to live in the marshes and swamps of the prairies and the Canadian north. There they eat crayfish, fish, small mammals, insects, roots, and berries. Efforts by the United States and Canada have helped increase the population from a low of 14 individuals in 1940 to 183 in 1999. The whooping crane may be a success story, and it may not. Chemical pesticides were the original human threat to the crane. However, it was already struggling.

During the fur trade southern sea otters were hunted to near extinction. They are still a threatened species, and may very well be endangered.

➡

Once widespread throughout North America, the whooping crane wild population dipped to just 15 birds in 1937. Through conservation efforts the whooping crane has begun a slow recovery. However, coastal and marine pollution, illegal hunting, and the draining of wetlands continue to threaten the species.

Cranes must fly a long way between their summer homes in the north and their winter homes on the Gulf of Mexico. Along the way they are vulnerable to hunting and accidents. In addition, the whooping crane reproduces very slowly. Each year females produce two eggs, however, only one will mature. The first fledgling to crawl from the egg kills its brother or sister. This ensures there will be enough food for the survivor. However, it is very difficult for the species to increase its numbers.

Scientists do not understand all the relationships between species ecosystems. They cannot predict what will happen if biodiversity is reduced, even by one species. If one species becomes extinct, it could be disastrous. The extent of the disaster may not be known until later. Sometimes the balance cannot be restored.

Reflecting on the Activity and the Challenge

In this activity you observed several very different living organisms. You then discovered that there are millions of other different organisms alive on Earth. There are reasons why it is important to make sure that these organisms do not disappear forever from the Earth. For your **Chapter Challenge** you may choose to research an issue that relates to the disappearance of a given species. You can now explain why it is important to maintain biological diversity. Whether or not your issue deals with biodiversity, the public still needs to understand why biological diversity should concern them. You need to provide the meaning and importance of biodiversity.

Biology to Go

1. Choose and identify two very different ecosystems.

   a) For each, name some of the populations that might be found in each community.

   b) Describe some of the abiotic factors that could affect each population.

2. What is biodiversity?

3. Explain how humans can influence biodiversity by changing the environment.

4. Why is maintaining biodiversity important?

5. a) Give an example of an ecosystem that has a high biodiversity.

   b) Give an example of an ecosystem that has a low biodiversity.

6. Choose an organism other than one that you studied in this activity. List at least three structures that have helped the organism adapt to its environment. Describe how each helps the organism live in its ecosystem.

Inquiring Further

1. The passenger pigeon and the human influence

Just over a century ago, the passenger pigeon was the most numerous species of bird on Earth. In the Eastern United States they numbered in the billions, more than all other species of North American birds combined. On September 1, 1914, at 1:00 PM the last surviving passenger pigeon died at the age of 29. Research and report on how humans were involved in the extinction of the passenger pigeon.

2. Extinction is forever

Humans were directly responsible for the extinction of passenger pigeons. However, this bird is not the only organism that has been threatened by humans. Research and report on another organism whose existence has been or is endangered by humans.

White rhinos are so large and powerful that in nature they must give way only to the elephant. Yet, humans are a major threat to their existence.

Activity 2

Who Eats Whom?

GOALS

In this activity you will:

- Distinguish between a food chain and a food web.

- Explain the roles of the producers, consumers, and decomposers.

- Understand the meanings of autotroph, heterotroph, herbivore, carnivore, and omnivore.

- Recognize the dependence of organisms on one another in an ecosystem.

What Do You Think?

You have probably heard the question, "If a tree falls in a forest and there is no one there to hear it, does it make a noise?"

- In ecology you might ask the question, "If a tree falls in a forest and there is no one there to haul it away, what happens to it?"

Write your answer to this question in your *Active Biology* log. Be prepared to discuss your ideas with your small group and other members of your class.

For You To Do

In this activity you will have an opportunity to explore how organisms in an ecosystem are dependent on one another.

Part A: A Food Chain

1. Look at the organisms in the pictures on the right.

   a) Link the names of the organisms together by the words "is eaten by."

   b) Show the relationship between the organisms as a linked word diagram or chain.

   c) Use arrows to show the direction in which food energy moves in the food chain you constructed in **Part (b)**.

   d) Identify the producer in the food chain.

   e) Identify the consumers in the food chain.

   f) Which consumer is a herbivore (feeds on plants)?

   g) Which consumers are carnivores (feed on other animals)?

   h) What elements are missing from this food chain?

Part B: A Food Web

1. Your teacher will provide you with a card that names an organism, what it does, what it eats, and what it is eaten by. You will also be given a name tag with your organism's name on it.

   Read your card and attach your "name" tag where others can readily identify you.

2. Clear a large area in your classroom, or find another large open area in or near your school. Form a large circle.

snake

grasshopper

frog

green plant

hawk

515

3. Obtain a big ball of string, about 35 m in length. Give the ball of string to one of the students.

4. The first student will say what organism he/she represents. Also, the student will indicate what the organism eats and what it is eaten by. The ball of string is then directed to one of students who represents the predator or the prey.

   a) As the game progresses, what appears to be forming in the center of the circle?

5. Suppose one organism is removed from the circle. Your teacher will direct you which organism will be removed.

   a) What happens to the web that was created?

   b) How does the removal of an organism impact on the other organisms in the circle?

6. Suppose that your circle has only a few organisms.

   a) What would happen to the web in this case if one of the organisms were removed?

   b) In which situation, a large or small "circle" of organisms, does the removal of an organism have a greater impact?

BioTalk

Bio Words

food chain: a series of organisms through which food energy is passed in an ecosystem

food web: a complex relationship formed by interconnecting food chains in an ecosystem representing the transfer of energy through different levels

autotroph: an organism that is capable of obtaining its energy (food) directly from the physical environment

heterotroph: an organism that must obtain its energy from autotrophs or other heterotrophs

producer: an organism that is capable of making its own food

consumer: a heterotrophic organism

herbivore: a heterotroph that feeds exclusively on plant materials

Food Chains and Webs

A bat ate a mosquito that had bitten a coyote that had eaten a grasshopper that had chewed a leaf. All these living things make up a **food chain**. A food chain is a step-by-step sequence that links together organisms that feed on each other. The story, however, is incomplete. It does not mention that many animals other than coyotes eat grasshoppers and mosquitoes bite other animals. It also does not consider that coyotes and bats eat and are eaten by a great many other living things. When you consider that the kind of plant a grasshopper might eat may also be eaten by various other consumers, you start to build a picture that links together a whole community of living things. Those links resemble a **food web** rather than a food chain. A food web is a series of interconnected food chains or feeding relationships. The diagram shows how members of a community interact in a food web.

Organisms in the Food Web

Autotrophs are organisms that are capable of obtaining their energy (food) directly from the environment. Most autotrophs obtain their energy through the process of photosynthesis. In this process solar energy is converted into a form of energy that can be used by the organism. **Heterotrophs** obtain their energy from autotrophs or other heterotrophs. For this reason autotrophs, the organisms that "make" the food, are called **producers**. In the diagram, grass, vegetables, and trees represent the producers. The heterotrophs are called **consumers**. **Herbivores** are first-order consumers. They feed directly on the plants. These organisms are removed by just one step

THE FOOD WEB

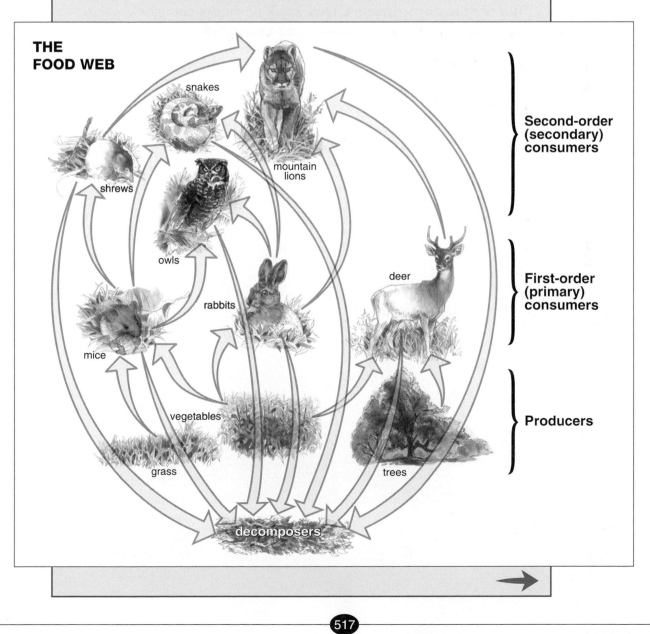

snakes

mountain lions

shrews

owls

deer

rabbits

mice

vegetables

grass

trees

decomposers

Second-order (secondary) consumers

First-order (primary) consumers

Producers

Bio Words

carnivore: an animal that feeds exclusively on other animals

omnivore: a heterotroph that feeds on both plant materials and animals

decomposers: organisms that break down the remains or wastes of other organisms to obtain their nutrients

in the food chain from the producers. In this example, they include mice, rabbits, and deer. **Carnivores** are second-order consumers. They feed on the animals that eat other plants. The owl and the mountain lion are just two examples of carnivores. **Omnivores** eat both plants and animals. A human is an example of an omnivore.

There is another group of organisms in the food web that is so important that these organisms are often treated as a separate group. They are the **decomposers**. They break down the complex organic molecules that are found in the wastes and bodies of other organisms. They do this to obtain food energy for their own use. In the process, they release nutrients back into the ecosystem. Bacteria and fungi make up most of the decomposers.

Alternative Pathways Maintain Stability in Food Webs

The alternative pathways in a food web help maintain the stability of the living community. If the rabbits in some area decrease in number, perhaps because of some disease, the owls might be expected to go hungry. However, this is not the case. The rabbits eat less vegetation. Hence, the greater number of plants produces more fruits, and seeds and furnishes better hiding places for mice. Soon a larger population of mice is present. The owls transfer their attention from rabbits to

The food habits of rabbits vary depending on location, time of year, and species of rabbit. They generally prefer to eat tender, green vegetation. They also eat leaves, bark, seeds, and even fruit of woody plants. Rabbits begin feeding in the evening and continue throughout the night.

mice. This reduces the danger for surviving rabbits, and these primary consumers have a better chance to rebuild their numbers. The greater the number of alternative pathways a food web has, the more stable is the community of living things which make up the web.

Owls are nighttime (nocturnal) birds of prey. Owls feed entirely on living animals. They eat everything from insects to mammals as large as rabbits. The size of the prey is proportional to the size of the owl.

Only a few of the possible offspring of a plant or animal survive to reproduce. Of all the seeds a plant forms, all but a few are eaten by animals. Some die from diseases. Others are killed by poor weather conditions. This can happen either as seeds or somewhat later in life, as young plants that have not yet formed seeds of their own. ➡

Humans are so used to thinking of the welfare of their own species, that they tend to regard as "wasted" all the offspring that do not survive. But there is another side to the picture. For one thing, the world lacks space for so many individuals of any one kind. Also, these individuals are needed as food by a great variety of consumers. Without the fruits, seeds, young plants, and foliage, the primary consumers could not exist. Without the primary consumers, the plants would die. They would become overcrowded or lack nutrients. Without the primary consumers, the secondary consumers would be reduced in numbers because of competition, or would become extinct. Without waste from plants and animals, including dead remains, the decomposers would not be able to get their nutrients. Without decomposers, nutrients that the producers require would not be returned to the soil or water. Through the presence of all these components in the food web, each species is held in check, and the community maintains its stability.

Reflecting on the Activity and the Challenge

In this activity you looked at how every organism is dependent on other organisms and how they are all held together by a food web. You can now begin to understand how the stability of any ecosystem depends on each one of its components. In the **Bio Talk** reading section you were also reintroduced to many terms that are used by ecologists. In discussing your environmental issue, you will be expected to use these terms correctly. You will probably also want to explain the importance of some of these terms in your booklet to educate the public.

How are primary consumers a benefit to plants?

Biology to Go

1. In what ways are living organisms affected by other living organisms?

2. What is the role of decomposers in a biological community?

3. What is the difference between a food chain and food web? Use an example to explain your answer.

4. a) Why are autotrophs called the producers in an ecosystem?

   b) Why are heterotrophs called consumers?

5. Are you a herbivore, carnivore, or omnivore? Explain your answer to show that you understand the meaning of each term.

6. Create a food web that includes you and at least five other organisms. Identify the decomposers, producers, and consumers as you diagram your food web.

7. In which ecosystem would the removal of an organism disrupt stability more, an Arctic ecosystem or a deciduous forest? Explain your answer.

Water makes up the largest part of the biosphere. Aquatic regions, both freshwater and marine, are home to many species of plants and animals. As you inquire further into aquatic food webs, you may be surprised at how many different types of aquatic ecosystems exist.

Inquiring Further

Aquatic food webs

Water covers over two-thirds of the surface of the Earth. Research and construct an aquatic food web. Identify the producers and consumers.

Integrated Coordinated Science for the 21st Century

Activity 3   Energy Flow in Ecosystems

GOALS

In this activity you will:

- Infer the loss of energy in the form of heat from the human body.

- Relate the laws of thermodynamics to the transfer of energy in a food chain.

- Calculate the energy lost at a given level in a food web.

- Explain the significance of a pyramid of biomass, a pyramid of numbers, and a pyramid of energy.

What Do You Think?

Heat stroke is caused by a failure of the heat-regulating mechanisms of the body. It can be caused by heavy exercise combined with hot and humid conditions.

- Where does the heat in the body come from?

Write your answer to this question in your *Active Biology* log. Be prepared to discuss your ideas with your small group and other members of your class.

For You To Do

As you work through this activity, consider whether there is any relationship between events like heat stroke and the heat that is stored and lost at each link in a food web.

1. Read through the steps of the activity.

   a) What are you investigating in this activity?

   b) Predict what you think will happen to the water temperatures in the containers.

2. You can now follow the steps to conduct the experiment. Put 600 mL of water in each of three containers. The temperature of the water should be 10°C. You may have to add ice. Remove the ice when the temperature gets to 10°C.

3. Have one student put one hand into the water in container A. Have that student put the other hand into the water in container B. In container A, move the fingers rapidly in the water. Do not move the hand in container B. Keep one hand moving and the other hand still for five minutes.

4. Another student will hold a thermometer in the water in container A. Read the temperature once each minute for 5 minutes.

a) What is the purpose of stirring the water?

b) Record the temperatures in the chart.

 Clean up any spilled water immediately.

Minutes	Temperature Container A (moving hand)	Temperature Container B (still hand)	Temperature Container C (no hand)
1			
2			
3			
4			
5			

a) Record the temperatures in a chart similar to the above.

5. A third student will hold a thermometer and read the temperatures in container B. Also, stir the water in this container using the stirring rod.

 Wash your hands after completing the activity.

6. A fourth student will hold a thermometer in container C. Stir the water in this container. Read the temperature once each minute for five minutes.

a) Why did you have a container that you did not put your hand in?

b) Record the temperature readings in the chart.

7. Make a line graph of the temperature readings for the three containers. You will have three lines on the same graph.

a) In container B, you held your hand in cold water without

moving it. What happened to the temperature? Does this data support your prediction?

b) In container A, you exercised your hand. How did the temperature of the water change? Do your data support your prediction?

Pyramids of Mass and Energy

One of the most important abiotic factors that affects relationships in a community is energy. Organisms in an ecosystem are tied together by the flow of energy from one organism to another. The food chain that exists when a herbivore eats a plant and a carnivore eats a herbivore depends on the energy entering the community in the form of sunlight. Without the Sun, there would be no green plants, no herbivores, and no carnivores. (There are a few ecosystems that get their energy from another source.)

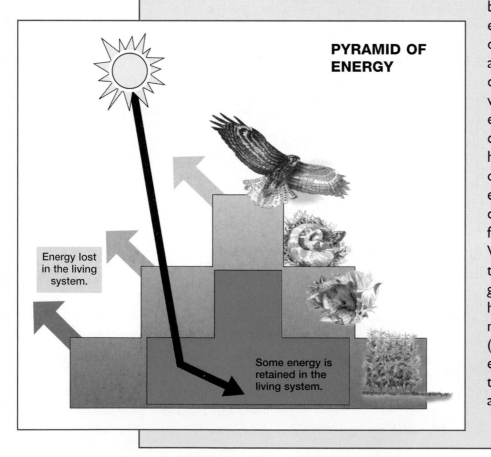

PYRAMID OF ENERGY

Energy lost in the living system.

Some energy is retained in the living system.

The size of a community, therefore, is limited by the amount of energy entering it through its producers. The total amount of chemical energy stored by photosynthesis is the gross primary productivity of the community. Much of that energy is used by the producers to grow and to maintain themselves. The remaining energy, which is available to the consumers as food, is the net primary productivity of the community.

The transfer of energy from producer to primary consumer to secondary consumer, and so on in a food web must follow the laws of **thermodynamics**.

The first law of thermodynamics states that although energy can be transformed, it cannot be created or destroy. Some energy from the Sun is transformed into a form that can be used by living organisms. However, if energy is not destroyed, what happens to it? Why is it necessary to keep adding energy in the form of sunlight? That is where the second law of thermodynamics comes into play. It states that in any energy transformation some energy is lost from the system in an unusable form.

Usually this is in the form of heat. In this activity, you actually measured the temperature increases that resulted from the heat loss from the human body. You noted that with exercise, the heat loss was even greater than without movement.

Among living beings, the transfer of energy in food from "eaten" to "eater" is really quite inefficient, and of course a great deal of the food does not get eaten at all. From grass to sheep the loss is about 90 percent.

Bio Words
thermodynamics:
the study of energy transformations described by laws

It takes about 10 kg of organic matter in the grass to support one kilogram of sheep.

Bio Words

pyramid of living matter: a pyramid developed on the basis of the mass of dry living matter at each trophic level

pyramid of energy: a pyramid developed on the basis of the energy at each trophic level

trophic level: the number of energy transfers an organism is from the original solar energy entering an ecosystem; the feeding level of one or more populations in a food web

For the sake of simplification, assume that each consumer lives entirely on one kind of food. Then a person on a lake might live entirely on a given type of fish, for example. To support one kilogram of this person it takes about 10 kg of fish, 100 kg of minnows, 1000 kg of water fleas, and 10,000 kg of algae. This information in graph form is called a **pyramid of living matter**. Mass is a measure of the amount of matter in an object. Because much of the mass of living organisms is water, the producers first must be dried for a truer estimate of their mass when constructing a pyramid of matter. The pyramid shows that the amount of matter is greatest at the producer level.

It is possible to measure the amount of energy available at each level. The **pyramid of energy** that results from graphing these values also

THEORETICAL PYRAMID OF LIVING MATTER

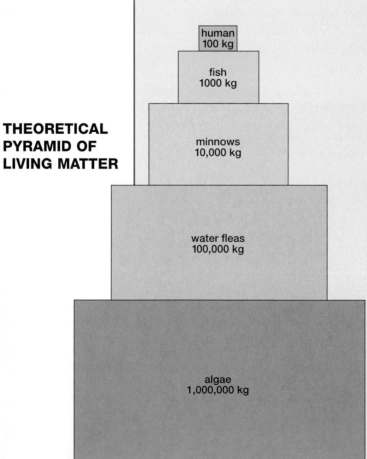

human
100 kg

fish
1000 kg

minnows
10,000 kg

water fleas
100,000 kg

algae
1,000,000 kg

Humans have relied on fish as a source of food throughout history. Most of the fish protein was provided by species caught in the wild.

shows that the energy available is greatest at the producer level and steadily decreases at the other levels. Each step in the pyramid is called a **trophic level** (energy level). Because energy is lost at each transfer, the steps in a pyramid of energy are limited. Usually, there are no more than about five trophic levels in a food chain.

It is also possible to construct a pyramid of numbers by counting the number of organisms in a food chain. Although the largest number of organisms is usually found at the base of the pyramid, this is not always the case. For example, in a meadow there will be many more grass plants than there will be grasshoppers. However, a single tree can sustain many caterpillars.

Reflecting on the Activity and the Challenge

In this activity, you observed the loss of heat from the human body. You then related that to the loss of energy at each step of a food chain. You learned that the further you go up a food chain, the less energy is available. As part of your challenge you are expected to explain how energy flows through an ecosystem. You should also consider how the flow of energy is affected in the environmental issue that you have chosen.

1. What is the relationship, if any, between the heat energy stored and dissipated at each link in a food web and the heat energy responsible for a heat stroke?

2. In the activity, the student who kept his/her hand in the water may have begun to shiver. Why do you suppose this happened?

3. Explain how the transfer of energy in a food chain follows the laws of thermodynamics.

4. Why is there a limit to the number of trophic levels in an energy pyramid?

5. Why is a pyramid of numbers not always a good example of the flow of energy through a food chain?

6. An energy pyramid illustrates the energy lost at each level of a food web. In general, each level of the pyramid has only 10% of the energy at the level below it. If the producer level (the lowest level) has 10,000 kilocalories available for the rest of the food web, how much energy is available for the other three levels?

7. An energy pyramid illustrates a great loss of energy as you go up the pyramid. When humans eat meat, they act as a top-level consumer. A steer eats a small amount of corn which contains 10 kilocalories. If you were to eat the same amount of corn you would get the same amount of energy from it as the steer. How much energy would you get from that small amount of corn if you ate some hamburger from that steer? Before you calculate this answer think about how this energy pyramid differs from the energy pyramid in the previous questions.

Inquiring Further

Biological amplification

What does biological amplification mean? Use the example of dichloro diphenyl trichloroethane, or DDT, to illustrate how biological amplification and food chains and energy pyramids are related.

The peregrine falcon is a bird of prey at the top of the food chain. As a result of biological amplification, falcons ingested high levels of the pesticide DDT. Falcons contaminated with DDT did not lay eggs or produced eggs with shells that broke.

Activity 4

Factors Affecting Population Size

GOALS

In this activity you will:

- Investigate the factors that affect the size of a population.

- Interpret a graph and make calculations to examine factors affecting fluctuations in populations.

- Calculate the doubling time of the human population.

- Distinguish between an open and closed population.

What Do You Think?

The population of your community may be going up, going down, or remaining the same. The change depends on whether individuals are being added to or taken away from your community.

- What can take place in your community, or any other community of living things, that can influence the size of the population?

Write your answer to this question in your *Active Biology* log. Be prepared to discuss your ideas with your small group and other members of your class.

For You To Do

This activity provides an opportunity for you to examine the factors that affect the changes (fluctuations) that occur in a population in an ecosystem.

Part A: Reindeer Population

1. In 1911, 25 reindeer, 4 males and 21 females, were introduced onto St. Paul Island near Alaska. On St. Paul Island there were no predators of the reindeer, and no hunting of the reindeer was allowed. Study the graph shown below and answer the questions in your *Active Biology* log.

a) In 1911 the population was 25 reindeer. What was the size of the population in 1920? What was the difference in the number of reindeer between 1911 and 1920? What was the average annual increase in the number of reindeer between 1911 and 1920?

b) What was the difference in population size between the years 1920 and 1930? What was the average annual increase in the number of reindeer in the years between 1920 and 1930?

c) What was the average annual increase in the number of reindeer in the years between 1930 and 1938?

d) During which of the three periods 1911—1920, 1920—1930, or 1930—1938, was the increase in the population of reindeer greatest?

e) What was the greatest number of reindeer found on St. Paul Island between 1910 and 1950? In what year did this occur?

f) In 1950, only eight reindeer were still alive. What is the average annual decrease in the number of reindeer in the years between 1938 and 1950?

2. In your group, discuss the questions on the next page. Then answer them in your *Active Biology* log.

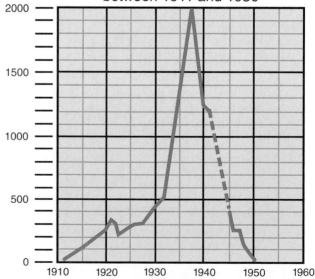

Changes in the
Reindeer Population on St. Paul Island
between 1911 and 1950

a) St. Paul Island is more than 323 km (200 miles) from the mainland. Could leaving or arriving at the island have played a major role in determining the size of the reindeer population? Explain your answer.

b) What might account for the tremendous increase in the population of reindeer between 1930 and 1938, as compared with the rate of growth during the first years the reindeer were on the island?

c) St. Paul Island is about 106 km^2 (41 square miles). What effect might 2000 reindeer have on the island and its vegetation?

d) Consider all the factors an organism requires to live. What might have happened on the island to cause the change in population size between 1938 and 1950?

e) Beginning in 1911, in which time spans did the reindeer population double? How many years did it take each of those doublings to occur? What happened to the doubling time between 1911 and 1938?

f) If some of the eight reindeer that were still alive in 1950 were males and some females, what do you predict would happen to the population in the next few years? Why?

g) What evidence is there that the carrying capacity (number of individuals in a population that the resources of a habitat can support) for reindeer on this island was exceeded?

h) What does this study tell you about unchecked population growth? What difference might hunters or predators have made?

Part B: Human Population

1. On a piece of graph paper, plot the growth of the human population using the following data.

Human Population Growth between A.D. 1 and 2000

Date A.D.	Human Population (millions)	Date A.D.	Human Population (millions)
1	250	1930	2070
1000	280	1940	2300
1200	384	1950	2500
1500	427	1960	3000
1650	470	1970	3700
1750	694	1980	4450
1850	1100	1990	5300
1900	1600	2000	6080
1920	1800	2010	?

2. Use your graph to determine the doubling times for the human population between A.D. 1 and 2000.

   a) How much time elapsed before the human population of A.D. 1 doubled the first time?

   b) Is the amount of time needed for the human population to double increasing or decreasing?

   c) What does that indicate about how fast the human population is growing?

3. Extend your graph to the year 2010.

   a) What do you estimate the human population will be in that year?

4. Using the equations below, estimate the doubling time for the current population based on the rate of growth from 1990 to 2000.

   a) In what year will the present population double?

c) In what ways is the Earth as a whole similar to an island such as St. Paul? Does the Earth have a carrying capacity? Explain your answer.

$$\text{Annual rate of growth (in percent)} = \frac{(\text{population in 2000} - \text{population in 1990}) \times 100}{\text{population in 1990} \times \text{number of years}}$$

$$\text{Doubling time} = \frac{70}{\text{annual rate of growth}}$$

5. In your group, discuss the following questions. Then answer them in your *Active Biology* log.

   a) What similarities do you see between the graph of the reindeer population and your graph of the human population?

   b) What are the three or four most important factors required to sustain a population?

   d) What might happen to the population of humans if the present growth rate continues?

   e) What methods could be used to reduce the growth rate?

   f) Suggest several problems in the United States that are related to the human population.

   g) What are the most important three or four factors to think about with regard to the world population?

Bio Talk

CHANGING POPULATION SIZES

Four Rates Determine Population Size

The size of a population changes through time. Suppose a biologist counted 700 ponderosa pines on a hill in Colorado in 1990. In 2000, when the biologist counted the trees again, there were only 500. In other words, there were 200 fewer trees in 2000 than in 1990.

There are many reasons that a population of trees may decrease. These include forest fires and logging. What else may contribute to the decrease of population?

This is a decrease in the population of ponderosa pines. This change in population may be expressed as a rate. To find the rate you divide the amount of change by the amount of time for the change to take place. The rate is an average. In this example, the rate of change in the number of trees divided by the change in time may be expressed as: -200 trees $\div$ 10 years $= -20$ trees per year. To the biologist, this means each year there were 20 fewer trees in the population. Keep in mind, however, that this rate is an average. It is unlikely the trees disappeared on a regular schedule. All of the trees may have been lost in one year due to a fire. Alternatively, selective cutting during several years may have caused the decrease.

533

Bio Words

death rate (mortality rate): the rate at which death decreases the size of a population

birthrate (natality): the rate at which reproduction increases the size of a population

immigration: the number of individuals of a species that move into an existing population

emigration: the number of individuals of a species that move out of an existing population

growth rate: the rate at which the size of a population increases as a result of death rate, birthrate, immigration, and emigration

What does the decrease of 200 pine trees in 10 years represent? Because pine trees cannot wander away, they must have died or have been cut down. In this situation, then, the decrease represents the **death rate**, or **mortality rate**, of the pine population. The number of deaths in the pine population per unit of time is the mortality rate. Mortality is not the only change that can affect a population, however. While some of the pines may have died, some young pine trees may have started to grow from seed. Death decreases a population; reproduction increases it. The rate at which reproduction increases the population is called the **birthrate**, or **natality.**

Organisms that can move have two other ways to bring about a change in population size. Suppose you were studying the pigeon population in your city or town. You might discover that a certain number of pigeons flew into the city in one year. This is called **immigration**. It occurs when one or more organisms move into an area where others of their type can be found. Immigration increases the population. While studying the pigeons, you might notice that a certain number flew out of the city. This is called **emigration**. It occurs when organisms leave the area. Emigration decreases the population. In any population that can move, then, natality and immigration increase the population. Mortality and emigration decrease the population. Thus, the size of any population is the result of the relationships among these rates.

The number of individuals of a species that move into and out of an area will affect the size of a population.

Natality, mortality, immigration, and emigration rates apply to every population, including the human population. The sum of these rates makes up the **growth rate** of a population. The growth rate of a population is the number of organisms added to (or subtracted from) a population in a year due to natural increase and net migration. Often, this rate is expressed as a percentage of the population at the beginning of the time period.

Population Density May Fluctuate

Any population has a built-in, characteristic growth rate. This is the rate at which the group would grow if food and space were unlimited and individuals bred freely. Environmental factors do affect a population's growth rate, however. The interaction of the population's natural growth rate and the environment determines the density of the surviving population. The maximum number of individuals that a given environment can support is called the **carrying capacity**.

Although there is variation among species, female ducks lay about 10 eggs per nesting attempt. The overall strategy for these birds is to get as many eggs out there as they can in the hopes that at least some will make it.

If you measure the density of a population at intervals during a given period of time, you seldom find any two consecutive measurements the same. Density increases or decreases continually. Most natural populations are **open populations**. These are populations in which individuals are free to emigrate or immigrate and in which the birth and death rates fluctuate. Variables in the environment, such as climate, available food, or the activities of natural enemies, are the causes of the fluctuations. In a closed population, birthrate and death rate are the only factors that affect the size of the population. The island of reindeer you studied in **Part A** is an example of a closed population.

Bio Words

carrying capacity: the maximum population that can be sustained by a given supply of resources

open population: a natural population in which all four factors that affect population size (death rate, birthrate, immigration, and emigration) are functioning

535

Sometimes population fluctuations are fairly regular, and the peaks are at approximately equal time intervals. For example, populations of lemmings often peak every three or four years. Many of the animals that live in the northern parts of Europe, Asia, and North America show similar population cycles. Although the data show very regular cycles when they are plotted on a graph, the reasons for the seemingly regular cycles are not well understood. A combination of purely chance events also can produce apparently regular cycles.

Although populations may change cyclically, many population changes are permanent. If a population becomes extinct, for example, the change is permanent. Any permanent change in a population is a change in the community to which the population belongs. Permanent changes in one population also may affect other populations of organisms in the same community.

Lemmings are known for repeated population explosions. During the peak, the population may increase a thousand times. Food becomes scarce and lemmings must migrate to new areas.

Reflecting on the Activity and the Challenge

In this activity you discovered that birthrate, death rate, immigration, and emigration affect the growth rate of a natural, open population. Review the issue you have identified for research.

Consider if any of the factors involving population size are relevant to the issue. You will be asked to explain to the public the importance of these factors in providing the science behind your stand.

Biology to Go

1. How do each of the four limiting factors affect population growth?

2. Explain how limiting factors could play a role in the extinction of a population.

3. Distinguish between an open and closed ecosystem. Use examples to illustrate your answer.

4. Scientists studying an area of the tundra reported that they found 5 lemmings per hectare. They returned the following year and discovered that the density of the lemmings in the same area were 20 per hectare. What is the rate of growth of lemmings in the area, expressed as a percentage?

5. According to the U.S. Census Bureau, the population of the United States is influenced by the following:

   1 birth every 8 s;

   1 death every 13 s;

   1 immigrant every 22 s.

   Use these figures to determine the time, in seconds, it takes for the net gain of one person. (Hint: Start by calculating the number of births, deaths, and immigrants every minute. Round off to whole numbers.)

Inquiring Further

1. Population growth in different parts of the world

Research a place in the world where population growth is a problem today. How is it a problem? Research a place in the world where population growth is not a problem today. Why is it not a problem?

2. The truth behind lemming suicide

During the filming of the 1958 Disney nature documentary *White Wilderness*, the film crew induced lemmings into jumping off a cliff and into the "sea" in order to document their supposedly suicidal behavior. Research and report on the truth of this statement and the truth about lemming "suicide."

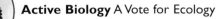
Activity 5

Competition Among Organisms

GOALS

In this activity you will:

- Observe the effects of competition among plants for space and nutrients.

- Describe the possible effects of introducing a nonnative species into an ecosystem.

- Explain why competition in nature is important.

What Do You Think?

Nature documentaries often feature the competition among animals for food, water, and space. These scenes are exciting to watch. However, plants seem to take a backstage to this type of activity.

- Do plants need to compete among themselves in any given environment?

- If plants do compete, how do they do it?

Write your answer to these questions in your *Active Biology* log. Be prepared to discuss your ideas with your small group and other members of your class.

For You To Do

This activity gives you an opportunity to observe the effect on plant growth when plants must compete for nutrients and space.

Part A: Competition among Plants

1. Fill five milk container bases with soil. Label the containers A through E.

2. Thoroughly moisten the soil in each container. Use the same amount of water to moisten the soil in each container.

   a) Why is it necessary to use the same amount of water in each container?

5. Place your containers in a low-light, room-temperature location (20°C is optimal). Keep the soil moist, but not soggy, by watering or misting every day or two.

6. When your plants sprout and begin to shed their hulls they are ready for light. Move them to a well-lighted location. If you go with sunlight be prepared to water more frequently. Room light will work as well and will not dry out the soil as quickly.

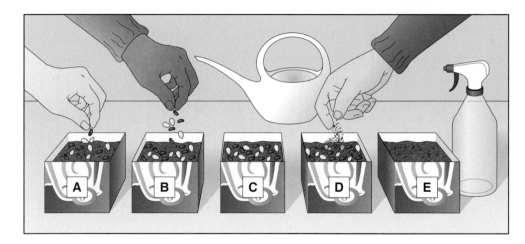

Do not eat any of the seeds in this activity. Wash your hands after handling the seeds and the soil.

3. Place seeds into the containers as follows:

   A. 5 crinkly cress (pepper grass) seeds
   B. 10 crinkly cress seeds
   C. 20 crinkly cress seeds
   D. 30 crinkly cress seeds
   E. 15 crinkly cress and 15 lettuce seeds.

   Spread seeds on the thoroughly moistened soil. (You are not expected to place them one at a time. Just spread them out as much as you can and as evenly as you can.)

4. Cover the seeds with a thin layer of soil.

   a) Count and record the number of seeds that germinated.

7. Keep the soil moist but not soggy by watering regularly. Water from the side if possible to prevent injuring the tiny plants. Again, make sure that each container is given the same amount of water.

8. Measure the heights of the plants and note the number and size of the leaves every two days for about three weeks.

   a) Record your observations.

   b) In which container were the cress plants the tallest?

c) In which container did the cress plants have the greatest number of leaves?

d) What happened to the appearance of the cress plants as the number of seeds in a container was increased?

e) Account for your observations when cress and lettuce seeds were planted together.

In the next part of this activity you will determine which plant species has an advantage under certain conditions. Each research group within the class can study a different set of variables.

Part B: Competition under Different Conditions

1. In this part of the activity you will once again use the bases of milk containers with moist potting soil to plant your seeds.

2. Plant seeds from various species according to the instructions on the packets. As a class, decide how you will control the mix of seeds in each container.

3. Water each of the milk cartons with the same amount of water every second day.

a) Record the amount of water used.

4. Once seeds start to germinate, store each of the milk cartons in a different environment. You might want to use temperature, amount of light, or amount of water as variables. Measure the growth of each of the plants daily.

a) Does one type of plant begin to dominate the community? Is it the same type of plant in all containers?

b) Present your data and draw a conclusion.

c) Speculate about why one plant might be better adapted for a specific environment.

Do not eat any of the seeds in this activity. Wash your hands after handling the seeds and soil.

Bio Talk

Plants and Animals Compete for Resources

It is not uncommon for two organisms to compete with one another. Often, this happens when there is a limited supply of resources like water, food, sunlight, or space. If there are not enough resources to satisfy the needs of both organisms, they will compete with one another.

Sometimes this competition occurs between members of the same species. Male birds of the same species will battle each other fiercely for the ownership of a territory. The territory would allow sufficient food and habitat for the male and the female birds to make a nest, eggs, and feed offspring. Competition among individuals of the same species is a very important factor in evolutionary change.

Plants must deal with competition in different ways. Usually the plants that grow the tallest or establish the "best" root system are the survivors. In some cases, plants even secrete chemicals, which prevent the seeds from other plants from growing.

Competition may occur among members of different species. In this case, limited resources are usually the cause for competition.

Female eagles usually lay one to three eggs a few days apart. One to two days is a normal age difference between eaglets. Older hatchlings often dominate the younger ones for food. In a three-egg brood, the third chick has little chance of survival. A large number of adult eagles are non-breeders, probably due to competition within the species and variable annual food supply.

541

Bio Words

nonnative (exotic, alien, introduced, or non-indigenous) species: any species, including its seeds, eggs, spores, or other biological material capable of propagating that species, that is not native to that ecosystem

invasive species: a nonnative species whose introduction does or is likely to cause economic or environmental harm or harm to human health

Purple loosestrife can produce up to 2.7 million seeds per plant yearly and spreads across approximately one million additional acres of wetlands each year.

Scientists have found that usually only one species survives in laboratory experiments studying this type of interaction. However, the real world is a much more complex situation. At times two competitive species can exist together. For example, both hawks and owls hunt mice. Hawks hunt by day and owls hunt by night.

Introducing Nonnative Species

Sometimes a new species that has not been there before is introduced into an ecosystem. This is called a **nonnative species**. (Other terms that you may hear used to refer to these organisms are **exotic**, **alien**, **introduced**, or **non-indigenous**.) The introduction can be either intentional or accidental. Introduction of a nonnative species can have negative effects on the ecosystem. When this happens the species is considered invasive. It can cause economic or environmental harm, or harm to human health. **Invasive species** can be plants, animals, and other organisms (e.g., microbes). All these terms are clearly defined by the U.S. government (Executive Order 13112).

Why is the government so concerned with invasive species? Why should the public be concerned? Most scientists believe that on a global basis, next to habitat destruction, the second greatest destroyers of biodiversity are invasive species. In some cases, the result is the extinction of an entire existing species.

Species have sometimes invaded new habitats naturally. However, human actions are the main means of invasive species introductions. When people settle far from home, they often bring with them familiar animals and plants. Other species, like rats, make the trip unintentionally. In their new habitat there may have fewer predators or diseases, so their populations grow out of control. Organisms that they might normally prey on may not have evolved defense mechanisms. Native species may not be able to compete successfully for space or food and so are often pushed to extinction. The spread of nonnative organisms destroys healthy, diverse ecosystems. It replaces them with biologically impoverished, homogeneous landscapes.

It is unfortunate, but increased travel and trade are providing many new opportunities for the spread of nonnative species. In addition to which, one important feature that makes a community susceptible to invasion by nonnative species is the level of human-induced disturbance. For example, nonnative birds such as European starlings and house sparrows do well in ecologically disrupted areas such as cities, suburbs, and farms.

One hundred house sparrows were introduced into Brooklyn in the 1850s. From this initial introduction, the species expanded throughout the eastern United States and Canada. House sparrows are closely tied to human activity. This sparrow is usually absent from extensive woodlands and forests and from grasslands and deserts.

Reflecting on the Activity and the Challenge

In this activity you looked at the competition among organisms. Sometimes this competition occurs among members of the same species. Other times it occurs among members of different species. Competition is not always bad. In fact, it plays an important role in evolutionary development. However, when a nonnative species is introduced into an ecosystem, the competition can have devastating results. Consider how your issue relates to the competition among organisms. Has the environmental issue that you are investigating for the **Chapter Challenge** been caused by competition?

Penguins breed in colonies and can be fiercely territorial. Since nearly all of Antarctica is covered in ice, competition for breeding space among penguins is great.

1. Why does competition occur among organisms?

2. What would be an advantage to competition between organisms of the same species?

3. Why do new species that are introduced into an ecosystem often become invasive?

4. What type of evidence would you look for in a natural setting to indicate that there is competition taking place among the plants?

5. Europeans, and their descendants in North America, often describe humans as being at the center of change. Not only do humans cause environmental changes, they are also responsible for those changes. In this worldview, the ideal human acts as a steward or protector for an ecosystem. By contrast, First Nations peoples often describe humans as belonging to an ecosystem. In this worldview, the ideal human lives in harmony with the ecosystem. How would the two worldviews differ in describing what has happened to ecosystems in the United States over the last century?

Inquiring Further

1. Investigating allelopathy

The production and release of substances by a plant that are toxic to neighboring plants is called allelopathy. Familiarize yourself with an allelopathic species in your area. Design an experiment to test which part of the plant is most toxic. Be sure to have your teacher approve your procedure if you plan on carrying out your experiment.

2. Invasive species

Research an invasive species in your area. Report your findings to the class.

Allelopathy benefited the sunflower growing in the wild. It reduced competition for nutrients, water, and sunlight. However, allelopathy works against sunflower crops. Sunflower crops must be rotated to avoid buildup of the "poison" in the soil.

Activity 6

Succession in Communities

GOALS

In this activity you will:

- Investigate succession after a natural disaster.
- Distinguish between primary and secondary succession.
- Explain how human activities can lead to succession.

What Do You Think?

Following a forest fire, all that remains is a charred landscape. Yet, within a few weeks the ground begins to turn green as living organisms return.

- From where does this new life come?
- How long will it take for the forest to return to its original condition?

Write your answers to these questions in your *Active Biology* log. Be prepared to discuss your ideas with your small group and other members of your class.

For You To Do

This activity provides you with an opportunity to examine how "life re-establishes itself" after a devastating blow.

1. On August 27, 1883, two volcanoes located on a single island in the Indian Ocean erupted at the same time. The blast was so great that a hole about 250 m deep remained where the peak of the volcano had been. The eruption on the island of Krakatoa has been said to be the loudest noise ever heard on Earth. The blast was heard in Hawaii, several thousands of kilometers away. Hot cinders and lava covered the island. Before the eruption, Krakatoa had been covered with a tropical forest. The eruption completely destroyed life on Krakatoa and two other nearby islands.

2. Two months after the eruption, scientists visited the island of Krakatoa. They found it steaming from a recent rain that had fallen on the lava that was still hot. In some places, the volcanic ash was washing away. In other places the ash was still more than 60 m deep. No life was visible.

3. Scientists visited the island nine months after the explosion, and at later times, to record the living things on Krakatoa. Some of the data recorded is shown in the diagram on the next page. Look for some interesting patterns in the rebirth of life on the island of Krakatoa. Study the plant life. (Reports of the animal life are interesting but too limited to use.)

a) What happens to the number of kinds of plants as the years pass?

b) Is there a change in the number of kinds of plant life?

c) Do the numbers of some kinds of plants change more than the numbers of other kinds?

d) Where do you think these plants might have come from? What reason do you have for your belief?

e) How long a period was needed for the complete recovery of the forest growth?

f) Write a statement that will describe the kinds of changes that have taken place on the island since the eruption.

g) Compare the "rebirth" of plant life on the coastal areas with the rebirth of plant life in the inland areas. How would you explain the difference?

SUCCESSION ON KRAKATOA

COASTAL AREAS   **INLAND AREAS**

3/4 years since eruption

Only algae and one lone spider found... mostly bare lava.

No plant or animal types found. Ground completely bare.

3 years since eruption

Ground completely covered with grasses. Many ferns, and many tropical seashore plants found. Insects also found.

A few grasses, many ferns and insects found.

13 years since eruption

Completely covered with young coconut trees, horsetail trees, and sugar cane plants. Lizards as well as insects found.

Almost all covered with grasses, orchids, and some horsetail trees. Lizards and insects found.

23 years since eruption

Completely covered as before, but with a greater number of trees.

Completely covered now with grasses, orchids, and groves of horsetail and young coconut trees.

47 years since eruption

By now a dense forest covers the area. All the previously listed plants and animals are found in abundance.

Inland areas now support same amount of plants and animals as the coast.

548

Bio Talk

Succession

The destruction of a mature forest by a severe fire is a devastating scene. Yet, even this charred scene holds promise of new life. Within a few weeks the ground will slowly turn green as annual and perennial plants return. These plants can tolerate full sunlight and the resulting high soil temperatures. They take root, grow, and reproduce in a soil made fertile by the mineral content of the ash. Within two or three years shrubs and young trees are evident and growing rapidly.

A few years later, an untrained observer would probably never know that the area had once been burned out. Over the long term, the forest will again reach maturity. This pattern is not limited to forests. It occurs in many other environments. This process of re-growth follows an environmental change. It is called **succession**. It describes the gradual change in an area. The change takes place as the area develops toward a final stable community. In every case, the final community that can exist is determined by the abiotic factors of the area.

Bio Words

succession: the slow and orderly replacement of community replacement, one following the other

Forest fires are one of the most destructive natural forces known. While sometimes caused by lightning, nine out of ten forest fires are caused by humans. Natural-occurring fires are vital in maintaining healthy ecosystems. However, human-caused fires have devastating effects on both wildlife and human lives.

Bio Words

primary succession:
the occupation by plant life of an area previously not covered with vegetation

secondary succession:
the occupation by plant life of an area that was previously covered with vegetation and still has soil

There are two types of succession: primary and secondary succession. **Primary succession** occurs in an area where no other community existed before. For example, this could happen on land left behind by a receding glacier. It could also happen on a newly formed volcanic island. **Secondary succession** occurs following destruction of a community. The re-growth after a forest fire is an example of secondary succession. Since soil is already present, the long time needed for soil to form in primary succession is not necessary.

Primary succession occurs on rock left behind by retreating glaciers, and transforms it into a living community. The process must begin with organisms that form organic soil, the pioneers or soil builders. This soil will be necessary to provide for the next group of plants to succeed.

After a forest fire, a sequence of ecological responses begins. Amid the charred forest remains, a pioneer community is established.

Each community goes through a succession of plant and associated animal species. The first community to appear is the **pioneer community**. It includes plants that are able to tolerate sunlight and the resulting high temperatures. This development of vegetation sets up new ground-level conditions. Eventually, conditions become more favorable to other plants that cannot tolerate full sunlight. These plants tend to be taller than the pioneer plants. This process continues through several in-between communities called **seral stages**. The plants and animals and their wastes at each stage contribute to the community development until a final community is reached. This final community is the one that can continue to perpetuate itself. It is called the **climax community**. Generally, both the biomass and the nonliving organic matter increase during the stages of succession. They then level off when the climax community is reached. The climate plant and animal life (biota) vary greatly by area. The types depend upon the tempereture and rainfall patterns.

Bio Words

pioneer community:
the first species to appear during succession

seral stages:
the communities in between the pioneer and climax community during the stages of succession

climax community:
the final, quite stable community reached during the stages of succession

Reflecting on the Activity and the Challenge

In this activity you observed some of the changes that occur after a dramatic environmental change. Sometimes, human activities are responsible for the environmental changes. Consider how the issue that you are researching for the **Chapter Challenge** came about. Can secondary succession be part of the solution to the problem?

Is the succession that occurs after a volcanic eruption primary or secondary succession?

Biology to Go

1. What is succession?

2. Explain the difference between primary and secondary succession.

3. Which community would support the greatest number and diversity of organisms, the pioneer community or the intermediate stages? Explain your answer.

4. Explain how abiotic factors change within a community as a result of the succession of vegetation.

5. Give two examples of how human activities can lead to secondary succession.

Inquiring Further

1. Primary succession

How does life establish itself on a rock surface? Describe the stages of succession that must occur to "transform" rock into a climax community.

2. Hydrarch succession

Hydrarch succession is the name for primary succession in a new freshwater environment. What type of organisms constitute the pioneer, seral, and climax communities in the stages of succession in fresh water?

3. Succession and Mt. St. Helens

At 8:32 Sunday morning, May 18, 1980, Mount St. Helens in southwestern Washington state erupted. About 600 km² of forest was blown over or left dead and standing. The eruption lasted nine hours, but Mount St. Helens and the surrounding landscape were dramatically changed within moments. Scientists and visitors follow the changes in the landscape and the volcano. Surviving plants and animals rise out of the ash, colonizing plants catch hold of the earth, birds and animals find a niche in a different forest on the slopes of Mount St. Helens. Research the succession pattern on Mt. St. Helens.

Volcanoes provide a unique opportunity to study plant succession, animal behavior, evolutionary and geologic processes, and ecology. Understanding how natural systems respond to disturbances is essential in facing environmental challenges of the future.

Activity 7

The Water Cycle

GOALS

In this activity you will:

- Measure the amount of water transpired by a plant.
- Describe the processes that take place in the water cycle.
- Provide examples of how human activities can affect the water cycle.
- Model the effects of acid rain on an ecosystem.

What Do You Think?

According to William Shakespeare, Caesar used part of his last breath to utter the words "Et tu, Brute" (even you, Brutus). His last breath would have been partly made up of water.

- Is it possible that the molecules of water that Caesar exhaled many centuries ago, are still a part of today's environment?
- Is it possible that these molecules could become a part of you?

Write your answer to these questions in your *Active Biology* log. Be prepared to discuss your ideas with your small group and other members of your class.

For You To Do

Plants absorb water through their roots and return water to the atmosphere through the process of respiration. In this activity you will measure the amount of water transpired by a plant over a period of time.

1. You will first construct a very simple "meter" to measure the loss of water. Place the tip of a 0.1 mL pipette into a piece of plastic tubing about 40 cm long.

2. Submerge the tubing and the attached pipette under water in the sink or a tray. Fill both with water. Make sure that all the air is drawn out of the tube and pipette. Leave the assembly under water while doing the next step.

3. Choose a branch from a plant. Suggested plants include Coleus and Zebrina. Submerge the end of the branch under water and make a small, slanted cut. This step is very important to ensure that no air bubbles are introduced into the xylem cells and the water will flow easily. Do not get the leaves wet. If you do, dry them gently with a paper towel before you begin your experiment.

4. While the branch and tubing are still under water, push the freshly trimmed end of the branch into the open end of the plastic tube. The end

of the branch should be about 1.5— 2.0 cm in the tube. There should be a very tight fit between the stem of the branch and the tube.

5. Bend the tubing into a U shape, as shown in the diagram. Clamp the tubing with the branch and the pipette onto a ringstand.

6. Once the "meter" is set up, wait about five minutes to make sure the plant is transpiring. After this initial waiting period, read the water level at "0 minutes." Then read the water level in the pipette every three minutes for a total of 30 minutes.

   a) Record your observations in a table.

7. At the end of your experiment, cut the leaves off the plant stem. Find the area of the leaf surfaces. You can do this by arranging all the cut-off leaves on a grid. Trace the edge of the leaves on to the grid. Count all of the grids that are completely within the tracing and estimate the number of grids that lie partially within the tracing.

   a) Record the area of the leaves in square centimeters.

   b) Calculate the water loss per square centimeter of leaf surface. Divide the water loss at each reading by the leaf surface area you calculated.

   c) Calculate and record the average loss per square centimeter for the class.

   d) Graph the loss per square centimeter over time.

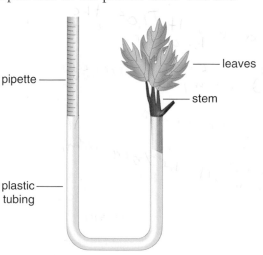

Be careful when cutting the plant. Cut away from yourself. Report any injuries.

pipette

leaves

stem

plastic tubing

 Wash your hands after the activity.

e) Assuming that your plant stem continued transpiration at the same rate, estimate the total volume of water that might be transpired in 24 h.

8. Use the results of your experiment to answer the following questions.

a) List some of the factors that might affect the results of this experiment. Explain how each factor might affect your results.

b) How could you improve the design of the experiment to reduce errors?

c) Consider what factors could affect the rate of transpiration of a plant. Develop a hypothesis and design an investigation to test your hypothesis.

The Water Cycle

Water is necessary to life in many ways. Land plants absorb water from the soil and land animals drink water or obtain it from their food. Water constantly bathes organisms that live in ponds, lakes, rivers, and the oceans. Other organisms rely on water to carry nutrients to their cells and organs. The cytoplasm in cells is mainly water.

Every day about 1200 km^3 of water evaporates from the ocean, land, plants, and ice caps. An equal amount of precipitation falls back on the Earth.

Bio Words

water (hydrologic) cycle: the cycle or network of pathways taken by water in all three of its forms (solid, liquid, and vapor) among the various places where is it temporarily stored on, below, and above the Earth's surface

evaporation: the process of changing from a liquid to a gas

condensation: the process of changing from a gas to a liquid

precipitation: water that falls to the Earth's surface from the atmosphere as liquid or solid material in the form of rain, snow, hail, or sleet

runoff: the part of the precipitation appearing in surface streams

groundwater: water contained in pore spaces in sediments and rocks beneath the Earth's surface

infiltration: the movement of water through pores or small openings into the soil and porous rock

aquifer: any body of sediment or rock that has sufficient size and sufficiently high porosity and permeability to provide an adequate supply of water from wells

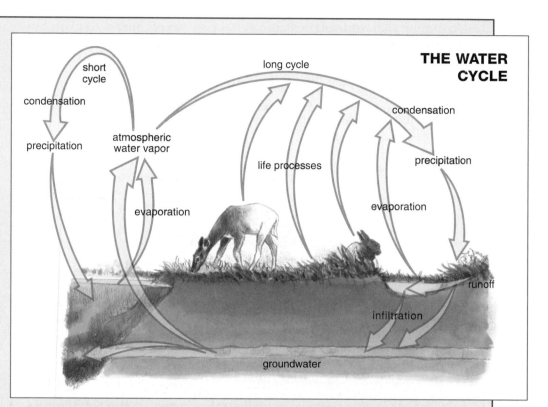

THE WATER CYCLE

The volume of water in the biosphere remains fairly constant through time. In fact, the water that you used today has been around for hundreds of millions of years. It has probably existed on the Earth's surface as a liquid, a solid, and a vapor. However, water is always moving from place to place. It is forever changing from one state to another. This complicated movement of the Earth's water is called the **water cycle** or **hydrologic cycle**. Some of the pathways of this cycle are shown in the diagram above.

One of the largest reserves of water on Earth is found in the oceans. The oceans contain about 97% of the Earth's water. Other surface water includes lakes, rivers, estuaries, marshes, and swamps. By contrast, the atmosphere holds less than 0.001% of the Earth's water. This means that rapid recycling of water must take place between the Earth's surface and the atmosphere.

By absorbing heat energy from the Sun, some of the water on the Earth's surface changes to water vapor by **evaporation**. It rises upward into the atmosphere until it reaches a point where the temperatures are low enough for the water vapor to condense to form tiny droplets of liquid water. This process is called **condensation**. These droplets of water are light. They collect around dust particles forming clouds or fog. They remain suspended in the atmosphere as clouds or fog and are supported by rising air currents and winds. When conditions are right, the droplets come together to form larger drops or sometimes ice crystals. Once the mass of the droplet or ice crystal can no longer be supported by air currents, **precipitation** occurs. Precipitation may take the form of rain, hail, sleet, or snow.

Snow falling high in the mountains or in the polar regions of the Earth may stay frozen there for years. Gradually, as layers of snow accumulate, the bottom layers of snow turn to ice, forming glaciers. Sometimes the snow or ice at the surface of the Earth can change directly back into water vapor. This process is called sublimation.

Other precipitation lands on the surface of the Earth and flows along the surface as **runoff**. The ground runoff gathers in streams, lakes, and oceans, and the cycle then repeats itself.

Approximately 1.7% of the water on Earth is stored in the polar icecaps, glaciers, and permanent snow.

However, some of the precipitation seeps into the Earth to form **groundwater**. This process is called **infiltration**. Sometimes the rock under the surface is very permeable. That is, water flows easily through it. In this case, some of the groundwater may seep to the surface, forming individual springs. **Aquifers** are large accumulations of underground water. They can provide an excellent source of water from wells. Groundwater

Bio Words

transpiration: the emission of water vapor from pores of plants as part of their life processes

flow, although measurable, is much slower than the flow in streams and rivers. That is because the passageways through the pore spaces in the materials beneath the Earth's surface are very small. Nonetheless, regardless of its speed, groundwater eventually also returns to the rivers, lakes, and oceans. And, the water cycle continues.

Plants and animals also play a very important role in the water cycle. Water enters living organisms by osmosis. However, through cellular respiration, water is released back into the atmosphere. As you saw in this activity, plants, especially broadleaf trees and shrubs play a major role in the water cycle through the process of **transpiration**. Transpiration is the loss of water through the leaves of a plant.

The Human Impact on the Water Cycle

The Earth's water supply remains constant, but humans can interfere with the water cycle. As population increases, living standards rise, and the industry and economy grow, humans place a greater demand on the supply of freshwater. The amount of freshwater needed increases dramatically, yet the supply of freshwater remains the same. As more water is withdrawn from rivers, lakes, and aquifers, local resources and future water supplies are threatened.

A larger population and more industry also mean that

A person can probably exist on about 4 L (four liters is about one gallon) of water a day for drinking, cooking, and washing. At present in the United States, people use almost 6000 L a day for their needs and comforts. These include recreation, cooling, food production, and industrial supply.

more wastewater is discharged. Domestic, agricultural, and industrial wastes include the use of pesticides, herbicides, and fertilizers. They can overload water supplies with hazardous chemicals and bacteria. Poor irrigation practices raise soil salinity and evaporation rates. Urbanization of forested areas results in increased drainage of an area as road drains, sewer systems, and paved land replace natural drainage patterns. All these factors put increased pressure on the water equation.

Pollutants that are discharged into the air can also affect the water cycle. Sulfur and nitrous oxides from the burning of fossil fuels, combustion in automobiles, and processing of nitrogen fertilizers enter the atmosphere. They combine with water droplets in the air to form acids. They then return to the surface of the Earth through the water cycle as acid precipitation.

Reflecting on the Activity and the Challenge

In this activity you observed one of the processes that take place in the water cycle. You learned that a great amount of water is transpired by a living plant. You also read about some of the other processes that are involved in the water cycle. The water cycle is very complex, and at any stage humans can have a significant impact. Perhaps the environmental issue you have chosen involves one part of the water cycle.

Biology to Go

1. Name and describe at least four processes that take place in the water cycle.

2. What is the energy source that drives the water cycle?

3. How has the water cycle determined partly where people live in the United States?

4. What would happen to the planet if the hydrologic cycle stopped functioning?

5. Describe three ways in which humans can have a negative effect on the water cycle.

Inquiring Further

Environmental models

Environmental models allow scientists to study what could happen to the plants and animals in an area if changes occurred. Models help check predictions without disrupting a large area.

Build an ecocolumn to research how acid rain affects an ecosystem.

(You will be allowed to use household vinegar as the acid.) An ecocolumn is an ecological model that is especially designed to cycle nutrients.

Record the procedure you will use. Have your teacher approve your procedure before you create your model.

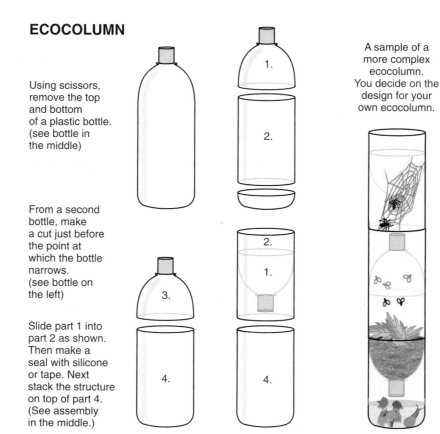

ECOCOLUMN

Using scissors, remove the top and bottom of a plastic bottle. (see bottle in the middle)

From a second bottle, make a cut just before the point at which the bottle narrows. (see bottle on the left)

Slide part 1 into part 2 as shown. Then make a seal with silicone or tape. Next stack the structure on top of part 4. (See assembly in the middle.)

A sample of a more complex ecocolumn. You decide on the design for your own ecocolumn.

Activity 8

Photosynthesis, Respiration, and the Carbon Cycle

GOALS

In this activity you will:

- Learn how oxygen cycles through photosynthesis and respiration.

- Practice safe laboratory techniques for using chemicals in a laboratory situation.

- Describe the cycling of carbon in an ecosystem.

- Speculate how human activities can affect the carbon cycle.

What Do You Think?

Consider the mass of a seed from a giant redwood tree and the tree itself. It is hard to believe that a giant of a tree began as a small seed.

- From where do the materials come to make up the mass of a mature tree?

Write your answer to this question in your *Active Biology* log. Be prepared to discuss your ideas with your small group and other members of your class.

For You To Do

In this activity you will investigate what happens when the exchange of carbon dioxide between a leaf and the atmosphere is blocked.

1. Three days before this activity, one plant was placed in the dark. A second plant of the same species was placed in sunlight.

a) Predict what you will find when you test a leaf from each plant for the presence of starch.

Day 1

2. Remove one leaf from each plant. Use scissors to cut a small notch in the margin of the one placed in sunlight. Using forceps, drop the leaves into a beaker of hot (60°C) tap water.

Isopropyl alcohol is flammable and toxic. Do not expose the liquid or its vapors to heat or flame. Do not ingest; avoid skin/eye contact. In case of spills, flood the area with water and then call your teacher. Make sure you wear goggles, apron, and gloves

3. When the leaves are limp, use forceps to transfer the leaves to a screw-cap jar about half full of isopropyl alcohol. Label the jar with your team symbol and store it overnight as directed by your teacher.

4. Select four similar leaves on the plant that has been kept in the dark, but do not remove them from the plant. Using a fingertip, apply a thin film of petroleum jelly to the upper surface of one leaf. Check to be sure the entire surface is covered. (A layer of petroleum jelly, although transparent, is a highly effective barrier across which many gases cannot pass.) Cut one notch in the leaf's margin.

5. Apply a thin film to the lower surface of a second leaf and cut two notches in its margin.

6. Apply a thin film to both upper and lower surfaces of a third leaf and cut three notches in its margin.

7. Do not apply petroleum jelly to the fourth leaf, but cut four notches in its margin; Place the plant in sunlight.

a) What is the purpose of the leaf marked with four notches?

8. Wash your hands thoroughly before leaving the laboratory.

Day 2

9. Obtain your jar of leaf-containing alcohol from Day 1. Using forceps, carefully remove the leaves from the alcohol and place them in a beaker of room-temperature water. (The alcohol extracts chlorophyll from the leaves but also removes most of the water, making them brittle.) Recap the jar of alcohol and return it to your teacher.

10. When the leaves have softened, place them in a screw-cap jar about half full of Lugol's iodine solution.

Lugol's iodine solution is used to test for the presence of small amounts of starch. Starch gives a blue-black color.

11. After several minutes, use forceps to remove both leaves, rinse them in a beaker of water, and spread them out in open Petri dishes of water placed on a sheet of white paper.

a) Record the color of each leaf. Recap the jar of Lugol's iodine solution and return it to your teacher.

b) What was the purpose of the iodine test on Day 2?

c) If you use these tests as an indication of photosynthetic activity, what are you assuming?

⚠ Lugol's iodine solution is poisonous if ingested, irritating to skin and eyes, and can stain clothing. Should a spill or splash occur, call your teacher immediately; flush the area with water for 15 minutes; rinse mouth with water.

12. Wash your hands thoroughly before leaving the laboratory.

Day 4

13. Remove from the plant the four notched leaves prepared on Day 1 and place them on paper towels. To remove the petroleum jelly, dip a swab applicator in the Histoclear™ and gently rub it over the surface of the film once or twice. Then gently use a paper towel to remove any residue of petroleum jelly. Discard the swab applicator and the paper towel in the waste bag.

14. Repeat **Steps 10** and **11**.

a) Compare the color reactions of the four leaves and record your observations.

b) In which of the leaves coated with petroleum jelly did photosynthetic activity appear to have been greatest? Least?

15. Wash your hands thoroughly before leaving the laboratory.

Histoclear is a combustible liquid. Do not expose to heat or flame. Do not ingest; avoid skin/eye contact. Should a spill or splash occur, call your teacher immediately; wash skin area with soap and water.

Bio Talk

The Carbon Cycle

You take in carbon in all the foods you eat. You return carbon dioxide to the air every time you exhale. A plant also returns carbon dioxide to the air when it uses its own sugars as a source of energy. When another plant takes in the carbon dioxide during photosynthesis, the cycle of carbon through the community is complete. In this activity you observed what happens when this exchange of carbon dioxide does not take place. However, when the exchange does take place, the plant can use the carbon from the carbon dioxide to live and grow.

Carbon dioxide is also returned to the air by decomposers. When producers or consumers die, decomposers begin their work. As its source of energy, a decomposer uses the energy locked in the bodies of dead organisms. It uses the carbon from the bodies to build its own body. Carbon that is not used is returned to the air as carbon dioxide. Eventually, almost all the carbon that is taken in by plants during photosynthesis is returned to the air by the activity of decomposers.

563

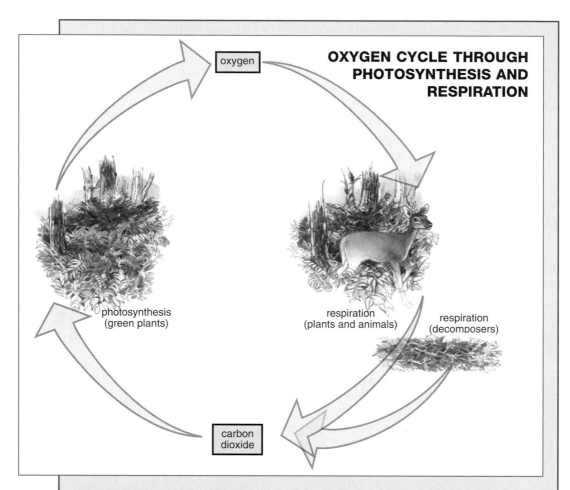

OXYGEN CYCLE THROUGH PHOTOSYNTHESIS AND RESPIRATION

oxygen

photosynthesis
(green plants)

respiration
(plants and animals)

respiration
(decomposers)

carbon
dioxide

Hundreds of millions of years ago, many energy-rich plant bodies were buried before decomposers could get to them. When that happened, the bodies slowly changed during long periods of time. They became a source of fuels like coal, oil, and natural gas. Today, when these fuels are burned, energy is released. The carbon in the fuels is returned to the air as carbon dioxide. You can see that even the energy obtained from fuels is a result of photosynthesis. The process in which carbon is passed from one organism to another, then to the abiotic community, and finally back to the plants is called the **carbon cycle**.

The Cycling of Matter

The energy from the Sun flows through the ecosystem in the form of carbon-carbon bonds in organic matter. When respiration occurs, the carbon-carbon bonds are broken and energy is released. The carbon is combined with oxygen to form carbon dioxide. The energy that is released is either used by the organism (to move, digest food, excrete wastes, etc.) or the energy may be lost as heat. In photosynthesis energy is used to combine the carbon molecules from the carbon dioxide, and oxygen is released. This is illustrated in the diagram. All the energy comes from the Sun. The ultimate fate of all energy in ecosystems is to be lost as heat. Energy does not recycle!

However, inorganic nutrients do recycle. They are inorganic because they do not contain carbon-carbon bonds. These inorganic nutrients include the phosphorous in your teeth, bones, and cell membranes. Also, nitrogen is found in your amino acids (the building blocks of protein). Iron is in your blood. These are just a few of the inorganic nutrients found in your body. Autotrophs obtain these inorganic nutrients from the inorganic nutrient pool. These nutrients can usually be found in the soil or water surrounding the plants or algae. These inorganic nutrients are then passed from organism to organism as one organism is consumed by another. Ultimately, all organisms die. They become detritus, food for the decomposers. At this stage, the last of the energy is extracted (and lost as heat). The inorganic nutrients are returned to the soil or water to be taken up again. The inorganic nutrients are recycled; the energy is not.

Bio Words

carbon cycle: the process in which carbon is passed from one organism to another, then to the abiotic community, and finally back to the plants

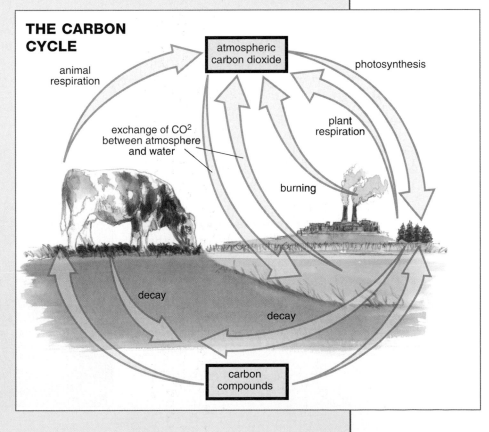

THE CARBON CYCLE

animal respiration

atmospheric carbon dioxide

photosynthesis

exchange of CO_2 between atmosphere and water

plant respiration

burning

decay

decay

carbon compounds

Integrated Coordinated Science for the 21st Century

Reflecting on the Activity and the Challenge

In this activity you learned that carbon is the key element in all organic matter. You investigated the process of photosynthesis and then related this process to respiration in the carbon-oxygen cycle. The cycling of matter like carbon is essential to the survival of any ecosystem. You will need to explain this cycle in your booklet.

1. Explain why photosynthesis and cellular respiration are considered to be paired processes.

2. What is the importance of decomposers in the carbon cycle?

3. What effect does the burning of fossil fuels have on the carbon cycle?

4. Scientists have expressed concerns about the burning of the rainforests to clear the land for the planting of crops.

    a) Explain how the burning of the forests could change oxygen levels.

    b) What impact would the change in oxygen levels have on living things?

Inquiring Further

The greenhouse effect

The term greenhouse effect was coined in the 1930s to describe the heat-blocking action of atmospheric gases. Research and report the connection between the greenhouse effect and the carbon cycle.

Activity 9   The Nitrogen and Phosphorous Cycles

GOALS

In this activity you will:

- Investigate the chemicals that promote and inhibit the growth of plant material.

- Explain the importance of nitrogen and phosphorous to organisms.

- Describe how nitrogen cycles in an ecosystem.

- Describe how phosphorous cycles in an ecosystem.

- Provide examples of how human activities can affect the nitrogen cycle.

What Do You Think?

Nitrogen is essential to all forms of life. Yet, recent studies have shown that excess nitrogen has been introduced into our ecosystems. It has had negative effects on the natural nitrogen cycle.

- What are the sources of the excess nitrogen?

- What are some of the negative effects of too much nitrogen?

Write your answer to these questions in your *Active Biology* log. Be prepared to discuss your ideas with your small group and other members of your class.

For You To Do

An excessive growth of algae (algal blooms) can make a lake very unappealing. More importantly, it places other organisms in the ecosystem in peril through lack of oxygen. In this activity you will investigate some of the chemicals that promote the growth of algae.

567

Handle all of the liquids and chemicals very carefully. They should all be considered contaminated and toxic. Keep hands away from eyes and mouth during the activity. Wash your hands well after the activity. Clean up any spills immediately.

1. Obtain three 1-L jars. Make sure the jars are rinsed thoroughly, so that there are no leftover traces of any chemicals, including soap. Fill each jar about three-fourths full with distilled water.

   a) Why is it important that the jars be cleaned before beginning this activity?

2. To each jar add a 10-mL sample of pond water. Stir the pond water thoroughly before taking the sample. The pond water will contain algae.

3. Label the jars A through C.

4. To each jar add the following:
   • To Jar A, add 15 gm of detergent.
   • To Jar B, add 15 gm of lawn fertilizer.
   • Do not add anything to Jar C.

   a) Many detergents contain phosphates. Fertilizers contain nitrogen and phosphates. Write as a question what you are investigating in this activity.

   b) What is the purpose of Jar C?

5. Cover each jar with plastic wrap so that dirt will not settle into the jar, but allow for some air to enter the jar.

6. Use a glass marker to mark the water level in each jar.

7. Set all the jars in a well-lighted place, but not in direct sunlight.

   a) Predict in which jar the algal growth will be the greatest? The least? Give reasons for your predictions.

8. Observe the jars each day for about two weeks. As water evaporates from the jars, add distilled water to bring the water back up to its original level. At the end of two weeks, you will pass the water in each jar through a separate filter.

   a) Record your observations every two or three days.

9. Find the mass of each of three pieces of filter paper.

   a) Record the mass of each in a table.

10. Fold the filter paper as shown and insert it into a funnel. Place the funnel in the mouth of another jar to collect the filtrate (the liquid that passes through the filter).

    Filter the liquid in each of the three jars.

11. Allow the filter papers and the algae residue to dry thoroughly.

    Find the mass of each piece of filter paper and algae. Calculate the mass of the algae.

    a) Record your findings in a table.

    b) Did your findings support your predictions? Explain any differences you found.

Be very careful with the liquid and the algae residue. You should assume that disease organisms have grown in the water during the activity. Be very careful to avoid ingesting any of the water or residue. Dispose of all materials as directed by your teacher when finished.

Place folded filter paper in funnel and soak with water.

Bio Talk

THE NITROGEN CYCLE

Nitrogen Fixation

Nitrogen is a basic building block of plant and animal proteins. It is a nutrient essential to all forms of life. Nitrogen is also required to make deoxyribonucleic acid or DNA. DNA is the hereditary material found in all living things. The movement of nitrogen through ecosystems, the soil, and the atmosphere is called the **nitrogen cycle**. Like carbon, nitrogen moves in a cycle through ecosystems. It passes through food chains and from living things to their environment and back again. Life depends on the cycling of nitrogen.

The largest single source of nitrogen is the atmosphere. It is made up of 78 percent of this colorless, odorless, nontoxic gas. With this much nitrogen available, you would think organisms would have no difficulty getting nitrogen. Unfortunately, this is not the case. Nitrogen gas is a very stable molecule. It reacts only under limited conditions. In order to be useful to organisms, nitrogen must be supplied in another form, the nitrate ion (NO_3-).

Bio Words

nitrogen cycle: the movement of nitrogen through ecosystems, the soil, and the atmosphere

nitrogen fixation: the process by which certain organisms produce nitrogen compounds from the gaseous nitrogen in the atmosphere

Three processes are responsible for most of the nitrogen fixation in the biosphere: atmospheric fixation by lightning, biological fixation by certain microbes, and industrial fixation. The enormous energy of lightning breaks nitrogen molecules apart. Only about five percent of the nitrates produced by nitrogen fixation are produced by lightning.

The nitrogen cycle is very complex. A simplified description is shown in the diagram on the next page. There are two ways in which atmospheric nitrogen can be converted into nitrates. The first method is lightning, and the second is bacteria in the soil. The process of converting nitrogen into nitrates is called **nitrogen fixation**.

A small amount of nitrogen is fixed into nitrates by lightning. The energy from lightning causes nitrogen gas to react with oxygen in the air, producing nitrates. The nitrates dissolve in rain, falling to Earth and forming surface water.

Integrated Coordinated Science for the 21st Century

The nitrates enter the soil and then move into plants through their roots. Plant cells can use nitrates to make DNA, and they can convert nitrates into amino acids, which they then string together to make proteins. When a plant is consumed by an animal, the animal breaks down the plant proteins into amino acids. The animal can then use the amino acids to make the proteins it needs.

Some bacteria are capable of fixing nitrogen. These bacteria provide the vast majority of nitrates found in ecosystems. They are found mostly in soil, and in small lumps called nodules on the roots of legumes such as clover, soybeans, peas, and alfalfa. The bacteria provide the plant with a built-in supply of usable nitrogen, while the plant

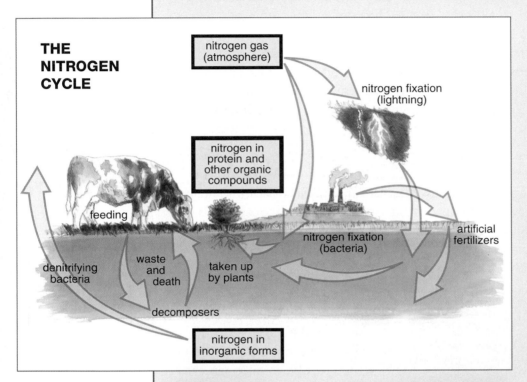

THE NITROGEN CYCLE

nitrogen gas (atmosphere)

nitrogen fixation (lightning)

nitrogen in protein and other organic compounds

artificial fertilizers

feeding

nitrogen fixation (bacteria)

denitrifying bacteria

waste and death

taken up by plants

decomposers

nitrogen in inorganic forms

The most familiar examples of biotic nitrogen fixing are the root nodules of legumes, plants like peas, beans, and clover.

supplies the nitrogen-fixing bacteria with the sugar they need to make the nitrates. This plant-bacteria combination usually makes much more nitrate than the plant or bacteria need. The excess moves into the soil, providing a source of nitrogen for other plants. The traditional agricultural practices of rotating crops and mixed plantings of crops, one of which is always a legume, capitalizes on bacterial nitrogen fixation.

All organisms produce wastes and eventually die. When they do, decomposers break down the nitrogen-containing chemicals in the waste or body into simpler chemicals such as ammonia (NH_3). Other bacteria convert ammonia into nitrites, and still others convert the nitrites back to nitrates. These bacteria all require oxygen to function. The nitrates then continue the cycle when they are absorbed by plant roots and converted into cell proteins and DNA.

Farmers and gardeners who use manure and other decaying matter take advantage of the nitrogen cycle. Soil bacteria convert the decomposing protein in the manure into nitrates. Eventually, the nitrates are absorbed by plants.

Denitrification

At various stages in the decay process, denitrifying bacteria can break down nitrates to nitrites, and then nitrites to nitrogen gas. Eventually, the nitrogen gas is released back into the atmosphere. This process

A gardening magazine stated, "grass can actually poison itself as a result of the various chemical processes that occur in the individual grass plants if the grass roots do not have enough air." To what "poison" is the magazine referring?

Bio Words

denitrification: the conversion of nitrates and nitrites to nitrogen gas, which is released into the atmosphere

phosphorous cycle: the cycling of environmental phosphorous through a long-term cycle involving rocks on the Earth's crust, and through a shorter cycle involving living organisms

is called **denitrification**, and is carried out by bacteria that do not require oxygen. Denitrification ensures the balance between soil nitrates, nitrites, and atmospheric nitrogen, and completes the nitrogen cycle.

Older lawns often have many denitrifying bacteria. The fact that denitrifying bacteria grow best where there is no oxygen may help explain why people often aerate their lawns in early spring. By exposing the denitrifying bacteria to oxygen, the breakdown of nitrates to nitrogen gas is reduced. Nitrates will then remain in the soil, and can be used by the grass to make proteins.

THE PHOSPHOROUS CYCLE

The **phosphorous cycle** is different from the water, carbon, and nitrogen cycles because phosphorous is not found in the atmosphere. Phosphorous is a necessary element in DNA, in many molecules found in living cells, and in the bones of vertebrate animals. Phosphorous tends to cycle in two ways: a long-term cycle involving the rocks of the Earth's crust, and a short-term cycle involving living organisms.

In the long cycle living things divert phosphates from the normal rock cycle. Phosphorous is found in bedrock in the form of

THE PHOSPHOROUS CYCLE

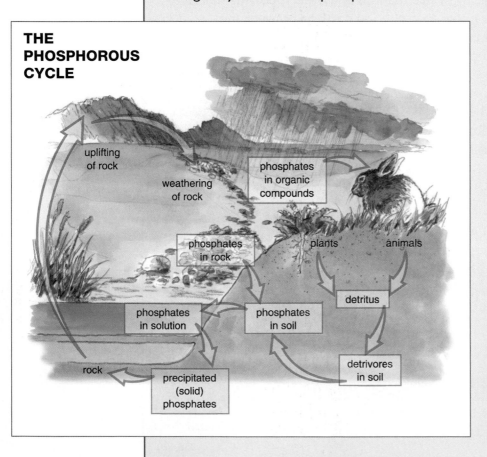

uplifting of rock

weathering of rock

phosphates in organic compounds

phosphates in rock

plants

animals

detritus

phosphates in solution

phosphates in soil

detrivores in soil

rock

precipitated (solid) phosphates

phosphate ions combined with a variety of elements. Phosphates are soluble in water and so can be drawn out of rock as part of the water cycle. Dissolved, phosphates can be absorbed by photosynthetic organisms and so pass into food chains. Phosphates eroded from rock are also carried by water from the land to rivers, and then to the oceans. In the ocean phosphates are absorbed by algae and other plants, where they can enter food chains. Animals use phosphates to make bones and shells. When they die, these hard remains form deposits on the ocean floor. Covered with sediment, the deposits eventually become rock, ready to be brought to the surface again. The cycle can take millions of years to complete. In the short cycle, wastes from living things are recycled by decomposers, which break down wastes and dead tissue and release the phosphates. The short cycle is much more rapid.

AGRICULTURE AND THE NITROGEN AND PHOSPHOROUS CYCLES

The seeds, leaves, flowers, and fruits of plants all contain valuable nutrients, which is why we eat them. However, as crops are harvested, the valuable nitrogen and phosphorous in these plant body parts are removed and do not return to the field or orchard they came from. This diversion of nitrates and phosphate from their cycles would soon deplete the soil unless the farmer replaced the missing nutrients. **Fertilizers** are materials used to restore nutrients and increase production from land. In this activity you investigated the effect fertilizer had on the growth of algae. Some estimates suggest that fertilizers containing nitrogen and phosphates can as much as double yields of cereal crops such as wheat and barley. However, fertilizers must be used responsibly. More is not necessarily better.

The accumulation of nitrogen and phosphate fertilizers produces an environmental problem. As spring runoff carries decaying plant matter and fertilizer-rich soil to streams and then lakes, the nutrients allow aquatic plants to grow more rapidly in what is called an algal bloom. When the plants die, bacteria use oxygen from the water to decompose them. Because decomposers flourish in an environment

Bio Words

fertilizer: a material used to provide or replace soil nutrients

Algae are generally thought of as simple, aquatic plants that do not have roots, stems, or leaves. A recurring problem in many bodies of water is algal bloom. An algal bloom is an abnormal increase of algae in a body of water. The most serious algal blooms are associated with human activities. Algal blooms deplete the water of oxygen and nutrients. In turn, this can kill other species in the water.

with such an abundant food source, oxygen levels in lakes drop quickly, so fish and other animals may begin to die. Dying animals can only make the problem worse, as decomposers begin to recycle the matter from the dead fish, allowing the populations of bacteria to grow even larger, and use still more oxygen.

Reflecting on the Activity and the Challenge

You have now investigated how several different types of matter cycle through ecosystems. You have also had an opportunity to learn about how humans can influence any one of these cycles. Consider how you will describe the importance of each of these cycles to the public. Also, consider whether or not the environmental issue that you have chosen deals specifically with one of these cycles. You will need to examine if any solution you provide will create a problem in any one of these cycles.

Biology to Go

1. Why is nitrogen important to organisms?

2. If plants cannot use the nitrogen in the atmosphere, how do they obtain the nitrogen they need?

3. How do animals obtain their usable nitrogen?

4. Explain why it is a good practice to aerate lawns.

5. Why is phosphorous important to living things?

6. With each harvest, nitrogen is removed from the soil. Farmers have traditionally rotated crops. Wheat, planted one year, is often followed by legumes planted the following year. Because the legumes contain nitrogen-fixing bacteria, nitrogen levels are replenished. The use of nitrogen-rich fertilizers has allowed farmers to not use crop rotation.

    a) What advantages are gained from planting wheat year after year?

    b) New strains of crops have been especially bred to take up high levels of nitrogen and harvests have increased dramatically. Speculate about some possible long-term disadvantages that these crops might present for ecosystems.

7. Before municipal sewers, the backyard outhouse was standard behind homes. They can still be found in some areas. To make an outhouse, a hole was dug in the ground to collect human wastes. Explain why the outhouse poses a risk to neighboring lakes, using information that you have gained about the nitrogen cycle.

Inquiring Further

1. The "new-tank syndrome"

Research to find out what is meant by the "new-tank" syndrome. How is it related to the nitrogen cycle?

2. Too much of a good thing

Which human activities impact on the nitrogen cycle? Choose one and explain how the impact of this activity on the environment could be reduced.

Biology at Work

Christy Todd Whitman

No person on the planet is more qualified to speak about the relationship between politics and environmental issues than Christy Todd Whitman. Whitman, 57, served as Governor of New Jersey from 1993 to 2000 and as the head of the Environmental Protection Agency from 2001 to 2003.

"Growing up on a farm I loved the outdoors. I loved to fish and swim and boat and bike and hike," Whitman says. "After seeing what happened as farms started to develop I got a real sense of the importance of protecting the environment."

Studying international government at Wheaton College in Massachusetts was also a natural extension of her curiosities as a child. "No matter what you're interested in—science or the arts or education—government impacts it in some way so I got interested in politics at an early age."

Whitman's work while EPA administrator forced her to deal with issues on a national level. She says that one of her biggest challenges was to educate the country–both individuals and corporate America–about the perils of ignoring the environment.

"A lot of the issues are very basic and we tried a lot of outreach programs. It's important to explain to people that everything you do has consequences, good and bad. For instance, we all live in a watershed so if you throw something out the window—a cigarette for example—that has an effect. If you change your oil in driveway or over-fertilize your lawn, it all will eventually wash down after a heavy rain. We found that every eight months there is as much oil deposited along the coastline from our everyday activities as was released for the Exxon Valdez spill. So what we're tying to get people to understand is that it

does matter what they do. Everything is cumulative."

And that includes big business. Although, Whitman is careful to point out that economic development does not have to be mutually exclusive to environmental protection.

"When you hear environmentalists yelling about business being bad for the planet or big corporations saying that they can't be profitable and environmentally conscious–you know that neither of those are true. You can have a cleaner, healthier environment, and a thriving economy. In fact, the environment needs the money produced by a healthy economy to invest in new technology. And there isn't a country in the world or a municipality or state in the world that is going to thrive economically if their environment is not good and healthy for the people who live there." Her solution? Incentives. The theory being that if you entice industries to develop environmentally sustainable practices, everybody wins.

Regardless of the fact that she is no longer head of the nations largest environmental group or governor of the 9th most populated state in the union, Whitman is still working to educate the public in an attempt to protect the planet's natural resources. "I am very proud of programs like Energy Star, which identifies energy efficient products such as washing machines, DVD players and other technologies to consumers," Whitman says. "In 2002, purchases from Energy Star saved consumers $7 billion and greenhouse gas emissions equivalent to the removal of 15 million cars from the road." And those are the kind of environmental impact numbers every politician would brag about.

Chapter 10

A HIGHWAY THROUGH THE PAST

10

A Highway Through The Past

Scenario

After much study, the State Department of Transportation decided that a stretch of road was needed to connect two very busy state highways. The study had included environmental assessment of the area that the road would be covering. Much to the frustration of the local people, this study had taken over a year to complete.

Now, by state law, before any road construction could begin paleontologists (scientists who study past life) from the state university had been given six months to study the land that would be covered by the new road. The local residents who would use this new road were very upset because of this further delay of six months. They were even more upset when they found out that the findings of the paleontologists would delay the road construction longer than six months, and maybe even indefinitely.

Chapter Challenge

The State Department of Transportation has concluded that in order to allow area residents a chance to express their views, a town-hall meeting should be held to discuss the issue. At this meeting, the paleontologists would also be given an opportunity to provide their findings and explain why they have asked for a delay or even an indefinite postponement of the construction. For your challenge, you may be asked to represent someone who is against building the road, someone who is for building the road, or one of the group of paleontologists. Or, you may be asked to represent a member of one of the levels of government involved in this project to explain why it is necessary to have all these studies

and subsequent delays. Your teacher will act as the chairperson. As you prepare for and participate in role-playing a town meeting, you will be expected to:

- explain why fossils are important;

- describe how the age of a fossil can be determined;

- indicate how a highway might impact on the natural-selection process of the living organisms in the area;

- explain why a great diversity of species is important for the survival of a community.

Criteria

How will your performance at the meeting be graded? Keep in mind that not everyone will be arguing every side of the issue. It is very important that you decide before the work begins how each person will be graded. Discuss this with your small group and then with your class. You may decide some or all of the following qualities are important:

- completeness and accuracy of the science principles presented in your side of the argument;

- accuracy of the science principles used to dispute your opponents' positions;

- forcefulness or conviction with which you present your argument;

- quality of questions you pose to the government officials.

Once you have determined the criteria that you wish to use, you will need to decide on how many points should be given to each criterion. Your teacher may wish to provide you with a sample rubric to help you get started.

Activity 1

Adaptations

GOALS

In this activity you will:

- Explain the meaning of adaptation.
- Speculate how adaptations help an organism survive in their environment.
- Distinguish between structural and behavioral adaptations.

What Do You Think?

Imagine surviving a temperature of −50°C and a blinding snowstorm. Imagine surviving a temperature of 50°C in an extremely dry landscape.

- How are plants and animals that live daily in these environments adapted for survival?

Write your answer to this question in your *Active Biology* log. Be prepared to discuss your ideas with your small group and other members of your class.

For You To Do

Part A: Observing Adaptations

An adaptation is an inherited trait or set of traits that improve the chances of survival and reproduction of organisms. In this part of the activity you will look at photographs of animals to observe and speculate about how the different types of adaptations help the organism survive.

1. Look closely at the following photographs. There is a living organism in each picture.

   a) Which organisms are exhibiting camouflage?

   b) How could this adaptation help an organism in capturing prey?

c) How could this adaptation help protect the organism from predators?

d) What other animals can you think of that use this type of adaptation for protection?

2. Some animals are not adapted to disappear into the background, but rather stand out.

Alligator.

Praying Mantis.

Snowshoe hare.

Chameleon.

Integrated Coordinated Science for the 21st Century

Hawk moth.

Hawk-moth
caterpillar.

Monarch butterfly.

Viceroy butterfly.

Look at the photographs of the hawk moth and caterpillar.

   a) At first glance, of what animal does each remind you?

   b) Why would birds avoid an animal with large eyes at the front?

   c) What advantage does this adaptation present for the moth and caterpillar?

3. A monarch butterfly stores bad-tasting chemicals in its body that birds hate. The viceroy butterfly also has a bitter taste.

   a) The monarch butterfly is brightly colored. Why do you think that this would be an advantage for the monarch butterfly?

   b) Would the bright colors and bitter taste protect all monarch butterflies? Explain your answer.

   c) Compare the appearance of the monarch and viceroy butterflies. Can you distinguish between them?

   d) How would the viceroy butterfly's coloration be an advantage for its survival?

4. Adaptations are not limited to animals. Look closely at the plants or plant parts shown on the next page for their adaptations to the environment.

a) For each plant shown above, explain the adaptation(s) that you can see. Consider the environment in which the plants live, how they reproduce, and how they get their nutrients when identifying adaptations.

5. Not all adaptations need to be structural. Some adaptations can be behavioral.

a) How is each animal in the photographs adapted to a change in the environmental conditions from summer to winter?

b) How do other animals adapt to an environmental change? Give at least two examples.

c) What type of behavioral adaptation is the plant at right exhibiting?

6. Invent an organism with specific adaptations. Consider one of the following:
   - camouflage
   - mimicry
   - warning coloration

Part B: How Well Adapted Are You?

In this part of the activity you will have an opportunity to examine one of your own adaptations that you probably take for granted.

1. Using masking tape, have your partner tape your thumb to your index finger on each hand. After your thumbs are securely taped, try each of the following activities. Rank the difficulty of each activity on a scale of 1 to 5.
   - picking up and carrying your textbook;

- writing your name and address on a piece of paper;
- picking up five coins from the floor and placing them in your pocket;
- unbuttoning and buttoning a button;
- tying up a shoe.

a) Did you find any of the activities impossible?

b) How did your ratings compare with others in your group and in your class?

c) Why do you think that an opposable thumb is an important adaptation for humans? (An opposable thumb is an arrangement in which the fleshy tip of the thumb can touch the fleshy tip of all the fingers.)

d) Do any other animals have opposable thumbs?

Adaptation

Bio Words

species: a group of organisms that can interbreed under natural conditions and produce fertile offspring

adaptation: an inherited trait or set of traits that improve the chance of survival and reproduction of an organism

Diversity is a striking feature of living organisms. There are countless types of organisms on Earth. They are the result of repeated formation of new **species** and adaptation. There is a type of organism that can live in almost every type of environment on Earth. Living organisms are unique in their ability to adapt. The accumulation of characteristics that improve a species' ability to survive and reproduce is called **adaptation**. Adaptation occurs over long time periods. It is the environment that "selects" the best and most useful inherited variations. In this activity you observed just a few of the large number of adaptations that exist.

Animals Adapt to the Demands of Their Environments

Animals cannot make their own food. Therefore, they must usually seek food. As a result, adaptations that allow animals to move are favorable. Movement is easier if the organism is elongated in the direction of movement. Fish, for example, are streamlined. This reduces water resistance as they swim. It is also easier to move if the sensory organs are concentrated in the head. The organs that detect food, light, and other stimuli should be in a position to meet the environment first. An organism can move more easily if it has a balanced body.

Animals have the type of body plan that is best suited to their lifestyle. The symmetry of an organism gives clues to its complexity and evolutionary development. Higher animals, including humans, are symmetrical along the mid-sagittal plane. This body plan is referred to as **bilateral symmetry**, in which the right and left halves of the organism are mirror images of each other. Some animals, however, are **radially symmetric**, or symmetric about a central axis.

How is body symmetry related to the speed at which an animal moves and to brain development? In general, animals that display radial symmetry are not highly adapted for movement. One explanation for the slower movement can be traced to the fact that no one region always leads. Only bilaterally symmetrical animals have a true head region. Because the head, or anterior region, always enters a new environment first, nerve cells tend to concentrate in this area. The concentration of

Bio Words

bilateral symmetry: a body plan that divides the body into symmetrical left and right halves

radial symmetry: a body plan that is symmetrical about a center axis

BODY SYMMETRY

radial symmetry

bilateral symmetry

anterior   posterior

ventral

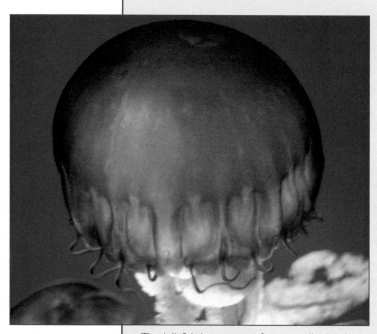

The jellyfish is a group of structurally simple marine organisms. The jellyfish has no head and a nervous system without a brain. The body exhibits radial symmetry.

nerve tissue at the anterior end of an animal's body, is an adaptation that enables the rapid processing of stimuli such as food or danger. Not surprisingly, the faster the animal moves, the more important is the immediate processing of environmental information. Every environment places special demands on the organisms living there. Seawater is fairly uniform. It poses the least stress for animal life. Oxygen is usually adequate. The temperatures and salt content are fairly constant. There is little danger that the organism will dry up. In contrast, the salt and oxygen contents of fresh water vary greatly.

Organisms that live in water have special adaptations. Gills, for example, allow the organisms to use the oxygen found in water. On land, oxygen is plentiful. However, the organisms that live there must protect themselves from the dangers of drying up. These dangers increase greatly because air temperatures change daily and seasonally. Air does not provide the same buoyancy as water. Therefore, large terrestrial, or land-dwelling, animals require good supportive structures. On the other hand, there is less resistance to movement in air than in water. Arms and legs, which would hinder an animal's movement in water, may help on land. Thus, long appendages specialized for locomotion have evolved in terrestrial animals.

Plant Adaptations

Plants lack the ability to move and must survive in the environment in which they are living. A plant must do more than simply survive and grow bigger. It must grow in such a way that it can take the best advantage of the light, water, and other conditions available to it.

Desert plants are an excellent example of adaptation to an environment. Some have a thick waxy coating to prevent them from drying out. Some have long vertical roots enabling a plant to reach water sources beneath the soil. Others develop shallow roots that extend horizontally. This maximizes water absorption at the surface. Many desert plants have small and narrow leaves. This decreases the heating from the Sun.

Even though plants are not able to move, they are still able to disperse. They produce seeds and fruits or other reproductive structures that may be distributed far from the parent plant.

Some plant adaptations are also behavioral. A vine spreads its leaves outward and receives as much light energy as possible. It sends its roots downward and receives more water. Tendrils of a vine touch an object and quickly coil it. This secures the vine in its upward growth. A vine would not live very long if it did not send its roots downward and its stem upward. The manner of plant growth is believed to be governed chiefly by hormones that are produced within the plant. The hormones are produced in response to conditions around the plant such as sunlight and gravity. Thus, the plant can fit itself to the environment in which it lives.

Some plants have even become adapted to feeding on animals. In this activity you looked at the Venus flytrap. Its leaves have been adapted to capture prey. These plants do photosynthesize. However, these plants live in bogs where there is very little nitrogen available. Therefore, they require the nutrients they receive from digesting their prey. Of course, the plant must therefore also be adapted to digest its prey with the secretion of chemicals.

Tendrils are modified stems or leaves that wrap around a support. They enable the plant to achieve fairly extensive horizontal and vertical spread without the use of much energy, since they don't have to support their own weight. Tendrils seem to respond to touch so if the stem or tendril touches an object, it wraps around it. This response is known as thigmotropism.

Reflecting on the Activity and the Challenge

In this activity you had an opportunity to look at adaptations of different organisms. You learned that every environment places various demands on the organisms living there. Organisms have developed special adaptations for living in any given environment. The animals and plants in the area of the highway construction have also adapted to their environment. In an environmental study scientists would have assessed the impact the highway would have had on the animals and plants. You may need to address this issue in the town-hall meeting if you are representing a government employee.

1. Explain the term adaptation.

2. Distinguish between a structural and a behavioral adaptation.

3. a) How can an animal's structure help it survive in different environments? Give three examples.

   b) How can an animal's behavior help it survive in different environments? Give three examples.

4. Do all animals living in the same environment have similar adaptations? Explain your answer.

5. A cross section represents a cut through the middle of an animal's body. Below are cross sections through an earthworm, sand worm, and a primitive insect.

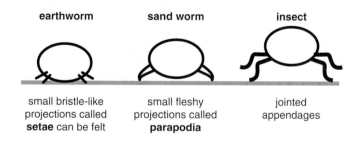

earthworm	sand worm	insect
small bristle-like projections called **setae** can be felt	small fleshy projections called **parapodia**	jointed appendages

   a) The jointed appendages of the insect lift the body from the ground. How does this help the insect move?

   b) What advantages might the fleshy projections of the sand worm have over the bristle-like projections of the earthworm?

   c) Predict which animal would be the fastest and give your reasons.

Inquiring Further

1. Animal adaptations to the arctic

Keeping warm is no easy task in the arctic where frigid weather lasts almost nine months of the year and where temperatures can plunge to −55°C. Even during the brief summer, when the land thaws and the Sun never sets, a sudden snowstorm can freeze everything. What adaptation have animals that live in this region developed?

2. Animal adaptations to the desert

Lack of water creates a survival problem for all desert organisms. However, animals have an additional problem. The biological processes of animal tissue can function only within a relatively narrow temperature range. Fortunately, most desert animals have evolved both behavioral and structural adaptations. Research the adaptations of animals living in desert regions.

Seals are well adapted to a cold environment. Their slick fur sheds water, and a thick layer of blubber beneath the skin keeps them warm in frigid temperatures.

The desert tortoise retreats to its burrow during the hottest times of the summer days. In the cold of winter it hibernates in its underground burrow.

Activity 2

Is It Heredity or the Environment?

GOALS

In this activity you will:

- Observe how an inherited trait can be influenced by the environment.
- Distinguish between a genotype and a phenotype.
- Explain how the environment can influence the development of an inherited characteristic.

What Do You Think?

"You've got your mother's hair and your father's eyes." Almost everyone has heard about heredity at some point.

- How are personal characteristics passed on from one generation to the next?
- Can a personal characteristic be changed?

Write your answer to these questions in your *Active Biology* log. Be prepared to discuss your ideas with your small group and other members of your class.

For You To Do

In this activity you will use tobacco seeds from parents that carried the characteristics for albinism (no chlorophyll) but did not show it. Your observations will help you to understand that traits are inherited but are also influenced by the environment.

3. Cover two dishes with a lightproof container.

4. Leave the other two dishes exposed to the light.

5. Let the seeds germinate for about a week, adding a few drops of water to the paper every other day or whenever the paper begins to dry.

6. On the tenth day, begin to make entries in your table of results.

   a) Make up tables on which to record your results. You may wish to use tables similar to the ones shown on the next page.

   b) Every day, record how many and what kind of seedlings you observe.

7. When all or most of the seeds have germinated in the darkened dishes (probably the twelfth day) remove the covering. Place these dishes in the light next to the others.

   a) Continue to record the appearance of the seedlings through the thirteenth day.

8. Study all the data you have accumulated.

   a) Try to draw any conclusions that you can from your data.

9. Using your data for the seedlings that were kept in the light all the time, answer the following questions:

   a) How might you explain the differences you observed?

   b) Are these differences caused by heredity or environment?

1. Place blotting paper in the bottom of each of four Petri dishes. Moisten the paper, but be sure that it is not floating in water. Sprinkle about 40 tobacco seeds evenly over the surface of the paper. Keep the seeds a few seed lengths apart from each other.

2. Replace the covers of the dishes and place the dishes in a well-lighted place, but not in the direct sunlight. The temperature should be approximately 22°C.

 Wash your hands after handling the seeds. If mold forms in the dish, have your teacher dispose of the affected seeds.

Kinds of Leaves from Germinating Tobacco Leaves
(Dishes Continuously Exposed to Light)

	Albino	Green	Percentage of albino each day
10th day			
11th day			
12th day			
13th day			

Kinds of Leaves from Germinating Tobacco Leaves
(Darkened Dishes)

	Albino	Green	Percentage of albino each day
10th day			
11th day			

Kinds of Leaves from Germinating Tobacco Leaves
(Covering Removed from Darkened Dishes)

	Albino	Green	Percentage of albino each day
12th day			
13th day			

10. Consider the seedlings that were kept in darkened dishes.

   a) How do the percentages of albino and green seedlings compare with the percentages of albino and green seedlings that were continuously exposed to light?

   b) What is the environmental factor that is varied in this activity?

   c) Is this difference in percentages of seedlings kept in the light and seedlings kept in the dark due to inherited or environmental factors?

   d) What do you think is causing the differences in the appearance of the seedlings that were in darkened dishes?

11. Consider the seedlings that were first in darkened dishes and then exposed to light.

   a) How do the percentages of green and albino seedlings compare with the percentages of green and albino seedlings in the other situations?

   b) What happened to the appearance of many of the seedlings after the cover was removed?

   c) Does this support your answer to **Step 10 (d)**?

   d) What are the effects of light upon seedlings that carry a certain hereditary characteristic?

Bio Talk

The Importance of Heredity and Environment

Why do offspring resemble their parents? Genetics, a branch of biology, tries to answer these types of questions about inheritance. Geneticists have found that most aspects of life have a hereditary basis. Many traits can appear in more than one form. A **trait** is some aspect of an organism that can be described or measured. For example, human beings may have blond, red, brown, or black hair. They may have tongues that they can roll or not roll. (Try it! Can you roll your tongue? Can your parents?) They may have earlobes that are attached or free. The passing of traits from parents to offspring is called **heredity**.

In *most* organisms, including humans, genetic information is transmitted from one generation to the next by deoxyribonucleic acid (DNA). DNA makes up the **genes** that transmit hereditary traits. Each gene in the body is a DNA section with a full set of instructions. These instructions guide the formation of a particular protein. The different proteins made by the genes direct a body's function and structure throughout life. **Chromosomes** carry the genes. They provide the genetic link between generations. The number of chromosomes in a cell is characteristic of the species. Some have very few, whereas others may have more than a hundred. You inherit half of your chromosomes from your mother and the other half from your father. Therefore, your traits are a result of the interactions of the genes of both your parents.

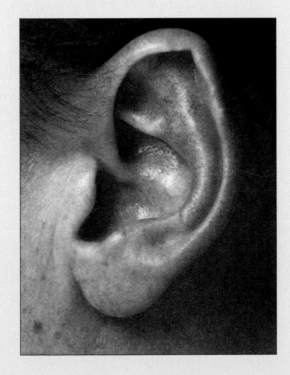

Bio Words

trait: an aspect of an organism that can be described or measured

heredity: the passing of traits from parent to offspring

gene: a unit of instruction located on a chromosome that produces or influences a specific trait in the offspring

chromosome: threads of genetic material found in the nucleus of cells

→

Bio Words

dominant: used to describe the gene that determines the expression of a genetic trait; the trait shows up

recessive: used to describe the gene that is overruled by a dominant gene; the trait is masked

genotype: the genes of an individual

phenotype: the observable traits of an organism that result because of the interaction of genes and the environment

Gregor Mendel was the first person to trace the characteristics of successive generations of a living organism. He was an Augustinian monk who taught natural science to high school students. His origins were humble. However, his work was so brilliant that it took many years for the rest of the scientific community to catch up to it.

The modern science of genetics started with the work of Gregor Mendel. He found that certain factors in a plant cell determined the traits a plant would have. Thirty years after his discovery these factors were given the name genes. Of the traits that Mendel studied, he found that one factor, or gene, could mask the effect of another. This is the principle of dominance. He called the factor that showed up in the offspring **dominant**, and the factor that was masked **recessive**.

Genotype refers to the genes that an organism contains for a particular trait. The **phenotype** is the observable traits of an individual. Phenotype is a product of the interaction between the genotype and the environment.

All genes interact with the environment. Sometimes it is difficult to tell how much of a phenotype is determined by heredity and how much is influenced by the environment. A familiar example of how the environment affects the phenotype is the coloring of Siamese cats. The cats have a genotype for dark fur. However, the special proteins (enzymes) that produce the dark color work best at low temperatures. That is why Siamese cats have dark markings on their ears, nose, paws, and tail. These are all areas that have a low body temperature. Suppose a Siamese cat's tail were shaved and then kept at a higher than normal temperature. It would soon be covered with light-colored fur. However, these changes are temporary and only present if the environmental conditions are met. There are other examples of the influence of the environment on a phenotype. For a fair-skinned person, exposure to sunlight may produce hair that has lightened and a face full of freckles. Primrose plants are red if they are raised at room temperature, but white if they are raised at temperatures about 30°C. Himalayan rabbits are black when raised at low temperatures and white when raised at high temperatures.

The Siamese is a cat in which color is restricted to the points, i.e., nose, ears, legs, and tail. This is known as the Himalayan pattern. This coloration is a result of both hereditary and environmental factors.

Reflecting on the Activity and the Challenge

In this activity you saw that both heredity and environment contribute to the expression of a trait in a plant. You then read about how this also applies to animals. When thinking about how organisms are able to adapt, you must consider both inherited characteristics as well as the influence that the environment has on the organism. You will need to understand this for your **Chapter Challenge**. Also, in the next activity, you will investigate natural selection. Heredity and the environment both play a role in natural selection.

595

Biology to Go

1. Distinguish between a genotype and a phenotype.

2. What is the difference between a dominant and a recessive gene?

3. A dominant gene for a specific trait is inherited along with a non-dominant gene for the same trait. Which gene's "building instructions" will be used to assemble the specific protein?

4. In guinea pigs black coat is dominant to white. Is it possible for a black guinea pig to give birth to a white guinea pig? Explain your answer.

5. Explain how both heredity and environment contribute to the expression of a trait in plants.

6. Review your observations from the activity. Comment on the following statement: heredity can determine what an organism *may* become, not what it *will* become.

7. Can the environment change the development of an inherited characteristic? Use your observations from this activity to justify your answer.

Inquiring Further

1. Analyzing a genetic condition

What is a genetic condition? Choose a condition from one of the more well-known conditions, such as achondroplasia, cystic fibrosis, hemophilia, Huntington's chorea, Marfan syndrome, dwarfism, Down syndrome, Fragile-X syndrome, Tay-Sachs disease, sickle cell anemia, neurofibromatosis, etc. You may wish to investigate a condition with which you are personally familiar. Construct a hypothetical family tree to do a pedigree analysis of the condition. (A pedigree is used to trace inheritance of a trait over several generations.)

Down syndrome is caused by abnormal cell division in the egg, sperm, or fertilized egg. This results in an extra or irregular chromosome in some or all of the body's cells.

Activity 3   Natural Selection

GOALS

In this activity you will:

- Investigate the process of natural selection.

- Describe the major factors causing evolutionary change.

- Distinguish between the accommodation of an individual to its environment and gradual adaptation of a species.

- Read about the meaning of a theory in science.

What Do You Think?

One hundred rabbits were trapped and introduced to an island with a huge diversity of plants. The rabbits had several noticeable variations. Thirty years later scientists returned to the island. They were amazed that although the number of rabbits was still around 100, the later generations did not vary as much as the earlier rabbits had.

- What happened to the variations that were evident in the original species?

- How would you explain why the variations seemed to have disappeared?

Write your answer to these questions in your *Active Biology* log. Be prepared to discuss your ideas with your small group and other members of your class.

For You To Do

In this part of the activity you will study the process of natural selection. You will work with a hypothetical population of organisms in a hypothetical environment.

You will use a sheet of newspaper as the environment. You will use paper squares to represent individual prey. You will be given a chance to capture five prey individuals. The remaining prey will reproduce. You will then have another chance to capture the prey.

Part A: Predator and Prey

1. Work in groups of four. One student (the keeper) sets up the environment before each round (generation). The other three in the group act as "predators." They remove prey from the environment.

2. Lay a sheet of newspaper flat on a table or floor.

3. Take at least 50 each of newspaper, white, and red paper squares (150 squares). Keep the three types separate, as each represents a different type of the *same* prey species. Some are brightly colored. The others are not. An example of such different populations is the species *Canis familiaris*, the common dog. Although dogs come in many different colors and sizes, they all belong to the same

species. The paper squares represent individuals of different colors, but of the same species.

4. The keeper collects 10 squares from each of the three prey populations. The keeper then mixes them and scatters them on the environment while the predators are not looking. Each predator may look at the environment *only* when it is her or his turn. When it is not your turn, simply close your eyes or turn your back until the keeper indicates that it is your turn. When it is your turn, remove five prey individuals as quickly as you can. Continue in order until each predator has removed five prey individuals.

5. Shake off the individuals left on the environment and count these survivors according to their type. They represent generation 1.

   a) Enter the data for your group in a table similar to the one shown.

   b) Place the data on the chalkboard also, so a class total can be reached.

Generation		Paper-Prey Species		
		Newspaper Individuals	White-Paper Individuals	Red-Paper Individuals
1	Team			
	Class			
2	Team			
	Class			
3	Team			
	Class			
4	Team			
	Class			

6. Analyze your data for the first generation. Record answers to the following questions in your *Active Biology* log:

a) Does any population have more survivors than the others?

b) Write a hypothesis that might explain this difference.

c) Consider your hypothesis. If it is valid, what do you predict will happen to the number of newspaper individuals by the end of the fourth generation? to the red-paper individuals? to the white-paper individuals?

7. The survivors will be allowed to "reproduce" before the next round begins. For each survivor, the keeper adds one individual of that same type. The next generation will then include survivors and offspring. This should bring the total prey number back up to 30.

8. The keeper scatters these 30 individuals on the habitat. Repeat the predation and reproduction procedures for three more generations.

a) Calculate the change in the number of all three populations after each round.

9. Look at your data and analyze your findings.

a) Does it take you a longer or shorter period of time to find one prey individual as you proceed through the generations? Give an explanation for this.

b) How does the appearance of the surviving individuals compare with the environment?

c) Is your hypothesis and your prediction in question supported, or do they need to be revised?

d) Were the red-paper individuals suited or unsuited for this environment? Explain.

e) Would you say this species *as a whole* is better adapted to its environment after several generations of selection by the predators? Explain.

10. Now think of the "real" world.

a) Is appearance the only characteristic that determines whether an individual plant or animal is suited to its environment? If so, explain. If not, give several other characteristics.

b) In your own words, what is natural selection? What role does reproduction play in your definition?

11. Now you may test some of your own ideas about natural selection.

• What would happen if there was a change in the environment, such as a change in color of the habitat?

• What would be the result if one type of paper square "reproduced" at a faster rate than the others?

Part B: Hypothetical Model

1. Examine the story shown in the pictures on the next two pages. It is purely a hypothetical model and not an actual situation that occurred.

2. Discuss the following questions in your small group. Then answer them in your *Active Biology* log.

   a) What change took place in the environment of the original moth population?

   b) What change was produced in the moth population as a result of this environmental change?

   c) Provide evidence that indicates that the change in the moth population is not simply an

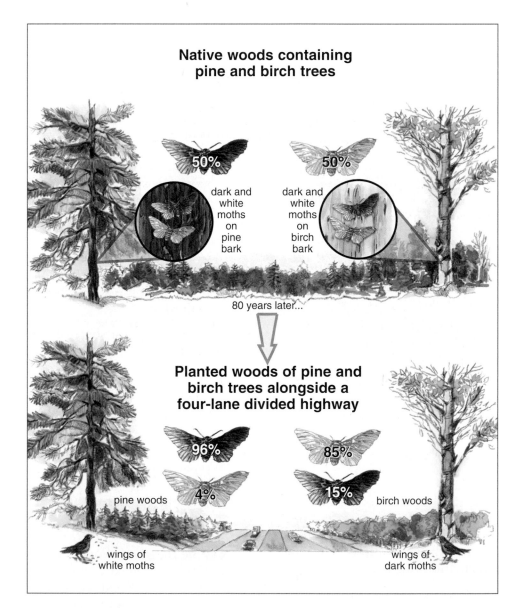

Native woods containing pine and birch trees

50%   50%

dark and white moths on pine bark   dark and white moths on birch bark

80 years later...

Planted woods of pine and birch trees alongside a four-lane divided highway

pine woods   96%   85%   birch woods

4%   15%

wings of white moths   wings of dark moths

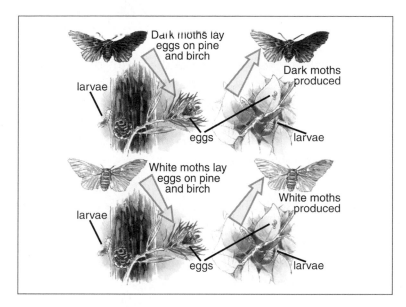

effect of the environment, but is really a hereditary population change.

d) Do you think that the change was a result of a change in reproductive capacity of the two kinds of moths? Do you think the change was a result of the survival of the moth best fit for the environment (selection pressure)?

e) What has happened to the frequency of the gene for speckled white color in the moth population now living in the pine woods?

f) What has happened to the frequency of the gene for speckled white color in the moth population living in the birch woods?

g) If environments change over a period of time, what must happen to populations if they are to survive?

h) If natural selection is responsible for the changes in frequency of black and of speckled-white moths in the two types of woods, what comparison can you make between the color of the favored type of moth and the color of the bark of the trees in each woods?

i) Assume there is benefit in protective coloration on the part of moths. What type of predators would you suspect to prey on moths?

j) What special abilities would these predators have to possess if they are really the agents of selection here?

k) Devise an experiment that would test this hypothesis.

601

Bio Talk

Theories in Science

The popular use and scientific use of the term "theory" are very different. Scientific theories attempt to provide explanations. Scientists make observations and then try to explain them. In popular terms you often hear the expression, "it's just a theory." That usually means that it is a guess. In scientific terms, a **theory** implies that an idea has been strongly supported by observations.

When scientists use the scientific method they often begin with questions from curious observations. They then develop hypotheses that can be tested experimentally. A **hypothesis** is a prediction between an independent (cause) variable and a dependent (result) variable. Hypotheses can either be supported or not, depending on the data collection. A hypothesis is not a guess. You developed and tested hypotheses in this activity. The hypothesis is then tested by further observations and experiments. Over time, if the observations and experiments satisfy the hypothesis, it becomes accepted as a scientific theory.

However, a theory is not the absolute truth. It only provides an explanation. The acceptance of a theory is often measured by its ability to enable scientists to make predictions or answer questions. A good theory provides an explanation that scientists can use to explain other observed events. Theories can be modified as new information becomes available or ideas change. Scientists continually "tinker" with a theory to make it more elegant and concise, or to make it more all encompassing.

Darwin's Hypothesis of Natural Selection

The theory of **evolution** owes much to the work of Charles Darwin. He presented his research in the mid-nineteenth century. However, Darwin never labeled his hypotheses as "evolution." He was interested in how species change and how new species come about. His many years of work led to explanations that have proved to be valid. But Darwin was not the first to think that existing species might evolve into new ones. However, Darwin was a most believable scientist for two reasons. First, he amassed a great deal of evidence. He verified its accuracy and presented it in a convincing way. Second, his hypothesis stated *how* change in organisms might take place, a contribution no one else had made.

Bio Words

theory: a proven and generally accepted truth

hypothesis: an idea that can be supported or not supported by observations and experiments

evolution: a gradual change in the characteristics of a population of organisms during successive generations, as a result of natural selection acting on genetic variation

From 1831 to 1836 Charles Darwin, a British naturalist, served aboard the H.M.S. Beagle on a science expedition around the world. The expedition visited places around the world, and Darwin studied plants and animals everywhere he went, collecting specimens for further study. In South America Darwin found fossils of extinct animals that were similar to modern species. On the Galapagos Islands in the Pacific Ocean he noticed many variations among plants and animals of the same general type as those in South America.

On November 24, 1859, the first edition of Darwin's *On the Origin of Species* was published. The book was so popular that its first printing was sold out in one day. There were, of course, many who disagreed with him. The theory of evolution has undergone many changes since Darwin's time. However, Darwin's original thinking still serves as a convenient introduction to the subject.

Here is his analysis:

• First, there are many differences among the individuals of every species. In a population, or group, of these individuals, variations occur. Usually it is safe to say that no two individuals are exactly alike. Darwin knew or suspected that many of the individual differences could be inherited.

• Second, the population size of all species tends to increase because of reproduction. One amoeba, for example, divides and produces two. These two divide, and the next generation numbers four. Then there will be 8, 16, 32, and so on.

• Third, this increase in the size of populations cannot go unchecked. If it did, the number of individuals of any species would outgrow the food supply and the available living space.

→

- Fourth, it is obvious that this huge increase seldom occurs in nature. The number of organisms in a species does not continue to increase over long periods of time. In fact, the sizes of many populations seem to remain nearly the same over time. How can this be explained? Observations of natural populations show that many individuals die before they are able to reproduce.

Why do some individuals die early, but not others? Darwin thought there must be a sort of "struggle for survival." The individuals of a species "compete" for food, light, water, places to live, and other things important for their survival. The "struggle" or "competition" may be either active or passive. That is, sometimes animals actually fight for food or the opportunity to mate. In other cases, there is no direct fight or competition. The first animal that happens to find a suitable living area may settle there. This prevents the area from being used by others. In either case, individuals with certain characteristics, or traits, will survive and produce offspring more often than individuals without them.

While chasing prey, cheetahs often reach speeds of 70 miles per hour. Unfortunately, their great speed may not be enough for this species to survive. Scientists have found that wild cheetahs have virtually no genetic variation. Cheetahs suffer from inbreeding. This lowers their resistance to diseases and also causes infertility and high cub-death rates.

Consider, for example, how the African cheetah came to be such a fast runner. Cheetahs are hunters. They capture their food; mostly antelopes, gazelles, and birds, by first stalking near their prey. Then they run the prey down with a terrific burst of speed over a short distance. In any population of cheetahs, some can run faster than others. Those that run fastest are most successful in getting food. Those that are better at getting food also are more likely to survive.

But survival is not the whole story. The characteristics that make an organism better able to survive in its environment are inherited. Therefore, those who survive are likely to pass on those characteristics to their offspring. For example, the surviving cheetah is likely to produce offspring with long, thin necks and powerful leg muscles, capable of great speed. Over many generations, then, one could expect an increase in the number of individuals that have these traits. The number with less beneficial characteristics would decrease. The organisms with the beneficial characteristics are likely to live longer and produce more offspring. Darwin called this process of survival and reproduction **natural selection**. Darwin thought that several factors were involved in natural selection:

1. The presence of variation among individuals in a population.

2. The hereditary basis of such variable characteristics.

3. The tendency of the size of populations to increase.

4. The "struggle for survival" (or competition for the needs of life).

5. A difference in the inherited characteristics that individuals pass on to succeeding generations.

Bio Words

natural selection: the differences in survival and reproduction among members of a population

Reflecting on the Activity and the Challenge

A change in the environment can have a large impact on the natural selection process. In this activity you investigated two situations. In the first, the "animals" that were best adapted to the environment were the ones to survive. In the second part you saw how a change in an environment could affect the natural selection process. Animals more suited to the changed environment would survive. You will need to explain the process of natural selection as part of your **Chapter Challenge**.

At one time some scientists believed that the necks of giraffes became long as a result of continually stretching to reach high foliage. Using what you know about natural selection, how would you explain the long necks?

1. What evidence supports the following idea: hereditary differences are important in determining whether or not an individual survives and leaves offspring?

2. What is the difference between natural selection and evolution?

3. What did Darwin emphasize as the major factors in causing evolutionary changes?

4. What did Darwin mean by natural selection?

5. Write a short paragraph expressing your ideas now of what happened to the rabbit population on the island in the **What Do You Think?** section.

6. Comment on the validity of the following statement: Breeders of domestic stock abandon natural selection. Only artificial selection plays an important role in animal-breeding programs.

Inquiring Further

1. Animal-breeding programs

What are the advantages and disadvantages to animal-breeding programs? Research and report on the pros and cons of human intervention in genetic processes.

2. Captive breeding

Captive breeding is one strategy used by governments and non-government organizations to preserve rare and endangered species. What are the advantages and disadvantages of captive breeding?

Activity 4   The Fossil Record

GOALS

In this activity you will:

- Model ways in which fossils are formed.
- Explain the difference between a body fossil and a trace fossil.
- Describe the importance of fossils.
- Predict which animals are more likely to be found in the fossil record.

What Do You Think?

To hold a fossil in the palm of your hand is to have millions of years of history at your grasp. Fossils tell you about history, and like all good history, they help you to understand both the present and the past.

- What is a fossil?

Write your answer to this question in your *Active Biology* log. Be prepared to discuss your ideas with your small group and other members of your class.

For You To Do

In this activity you will have an opportunity to model different ways in which some fossils are formed. You will visit several stations.

Integrated Coordinated Science for the 21st Century

Station 1: Preservation in Rock

You will mold a clamshell in plaster to model how it might be preserved in rock.

1. Obtain a large paper cup. Identify the cup with the name of your group. With a paper towel, smear petroleum jelly over the inside of the cup.

2. Mix plaster in another container following the directions on the package. Work quickly to complete the next four steps.

3. Fill the cup half full of plaster.

4. With the paper towel smear some petroleum jelly on both surfaces of a clamshell. Gently press the clamshell into the plaster.

5. Sprinkle a few pieces of confetti over the surface, enough to cover about 50% of the surface.

6. Fill the rest of the container with plaster.

7. Let the plaster harden overnight.

8. In the next class, remove the hardened plaster from the container. Set the plaster on its side and cover it with a towel. With a hammer gently hit the plaster to break it at the layer of confetti.

Wear goggles when using the hammer. Be sure others nearby are also wearing goggles. To contain any bits of plaster, cover the fossil model with cloth or paper before hitting it.

9. Observe your plaster molds and answer the following questions in your *Active Biology* log:

   a) What does the plaster represent?

   b) If you had never seen the clamshell, how would you figure out what the shell looked like by studying the fossil?

   c) Clamshells have two parts to their shell. How many possible imprints could a clamshell form?

   d) Why are fossils most often found in sedimentary rock formations?

Station 2: Preservation in Resin

You will encase a seed in glue to model how it might be preserved in a material like resin.

1. Obtain a small paper plate. Write your group's name on it. Use a paper towel to smear a small amount of petroleum jelly on a spot on the plate.

2. Using a hot-glue gun, put a bead of glue on the greased area of the plate.

3. Using tweezers, place the seed on the bead of glue. Add a few more drops of glue on top of the seed.

4. Let the glue harden overnight.

Wear goggles and be very careful when handling the hot-glue gun. Keep the hot part of the glue gun away from skin and flammable materials. Keep the glue away from skin, cloth, or other materials that may be damaged by it. Work on a surface that will not be damaged by the heat or the glue. Tell the teacher immediately of any accidents, including burns.

clamshell

confetti

plaster

5. In the next class, remove the bead of glue and observe. Answer the following questions in your *Active Biology* log:

a) Compare your preserved seed with a sample of amber provided by your teacher. How are they different? How are they similar?

b) Explain how a seed might end up being preserved in the resin.

c) Would you ever expect to see a large animal preserved in resin? Explain your answer.

d) Which type of fossil would be easier to identify: one preserved in rock, or one preserved in resin? Explain your answer.

Station 3: Preservation in Ice

You will freeze a small object in a cup of water to model how organisms can be preserved in ice.

1. Your teacher will provide you with a paper cup half full of water that is beginning to freeze. Put your group's name on the cup.

2. Gently push the object under the surface of the ice.

3. Add more water on top of the object.

4. Let the water freeze overnight.

5. In the next class, remove the ice from the paper cup. Answer the following questions in your *Active Biology* log:

Do not attempt to remove the object from the ice.

a) How do you think an organism could end up being preserved in ice?

b) What type of organisms could be preserved in ice?

Station 4: Preserving Animal Traces

1. Flatten or roll out a piece of modeling clay to create a flat surface.

2. On the surface of the modeling clay, produce the pathway that an organism might leave in a muddy surface. Use your imagination to produce the pathway. You could represent anything from a worm crawling to a dinosaur trudging.

3. With a paper towel spread a small amount of petroleum jelly over the imprints you left in the modeling clay.

4. Mix plaster in a small plastic bag following the directions on the package. Cut the corner off the plastic bag. Squeeze enough plaster over the impression to fill the area.

5. Let the plaster dry overnight.

6. In the next class, remove the modeling clay from the plaster. Answer the following questions in your *Active Biology* log:

a) In what kind of ancient environment(s) might you expect to have footprints formed?

b) Once a set of fresh footprints have been made in the mud, what would have to happen to preserve them as rock?

Bio Talk

THE NATURE OF THE FOSSIL RECORD

Making Models

Scientists often make models to help them understand how living things work. Models can be small-scale structures that simulate what is found in nature. For example, a scientist might reconstruct the climatic conditions of 65 million years ago to uncover what might have happened to the dinosaurs. Another type of model could be nonliving structures that work in a similar fashion. The human heart is often understood from the model of a pump. Recently, scientists have begun using computers to make mathematical models. Unlike the structural models, these models only exist as numbers. In this activity you modeled the formation of fossils.

The Importance of Fossils

What does the fossil record tell you? Among a number of things, it tells you that species are not unchangeable. The species you see around you today are not the ones that have always existed. Fossils provide direct evidence that organisms are continually evolving. However, it is important to note that evidence of evolution is very different from the theories of evolution, which you read about in the previous activity. Fossils tell you that life forms on Earth have changed. The theories attempt to explain how and why these changes took place.

Fossil Formation

Fossils are preserved evidence of ancient life. Some fossils are called **body fossils**. These are the preserved parts of plants and animals. Fossils may also be **trace fossils**. These fossils are traces of the activities of plants and animals, for example, tracks, trails, or scratch marks.

As you investigated in this activity, fossils form as a result of many processes. For example, most animals become fossilized by being buried in sediment. The sediments then accumulate and consolidate to form rock. Molds are fossils formed from the impressions in soft sediment of shells or leaves, for example, or from footprints or tracks. Casts are replicas formed when a hollow mold is subsequently filled with sediment—mud, sand, or minerals. Sometimes an insect might

→

Bio Words

fossil: any evidence of past life preserved in sediments or rocks

body fossil: a fossil that consists of the preserved body of an animal or plant or an imprint of the body

trace fossil: any evidence of the life activities of a plant or animal that lived in the geologic past (but not including the fossil organism itself)

become trapped in a sticky substance called resin, produced by some types of trees. The resin hardens to form amber. The insect fossil is preserved in amber, often perfectly. At other times natural mummies form when organisms are buried in areas like tar pits and peat bogs or dry environments like deserts or certain caves. Organisms buried in

Body fossil.

Trace fossil.

Cast.

glacial ice also can remain preserved for thousands of years. Finally, the cells and pore spaces of wood and bone can be preserved if filled with mineral deposits, a process called petrifaction.

Not all organisms become fossils. To begin with, very few escape the food chain. They are either eaten by other organisms or are broken down by decomposers. Soft body parts decay very quickly. You know from experience that it takes little time for meat and vegetables to spoil if left out of the refrigerator. More resistant parts, such as the exoskeletons of insects, vertebrate bones, wood, pollen, and

spores take much longer to decay. Thus, the likelihood of finding these in the fossil record is much greater.

The Fossil Record

Fossils typically form where sediments such as mud or sand accumulate and entomb organisms or their traces. The layers of hardened mud, sand, and other sedimentary materials are like a natural book of the Earth's history. Interpreting each layer is like reading the pages of a book. Unfortunately, there are many surfaces on the Earth where layers are not

Major Divisions of Geologic Time (boundaries in millions of years before present)			
Era	Period	Event	
Cenozoic	Quaternary	modern humans	
			1.8
	Tertiary	abundant mammals	
			65
Mesozoic	Cretaceous	flowering plants; dinosaur and ammonoid extinctions	
			145
	Jurassic	first birds and mammals; abundant dinosaurs	
			213
	Triassic	abundant coniferous trees	
			248
Paleozoic	Permian	extinction of trilobites and other marine animals	
			286
	Pennsylvanian	fern forests; abundant insects; first reptiles	
			325
	Mississippian	sharks; large primitive trees	
			360
	Devonian	amphibians and ammonoids	
			410
	Silurian	early plants and animals on land	
			440
	Ordovician	first fish	
			505
	Cambrian	abundant marine invertebrates; trilobites dominant	
			544
Proterozoic		primitive aquatic plants	
			2500
Archean		oldest fossils; bacteria and algae	

Time Not to Scale

Bio Words

index fossil: a fossil of an organism that was widespread but lived for only a short interval of geological time

accumulating or where erosion is removing other layers. Thus, interpreting the layers is like reading a novel that is missing most of its pages. You can read the pages that are preserved and even group them into chapters, but much important information is missing from each chapter. Paleontologists (scientists who study fossils) use **index fossils**. These are fossils of organisms that were widespread but lived for only a short interval of geological time. They use index fossils to divide the fossil record into chapters. For example, dinosaurs are index fossils for the Mesozoic era, the unit of time that runs from roughly 245 million years ago (abbreviated Ma) to 65 Ma. In other

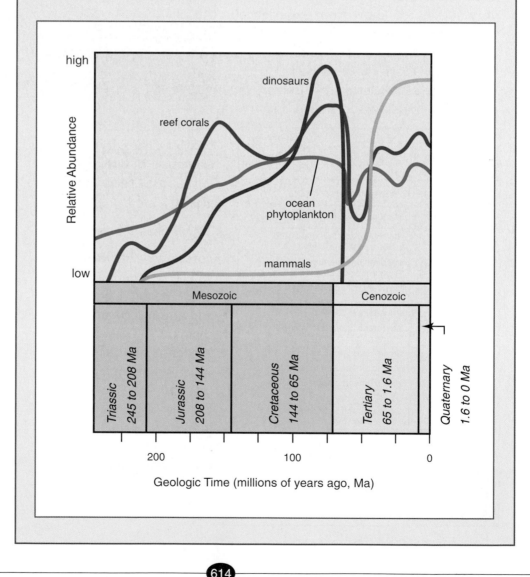

words, all dinosaur species evolved and became extinct during the Mesozoic era. Whales, horses, and many other mammal groups, on the other hand, are index fossils of the Cenozoic era, the unit of time that runs roughly from 65 Ma to the present. Using this and additional fossil evidence, paleontologists infer that the Mesozoic and Cenozoic eras represent two of the major chapters in the history of life.

The graph on the previous page summarizes the distribution of four groups of animals during the Mesozoic and Cenozoic eras. (Please note that this graph is not drawn to scale along the vertical axis; for example, the peak in dinosaur diversity is comparatively a small fraction of present day mammal diversity.) Although the graph is a rough summary of just a small part of the fossil record, paleontologists can get a much more accurate picture of life's history by examining specific pages in the record. You will do this in the next activity.

Reflecting on the Activity and the Challenge

In this activity you modeled some of the ways in which fossils can form. You also read about different types of fossils and the incomplete nature of the fossil record. You may have now developed a sense of the importance of fossils.

You can begin to appreciate what might be lost if fossil records were destroyed or disrupted. You will need to explain this at the town-hall meeting if you are representing one of the paleontologists.

Biology to Go

1. What is the difference between a body fossil and a trace fossil?

2. What are the chances of an organism becoming a fossil? Explain your answer.

3. a) What is an index fossil?

   b) How do paleontologists use index fossils?

4. Use evidence from this activity to explain how the biosphere and the geosphere are connected.

Inquiring Further

1. Carbon-14 dating

How is it possible to determine the age of organic matter using carbon-14? Research to find the physical and chemical principles on which this technique is based. What are the limitations of carbon-14 dating?

Activity 5   Mass Extinction and Fossil Records

GOALS

In this activity you will:

- Investigate fossil data for evidence of mass extinction and adaptive radiation.
- Explain the meaning of mass extinction and adaptive radiation.
- Describe the meaning of niche in an ecosystem.

What Do You Think?

Sixty-five million years ago the curtain came down on the age of dinosaurs when a catastrophic event led to their mass extinction.

- What type of disastrous event could have led to the extinction of such a large group of animals?
- Did any other life forms become extinct at this time in geological history?

Write your answer to these questions in your *Active Biology* log. Be prepared to discuss your ideas with your small group and other members of your class.

For You To Do

In this activity, you will investigate fossil data from those "pages" that represent the boundary between the Cretaceous and Tertiary periods (about sixty-five million years ago).

1. Your teacher will divide the class into groups of three or four students. With the other members of your group,

Integrated Coordinated Science for the 21st Century

Wash your hands after handling the fossils.

examine the six brachiopod fossils. Brachiopods are a group of marine animals.

a) What characteristics might paleontologists use to assign these fossils to different species?

b) What characteristics might paleontologists use to assign these fossils to one group?

2. Now examine **Graph A**. It plots the ranges of 50 different species of brachiopods across 15 m of sedimentary rock at one location in Denmark. This is one of the few places in the world that contains a continuous record of layers that represent the boundary between the

Cretaceous and Tertiary periods. Using a technique known as *magnetostratigraphy*, geologists infer that each meter of this sedimentary sequence represents 0.1 million years of history. The point "0 m" represents the boundary between the Cretaceous and Tertiary systems, 65 Ma (millions of years ago). Paleontologists sampled fossils from the locations shown along the left axis.

a) Which species became extinct at the Cretaceous-Tertiary (K-T) boundary?

b) Which species evolved after the K-T boundary?

c) Which species appear to have become extinct and then reappeared later?

d) What conclusions can you draw from this graph?

e) What are the limitations of the data shown in **Graph A**? (Hint: recall the processes by which fossils are preserved.)

Graph A: Range of Different Species of Brachiopods

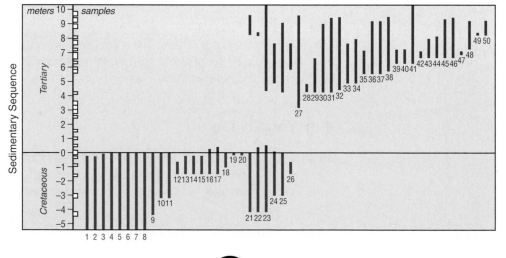

Graph B: Number of Families of Marine Organisms through Time

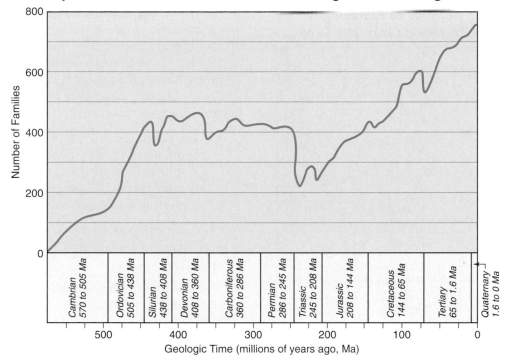

3. Paleontologists have compiled similar data on the ranges of existence of numerous other organisms during the Cretaceous and Tertiary periods. Examine **Graph B**, which shows a set of data assembled to illustrate the number of *families* (groups of closely related species) of marine animals through geological time.

   a) When was the number of families the greatest?

   b) Has the growth in the number of families been steady? Explain your answer.

   c) What do the dips in the graph represent?

   d) What inferences can you draw from this graph?

   e) What are the limitations of the graph shown in **Graph B**?

4. Now re-examine **Graph B**. Locate the times of the five greatest decreases in the number of families. Discuss why this might represent mass extinctions. Locate the times of the five greatest increases in the number of families. Discuss why this might represent adaptive radiations. (Adaptive radiation describes the rapid changes in a single or a few species to fill many empty functions in an ecosystem.)

   a) In your *Active Biology* log, construct a chart that summarizes your findings. Your chart should have two vertical columns, one labeled "Times of Mass Extinction" and the other labeled "Times of Adaptive Radiation." Fill in the chart with the estimated date that each event began and the name of the time period (e.g., "beginning of the Devonian period, roughly 410 Ma").

Graph C: Number of Families of Terrestrial Tetrapods through Time

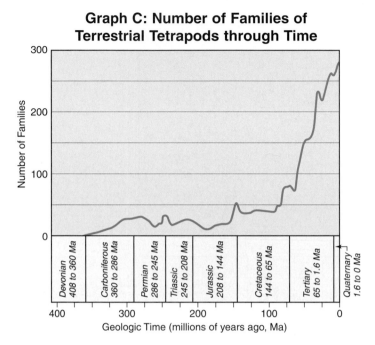

5. Now analyze **Graph C**, a graph constructed to show the number of families of terrestrial tetrapod families (land animals with four limbs) through geological time. Locate the greatest extinction events and adaptive radiations.

   a) Compare these events to the events listed in your chart for **Graph B**. Propose a hypothesis to account for the differences and similarities in these two graphs.

6. Consider the pattern of extinction and adaptive radiation in **Graph B** and **C**.

   a) How might adaptive radiation be related to mass extinctions? (Hint: consider how life on Earth might be different if dinosaurs still existed.)

Making Inferences in Science

Have you ever wondered how scientists know so much about dinosaurs? No human ever saw a dinosaur eat or run. The huge lizards disappeared from Earth about 65 millions years ago. No fossil evidence of the human species, Homo sapiens, appears before 500,000 years ago.

The skeletons of dinosaurs have been reconstructed using fossil records. The skeletons provide indirect evidence of how the dinosaur might have lived. Evidence from the skull of a dinosaur may indicate that the dinosaur might have been a meat eater. The premise that this dinosaur killed other dinosaurs is called an inference. No one ever saw the dinosaur eating meat, the evidence to support this conclusion came from examining the skull shape and the structure of the teeth. Unlike a hypothesis, an inference cannot be tested.

Mass Extinction and Adaptive Radiation

Extinction is the total disappearance of a species. Extinction means that not a single organism of the species lives anywhere on Earth. The fossil record is a virtual graveyard of extinct species. It is strewn with the fossilized remains of millions of extinct species. David Raup, a paleontologist at the University of Chicago, notes that "only about one in a thousand species [that have lived on Earth] is still alive—a truly lousy survival record: 99.9 percent failure!"

Even more striking, however, is the fossil evidence of **mass extinctions**. These are episodes during which large numbers of species became extinct during short intervals of geological time. In geological time a few million years or less is a short period! The extinction of one species often has a domino effect. If one species vanishes, so do many others. Yet mass extinctions can present new opportunities to survivors.

Those best able to survive fill empty **niches**. (An ecological niche is the function a species plays in an ecosystem.) Plants and animals that have the greatest genetic variation are most often best able to fill these empty "spaces." This process is called **adaptive radiation**. In this activity, you investigated evidence of mass extinctions and adaptive radiations by analyzing data from the fossil record. Rapid evolution can also occur when a species moves into a new area. Natural variation within a species makes it easier for the species to adapt to different environments.

One remarkable mass extinction event occurred at the boundary between the Cretaceous and Tertiary periods, roughly 65 million years ago. This boundary separates the age of the reptiles and the age of the mammals. Geologists recognized this event over one hundred years ago when they realized that there was a striking change in the types of fossils deposited on either side of this boundary. This is where the language of science may become difficult to follow. However, no matter how it is said, the concepts are the same. This boundary ➤

Bio Words

extinction: the permanent disappearance of a species from Earth

mass extinction: the extinction of a large number of species during short intervals of geological time

niche: the ecological function of a species; the set of resources it consumes and habitats it occupies in an ecosystem

adaptive radiation: the diversification by natural selection, over evolutionary time, of a species or group of species into several different species that are typically adapted to different ecological niches

Model of a Brachiosaurus.

also separates two eras. These two eras are called the Mesozoic and Cenozoic. Dinosaurs were prevalent during the Mesozoic Era and extinct during the Cenozoic Era. The last segment of the Mesozoic Era is called the Cretaceous Period. The first segment of the Cenozoic Era is called the Tertiary Period. The abbreviation for the boundary between the Cretaceous and Tertiary periods is often referred to as the K-T boundary, where K is the abbreviation for the German form of the word Cretaceous. You may also hear of this time referred to the Mesozoic and Cenozoic boundary. No matter what you call it, there were dinosaurs before and there are no dinosaurs now, and it happened about 65 million years ago!

Moreover, at the end of the Cretaceous period virtually all plant and animal groups were lost from Earth, not just the dinosaurs. Yet, the beginning of the Tertiary period marks the start of the adaptive radiation of mammals.

The ultimate cause of the mass extinction at the Cretaceous/Tertiary boundary is still a debate among scientists. However, more and more evidence suggests that a meteorite impact caused the mass extinction. The impact of the meteorite created a chain of devastating environmental changes for living organisms.

Reflecting on the Activity and the Challenge

In this activity you had an opportunity to see that life forms that dominated the Earth many (geological) years ago are not here now. You also learned that the evidence to support this fact is found in fossil records. The new organisms that evolved to fill the ecological place of the extinct organisms are also part of fossil records. You probably have developed an even further appreciation of the importance of fossil records. You may wish to argue for a delay of construction of the new highway whether you represent the paleontologists or a concerned citizen.

Biology to Go

1. Explain the meaning of adaptive radiation in your own words.

2. What evidence do scientists use to support the idea of mass extinctions?

3. After a mass extinction, which organisms are most likely to survive? Explain your answer.

4. Explain why the extinction of one species can have a domino effect on an ecosystem.

Inquiring Further

1. The Cretaceous and Tertiary boundary event

Research the proposed causes of the mass extinction during this time period. Provide at least two explanations. Which one do you think is more plausible?

Biology at Work

Pat Holroyd

Paleontologist, University of California Berkeley Museum of Paleontology

"Believe it or not," says Pat Holroyd, "the science of paleontology owes a lot to the oil industry and construction projects in general." This statement may be surprising to you, coming from one of the best paleontologists in the world.

Holroyd's position at the University of California Berkeley Museum of Paleontology (UCBMP) has her in the field looking for rare fossils and overseeing construction projects as much as 12 weeks a year. "Under California law every construction project must produce an environmental impact statement before ever breaking ground," she explains, "and that must include a paleontology component. So, if someone wants to put in a transmission line or a road they must first look at how all the natural resources might be affected."

Yet, according to Holroyd, that rarely means development projects are blocked or even seriously delayed. "Mitigation is the word we like to use," she says. "When excavation begins, a paleontologist will be there to see if anything is coming out of the hole. What usually happens is that the paleontologist will jump in the hole and excavate for as long as she or he has to and then the project continues." As Holroyd explains, "Most important fossil finds do not happen despite development, but rather because of them. Most of the fossils we've found are only found because of construction projects. "The fact is that there are only a few thousand paleontologists in the entire

Pat Holroyd examines a juvenile sea turtle skull, *Puppigerus camperi.*

world and they don't have the money to dig a 30-meter hole in the ground."

As a child, she loved playing in the dirt, but thought more about discovering pyramids than fossils. "It wasn't until college that I became interested in paleontology," Holroyd says. After graduating from the University of Kansas, she received a Ph.D. from Duke University in biological anthropology and anatomy. "I usually just say my degree is in paleontology," Holroyd laughs. During graduate school she worked with the U.S. Geological Survey in Denver and continued there for a year after graduation before moving over to UCBMP, where she's been happily digging in the dirt ever since.

In the larger sense, Holroyd's work is the study of small mammals and the effects of global warming. She and other scientists are actively trying to determine what a phenomenon like that does to a whole ecosystem, in an attempt to see what might be happening now. "If there is global warming now, then it's important to look at a period in the past when the globe went through similar changes," she explains. "Almost everything that we, as scientists, look at in terms of the impact humans are having or might have on the environment are things that we can find examples of in the fossil record."

Glossary: Unit 1

Chapters 1-3
Earth's Dynamic Geosphere

ash: fine pyroclastic material (less than 2 mm in diameter)

asthenosphere: the part of the mantle beneath the lithosphere. The asthenosphere undergoes slow flow, rather than behaving as a rigid block, like the overlying lithosphere

basalt: a kind of volcanic igneous rock, usually dark colored, with a high content of iron

caldera: a large basin-shaped volcanic depression, more or less circular, the diameter of which is many times greater than that of the included vent or vents

composite cone (stratovolcano): a volcano that is constructed of alternating layers of lava and pyroclastic deposits

continental accretion: the growth of a continent along its edges

contour interval: the vertical distance between the elevations represented by two successive contour lines on a topographic map

contour line: a line on a map that connects points of equal elevation of the land surface

convergent plate boundary: a plate boundary where two plates move toward one another

core: the solid, innermost part of the Earth, consisting mainly of iron

crust: the thin outermost layer of the Earth. Continental crust is relatively thick and mostly very old. Oceanic crust is relatively thin, and is always geologically very young

density: the mass per unit volume of a material or substance

divergent plate boundary: a plate boundary where two plates move away from one another

earthquake: a sudden motion or shaking in the Earth caused by the abrupt release of slowly accumulated strain

elastic rebound: the return of a bent elastic solid to its original shape after the deforming force is removed

epicenter: the point on the Earth's surface directly above the focus of an earthquake

extrusive igneous rock: an igneous rock that has formed by eruption of lava onto the surface of the Earth

fault: a fracture or fracture zone in rock, along which the rock masses have moved relative to one another parallel to the fracture

focus: the point of an earthquake within the Earth where rupture first occurs to cause an earthquake

friction: the force that resists the motion of one surface against another surface

Global Positioning System (GPS): a satellite-based system for accurate location of points on the Earth

hazard: a natural event, like an earthquake, that has the potential to do damage or harm

hot spot: a fixed source of abundant rising magma that forms a volcanic center that has persisted for tens of millions of years

igneous rock: rock or mineral that solidified from molten or partly molten material, i.e., from magma

intrusive igneous rock (plutonic igneous rock): igneous rock formed at considerable depth by the crystallization of magma

isoseismal map: a map showing the lines connecting points on the Earth's surface at which earthquake intensity is the same

lahar: a wet mixture of water, mud, and volcanic rock fragments, with the consistency of wet concrete, that flows down the slopes of a volcano and its river valleys

lapilli: pyroclastics in the general size range of 2 to 64 mm

lava: molten rock that issues from a volcano or fissure

lava flow: an outpouring of molten lava from a vent or fissure; also, the solidified body of rock so formed

lithosphere: the outermost layer of the Earth, consisting of the Earth's crust and part of the upper mantle. The lithosphere behaves as a rigid layer, in contrast to the underlying asthenosphere

magma: naturally occurring molten rock material generated within the Earth. Magma also contains dissolved gases, and sometimes solid crystals

mantle: the zone of the Earth below the crust and above the core. It is divided into the upper mantle and lower mantle with a transition zone between

map projections: the process of systematically transforming positions on the Earth's spherical surface to a flat map while maintaining spatial relationships

mercator projection: a map projection in which the Equator is represented by a straight line true to scale, the meridians by parallel straight lines perpendicular to the Equator and equally spaced according to their distance apart at the Equator, and the parallels by straight lines perpendicular to the meridians and the same length as the Equator. There is a great distortion of distances, areas, and shapes at the polar regions

mid-ocean ridge: a chain of undersea ridges extending throughout all of the Earth's ocean basins, and formed by sea-floor spreading

paleomagnetism: the record of the past orientation and polarity of the Earth's magnetic field recorded in rocks containing the mineral magnetite

pangea: Earth's most recent supercontinent which was rifted apart about 200 million years ago

plate tectonics: the field of study of plate motion

primary wave (P wave): a seismic wave that involves particle motion (compression and expansion) in the direction in which the wave is traveling. It is the fastest of the seismic waves

pyroclastic flow: a high-density mixture of hot ash and rock fragments with hot gases formed by a volcanic explosion or aerial expulsion from a volcanic vent

relief: the physical configuration of a part of the Earth's surface, with reference to variations of height and slope or to irregularities of the land surface

resonance: a condition in which a vibration affecting an object has about the same period as the natural vibration period of the object

rift valley: a large, long valley on a continent, formed where the continent is pulled apart by forces produced when mantle material rises up beneath the continent

rift valley: the deep central cleft in the crest of the mid-oceanic ridge

risk: the potential impact of a natural hazard on people or property

seamount: a peaked or flat-topped underwater mountain rising from the ocean floor

secondary wave (S wave): a seismic wave produced by a shearing motion that involves vibration perpendicular to the direction in which the wave is traveling. It does not travel through liquids, like the outer core of the Earth. It arrives later than the P wave

seismic (earthquake) waves: a general term for all elastic waves in the Earth, produced by earthquakes or generated artificially by explosions

seismogram: the record made by a seismometer

seismology: the study of earthquakes and of the structure of the Earth

seismometer: an instrument that measures seismic waves. It receives seismic impulses and converts them into a signal like an electronic voltage

shear strength: the shear force needed to break a solid material

shield volcano: a broad, gently sloping volcanic cone of flat-dome shape, usually several tens or hundreds of square miles in extent

silica: material with composition SiO_2

subduction: the movement of one plate downward into the mantle beneath the edge of the other plate at a convergent plate boundary. The downgoing plate always is oceanic lithosphere. The plate that stays at the surface can have either oceanic lithosphere or continental lithosphere

subduction zone: a long, narrow belt in which one plate descends beneath another

supercontinent: a large continent consisting of all of the Earth's continental lithosphere. Supercontinents are assembled by plate-tectonic processes of subduction and continent–continent collision

surface wave: a seismic wave that travels along the surface of the Earth

suture zone: the zone on the Earth's surface where two continents have collided and have been welded together to form a single continent

tephra: a collective term for all the particles ejected from a volcano and transported through the air. It includes volcanic dust, ash, cinders, lapilli, scoria, pumice, bombs, and blocks

thermal convection: a pattern of movement in a fluid caused by heating from below and cooling from above. Thermal convection transfers heat energy from the bottom of the convection cell to the top

topographic map: a map showing the topographic features of the land surface

transform fault: a vertical surface of slippage between two lithospheric plates along an offset between two segments of a spreading ridge

transform plate boundary: a plate boundary where two plates slide parallel to one another

tsunami: a great sea wave produced by a submarine earthquake (or volcanic eruption or landslide)

viscosity: the property of a fluid to offer internal resistance to flow

volcanic bomb: a blob of lava that was ejected while viscous and received a rounded shape (larger than 64 mm in diameter) while in flight

Volcanic Explosivity Index: the percentage of pyroclastics among the total products of a volcanic eruption

Glossary: Unit 2

Chapters 4-6
Active Physics

amplitude: the height of a wave crest; it is related to a wave's energy

analog: a description of a continuously variable signal or a circuit; an analog signal can be represented as a series of waves

angle of incidence: the angle a ray of light makes with a perpendicular to the surface at the point of incidence

angle of reflection: the angle a reflected ray makes with a perpendicular to the surface at the point of reflection

angle of refraction: the angle a refracted ray makes with the perpendicular to the surface separating the two media traversed by the ray

capacitor: a component of an electrical circuit used to temporarily store charge

circuit diagram: a drawing that uses a special set of symbols to represent the electrical components and wiring in an electric circuit

circuit: a route laid out with wires that connect circuit components along which electrical current flows

compression pulse or wave: a longitudinal pulse or wave caused by means of the compression of a fluid, as a sound wave in air

concave lens: a lens that causes parallel light rays to diverge; a lens that is thicker at its edges than in the center

converging lens: a parallel beam of light passing through the lens and is brought to a real point or focus (convex lens)

convex lens: a lens that causes parallel light rays to converge; a lens that is thinner at its edges than in the center

crest: the highest point on a wave

critical angle: the smallest angle of incidence at which a light ray passing from one medium to another can be totally reflected

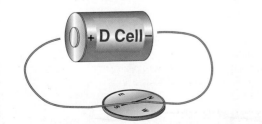

digital: description of data that is stored or transmitted as a sequence of discrete symbols; usually this means binary data (1s and 0s) represented using electronic or electromagnetic signals

diverging lens: a parallel beam of light passing through the lens diverges as though it came from a point behind the lens (concave lens)

Doppler Effect: a change in the observed frequency of a wave when the source and an observer are in motion relative to each other; the frequency increases when the source or observer approach each other and decreases when they move apart

electromagnetic spectrum: the entire range of radiation extending in frequency from approximately 10^{23} hertz to 0 hertz; this includes gamma rays, x-rays, ultraviolet radiation, visible light, infrared radiation, microwaves, and radio waves

focal length: the distance from the center of a lens or mirror to its focal point

focus: the place at which light rays converge or from which they appear to diverge after refraction or reflection; also call focal point

frequency: the number of waves produced per unit time; the frequency is the reciprocal of the amount of time it takes for a single wavelength to pass a point

image: the likeness of a physical object formed by a lens, mirror or other optical instrument

index of refraction: a property of a medium that is related to the speed of light through it; it is calculated by dividing the speed of light in a vacuum by the speed of light in the medium

lens: a curved, ground and polished piece of glass or other transparent material used for the refraction of light

light-year: the distance that light travels in one year (9.46×10^{12}km)

longitudinal pulse or wave: a pulse or wave in which the motion of the medium is parallel to the direction of motion of the wave motion

node: a spot on a standing wave where the medium is motionless

normal: at right angles; perpendicular

parallax: the apparent difference of position of an object as seen from two different places, or points of view

periodic wave: a repetitive series of pulses; a wave train in which the particles of the medium undergo periodic motion (after a set amount of time the medium returns to its starting point and begins to repeat its motion)

Integrated Coordinated Science for the 21st Century

pitch: the quality of a sound dependent primarily on the frequency of the sound waves produced by its source

principal axis: the line drawn through the point of sight perpendicular to the perspective plane

ray: the path followed by a very thin beam of light

real image: an image that will project on a screen or on the film of a camera; the rays of light actually pass through the image

reflecting telescope: an optical device that uses a concave mirror to gather light and make distant objects appear larger

reflection: the return of light or sound waves from a surface; the action of bouncing or folding back

refracting telescope: an optical device that uses lenses to gather light and make distant objects appear larger

refraction: the change in direction (bending) of a light beam as it passes obliquely from one medium to a different one

resistor: an electric device used to impede (resist) the flow of electrons in conductors

Snell's law: describes the relationship between the index of refraction and the ratio of the sine of the angle of incidence and the sine of the angle of refraction

standing wave: the superposition of two waves traveling in opposite directions characterized by lack of vibration at certain points, between which areas of maximum vibration occur periodically; produced whenever a wave is confined within boundaries, as in the vibrating string of a musical instrument

transverse pulse or wave: a pulse or wave in which the motion of the medium is perpendicular to the motion of the wave

trough: the lowest point on a wave

virtual image: an image from which rays of reflected or refracted light appear to diverge, as from an image seen in a plane mirror; no light comes directly from or passes through the image

wave pulse: a wave of a fixed (or short) duration; the particles of the medium are at rest until the pulse arrives, and they return to rest after it passes

wave train: a continuous series of wave pulses; the particles of the medium are in continuous motion

wavelength: the distance (measured in the direction of propagation) between two identical points in consecutive cycles of a wave

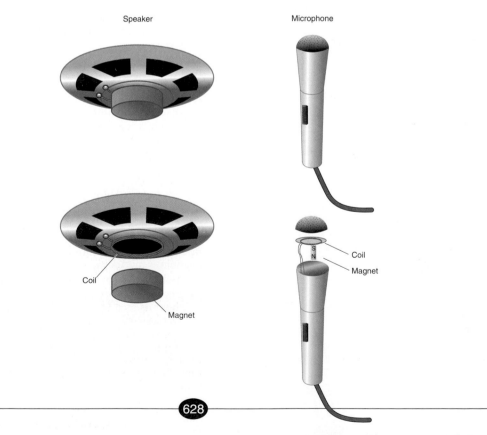

Speaker

Microphone

Coil

Magnet

Coil

Magnet

Glossary: Unit 3

Chapters 7-8
Active Chemistry

accuracy: how close the measured value is to the standard or accepted value of that measurement

acid: a substance that produces hydrogen ions in water, or is a proton donor

acid-base indicator: a dye that has a certain color in an acid solution and a different color in a base solution

alloy: a substance that has metal characteristics and consists of two or more different elements

anion: a negatively charged ion

atom: the smallest representative part of an element

atomic mass: atomic mass is determined by the mass of the protons and neutrons of the atom

atomic mass unit (amu): a unit of mass defined as one-twelfth of the mass of a carbon-12 atom

Avogadro's number: the number of atoms contained in 12 grams of carbon-12. The number is 6.022×10^{23}

base: a substance that releases hydroxide ions (OH–) in water, or is a proton acceptor

binary compound: a compound formed from the combining of two different elements

bounce: the ability of an object to rebound to its original position when dropped from a given height

catalyst: a substance that changes the speed of a chemical reaction without being permanently changed itself

cation: a positively charged ion

chemical change: a change that converts the chemical composition of a substance into different substance(s) with different chemical composition

chemical formula: the combination of the symbols of the elements in a definite numerical proportion used to represent molecules, compounds, radicals, ions, etc.

chemical group: a family of elements in the periodic table that have similar electron configurations

chemical property: a characteristic that a substance undergoes in a chemical reaction that produces new substance(s)

chemical reaction: a process in which new substance(s) are formed from starting substance(s)

chemical test: a physical procedure or chemical reaction used to identify a substance

colligative property: a property such as freezing-point depression or boiling-point elevation whose physical value depends on only the ratio of the particles of solute and solvent particles and not on their chemical identities

colloid: a mixture containing particles larger than the solute but small enough to remain suspended in the continuous phase of another component. This is also called a colloidal dispersion

combustion: the rapid reaction of a material with oxygen accompanied by rapid evolution of flame and heat

composite: a solid heterogeneous mixture of two or more substances that make use of the properties of each component

compound: a material that consists of two or more elements united together in definite proportion

concentration: a measure of the composition of a solution, often given in terms of moles of solute per liter of solution

conductivity: the property of transmitting heat and electricity

covalent bond: a bond formed when two atoms combine and share their paired electrons with each other

decomposition: a chemical reaction in which a single compound reacts to give two or more products

density: the mass per unit volume of a material

double-displacement reaction: a chemical reaction in which two ionic compounds "exchange" cations to produce two new compounds

ductility: a property that describes how easy it is to pull a substance into a new permanent shape, such as, pulling into wires

elasticity: the property of a material to resist deformation and return to its normal size or shape after a force has been applied to it

electrolysis: the conduction of electricity through a solution that contains ions or through a molten ionic compound that will induce chemical change

electromagnetic spectrum: the complete spectrum of electromagnetic radiation, such as radio waves, microwaves, infrared, visible, ultraviolet, x-rays, and gamma rays

electron: a subatomic particle that occurs outside of the nucleus and has a charge of −1 and mass of 9.109×10^{-28}g

electron configuration: the distribution of electrons in an atom's energy levels

element: a substance in which all of the atoms have the same atomic number

emulsion: a colloid or colloidal dispersion of one liquid suspended in another

endothermic change or reaction: a change in which energy in the form of heat is absorbed from the surrounding environment resulting in an increase in the internal energy of the system

exothermic change or reaction: a change in which energy in the form of heat is released from a system resulting in a decrease in the internal energy of the system

fission: the process of breaking apart nuclei into smaller nuclei and with the release of a large amount of energy

flame test: an experimental technique or process in identifying a metal from its characteristic flame color

frequency: the number of waves per second or cycles per second or hertz (Hz)

fusion: nuclei of lighter atoms combining to form nuclei with greater mass and release of a large amount of energy

halogens: Group VIIA (17) on the periodic table consisting of fluorine, chlorine, bromine, iodine, and astatine

hydrocarbon: a molecular compound containing only hydrogen and carbon

inorganic compound: a compound not based on molecular compounds of carbon

ion: an electrically charged atom or group of atoms that has acquired a net charge, either negative or positive

ionic bond: the attraction between oppositely charged ions

ionic compound: a compound consisting of positive or negative ions

ionization energy: the energy required to remove an electron from a gaseous atom at ground state

isotope: atoms of the same element but different atomic masses due to different number of neutrons

kinetic energy: a form of energy related to the motion of a particle (KE $= \frac{1}{2}mv^2$)

Law of Definite Proportions: the composition of a pure substance is always the same or the elements of the compound always combine in the same proportion by mass

luster: the reflection of light from the surface of a material described by its quality and intensity

malleability: the property of a material to be able to be hammered into various shapes without breaking

metal: classes of materials that exhibit the properties of conductivity, malleability, reactivity, and ductility. Metal elements readily lose electrons to form positive ions

mole: a collection of objects that contains Avogadro's number (6.022×10^{23})

molecular compound: two or more atoms bond together by sharing electrons (covalent bond)

neutralization: the process of an acid and base reacting to form water and salt

neutron: neutral subatomic particle with a mass of 1.675×10^{-24} g located in the nuclei of the atom

noble gas: a family of elements (Group 18 or VIIIA) of the periodic table

nonmetal: elements that do not exhibit the properties of conductivity, malleability, reactivity, and ductility. These elements tend to form negative ions. The oxides of the elements are acidic

normal boiling point: the temperature at which the vapor pressure of the pure liquid equals 1 atm

normal freezing point: the characteristic temperature, at 1 atm, at which a material changes from a liquid state to its solid state

normal melting point: the characteristic temperature, at 1 atm, at which a material changes from a solid state to its liquid state

nucleus: the very dense core of the atom that contains the neutrons and protons

orbit: the path of the electron in its motion around the nucleus of Bohr's hydrogen atom

orbital: in the quantum mechanical model of an atom, it is the region surrounding the atomic nucleus in which the electron distribution is given by a wave function

organic compound: a molecular compound of carbon

oxidation: the process of a substance losing one or more electrons

oxidation number: a number assigned to an element in a compound designating the number of electrons the element has lost, gained, or shared in forming that compound

period: a horizontal row of elements in the periodic table

pH: a quantity used to represent the acidity of a solution based on the concentration of hydrogen ions (pH $= -\log[H+]$)

phase change: the conversion of a substance from one state to another state at a specific temperature and pressure. Example: solid to liquid, liquid to gas, or solid to gas (sublimation)

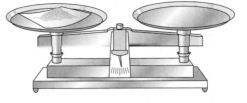

physical change: a change that involves changes in the state or form of a substance but does not cause any change in chemical composition

physical property: a property that can be measured without causing a change in the substance's chemical composition

Planck's constant: a proportionality constant of the energy of a photon to its frequency, derived by Max Planck in 1900. His equation was: E = hf and Planck's constant is (h) = 6.626×10^{-34} J·s

polyatomic ion: an ion that consists of 2 or more atoms that are covalently bonded and have either a positive or negative charge

polymer: a substance that is a macromolecule consisting of many similar small molecules (monomers) linked together in long chains

polymerization: a chemical reaction that converts small molecules (monomers) into large molecules (polymers)

potential energy: stored energy of the material as a result of its position in an electric, magnetic, or gravitational field

precipitate: an insoluble solid formed in a liquid solution as a result of some chemical reactions

precision: the closeness of agreement of several measurements of the same quantity

product: the substance(s) produced in a chemical reaction

proton: a positively charged subatomic particle contained in the nucleus of an atom. The mass of a proton is 1.673×10^{-24}g and it has a charge of +1

pure material: an element or compound that has a defined composition and properties

pure substance: a substance that contains only one kind of particle

radioactive: an atom that has an unstable nuclei and will emit alpha, positron, or beta particles in order to achieve more stable nuclei

reactants: the starting materials in a chemical reaction

reactivity: a property that describes how readily a material will react with other materials

reduction: a process in which the substance under consideration gains electron(s)

saturated solution: the maximum amount of solute that can be dissolved at a given temperature and pressure

single-displacement reaction: a reaction in which an element displaces or replaces another element in a compound

solute: the substance that dissolves in a solvent to form a solution

solution: a homogeneous mixture of two or more substances

solvent: the substance in which a solute dissolves to form a solution

strength: the property of how well a material withstands the application of a force.

sublimation: The change of state of a solid material to a gas without going through the liquid state

supersaturated solution: a solution containing more solute than a saturated solution and therefore not at equilibrium. This solution is not stable and cannot be maintained indefinitely

surface area: changing the nature of the reactants into smaller particles increases the surface exposed to react. Successful reaction depends on collision and increasing the area of the reactant increases the chance of a successful collision taking place. Lighting a log is more difficult than lighting wood shavings. The shavings have a greater surface area and speed up the reaction

suspension: heterogeneous mixture that contains fine solid or liquid particles in a fluid that will settle out spontaneously. By shaking the container they will again be dispersed throughout the fluid

synthesis reaction: a chemical reaction in which two or more substances combine to form a compound

temperature: the measure of the average kinetic energy of all the particles of the material

texture: the characteristics of the surface of a material, like how smooth, rough, or coarse it is

titration: an analytical procedure in which the concentration of an unknown solution is added to a standard solution until a color change of some indicator indicates that equivalent quantities have reacted

Tyndall effect: the scattering of a light beam as it passes through a colloid

uniformity: the property of how consistent a material is throughout

valence electrons: the outermost electrons of an atom. These electrons are used for chemical bonding of atoms

vaporization: the change of state from a liquid to a gas

viscosity: a property related to the resistance of a fluid to flow

wavelength: the distance measured from crest to crest of one complete wave or cycle

Glossary: Unit 4

Chapters 9-10
Active Biology

abiotic: the nonliving components of an ecosystem

adaptation: an inherited trait or set of traits that improve the chance of survival and reproduction of an organism

adaptive radiation: the diversification by natural selection, over evolutionary time, of a species or group of species into several different species that are typically adapted to different ecological niches

aquifer: any body of sediment or rock that has sufficient size and sufficiently high porosity and permeability to provide an adequate supply of water from wells

autotroph: an organism that is capable of obtaining its energy (food) directly from the physical environment

bilateral symmetry: a body plan that divides the body into symmetrical left and right halves

biodiversity: the sum of all the different types of organisms living on Earth

biosphere: the area on Earth where living organisms can be found

biotic: the living components of an ecosystem

birthrate (natality): the rate at which reproduction increases the size of a population

body fossil: a fossil that consists of the preserved body of an animal or plant or an imprint of the body

carbon cycle: the process in which carbon is passed from one organism to another, then to the abiotic community, and finally back to the plants

carnivore: an animal that feeds exclusively on other animals

carrying capacity: the maximum population that can be sustained by a given supply of resources

chromosome: threads of genetic material found in the nucleus of cells

climax community: the final, quite stable community reach during the stages of succession

community: all the populations of organisms occupying a given area

condensation: the process of changing from a gas to a liquid

consumer: a heterotrophic organism

death rate (mortality rate): the rate at which death decreases the size of a population

decomposers: organisms that break down the remains or wastes of other organisms to obtain their nutrients

denitrification: the conversion of nitrates and nitrites to nitrogen gas, which is released into the atmosphere

dominant: used to describe the gene that determines the expression of a genetic trait; the trait shows up even when the gene is present as a single copy

ecosystem: a community and the physical environment that it occupies

emigration: the number of individuals of a species that move out of an existing population

evaporation: the process of changing from a liquid to a gas

evolution: a gradual change in the characteristics of a population of organisms during successive generations, as a result of natural selection acting on genetic variation

extinction: the permanent disappearance of a species from Earth

fertilizer: a material used to provide or replace soil nutrients

food chain: a series of organisms through which food energy is passed in an ecosystem

food web: a complex relationship formed by interconnecting food chains in an ecosystem representing the transfer of energy through different levels

fossil: any evidence of past life preserved in sediments or rocks

gene: a unit of instruction located on a chromosome that produces or influences a specific trait in the offspring

genotype: the genes of an individual

groundwater: water contained in pore spaces in sediments and rocks beneath the Earth's surface

growth rate: the rate at which the size of a population increases as a result of death rate, birthrate, immigration, and emigration

herbivore: a heterotroph that feeds exclusively on plant materials

heredity: the passing of traits from parent to offspring

heterotroph: an organism that must obtain its energy from autotrophs or other heterotrophs

hypothesis: a statement that can be proved or disproved by experimental or observational evidence

immigration: the number of individuals of a species that move into an existing population

index fossil: a fossil of an organism that was widespread but lived for only a short interval of geological time

infiltration: the movement of water through pores or small openings into the soil and porous rock

invasive species: a nonnative species whose introduction does or is likely to cause economic or environmental harm or harm to human health

mass extinction: the extinction of a large number of species during short intervals of geological time

motile: having the ability to move spontaneously

natural selection: the differences in survival and reproduction among members of a population

niche: the ecological role of a species; the set of resources it consumes and habitats it occupies in an ecosystem

nitrogen cycle: the movement of nitrogen through ecosystems, the soil, and the atmosphere

nitrogen fixation: the process by which certain organisms produce nitrogen compounds from the gaseous nitrogen in the atmosphere

nonnative (exotic, alien, introduced, or non-indigenous) species: any species, including its seeds, eggs, spores, or other biological material capable of propagating that species, that is not native to that ecosystem

omnivores: a heterotroph that feeds on both plant materials and animals

open population: a natural population in which all four factors that affect population size (death rate, birthrate, immigration, and emigration) are functioning

organism: an individual living thing

phenotype: the observable traits of an organism that result because of the interaction of genes and the environment

phosphorous cycle: the cycling of environmental phosphorous through a long-term cycle involving rocks on the Earth's crust, and through a shorter cycle involving living organisms

pioneer community: the first species to appear during succession

population: a group of organisms of the same species occupying a given area

precipitation: water that falls to the Earth's surface from the atmosphere as liquid or solid material in the form of rain, snow, hail, or sleet

primary succession: the occupation by plant life of an area previously not covered with vegetation

producer: an organism that is capable of making its own food

pyramid of energy: a pyramid developed on the basis of the energy at each trophic level

pyramid of living matter: a pyramid developed on the basis of the mass of dry living matter at each trophic level

radial symmetry: a body plan that is symmetrical about a center axis

recessive: used to describe the gene that is overruled by a dominant gene; the trait is masked

runoff: the part of the precipitation appearing in surface streams

secondary succession: the occupation by plant life of an area that was previously covered with vegetation and still has soil

seral stages: the communities in between the pioneer and climax community during the stages of succession

sessile (non-motile): an organism that is permanently attached rather than free-moving

species: a group of organisms that can interbreed under natural conditions and produce fertile offspring

succession: the slow and orderly replacement of community replacement, one following the other

theory: a proven and generally accepted truth

thermodynamics: the study of energy transformations described by laws

trace fossil: any evidence of the life activities of a plant or animal that lived in the geologic past (but not including the fossil organism itself)

trait: an aspect of an organism that can be described or measured

transpiration: the emission of water vapor from pores of plants as part of their life processes

trophic level: the number of energy transfers an organism is from the original solar energy entering an ecosystem; the feeding level of one or more populations in a food web

water (hydrologic) cycle: the cycle or network of pathways taken by water in all three of its forms (solid, liquid, and vapor) among the various places where is it temporarily stored on, below, and above the Earth's surface

Spanish Glossary: Unit 1

Chapters I-3
Earth's Dynamic Geosphere

astenósfera (asthenosphere): la parte del manto debajo de la litosfera. La astenósfera pasa por un movimiento lento, en vez de actuar como un bloque rígido, como es la capa encima de la litosfera

basalto (basalt): tipo de piedra ígnea volcánica, generalmente de color oscuro, con un alto contenido de hierro

bomba volcánica (volcanic bomb): una masa de lava que fue expulsada cuando estaba viscosa y recibió una forma redonda (de más de 64 mm en diámetro) mientras estaba en vuelo

caldera: una gran depresión volcánica en forma de cuenca, más o menos circular, la cual muchas veces tiene un diámetro más grande que cualquiera de las aberturas

calentamiento termal (thermal convection): un patrón de movimiento en un flujo causado por calentamiento de abajo y enfriamiento de arriba El calentamiento termal transfiere energía de calor del fondo de la célula de calor a la superficie

cenizas (ash): material fino piroclástos (de menos de 2 mm en diámetro)

cono de escoria - estratovolcanes (composite cone - stratovolcano): un volcán que es construido de capas alternas de lava y depósitos piroclástos

cordilleras submarinas (mid-ocean ridge): una cadena de cordilleras debajo del agua que se extienden a través de todas las cuencas del océano, formadas y extendidas por el suelo marino

corteza (crust): la capa externa más delgada de la Tierra. La corteza continental es relativamente gruesa y mayormente muy vieja. La corteza oceánica es relativamente delgada, y siempre es geológicamente muy joven

declive continental (continental accretion): el crecimiento de un continente a lo largo de sus orillas

densidad (density): la masa por unidad de volumen de un material o una sustancia

epicentro (epicenter): el punto de la superficie de la Tierra directamente encima del foco de un terremoto

falla (fault): la rotura o la zona de rotura en la roca, por la cual las masas de roca se han movido relativamente de una a otra paralelamente a la rotura

falla transformante (transform fault): una superficie vertical de deslizamiento entre dos placas litosféricas por entre dos segmentos de una cima extendida

flujo de piroclástos (pyroclastic flor): una mezcla de alta densidad de ceniza caliente y fragmentos de rocas con gases calientes formados por una explosión volcánica o una expulsión aérea desde una abertura volcánica

foco (focus): el punto de un terremoto dentro de la Tierra donde primero ocurre la ruptura que causa un terremoto

fricción (friction): la fuerza que resiste el movimiento de una superficie contra otra superficie. El Sistema de Posicionamiento Global (GPS, por sus siglas en inglés): un sistema que utiliza un satélite para localizar con exactitud puntos en la Tierra

fuerza de rompimiento (shear strength): la fuerza de rompimiento necesaria para romper material sólido

guyote (seamount): una montaña debajo del agua que surge del suelo oceánico con una cima plana

Índice de explosividad volcánica (volcanic explosivity index): el porcentaje de piroclástos entre el total de productos de una erupción volcánica

intervalo de curvas de nivel (contour interval): la distancia vertical entre las elevaciones representadas por dos líneas sucesivas de curvas de nivel en un mapa topográfico

lahar: una mezcla húmeda de agua, barro, y fragmentos de roca volcánica, con la consistencia de concreto húmedo, que fluye por las pendientes de un volcán y sus valles

lapilli: piroclástos con un tamaño general entre 2 a 64 mm

lava: roca fundida que sale de un volcán o una fisura

límite convergente (convergent plate boundary): el límite de placas donde dos placas se mueven una en dirección a la otra

límite de transformación (transform plate boundary): el límite de placas donde dos placas se deslizan paralelamente una hacia la otra

límite divergente (divergent plate boundary): el límite de placas donde dos placas se mueven en dirección contraria una de la otra

línea de contorno (contour line): una línea en el mapa que conecta puntos con una elevación igual a la de la superficie terrestre

litosfera (lithosphere): la capa más externa de la Tierra, que consiste de la corteza terrestre y parte del manto superior. La litosfera actúa como una capa rígida, en contraste con la astenósfera

magma: material fundido de roca que ocurre naturalmente dentro de la Tierra. El magma contiene gases disueltos y algunas veces cristales

manto (mantle): la zona de la Tierra debajo de la corteza y sobre el núcleo. Esta dividida entre el manto superior y el manto inferior con una zona de transición entre ellas

mapa isosísmico (isoseismal map): un mapa que muestra las líneas conectando puntos en la superficie de la Tierra en el cual la intensidad de un terremoto es igual

mapa topográfico (topographic map): un mapa mostrando las características topográficas de la superficie terrestre

movimiento de lava (lava flow): un derramamiento de lava fundida de una abertura o fisura; también, el cuerpo sólido de una roca formada de esta manera

núcleo (core): la parte sólida más interna de la Tierra, que consiste mayormente de hierro

onda de superficie (surface wave): una onda sísmica que viaja a lo largo de la superficie de la Tierra

onda primaria (primary wave - P wave): una onda sísmica que envuelve movimientos de partículas (compresión y expansión) en la dirección en la cual la onda viaja. Es la más rápida de las ondas sísmicas

onda secundaria (secondary wave - S wave): onda sísmica producida por un movimiento repetitivo que envuelve vibración perpendicular en la dirección en la cual la onda esta viajando. Esta no viaja a través de líquidos, como el núcleo exterior de la Tierra. Esta llega más tarde que la onda P. ondas sísmicas

(seismic earthquake waves): un término general para todas las ondas elásticas en la Tierra, producidas por terremotos o generadas artificialmente por explosiones

paleomagnetismo (paleomagnetism): el récord de la orientación pasada y la polaridad del campo magnético de la Tierra registrado en las rocas que contienen el mineral magnetita

pangea: el supercontinente más reciente de la Tierra que fue separado alrededor de 200 millones de años atrás

peligro (hazard): un evento natural, como un terremoto, que tiene la posibilidad de hacer daños

placas tectónicas (plate tectonics): el campo de estudio del movimiento de placas

proyección de Mercator (Mercator projection): una proyección de mapa en el cual el Ecuador es representado por una línea recta hecha a escala, los meridianos por líneas rectas perpendiculares al Ecuador y con espacios iguales de acuerdo a la distancia que las separa del Ecuador, y los paralelos por líneas rectas perpendiculares a los meridianos en la misma longitud al Ecuador. Hay una gran distorción de las distancias, áreas y formas en las regiones polares

proyecciones de mapa (map projections): el proceso sistemático de transformar posiciones en la superficie esférica de la Tierra a un mapa plano mientras se mantienen relaciones espaciales

punto caliente (hot spot): una fuente fija de abundante magma que forma un centro volcánico y que ha existido por decenas de millones de años

rebote elástico (elastic rebound): el regreso de un sólido elástico doblado a su forma original después de remover la fuerza deformante

relieve (relief): la configuración física de una parte de la superficie de la Tierra, con referencia a las variaciones de altura y pendiente o las irregularidades en la superficie terrestre

resonancia (resonance): una condición en la cual una vibración afectando un objeto tiene el mismo periodo de tiempo a la vibración natural del objeto

riesgo (risk): el potencial impacto de un peligro natural en personas o propiedad

roca ígnea (igneous rock): roca o mineral que se ha solidificado de material fundido o parcialmente fundido, i.e., de magma

roca ígnea extrusiva - roca ígnea volcánica (extrusive igneous rock): una roca ígnea que se ha formada por la erupción de lava en la superficie de la Tierra

roca ígnea intrusiva - roca ígnea plutónica (intrusive igneous rock - plutonic igneous rock): roca ígnea formada a considerable profundidad por la cristalización de magma

sílice (silica): material con composición SiO_2

sismógrafo (seismometer): un instrumento que mide las ondas sísmicas. Recibe impulsos sísmicos y los convierte en una señal con un voltaje electrónico

sismograma (seismogram): el registro hecho por un sismógrafo

sismología (seismology): el estudio de terremotos y la estructura de la Tierra

subducción (subduction): movimiento de una placa hacia abajo del manto, debajo del borde de la otra placa en el límite convergente de la placa. La placa de abajo es siempre la litosfera oceánica. La placa que permanence en la superficie puede tener tanto litósfera oceánica o litósfera continental

supercontinente (supercontinent): un continente grande consistiendo de toda la litosfera continental de la Tierra. Los supercontinentes son formados por procesos placa-tectónico de conducción subterránea y colisión de continente a continente

tefra (tephra): un término colectivo para todas las partículas expulsada de un volcán y transportadas a través del aire. Incluyendo polvo volcánico, cenizas, rescoldos, lapilli, escoria, piedra pómez, bombas volcánicas y bloques volcánicos

terremoto (earthquake): un movimiento rápido o temblor en la Tierra causado por una liberación repentina de una tensión acumulada lentamente

tsunami: una gran ola producida por un terremoto submarino (o una erupción volcánica o deslizamiento de tierra)

valle de hendiduras (rift valley): la profunda grieta central en la cima de la cordillera medio-oceánica

valle de hendiduras (rift valley): un valle largo y grande en un continente, formado donde el continente es separado por fuerzas producidas cuando los materiales del manto se levantan bajo el continente

viscosidad (viscosity): la propiedad de un flujo que ofrece resistencia interna de movimiento

volcán escudo (shield volcano): un cono volcánico de cúpula plana, ancha y con una pendiente suave, generalmente con una extensión de varias decenas o cientos de millas cuadradas

zona de subducción (subduction zone): un cinturón largo y estrecho en el cual una placa desciende bajo otra

zona de sutura (suture zone): la zona en la superficie de la Tierra donde dos continentes han chocado y se han soldado para formar un solo continente

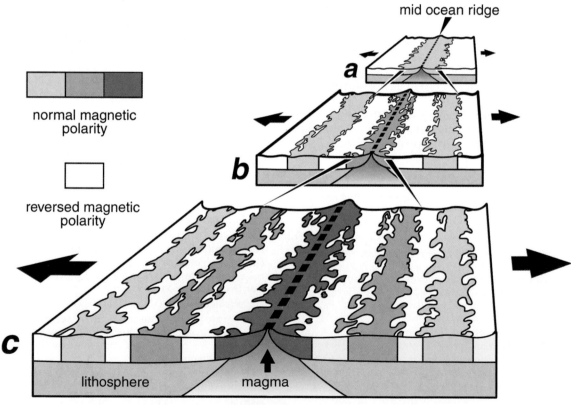

Spanish Glossary: Unit 2

Chapters 4-6
Active Physics

amplitud (amplitude): la altura de la cresta de una onda; está relacionado con la energía de la onda

análoga (analog): la descripción de una señal variable continúa o un circuito; una señal análoga puede ser representada como una serie de ondas

ángulo crítico (critical angle): el ángulo incidente más pequeño que hace que el rayo de luz pasando de un medio a otro pueda ser reflejado completamente

ángulo de incidencia (angle of incidence): el ángulo que se forma entre el rayo de luz y la normal o perpendicular de la superficie en el punto de incidencia

ángulo de reflexión (angle of reflection): el ángulo que hace un rayo reflejado con la normal o perpendicular de la superficie en el punto de reflexión

ángulo de refracción (angle of refraction): el ángulo que forma el rayo refractado con la normal o perpendicular de la superficie separando las dos materias atravesadas por el rayo

año luz (light-year): la distancia que viaja la luz en un año (9.46×10^{12}km)

capacitor: un componente de un circuito eléctrico usado para guardar carga temporalmente

circuito (circuit): una trayectoria de conducción cerrada con cables o alambres que conecta los componentes del circuito, a través de la cual fluye una corriente eléctrica

cresta (crest): el punto más alto de una onda

diagrama de un circuito (circuit diagram): un dibujo que usa un conjunto especial de símbolos para representar los componentes eléctricos y alambrado en un circuito eléctrico

digital: descripción de datos que han sido guardados o transmitidos como una secuencia de símbolos discretos; normalmente esto significa datos binarios (1s y 0s) representados usando señales electrónicas o electromagnéticas

efecto Doppler (Doppler effect): un cambio en la frecuencia observada de una onda cuando la fuente y un observador están en movimiento el uno hacia el otro; la frecuencia aumenta cuando la fuente o el observador se aproximan y se reduce cuando estos se separan

eje principal (principal axis): la línea que pasa por el punto de vista perpendicular al plano de perspectiva

espectro electromagnético (electromagnetic spectrum): el alcance completo de radiación extendiéndose en una frecuencia de aproximadamente 10^{23} hertz a 0 hertz; este incluye rayos gamas, rayos x, radiación ultravioleta, luz visible, radiación infrarroja, microondas y ondas de radio

foco (focus): el lugar en el cual los rayos de luz convergen o donde estos parecen divergir después de la refracción o reflejo; también llamado punto focal

frecuencia (frequency): el número de oscilaciones producidas por unidad de tiempo; la frecuencia es el recíproco de la cantidad de tiempo que le toma a una sola longitud de onda pasar un

imagen (image): reproducción de un objeto físico formado por un lente, espejo u otro instrumento óptico

imagen real (real image): una imagen que se proyecta sobre una pantalla o en la película de una cámara; los rayos de luz pasan a través de la imagen

imagen virtual (virtual image): una imagen de la cual los rayos reflejados o la luz refractada aparece divergida, como es la imagen vista en un espejo plano, no hay luz que venga directamente o que pase a través de la imagen

índice de refracción (index of refraction): la propiedad de un medio que esta relacionado con la velocidad de la luz a través de este; es calculado dividiendo la velocidad de la luz en el vacío por la velocidad de la luz en el medio

lente (lens): un pedazo de cristal curvo y pulido u otro material transparente usado para la refracción de luz

lente cóncavo (concave lens): un lente que causa que los rayos de luz paralelos se divergen; un lente que es más grueso en las orillas que en el centro

lente convexo (convex lens): un lente que causa que los rayos de luz paralelos converjan; un lente más delgado en las orillas que en el centro

lente convergente (converging lens): un rayo de luz paralelo pasando a través del lente es conducido a un punto real o enfoque (lente cóncavo)

lente divergente (diverging lens): rayos de luz paralelos que pasan a través del lente se divergen como si pasaran desde un punto detrás del lente (lente cóncavo

ley de Snell (Snell's law): describe la relación entre el índice de refracción y la proporción del seno del ángulo de incidencia y el seno del ángulo de refracción

longitud de la onda (wavelength): la distancia (medida en la dirección de la propagación) entre dos puntos idénticos en ciclos consecutivos de una onda

longitud focal (focal length): la distancia desde el centro de un lente o espejo hasta el punto focal

nodo (node): punto estacionario de una onda donde su desplazamiento es de cero

normal: en ángulos rectos; perpendicular

onda estacionaria (standing wave): la sobre posición de dos ondas viajando en direcciones opuestas caracterizada por la falta de vibración en ciertos puntos, entre las cuales la vibración máxima ocurre periódicamente; producida donde quiera que una onda es reducida entre límites, como es la vibración de la una cuerda de un instrumento musical

onda o pulso transversal (transverse pulse or wave): un pulso u onda en la cual el movimiento del medio es perpendicular al movimiento de la onda

onda o vibración de compresión (compression pulse or wave): una onda o vibración longitudinal causada mediante la compresión de un líquido, como es el sonido de una onda en el aire

onda periódica (periodic wave): una serie repetitiva de pulsaciones; una serie de ondas en la cuales las partículas de un medio atraviesan un movimiento periódico (después de un tiempo definido el medio vuelve a u punto de partida y comienza la repetición del movimiento)

paralaje (parallax): el cambio aparente en la posición de un objeto que sucede cuando se observa desde distintos ángulos o puntos de vista

pulsaciones u ondas longitudinales (longitudinal pulse or wave): una vibración u onda que desplaza la materia paralelamente a la dirección del movimiento de la onda

pulso de onda (wave pulse): una onda de duración fija (o corta); las partículas de un medio están en reposo hasta que llega el pulso y vuelven a reposar después que este pasa

rayo (ray): la trayectoria seguida por un rayo muy fino de luz

reflejo (reflection): el regreso de la ondas de luz o las ondas de sonido desde una superficie; la acción de rebote o doblamiento

refracción (refraction): el cambio en la dirección de los rayos de luz que pasan indirectamente entre dos medios diferentes

resistor: un instrumento eléctrico usado para impedir (resistir) el flujo de electrones en los conductores

seno (trough): el punto más bajo de la onda

telescopio de reflexión (reflecting telescope): instrumento óptico que usa un espejo cóncavo para acumular luz y hace que los objetos distantes parezcan más grandes

telescopio refractorio (refracting telescope): un instrumento óptico que usa lentes para acumular luz y hace que los objetos distantes parezcan más largos

tono (pitch): la calidad de un sonido depende principalmente en la frecuencia que las ondas de sonido producen por su fuente

tren de ondas (wave train): una serie continúa de ondas de pulso; las partículas de un medio están prolongadas

Active Physics

Spanish Glossary: Unit 3

Chapters 7-8
Active Chemistry

ácido (acid): una sustancia que produce iones de hidrógeno en agua, o es un donante de protones Indicador a base de ácido: una tinta tiene cierto color en una solución de ácido y un color diferente en una solución de base

aleación (alloy): una sustancia que tiene características de metales y consiste de dos o más elementos diferentes

anión (anion): un ión con carga negativa

área de superficie (surface area): cambiar la naturaleza de los reactivos a pequeñas partículas aumenta la superficie expuesta a la reacción. Una reacción exitosa depende en el choque y aumento de área de los reactivos aumentando así la oportunidad de que un choque exitoso se lleve a cabo. Encender un tronco es más difícil que encender virutas de madera. Las virutas tienen un área de mayor superficie y aceleran la reacción

átomo (atom): la parte representativa más pequeña de un elemento

base: una sustancia que libera iones de hidróxido (OH-) en agua, o es un aceptador de protones

brillo/lustre (luster): el reflejo de la luz desde la superficie de un material descrito por su calidad e intensidad

cambio de fase (phase change): la conversión de una sustancia de un estado a otro a una temperatura y presión específica. Ejemplo: sólido a líquido, líquido a gaseoso, o sólido a gaseoso (sublimación)

cambio físico (physical change): un cambio que envuelve cambios en el estado o forma de una sustancia pero que no causa ningún cambio en su composición química

cambio químico (chemical change): un cambio que convierte la composición química de una sustancia a una(s) sustancia(s) diferente con una composición química diferente

catalizador (catalyst): una sustancia que cambia la velocidad de una reacción química sin cambiarse a si misma permanentemente

catión (cation): un ión con carga positiva

coloide (colloid): una mezcla que contiene partículas más grande que el soluto pero suficientemente pequeñas para mantenerse suspendidas en un fase continúa en otro componente. Esta mezcla tambien es conocida como una dispersión coloidal

combustión (combustion): la reacción rápida de un material con oxígeno acompañado por una evolución rápida por la flama y el calor

compuesto (composite): una mezcla heterogénea sólida de dos o más sustancias que hacen uso de las propiedades de cada componente

compuesto binario (binary compound): un compuesto formado por la combinación de dos elementos diferentes

compuesto iónico (ionic compound): un compuesto que consiste de iones positivos y negativos

compuesto molecular (molecular compound): dos o más átomos enlazados al compartir electrones (enlace covalente)

compuesto orgánico (organic compound): un compuesto molecular de carbono

concentración (concentration): la medida de la composición de una solución, algunas veces dada en términos de moles de un soluto por litro de solución

conductibilidad (conductivity): la propiedad de transmitir calor y electricidad

configuración de un electrón (electron configuration): la distribución de electrones en los niveles de energía de un átomo

constante de Planck (Planck's constant): una constante proporcional de energía de un fotón a su frecuencia, derivada por Max Planck en el 1900. Su ecuación fue E = hf y la constante de Planck es (h) = 6.626×10^{-34} J·s

densidad (density): la masa por unidad de volumen de un material

descomposición (decomposition): una reacción química en la cual un compuesto sencillo reacciona para dar dos o más productos

ductibilidad (ductility): una propiedad que describe cuan fácil es convertir una sustancia a una forma nueva y permanente, como es, cambiarla a alambres

efecto Tyndall (Tyndall effect): la diseminación de un rayo de luz cuando este pasa a través de un coloide

elasticidad (elasticity): la propiedad de un material al resistir una deformación y regresar a su tamaño o forma normal después que se le ha aplicado fuerza

electrólisis (electrolysis): la conducción de electricidad a través de una solución que contiene iones o a través de un compuesto iónico fundido que induzca cambio químico

electrón (electron): una particular subatómica que ocurre fuera del núcleo y que tiene una carga de -1 y una masa de 9.109×10^{-28}g

electrones de valencia (valence electrons): los electrones más externos de un átomo. Estos electrones son usados para enlazar químicamente a los átomos

elemento (element): una sustancia en la cual todos los átomos tienen el mismo número atómico

emulsión (emulsion): un coloide o una dispersión coloidal de un líquido suspendido en otro

energía cinética (kinetic energy): una forma de energía relacionada al movimiento de una partícula ($KE = \frac{1}{2}mv^2$)

energía ionizante (ionization energy): la energía requerida para remover un electrón en un átomo gaseoso en un estado firme

energía potencial (potential energy): energía reservada de un material como resultado de su posición en un campo eléctrico, magnético o gravitacional

enlace covalente (covalent bond): un enlace formado cuando dos átomos se combinan y comparten pares de electrones entre ellos

enlace iónico (ionic bond): la atracción entre iones con cargas opuestas

espectro electromagnético (electromagnetic spectrum): el espectro completo de radiación electromagnética, como son las ondas de radio, microondas, infrarrojas, visible, ultravioleta, rayos-x y rayos gama

fisión (fission): el proceso de dividir el núcleo en núcleos más pequeños y con la liberación de grandes cantidades de energía

formula química (chemical formula): la combinación de los símbolos de los elementos en una proporción numérica definida usada para representar moléculas, compuestos, radicales, iones, etc.

frecuencia (frequency): el número de ondas por segundo o ciclos por segundo o hertz (Hz)

fuerza (strength): la propiedad de cuan bien un material resiste el empleo de una fuerza

fusión (fusion): núcleos de átomos ligeros combinados para formar núcleos con mayor masa y liberando una cantidad mayor de energía

gas noble (noble gas): una familia de elementos (Grupo 18 o VIIIA) de la tabla periódica

grupo químico (chemical group): una familia de elementos en la tabla periódica que tienen la configuración de electrones similares

halógenos (halogens): Grupo VIIA (17) en la tabla periódica consistiendo de flúor, cloro, bromo, yodo, y astatín

hidrocarbono (hydrocarbon): un compuesto molecular conteniendo solamente hidrógeno y carbón

compuesto inorgánico: un compuesto que no esta basado en compuestos moleculares de carbón

ión (ion): un átomo o grupo de átomos cargados eléctricamente que han adquirido una carga neta, positiva o negativa

ión poliatómico (polyatomic ion): un ión que consiste de 2 ó más átomos que están enlazados covalentemente y tiene una carga positiva o negativa

isótopo (isotope): Átomos del mismo elemento pero con diferente masa atómica debido a diferente número de neutrones

ley de proporciones definida (law of Definite Proportions): la composición de una sustancia pura es siempre la misma o los elementos del compuesto siempre se combinan en la misma proporción de masa

longitud de la onda (wavelength): la distancia medida de una cresta a otra en una onda o ciclo completo

maleabilidad (malleability): la propiedad de un material de poder ser martillado a varias formas sin romperse

masa atómica (atomic mass): la masa atómica es determinada por la masa de protones y neutrones de un átomo

material puro (pure material): un elemento o compuesto que tiene una composición y propiedades definidas

metales (metal): tipos de materiales que exhiben las propiedades de conductividad, maleabilidad, reactividad y ductilidad. los elementos de metales fácilmente pierden electrones para formar iones positivos

mezcla (compound): un material que consiste de dos o más elementos unidos en una proporción definida

mol (mole): una colección de objetos que contienen el número de Avogadro (6.022×10^{23})

neutralización (neutralization): el proceso de un ácido y una base reaccionando para formar agua y sal

neutrón (neutron): partícula neutral subatómica con una masa de 1.675×10^{-24} g situada en el núcleo del átomo

no metales (nonmetal): elementos que no exhiben las propiedades de maleabilidad, reactividad, y ductilidad. Estos elementos tienden a formar iones negativos. El óxido de los elementos es acídico

núcleo (nucleus): el bien denso corazón del átomo que contiene los neutrones y protones

número de Avogadro (Avogadro's number): el número de átomos que hay en 12 gramos de carbón-12. El número es 6.022×10^{23}

número de oxidación (oxidation number): un número asignado a un elemento en un compuesto designando el número de electrones que el elemento ha perdido, ganado o compartido al formar ese compuesto

órbita (orbit): la trayectoria de un electrón en su movimiento alrededor del núcleo del átomo de hidrógeno de Bohr

orbital (orbital): en el modelo mecánico quanta de un átomo, es la región que rodea el núcleo atómico en el cual la distribución del electrón es dada por una función de onda

oxidación (oxidation): el proceso de perdida de uno o más electrones en una sustancia

periodo (period): una línea horizontal de elementos en la tabla periódica

pH (pH): la cantidad usada para representar la acidez en una solución basada en la concentración de iones de hidrogeno $(pH = -\log[H+])$

polimerización (polymerization): una reacción química que convierte moléculas pequeñas (monómeros) a moléculas grandes (polímeros)

polímero (polymer): una sustancia que es una macromolécula consistiendo de muchas moléculas pequeñas similares (monómeros) enlazadas en largas cadenas

precipitar (precipitate): un sólido insoluble formado en una solución líquida como resultado de algunas reacciones químicas

precisión (precision): la proximidad de acuerdo en muchas medidas de la misma cantidad

presición (accuracy): cuán cerca es el valor de la medida al estándar o al valor aceptado de esa medida

producto (product): la(s) sustancia(s) producida(s) en una reacción química

propiedad coligativa (colligative property): una propiedad como la depresión del punto de congelación o la elevación del punto de ebullición en las cuales su valor físico depende solamente en la proporción de las partículas del soluto y el solvente y no en sus identidades químicas

propiedad física (physical property): una propiedad que puede ser medida sin causar un cambio en la composición química de la sustancia

propiedad química (chemical property): una característica que sufre una sustancia en una reacción química que produce una(s) nueva(s) sustancia(s)

protón (proton): una partícula subatómica cargada positivamente contenida en el núcleo de un átomo. La masa de un protón es 1.673×10^{-24}g y tiene una carga de $+1$

prueba de llama (flame test): una técnica o proceso experimental para identificar a un metal por sus características de color en una llama

prueba química (chemical test): un procedimiento físico o reacción química usada para identificar una sustancia

punto normal de congelación (normal freezing point): La temperatura característica, de 1 atm, en la cual un material cambia de un estado líquido a uno sólido

punto normal de ebullición (normal boiling point): la temperatura en la cual la presión de vapor de un líquido puro iguala 1 atm

punto normal de fundición (normal melting point): la temperatura característica, de 1 atm, en la cual un material cambia de un estado sólido a uno líquido

radioactivo (radioactive): un átomo que tiene un núcleo inestable y emitirá partículas alfa, positrón o beta para poder conseguir un núcleo más estable

reacción de desplazamiento doble (double-displacement reaction): una reacción química en la cual dos compuestos iónicos "intercambian" cationes para producir dos nuevos compuestos

reacción de reemplazo simple (single-displacement reaction): una reacción en la cual un elemento desplaza o reemplaza a otro elemento en un compuesto **reacción de síntesis (synthesis reaction):** una reacción química en la cual dos o más sustancias se combinan para formar un compuesto

reacción o cambio endotérmico (endothermic change or reaction): un cambio en el cual la energía en la forma de calor es absorbida por el ambiente circundante resultando en un aumento en la energía interna del sistema

reacción o cambio exotérmico (exothermic change or reaction): un cambio en el cual la energía en la forma de calor es liberada por el ambiente circundante resultando en un disminución en la energía interna del sistema

reacción química (chemical reaction): el proceso en el cual una(s) nueva(s) sustancia(s) es (son) formada(s) por una(s) primera(s) sustancia(s)

reactividad (reactivity): una propiedad que describe cuan fácilmente un material reaccionará con otro

reactivos (reactants): los materiales que empiezan una reacción química

rebote (bounce): la habilidad de un objeto para regresar a su posición original cuando es tirado desde cierta altura

reducción (reduction): un proceso en el cual la sustancia bajo consideración gana electrón(es)

solución (solution): una mezcla homogénea de dos o más sustancias

solución saturada (saturated solution): la cantidad máxima de un soluto que puede ser disuelta a cierta temperatura y presión

solución sobresaturada (supersaturated solution): una solución conteniendo más soluto que solución saturada y que por lo tanto está desequilibrada. Esta solución no es estable y no se puede mantener indefinidamente

soluto (solute): la sustancia que se disuelve en un solvente para formar una solución

solvente (solvent): la sustancia en la cual un soluto se disuelve para formar una solución

sublimación (sublimation): el cambio en el estado de un material sólido a gaseoso sin pasar por el estado líquido

substancia pura (pure substance): una sustancia que solamente contiene un tipo de partícula

suspensión (suspension): mezcla heterogénea que contiene partículas sólidas finas o líquidas en un líquido y que se asentarán espontáneamente. Al agitar el envase volverán a dispersarse a través del líquido

temperatura (temperature): la medida de la energía cinética promedio de todas las partículas en el material

textura (texture): las características en la superficie de un material, como cuan suave, áspera, o gruesa es

titración (titration): un procedimiento analítico en el cual la concentración de una solución desconocida es añadida a una solución estándar hasta que el color de algún indicador cambia indicando que las cantidades equivalentes han reaccionado

unidad de masa atómica (atomic mass unit - amu): una unidad de masa definida como una doceava parte de la masa de un átomo de carbono-12

uniformidad (uniformity): la propiedad de consistencia que tiene un material

vaporización (vaporization): el cambio de estado líquido a gaseoso

viscosidad (viscosity): una propiedad relacionada con la resistencia de un líquido a fluir

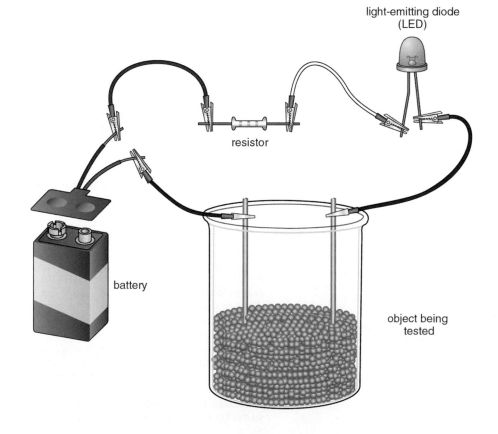

light-emitting diode (LED)

resistor

battery

object being tested

Spanish Glossary: Unit 4

Chapters 9-10
Active Biology

abiótico (abiotic): los componentes sin vida de un ecosistema

acuífero (aquifer): cualquier cuerpo de sedimento o roca que tiene suficiente tamaño, nivel de porosidad y permeabilidad para permitir un suministro adecuado de agua de los pozos

adaptación (adaptation): un rasgo o conjunto de rasgos heredados que mejoran las posibilidades de supervivencia y reproducción de un organismo

agua subterránea (groundwater): agua que se encuentra en los poros de las rocas y el sedimento debajo de la superficie de la Tierra

autótrofo quimio-sintético (autotroph): un organismo que puede sintetizar su propia energía (alimento) directamente del ambiente físico

biodiversidad (biodiversity): la suma de todos los tipos diferentes de organismos vivos en la Tierra

biosfera (biosphere): el área en la Tierra donde se puede encontrar organismos vivos

biótico (biotic): los componentes vivos en un ecosistema

cadena alimenticia (food chain): una serie de organismos por los cuales pasa energía alimenticia en un ecosistema

capacidad de carga (carrying capacity): la población máxima que puede se sostenida por un suministro determinado de recursos

carnívoro (carnivore): un animal que se alimenta exclusivamente de otros animales

ciclo (hidrológico) del agua (water–hydrologic–cycle): el ciclo o la red de senderos tomados por el agua en todas sus formas (sólida, líquida y gaseosa) entre los varios lugares donde es guardada temporalmente en, bajo o sobre la superficie de la Tierra

ciclo de nitrógeno (nitrogen cycle): el movimiento del nitrógeno a través de los ecosistemas, el suelo y la atmósfera

ciclo del fósforo (phosphorous cycle): el ciclismo del fósforo ambiental a través de un ciclo a largo plazo envolviendo rocas en la corteza de la tierra y a través de un ciclo corto envolviendo organismos vivos

ciclo de carbono (carbon cycle): el proceso en el cual el carbono es pasado de un organismo a otro, de ahí a la comunidad abiótica y finalmente de vuelta a las plantas

comunidad (community): todas las poblaciones de organismos ocupando una área determinada

comunidad culminante (climax community): el final que una comunidad estable alcanza durante las etapas de sucesión

comunidad pionera (pioneer community): las primeras especies en aparecer durante la sucesión

condensación (condensation): el proceso de cambio de gas a líquido

consumidor (consumer): un organismo heterótrofo

cromosoma (chromosome): hilo de material genético encontrado en el núcleo de las células

desnitrificación (denitrification): la conversión de nitratos y nitritos a gas nitrógeno, el cual es liberado en la atmósfera

dominante (dominant): se usa para describir el gene que determina la expresión de un rasgo genético; el rasgo que se muestra

ecosistema (ecosystem): una comunidad y el medio ambiente físico que esta ocupa

emigración (emigration): el número de individuos en una especie que se muda fuera de una población existente

escurrimiento superficial (runoff): la parte de la precipitación que aparece en chorros superficiales

especies (species): un grupo de organismos que pueden ser reproducidos entre si bajo condiciones naturales y producir descendencia fértil

especies invasivas (invasive species): una especie que no es natural del área y que su introducción causa o puede causar daño económico, ambiental o a la salud humana

especies no naturales – exóticas, extranjeras, introducidas o no indígenas (nonnative - exotic, alien, introduced, or non-indigenous) species: cualquier especie, incluyendo sus semillas, huevos, esporas u otro material biológico capaz de propagar la especie y que no es natural de ese ecosistema

etapas serales (seral stages): las comunidades entre la comunidad pionera y la culminante durante las etapas de sucesión

evaporación (evaporation): el proceso de cambio de un líquido a un gas

evolución (evolution): cambio gradual en las características de una población de organismos durante generaciones sucesivas, como resultado de selección natural o variación genética

extinción (extinction): la desaparición permanente de una especie en la Tierra

extinción en masa (mass extinction): la extinción de un gran número de especies durante intervalos cortos en una era geológica

fenotipo (phenotype): los rasgos externos de un organismo que son el resultado de una interacción de los genes y el medio ambiente

fertilizador (fertilizer): un material usado para proveer o reemplazar nutrientes en el suelo

fijación del nitrógeno (nitrogen fixation): el proceso por el cual algunos organismos producen compuestos de nitrógeno del nitrógeno gaseoso en la atmósfera

fósil (fossil): cualquier evidencia de vida pasada preservada en sedimento o rocas

fósil de organismo (body fossil): un fósil que consiste del cuerpo preservado de un animal, planta o la impresión de un cuerpo

fósil índice (index fossil): el fósil de un organismo que se extendió pero vivió solamente por un corto intervalo de una era geológica

gene: una unidad de instrucción ubicada en un cromosoma que produce o influye un rasgo específico en la descendencia

genotipo (genotype): los genes de un individuo

herencia (heredity): el paso de rasgos de los padres a los descendientes

hervíboro (herbivore): un heterótrofo que se alimenta exclusivamente de plantas

heterótrofo (heterotroph): un organismo que debe obtener su energía de autótrofos u otros heterótrofos

hipótesis (hypothesis): proposición que puede ser probada o refutada por evidencia experimental o de observación

huella de fósil (trace fossil): cualquier evidencia de las actividades de vida de una planta o un animal que vivió en el pasado geológico (pero sin incluir el organismo fósil)

infiltración (infiltration): el movimiento del agua pasando por poros o pequeñas aberturas en el suelo o en roca porosa

inmigración (immigration): el número de individuos en una especie que se mueve adentro de una población ya existente

móvil (motile): tener la habilidad de moverse espontáneamente

nicho (niche): el rol ecológico de las especies; el conjunto de recursos que consume y los medios físicos ocupados en un ecosistema

nivel trófico (trophic level): el número de transferencias de energía un organismo tiene de la energía solar original que está entrando en un ecosistema; el nivel de alimentación de una o más poblaciones en una red alimenticia

omnívoro (omnivores): un heterótrofo que se alimenta tanto de plantas como de animales

organismo (organism): un ser vivo individual

organismos de descomposición (decomposers): organismos que descomponen los restos o desperdicios de otros organismos para obtener sus alimentos

pirámide de energía (pyramid of energy): una pirámide desarrollada basada en energía en cada nivel trófico

pirámide de material viviente (pyramid of living matter): una pirámide desarrollada basada en la masa de material viviente seca en cada nivel trófico

población (population): un grupo de organismos de la misma especie ocupando una área determinada

población abierta (open population): una población natural en la cual los cuatro factores que afectan el tamaño de la población (tasa de mortalidad, tasa de natalidad, inmigración y emigración) están en funcionamiento

precipitación (precipitation): agua que cae de la atmósfera sobre la superficie de la Tierra como material líquido o sólido en forma de lluvia, nieve, cellisca o granizo

primera sucesión (primary succession): la ocupación de una vida vegetal en un área que anteriormente no estaba cubierta por vegetación

productor (producer): un organismo que sintetiza su propio alimento

radiación adaptativa (adaptive radiation): la diversificación por selección natural, a través de tiempo evolutivo, de especies o grupos de especies a muchas diferentes especies que se adaptan regularmente a diferentes nichos ecológicos

rasgo (trait): característica de un organismo que puede ser descrito o medido

recesivo (recessive): se usa para describir el gene que es anulado por un gene dominante; el rasgo está encubierto

red alimenticia (food web): relación compleja formada por cadenas alimenticias interconectadas en un ecosistema representando el traslado de energía a través de diferentes niveles

selección natural (natural selection): la diferencia en supervivencia y reproducción entre los miembros de una población

sésil (sessile; non-motile): un organismo que está permanentemente unido, sin movimiento libre

simetría bilateral (bilateral symmetry): disposición de las partes de un organismo que se divide en dos mitades simétricas, derecha e izquierda

simetría radial (radial symmetry): disposición de las partes de un organismo que tiene simetría sobre el eje central

sucesión (succession): el lento y ordenado reemplazo de la comunidad de reemplazo, una siguiendo a la otra

sucesión secundaria (secondary succession): la ocupación de vida vegetal en una área que estaba cubierta anteriormente por vegetación y que todavía tiene tierra

tasa de crecimiento (growth rate): la proporción a la cual el tamaño de la población aumenta como resultado de la tasa de mortalidad, la tasa de natalidad, la inmigración y la emigración

tasa de mortalidad (death rate – mortality rate): la proporción a la cual las muertes disminuyen el tamaño de la población

tasa de natalidad (birthrate – natality): la proporción a la cual la reproducción aumenta el tamaño de la población

termodinámicas (thermodynamics): el estudio de la transformación de la energía descrita por las leyes

transpiración (transpiration): la emisión de vapor de agua de los poros de las plantas como parte de sus procesos de vida

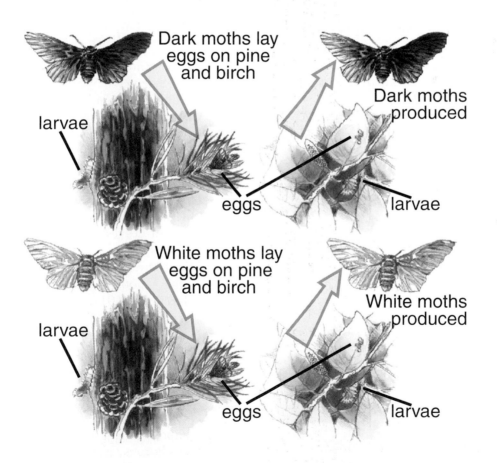

Charts/Graphs/Tables

Index: Unit 1

Chapters 1-3
Earth's Dynamic
Geosphere

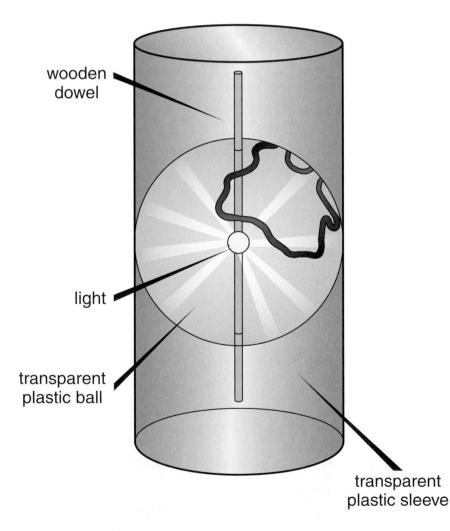

wooden dowel

light

transparent plastic ball

transparent plastic sleeve

Index: Unit 2

Chapters 4-6
Active Physics

Index: Unit 3

Chapters 7-8
Active Chemistry

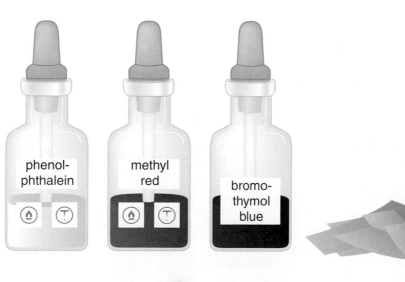

Index: Unit 4

Chapters 9-10
Active Biology

Photos and Illustrations

Chapters 1-3: EarthComm

4 Krakatoa: Source National Geophysical Data Center (NGDC) (P. Hedervari)

7, 10, 12 17, 65, 708, 72, 77, 78, 81, 84, 85 *Fig. 5*, 95, 109, 110, 115, 116, 117, 118, 125, 126, 129, 134, 135, 137, 141, 150, 151, 159, 160, 170 illustrations by Stuart Armstrong

8, 18, 20, 24, 27, 34, 37, 39, 46, 49, 71, 92 source United States Geological Survey (U.S. Geological Survey)

9 photo by R.T. Holcomb U.S. Geological Survey Hawaii Volcanoes Observatory (U.S. Geological Survey HVO) 1974.

11, 13, 31, 34, 35, 36, 44, 51, 57, 68, 83, 85 *Fig. 4*, 93, 94, 98, 101, 153 illustrations by Stuart Armstrong, source U.S. Geological Survey

12 *Fig 4* photo by Lina Galtieri.

15 photo by D.W. Peterson U.S. Geological Survey HVO 1972.

18, 47, 59, 36 photos by Bruce Molnia

20 adapted from Earth Science, 7th Edition, Tarbuck and Lutgens, 1994.

21 *Fig 2* photo by Jim. D Griggs U.S. Geological Survey HVO, *Fig 3* photo by Gary Smith

22 *Fig 4* University of Colorado *Fig 5*

23 *Fig 6* photo by Gary Smith

29 Photos by Jim D. Griggs U.S. Geological Survey HVO. 1989, 1990.

30 *Fig 4* photo by Department of Natural Resources, State of Washington.

37 *Fig 2 (left)* photo by T.J. Casadevall 1991 *(right)* photo by R.L. Rieger, U.S. Navy

46 photos by Rich Busch, map source U.S. Geological Survey

48, 49, 89 photos by Rich Busch

52 photo courtesy Dia Met Minerals Ltd.

54 Montserrat Observatory

65, 66 illustrations by Stuart Armstrong, source MIT Global Time Series webpage

62 photo by R.W. Griggs U.S. Geological Survey HVO 1989

63 photo by Jim D. Griggs U.S. Geological Survey HVO 1971

71 *Fig 2* photo by Laszlo Kesthelyi U.S. Geological Survey 1997.

73, 74 National Ocean and Atmospheric Administration

86 photo by P. Rona, NOAA, OAR/National Undersea Research Program (NURP)

99 illustration by Stuart Armstrong, source This Dynamic Planet Map – USGS, Smithsonian, US Naval Research Laboratory

104 photo by Jennifer Wang 1998.

113, 122 Photo Disk

123 source University of Colorado

125 photo by Eric Shih, American Geological Institute

130 illustration by Stuart Armstrong adapted from B.A. Bolt.

132 photo courtesy Veritas DGC, Inc.

138 illustration by Stuart Armstrong, source American Geological Institute

139 photo by Peter Bormann

142 Reinsurance Company, Munich, Germany

146 photo by J. Dewey U.S. Geological Survey Northridge Earthquake 1994

156 EROS Data Center, U.S. Geological Survey.

161 IRIS

165 United State Department of the Interior

168 photo by Roger Hutchison

169 *(top)* Reinsurance Company, Munich, Germany; *(middle)* University of California, Berkeley; *(bottom)* NOAA NGDC

Chapters 4-6: Active Physics

182, 194, 201, 210, 216, 223, 230, 236, 243, 254, 259, 264, 270, 276, 281, 291, 300, 306, 311, 316, 323, 329, 335, 340, 345, illustrations by Tomas Bunk

183-186, 195, 196, 203, 204 *(top)*, 211-214, 217-219, 224, 225, 231, 237, 238, 241, 244, 255, 256, 265-267, 276-278, 282, 301-304, 306, 307, 324, 325, 331, 336, 339 technical illustrations by Burmar

200 photo Courtesy of Steinway & Sons

289 photo by Mekea Z. Hurwitz, Courtesy of The Riverdale Press,

313 photo Courtesy of National Space Science Data Center

all other photos by PhotoDisc Inc.

Chapters 7-8: Active Chemistry

425 photo by Doug Brown of Robert Hobbs, Physics Instructor, Bellevue Community College, Bellevue, Washington

358, 360, 366, 377, 385, 395, 404, 412, 419, 436, 443, 449, 456, 466, 473, 480, 490 illustrations by Tomas Bunk

361, 362, 368, 369, 378, 380, 382, 386, 390, 392, 398, 399, 421, 438, 445, 446, 451, 458, 461, 467, 468, 469, 474, 475, 481, 482, 486, 489 Illustrations by Burmar

371 CHF Chemistry Web Quest

389, 428, 472, 494 by Digital Stock

370 Liberty on Line (libertyonline.hypermall.com/Aristotle)

357 The Nature of Physical Science (www.hcc.hawaii.edu)

381 388, photos by The Nobel Foundation

440, 454, 487 photos by John Nordland

Chapter 7 and 8 Sidebars, 355, 356, 357, 364, 373, 375, 389, 391, 394, 415, 418, 433, 434, 435, 439, 447, 469, 477, 479, 488, 491, 492 by PhotoDisc

457 photo by A.R.Smith, Department of Chemistry, Appalachian State University

Chapters 9-10: Active Biology

498, 502, 514, 522, 529, 538, 546, 553, 561, 567, 576, 580, 590, 597, 607, 617, illustrations by Tomas Bunk

503, 504, 505, 506, 507, 515, 517, 523, 524, 548, 556, 562, 564, 565, 570, 572, 585, 600, 601, illustrations by Dennis Falcon

539, 540, 569, 591, 608, 609 top, 610, 614, 618 bottom, 619, 620, illustrations by Burmar

554, 560, illustrations by Kadi Sarv

500-501 top, 578-579 bottom, photos by Digital Stock

512, 528, 581 top right, 583 middle right, photos courtesy of U.S. Fish and Wildlife Service

536, photo courtesy of The Funke Foundation

543, photo by David Jones

552, photo by Department of Natural Resources, State of Washington

570 bottom, photo courtesy of Oklahoma State University

582 middle right, photo courtesy of kidzone.ws

594, 603, photos by Photo Researchers, Inc.

609 bottom, photo by Albert M. Hines

612 top left, photo by Doug Sherman; 612 top right, photo by Bruce Molina; 612 bottom, photo courtesy of Peabody Museum of Natural History

618 top, photo courtesy of Paleontological Research Institution

622, photo by Araki Kazunari

623, photo courtesy of Smithsonian Institution

624, photo by Pat Holroyd

all other photos by Getty Images

Periodic Table of the Elements

GROUP

| 1 | 2 | 3 | 4 | 5 | 6 | 7 | 8 | 9 |

KEY

```
1  ──── Atomic Number
      2.1  ──── Electronegativity
   1  ──── Oxidation Number
   H  ──── Symbol
1.00794  ──── Average Atomic Mass
   1s'  ──── Electron Configuration
Hydrogen  ──── Name
```

- Gases at room temperature
- Liquids at room temperature
- Solids at room temperature
- Metals
- Metalloids
- Nonmetals

PERIOD

Period 1

IA/1A — Alkali Metals

1	2.1
1	
H	
1.00794	
$1s^1$	
Hydrogen	

Period 2

IIA/2A — Alkaline Earth Metals

3	1.0	4	1.5
1		2	
Li		**Be**	
6.941		9.012182	
$1s^22s^1$		$1s^22s^1$	
Lithium		Beryllium	

Period 3

11	0.9	12	1.2
1		2	
Na		**Mg**	
22.98977		24.3050	
$[Ne]3s^1$		$[Ne]3s^2$	
Sodium		Magnesium	

Transition Metals

| IIIB/3B | IVB/4B | VB/5B | VIB/6B | VIIB/7B | VIIIB/8B |

Period 4

19 0.8	20 1.0	21 1.3	22 1.5	23 1.6	24 1.6	25 1.5	26 1.8	27 1.9
1	2	3	3,4	2,3,4,5	2,3,6	2,3,4,6,7	2,3	2,3
K	**Ca**	**Sc**	**Ti**	**V**	**Cr**	**Mn**	**Fe**	**Co**
39.0983	40.078	44.95591	47.867	50.9415	51.9961	54.93805	55.847	58.93320
$[Ar]4s^1$	$[Ar]4s^2$	$[Ar]4s^23d^1$	$[Ar]4s^23d^2$	$[Ar]4s^23d^3$	$[Ar]4s^23d^4$	$[Ar]4s^23d^5$	$[Ar]4s^23d^6$	$[Ar]4s^23d^7$
Potassium	Calcium	Scandium	Titanium	Vanadium	Chromium	Manganese	Iron	Cobalt

Period 5

37 0.8	38 1.0	39 1.2	40 1.4	41 1.6	42 1.8	43 1.9	44 2.2	45 2.2
1	2	3	4	3,5	2,3,4,5,6	7	2,3,4,6,8	2,3,4
Rb	**Sr**	**Y**	**Zr**	**Nb**	**Mo**	**Tc**	**Ru**	**Rh**
85.4678	87.62	88.90585	91.224	92.90638	95.94	98.9072	101.07	102.90550
$[Kr]5s^1$	$[Kr]5s^2$	$[Kr]5s^24d^1$	$[Kr]5s^24d^2$	$[Kr]5s^24d^3$	$[Kr]5s^24d^4$	$[Kr]5s^24d^5$	$[Kr]5s^24d^6$	$[Kr]5s^24d^7$
Rubidium	Strontium	Yttrium	Zirconium	Niobium	Molybdenum	Technetium	Ruthenium	Rhodium

Period 6

55 0.7	56 0.9	57 1.1	72 1.3	73 1.5	74 1.7	75 1.9	76 2.2	77 2.2
1	2	3	4	5	2,3,4,6,8	2,4,6,7	2,3,4,6,8	2,3,4,6
Cs	**Ba**	***La**	**Hf**	**Ta**	**W**	**Re**	**Os**	**Ir**
132.90543	137.327	138.9055	178.49	180.9479	183.85	186.207	190.23	192.22
$[Xe]6s^1$	$[Xe]6s^2$	$[Xe]6s^24f^1$	$[Xe]6s^24f^{14}5d^2$	$[Xe]6s^24f^{14}5d^3$	$[Xe]6s^24f^{14}5d^4$	$[Xe]6s^24f^{14}5d^5$	$[Xe]6s^24f^{14}5d^6$	$[Xe]6s^24f^{14}5d^7$
Cesium	Barium	Lanthanum	Hafnium	Tantalum	Tungsten	Rhenium	Osmium	Iridium

Period 7

87 0.7	88 0.9	89 1.1	104	105	106	107	108	109
1	2	3						
Fr	**Ra**	****Ac**	**Rf**	**Db**	**Sg**	**Bh**	**Hs**	**Mt**
223.0197	226.0254	227.0278	(261)	(262)	(263)	(262)	(265)	(265)
$[Rn]7s^1$	$[Rn]7s^2$	$[Rn]7s^25f^1$	$[Rn]7s^25f^{14}6d^2$	$[Rn]7s^25f^{14}6d^3$	$[Rn]7s^25f^{14}6d^4$	$[Rn]7s^25f^{14}6d^5$	$[Rn]7s^25f^{14}6d^6$	$[Rn]7s^25f^{14}6d^7$
Francium	Radium	Actinium	Rutherfordium	Dubnium	Seaborgium	Bohrium	Hassium	Meitnerium

*Lanthanide Series

58 1.1	59 1.1	60 1.1	61 1.1	62 1.2
3,4	3,4	3	3	2,3
Ce	**Pr**	**Nd**	**Pm**	**Sm**
140.115	140.90765	144.24	144.9125	150.36
$[Xe]6s^24f^2$	$[Xe]6s^24f^3$	$[Xe]6s^24f^4$	$[Xe]6s^24f^5$	$[Xe]6s^24f^6$
Cerium	Praseodymium	Neodymium	Promethium	Samarium

**Actinide Series

90 1.3	91 1.5	92 1.4	93 1.4	94 1.3
4	4,5	3,4,5,6	3,4,5,6	3,4,5,6
Th	**Pa**	**U**	**Np**	**Pu**
232.0381	231.03588	238.0289	237.0482	244.0642
$[Rn]7s^25f^2$	$[Rn]7s^25f^3$	$[Rn]7s^25f^4$	$[Rn]7s^25f^5$	$[Rn]7s^25f^6$
Thorium	Protactinium	Uranium	Neptunium	Plutonium